PROGRESS IN BRAIN RESEARCH

VOLUME 17
CYBERNETICS OF THE NERVOUS SYSTEM

PROGRESS IN BRAIN RESEARCH

PROGRESS IN BRAIN RESEARCH

VOLUME 17

CYBERNETICS
OF THE NERVOUS SYSTEM

EDITED BY

THE LATE NORBERT WIENER

Massachusetts Institute of Technology, Cambridge, Mass. (U.S.A.)

AND

J. P. SCHADÉ

Central Institute for Brain Research, Amsterdam (The Netherlands)

ELSEVIER PUBLISHING COMPANY

AMSTERDAM / LONDON / NEW YORK

1965

ELSEVIER PUBLISHING COMPANY
335 JAN VAN GALENSTRAAT, P.O. BOX 211, AMSTERDAM

AMERICAN ELSEVIER PUBLISHING COMPANY, INC.
52 VANDERBILT AVENUE, NEW YORK, N.Y. 10017

ELSEVIER PUBLISHING COMPANY LIMITED
RIPPLESIDE COMMERCIAL ESTATE, BARKING, ESSEX

LIBRARY OF CONGRESS CATALOG CARD NUMBER 65–20131

WITH 143 ILLUSTRATIONS AND 13 TABLES

PRINTED IN THE NETHERLANDS

List of Contributors

R. C. Atkinson, Institute for Mathematical Studies in the Social Sciences, Stanford University, Stanford, Calif. (U.S.A.).

V. Braitenberg, Scuola di Perfezionamento in Fisica Teorica e Nucleare, University of Naples, Naples (Italy).

D. B. Brick, Sylvania Electronic Systems. Applied Research Lab., Waltham, Mass. (U.S.A.).

D. E. Broadbent, Medical Research Council, Applied Psychology Research Unit, Cambridge (England).

R. C. Calfee, Institute for Mathematical Studies in the Social Sciences, Stanford University, Stanford (U.S.A.).

J. D. Cowan, Imperial College of Science and Technology, University of London, London (England).

H. Frank, Institut für Nachrichtenverarbeitung und Nachrichtenübertragung, Karlsruhe (Germany).

J. H. Holland, Communication Sciences, The University of Michigan, Ann Arbor, Mich. (U.S.A.).

F. Jenik, Institut für Allgemeine Nachrichtentechnik, Darmstadt (Germany).

A. B. Kogan, Dept. of Physiology, Rostov-Don State University, Rostov on Don (U.S.S.R.).

L. Krushinsky, Laboratory of Pathophysiology, Moscow State University, Moscow (U.S.S.R.).

D. M. Mackay, Dept. of Communication, University of Keele, Keele (England).

M. E. Maron, The Rand Corporation, Santa Monica, Calif. (U.S.A.).

G. E. Olson, Neth. Centr. Institute for Brain Research, Amsterdam (the Netherlands)

W. Reichardt, Max-Planck Institut für Biologie, Tübingen (Germany).

J. M. Samsó-Dies, Vila Badó et Torres Gasco, Barcelona (Spain).

J. P. Schadé, Neth. Centr. Institute for Brain Research, Amsterdam (The Netherlands).

T. Shelton, J.R., Institute for Mathematical Studies in the Social Sciences, Stanford University, Stanford, Calif. (U.S.A.).

D. Stanley-Jones, Buckshead, Cornwall (England).

W. K. Taylor, Department of Electr. Engineering, London (England).

J. R. Ullmann, National Physical Laboratory, Teddington, Middlesex (England).

D. Varjú, Max-Planck Institut für Biologie, Tübingen (Germany).

J. Zeman, Filosofický ústav ČSAV, Prague (Czechoslovakia).

OTHER VOLUMES IN THE SERIES
PROGRESS IN BRAIN RESEARCH

Preface

In January 1964 Prof. Norbert Wiener came to Amsterdam to act as visiting professor and honorary head of the department of neurocybernetics at the Netherlands Central Institute for Brain Research. During the first months of his stay we discussed in great detail the publication of a second volume on cybernetical and theoretical aspects of the nervous system, to be published in the series PROGRESS IN BRAIN RESEARCH. Prof. Wiener had already served as editor of the first volume on this subject (Nerve, Brain, and Memory Models, edited by N. Wiener and J. P. Schadé, volume 2, Progress in Brain Research).

It was decided to try to cover all aspects of neurocybernetics by a number of outstanding scientists in this field. They were asked to discuss their own research as comprehensively as possible, against the background of relevant data in the literature.

In the course of conversations with some senior members of our staff we decided to publish this volume as a celebration volume, marking the occasion of Prof. Wiener's 70th birthday. He was to choose the contributors for the volume without knowing that the authors were asked to write the survey of their work in honour of the great pioneer of cybernetics. Due to the untimely death of Norbert Wiener in March 1964 the anniversary volume had to be changed into a memorial volume.

The collection of the material of this book was made possible in part by a grant (No. 146) from the NATO Research Grants Programme.

J. P. Schadé.

Contents

Norbert Wiener (1894–1964)

A Tribute to Norbert Wiener

GORDON E. OLSON AND J. P. SCHADÉ

Central Institute for Brain Research, Amsterdam (The Netherlands)

It was one of Dr. Wiener's favorite occupations to sit amongst many kinds of scientists and together project whole systems of ideas to and beyond the limits of man's scientific understanding. The relaxed, untroubled atmosphere of a small discussion group was his kind of study-laboratory. One could talk with each other freely, could have time to think and to see something fit, and to make headway. People came into close association with each other; they effected each other. With clear scientific understanding and the right amount of imagination, people could become productive together in a *rhythm* of mutual participation. Wiener hardly ever got away from this.

But of course, this was Wiener's whole point, this mutual working together. Wiener had long brought people to the realization that in the natural world there exist a multitude of rhythmic phenomena which work together: it is a pooling-effect. Wiener always saw these rhythmic systems and this self-orientation, pooling behavior between them. Because he was able to supply the mathematical formula to such behaviors, he became a tremendous impetus to the scientific world.

The pooling effect between rhythmic systems he called: 'Non-Linear Interactions between Independent Rhythms'; He meant by this that randomly distributed objects or particles in a state of rhythmic oscillation can effect one another through interactions between them, generally consisting of a feed-back of information and because this effect is non-linear, it must be a pooling-effect. He found it in electrical generators; he found it in the electrical circuitries of computers; he found it in the biological organism (the application of control mechanisms to both machines and animals is the science of Cybernetics); with neurocybernetics and medical cybernetics he found further examples of control mechanism.

Members of our Laboratory can remember just a short time before his death, when Wiener rose during a recent conference on neurocybernetics and reminded those present something they probably knew from childhood, or what surely they had noticed anytime since on warm pleasant evenings in the countryside. 'Haven't you noticed that *frogs* all croak in unison? And fire-flies, they all flicker together. Haven't you noticed this?', he said.

The point Wiener was making was that here is an example of control mechanism in behavior between animals. Frogs and fire-flies probably have individual 'natural rhythms' of either croaking or flickering, but as a group, Wiener remarked they only produced one synchronized rhythm. Here again was this pooling-effect, this control mechanism, where animals responded to each other.

Some members of our Institute, with Dr. Wiener's participation, then began a set of experiments to scientifically test this pooling behavior of animals which Wiener had noticed in frogs and fire-flies. And what started out as just a small experiment, later became one of significance, and for us one of particular emotional attachment, for it became the last scientific experiment of Dr. Wiener before his death. Though Wiener lived to see the first results of this work, most of the thorough experimentation and evaluation is not yet completed.

The idea was quite simple. Small chicks, make soft periodic *peeping* sounds when left together in a cage. We would test for synchronization of these peeping sounds, to see if a control mechanism functioned. Chick peeping of isolated birds was first recorded into a tape recorder, to see if peeping was done at any pattern of constant rhythm. What we found was that chicks really do have definite patterns of peeping rhythms, so distinct that each bird could be type-classed (fast peeping, slow peeping, etc.). Here then was a biological example of a 'natural rhythm'; when not put together with others a bird has its own characteristic peeping behavioral pattern. To test Wiener's basic idea, whether one could find a control mechanism which influences the change to synchronization of such natural rhythms when several birds are brought together, we then brought two birds together, then three, then four, six, ten, etc. Did the birds synchronize their rhythms of peeping to a group rhythm while in the presence of other birds? Yes, they did, very definitely. Though Wiener never saw the final summarization of this work, we found that a control mechanism is so distinct in the peeping of these birds, that one can make general statements about the degree of synchronization, dominancy and recessiveness in birds, optimal group size for distinct synchronization.

If one looks back at Wiener's long career, one notices that there has been a continuous line of this same kind of interaction and rhythmic synchronization in his own conduct. He talked with people and in discussion groups gave them his ideas; they in turn shared with him their knowledge. It was always the same: a discussion, an exchange of ideas, and then the development of some new scientific understanding. Wiener was always creative in this way.

Being the international exportation from the Mathematics Department of Massachusetts Institute of Technology, he came to influence and stimulate a great number of people all over the world. In traveling to so many lands he saw no distinction between peoples; with scientific enlightenment he set no limits, being always in the process of adding new idea upon new idea; about science, he had long come to the conclusion that in no *real* sense are there separate branches within science, there only being special ways of looking at the same thing. His discussion groups consisted of learned men from all the sciences.

His boundaries were the very limit of the infinity of his mathematics. And they were also at the same level of awareness that exists within the pepole he came in contact with.

In 1913, a young fellow by the name of Norbert Wiener residing in the New England city of Boston, Massachusetts had just received his Ph.D. in philosophy from nearby Harvard University at the early age of 18. He was born in the little midwest town of Columbia, Missouri (November 26, 1894), and now he had made quite a big step forwards. As we look at it his later career would consist of an early period when many of his basic concepts would be established; a second period when he would come into permanent relationship with M.I.T. and when his work in computer systems would take on practical realizations; and then finally a third period when he would become the cyberneticist with his application of mathematical analysis to biological organisms. But throughout his career the ability of vision and to see beyond the limit of scientific understanding never left him.

It is perhaps difficult for many of us to imagine quite how it was back in 1913. Today's age of automation, not to mention the other atomic and space-ages, would at that time seem to be a *miracle*. Speed for one thing has been one of its big changes, where fifty years ago the tempo particularly in scientific research was slow. The big new principles in the field of physics were slowly being contemplated. Men like Wiener searched for basic concepts, like the random distribution of matter, and re-lation of matter and electromagnetic radiation, the quantum state of energy in matter, relativity, etc. and with Wiener's concentration in Philosophy at this time (for his Ph.D. studying under Santayana), it would make him the kind of scientist who al-ways looked for such basic principles. Even today, in his books and conversations, one finds in Wiener the thinly disguise of a philosopher always talking. For example recently he said: 'When you are doing your work don't read too much'; or while talking about Lewis Carroll who frequently feed through his mind, he said: 'The filter system is actually the educational system' or at another time, he said: 'The art of scientific integrity is not throwing away an idea *until* you have found a hole in it'.

That same year he received his doctoral degree from Harvard, Norbert Wiener was honored with the John Thornton Kirkland Fellowship Award. It was for a one-year study program abroad to Cambridge, England, to study mathematics under the fore-most mathematician Bertrand Russell. The fellowship also included travel to Goet-tingen, Germany, to study under Hilbert. For Wiener, the fellowship was particularly significant in at least one sense, in that it immediately set a pattern of travel and coming into personal contact with men in the scientific world. As we all know, he became science's foremost traveler. This was his *rhythm of behavior*.

It is remarkable to compare the two careers of Wiener and of his early school-master, Sir Bertrand Russell, the person Wiener always said gave him constant in-spiration. In one aspect their careers are similar, and in another quite different. Wiener was the philosopher who turned mathematician, and for Russell it was just the other way around, the mathematician turned philosopher. Here we again see the inner-blending in people of mathematics and philosophy, and shifting from one of these viewpoints to the other only occurring when men are caught up in different issues of the day.

The following year, 1914, Wiener was back once again studying under Russell, both at Cambridge University and at Columbia University, New York City, this time holder of the Frederick Sheldon Fellowship. At this time he also came under the influence of G. H. Hardy.

In this early period of Wiener, culminating with his production of the book 'The Fourier Integral and Certain of its Applications' in 1933, one sees a young enthusiast being taken up with many of the mathematical and physical problems of the day. There would be moments of tangential off-shoots, like when in 1918 he became staff writer for the Encyclopedia Americana and then in 1919 he became a reporter for the Boston Herald newspaper. Some of his scientific writings showed the restless philosopher in search of intangibles, like the articles 'The Highest Good' and 'Relativeness' in 1914, and 'On the Nature of Mathematical Thinking' in 1923. There were great influences that came from the expanding, highly theoretical field of physics. By the middle or late 1920s, Wiener was publishing such articles as 'Quantum Theory and Gravitational Relativity', 'The Fifth Dimension in Relativistic Quantum Theory' and 'On the Spherically Symmetrical Statistical Field in Einstein's Unified Theory of Electricity and Gravitation'.

Wiener during this period of time, had become serious about several things. His mathematical thinking began centered and oriented along certain lines; certain concepts began dominating his thoughts. In many ways his later career consisted mainly of concentrating on further developing these concepts into practical applications. His work in computers was one example of this.

To the neurophysiologist many of Wiener's highly complex systems of mathematics perhaps at times appeared somewhat unreal. But one should remember, that the scope of his insight had taken a slow time to develop. And when he first came to realize the existence of control mechanisms in a biological organism, he was probably as dumb founded at first as all of us. So it is very important for us to understand Wiener's mathematical approach to neurophysiology from a historical view of his work.

With quantum theory being established in physics there was brought to light the high priority of statistics in the evaluation of natural phenomena. The code of absolute knowledge as it had existed before in classical physics had been reduced to the level of statistical probability. Statistical analysis was now made the essential tool for the physics scientist. Mathematics adjusted by the development of new systems of mathematical equations, mostly those of *transformations*, to allow one to follow particles' motions from one set of conditions to another.

One of Wiener's important considerations at this time was the phenomenon of *Brownian motion*, the familiar short-distant movement between particles. To men like Wiener (another was Einstein) who followed their pattern of motion, this interesting common phenomenon is an excellent model for the study of *randomness*. One tries with a set of mathematical matrices and equations to calculate the distribution of the particles. Wiener realized at that time that the analysis of these arbitrary existing movements was unimaginably difficult, but recently he remarked: 'That type of work is continuing now'.

Another consideration of Wiener at this time was the phenomenon of *harmonic analysis* of particles. This is related to the study of Brownian motion, and is the natural outgrowth from quantum mechanics' representations of matter in the form of wave functions. With harmonic analysis this clearly is Wiener's earliest work into 'rhythmic systems'. This would later come to dominate all his work, and he stressed the importance for neurophysiology.

We can then see a growth pattern from Wiener's original work in Brownian motion: this led at once to the development of a system of statistical mathematics for the calculation of the *random distribution* of particles; with quantum theory's use of wave functions this gives a picture of *harmonic analysis*, and this sort of thing is just another way of saying a *rhythmic system*; and one thing further is the dependence of these phenomena on the element of time; and for this element Wiener developd the mathematics of what he called *time series* for his theories on information and communication. What was needed now was a set of equations or transformation functions that could relate all these purely theoretical considerations to a practical problem. This important link between theory and practical application, Wiener was able to supply with his work on Fourier analysis, which he published in the book 'Fourier Integral and Certain of its Applications' in 1933. It turned the tables on complete theory and established a firm footing for practical, statistical analysis. Wiener had reached a milestone.

The year 1923 for Norbert Wiener was a particular important one. He had just returned to M.I.T. from Cambridge, England, where he had written his book on Fourier analysis and where he had also been a guest lecturer at the University. He was then given the appointment of full Professor of Mathematics at M.I.T., a position he held until his retirement in 1959 (up to this time, his association with M.I.T. had been at various levels of appointments: Instructor of Mathematics, ass. Professor of Math., Associate Professor of Math., beginning back in 1919). And 1932 was also the year he won the Boucher Prize from the American Mathematical Society. He became that Society's Vice-President two years later holding the honorary post for two years.

In the succeeding years up to about 1943, Wiener's career was one of expansion. He was continuing his work on developing mathematics on the principle of feed-back for the building of computer systems. His habit of going off on great wandering scientific safari took him next in 1933 to the Tsing Hua University of Peiping, China for a one year appointment as Visiting Professor. As the continuous rebellious philosopher Wiener published such articles as 'The Homogeneous Chaos', but also 'The Use of Statistical Theory in the Study of Turbulence Nature'. He lent assistance towards the development of aiming devices for the military during the war, but when offers were made to him to join in the effort to produce the destructive H-bomb, he said he would not be available. Science is not the pawn of destruction, was his defiant position.

One can point to the year 1943 as the beginning of Wiener's final decisive period of accomplishment. This was the year the original small group of outstanding scientists–physicists, engineers, mathematicians, physiologists, began holding their first discussion groups for the purpose of advancing the new application of control principles on to the biological organism. For this new kind of study which *pooled* men from all branches of science, Wiener in 1947 gave the name CYBERNETICS (the greek word κυβερνητης meaning steersman, or its stem meaning *governor*). Besides Wiener those originally participating were such men as: Dr. Arturo Rosenblueth, Dr. Warren McCulloch (Medical School, University of Illinois), Dr. J. von Neumann (Institute for Advanced Studies, Princeton, U), Mr. Walter Pitts (later associated with M.I.T.), Dr. I. Aiken (Harvard University), the late Dr. Walter B. Cannon and Mr. Julian H. Bigelow. From the work of these early men, the great reservoirs of knowledge in physics, mathematics and engineering, for the first time started spilling over into the biological sciences.

The advent of cybernetics into neurophysiology, with its *a priori* point of mathematical view, was bound to cause changes the in conventional ways of thinking. To the strict experimental neurophysiologist, these new theoretical-men who could come to a solution to nerve function without first gathering all the necessary experimental facts, appeared high-handed. Wiener argued on many occasions and told the students in his lectures all around the world that: particles in matter, machines and biological tissue were all equally comparable. Control mechanism is a general phenomenon. But the cybernetic approach was able to grow rapidly into neurophysiology, with now that area of study being called neurocybernetics. Neurophysiology was itself in the process of rapid advancement at the same time cybernetics was being developed. The view of the nervous system as a dynamic system capable of spontaneous activation, replaced the previous view, mostly of Sherrington and Pavlov, that the nervous system is a static system. Ideas of nerve excitation and inhibition were added. Cybernetics brought about only one kind of new neurological view. Between cybernetics and neurophysiology there was a remarkable interchange of ideas. Was cybernetics an aiming too high for a thorough understanding of neural function?

The answer is found in a statement by the Russian neurophysiologist A. V. Napalkov. 'We believe that new research methods, engendered by the development of cybernetics lead to a radical change in the methods which so far have been used in the study of the brain. They enable the researcher to pass mere accumulation of facts to purposeful experimental investigations based on an elaborate scientific theory'. The answer Dr. Wiener has given us, is that whereas the resolution of most of our basic problems in neurophysiology is still anywhere between experimental and theoretical guess, cybernetics can make *predictions* toward some of these.

Wiener's latest thoughts about the function of the brain were characteristically the combination of contemporary knowledge and searching imagination. They were constant towards the application of control principles, within this pursuit some of his concepts had changed. And new ideas had been added. His concern was to look ahead. 'You don't mind my talking science fiction with you, do you?' Wiener asked the Thursday afternoon discussion group into neurocybernetics, several months before his death. An amusing thing about Wiener was how he would approach a new idea of his. 'I don't say this is true,' he would prefex himself. And afterwards he might say, 'What do you think of such wild ideas?'

Wiener was first concerned with the types of neurophysiological phenomenon one deals with in applying control mechanism principles to the brain. His earlier thoughts had centered on the evaluation of cortical 'alpha rhythms'. These types of constant rhythms which must be the product of millions of cortical neurons, suggest a high degree of synchronization between these neurons; Wiener saw that a control mechanism must function here. While electroencephalography has never been able to characterize all the various patterns of brain waves, this basic alpha rhythm at about 10 cycles per second is easily recognized. There must be a high degree of orientation of individual neuron 'natural rhythms' for this to be produced. The question Wiener now raises is, are these rhythms the same as you find throughout the nervous system, following known laws of nerve function, such as the all-or-nothing law. Answering in the negative he finds that there must be some *other* phenomenon which exists in brain function, something which we haven't been able to measure yet. His reasons for thinking this, can be understood from our present day knowledge. Wiener expresses the belief that whereas the all-or-nothing law applies for the long, myelinated nerve fibers in the body, some other law must function for the short branches of these neurons. A full 'spike' potential complex cannot develop over short distances of branches, and what one is dealing with here are impulses of all degrees of complexity.

In Wiener's belief the property of brain waves is one of *highly specific micro-radiation*. The reason why such radiation has not yet been recorded is that they are of a very small quantity. As Dr. Wiener said to us: 'My idea is that we do have radiation within the nervous system but for a very short range. What you will ultimately get is a radiant phenomenon which is of such short weak range that you don't get it to the outside. 'Alpha rhythms then could be thought as the synchronization of micro-radiation of individual neurons. The concept fits with quantum analysis where wave functions are used to characterize vibrating particles. The next point to consider is how are these specific micro-radiations produced? The factor would have to account for the control synchronization of alpha rhythms. 'This is just a suggestion. *Nucleic Acid Complexes*. It maybe a phenomenon of this type of crystalline vibrations at a high frequency that a resonance phenomenon tends to pull one another together'. An interaction between such crystalline nucleic acid complexes in neurons very likely falls under a control mechanism, as the specific frequencies of vibrations of radiations of these complexes could cause a resonance effect. The reason why these nucleic acid complexes are so important, is that they are the basis of *memory* in the brain tissue; this follows directly from the fact that all crystalline structures have *specific* spectrums of vibrations, and therefore could answer the specificity of memory.

What influence this new concept of nucleic acid complexes which stores 'memory' information will have on computer systems, could be of great significance. 'This is another wild conjecture. Why couldn't these memory particles be used as initial memories in machines. Why can't the next step in automation after transistor, solid-state memories be *nucleic acid memories*. Maybe that will come in twenty years, but that is much too long of time, I believe'. Wiener's idea was directed towards supplying the means for building future computers with a much higher information-storage bit index. Large amounts of information could be stored on nucleic acid complexes over micro-distances. Dr. Wiener finds that his ideas about specific types of radiation associated with nucleic acid complexes randomly scattered within neurons, when applied to encephalography should bring about productive results. 'Encephalography has been too much in recognizing wave patterns subjectively. Too little has been done for determining what actually happens there . . . . We have not done enough work making atlases of frequency distribution . . . . This method is looking for specific numbers'.

As he continued into cybernetics, the ramifications of his thoughts into the biological sciences brought him to a growing awareness of the social implications to his work. He became concerned with the impact of automation on industry, and began consulting with labor leaders to bring about better understanding of it with them. And he participated in the field of medicine. People are well aware of Dr. Wiener's persistent work towards developing artificial prostheses for the rehabilitation of paralyzed limbs. This seemingly insurmountable project is to use the remaining receptor organs and nerve fibers in a paralyzed limb or one that has been amputated, and by means of an electrical computer apparatus resupply the missing nerve activity and restore the limb to normal function. This would use feed-back looping mechanisms between the various neural, muscular and electronic structures; a full reconstruction of reflex pathways could be anticipated.

In this last period of Wiener's career there continued a regular outpouring of publications. His most famous one of course was the book, 'CYBERNETICS: or control and communication in the animal and in the machine' originally published in 1948, and which decidely established the science of cybernetics. In a recent 1961 second edition, he added two more chapters. He also became the author of such books as, 'The Human Use of Human Beings', 'I Am a Mathematician', 'Nonlinear Problems in Random Theory', etc. He continued his world traveling, going to such places as Instituto Nacional de Cardiologica, Mexico, a Fullbright Teaching Fellowship to the University of Paris, University of California at Los Angeles, University of Naples. Here at our Laboratories of the Central Institute of Brain Research, Amsterdam, Holland, he held regular study-groups in neurocybernetics. A complete account of Dr. Wiener's work is not possible at present, for a great portion of that work continues to exist in the present, and will continue into the future. Only in the future will there be the complete resolution to all the things Wiener participated in and contributed to. Wiener's long scientific career is a model of creativity. He participated best in the quiet small study group, where the brew of coffee and ideas went together. His temperament was always:

'Couldn't this be so'.

The Problem of Organismic Reliability

JACK D. COWAN

*Department of Electrical Engineering, Imperial College of Science and Technology,
London (Great Britain)*

CONTENTS

1. INTRODUCTION

> "To reconcile the high durability of the heredity substance with its minute size, we have to evade the tendency to disorder by 'inventing the molecule', in fact, an unusually large molecule which has to be a masterpiece of highly differentiated order, safeguarded by the conjuring rod of quantum theory."
>
> E. SCHRÖDINGER

In 1944 there was published a monograph by E. Schrödinger, based on a set of lectures given by the eminent physicist, on the possibility of accounting for the spatio-temporal events occurring within living organisms, by the sole use of physics and chemistry. Some notable points made in this monograph were:

(a) The living organism seems to be a macroscopic system which in part of its behaviour approaches to that purely mechanical (as contrasted with thermodynamical) conduct to which all systems tend, as the temperature approaches the absolute zero and the molecular disorder is removed.

(b) (Whereas) non-living systems tend to converge to thermodynamic equilibrium — a state of 'maximum entropy' or 'complete randomness', living systems tend to avoid this by the process of metabolism, in which the excess entropy acquired by the organism is reduced, *i.e.*, the living organism 'feeds' on 'negative entropy'.

(c) The power to perform this entropy transformation seems to be connected with the presence of aperiodic solids — the chromosome molecules which doubtless represent the highest degree of well-ordered atomic association we know of – much higher than the ordinary periodic crystal – in virtue of the individual role every atom and every radical is playing (in the molecule).

(d) It is a fact of observation that the guiding principle in every cell is embodied in a single atomic association existing in only one (or sometimes two) copies — and it results in (the production of) events which are a paragon of orderliness, *i.e.*, quantum indeterminacy and in effect statistics, plays no part in the organisation of living cells. The effect of this is that whereas in physics, order breeds disorder, in biology, order breeds new order. Underlying this (seems to be) the fact that life is a sequence of events of a dynamical, small-scale kind, and not a sequence of events of a statistical, large-scale kind. Such a 'fact' relates to the problem the basic principle of quantum theory — that small-scale systems (on the order of the atomic scale) possess only discretely connected stable states, *i.e.* continuous transitons between these states are 'forbidden'.

(e) Macroscopic physical systems, *e.g.* clockworks, are capable of functioning dynamically, and not statistically because they are built of solids, which are kept in shape by Heitler — London forces strong enough to elude the disorderly tendency of heat motion at ordinary temperatures. Biological systems also impinge upon solids — aperiodic — largely withdrawn from the disorder of heat motion. *Only systems in molecular disorder that are homogeneous obey the entropy law; biological systems, which are highly organised, heterogeneous, and stable, do not.*

It is obvious that this brilliant little monograph contains intimations of contemporary molecular biology and genetics, and of information theory. The present picture in molecular biology may be represented (for our purposes) as follows:

(A) There exists in the living cell a complex molecular assembly involved in the storage and replication of hereditary information (the genetic system) and in the synthesis of molecules such as proteins, lipids, and so forth, which have enzymatic activity and which play an important role in cellular metabolism (the epigenetic system).

(B) There are two main aspects involved in understanding such molecular assemblies, namely the so called Coding problem, and the Control problem. The coding problem was first recognised as such by Gamow (1955) following the elucidation of the structure of what is commonly taken to be the primary carrier of hereditary information — deoxyribonucleic acid, DNA — *alias* the chromosome, by Watson and Crick (1953). Recent work by Nihrenberg and Matthai (1961) and by Lengyel *et al.* (1962) has contributed manifestly to our understanding of the code, although the actual details remain to be considered. Suffice it to say the code appears to be a 4 letter one, written in the language of nucleic acid chemistry (the 4 letters being in DNA, ademine, thymine, guanine and cytosine), and that it appears to be *universal*, *i.e.* the same combinations of letters are used throughout the biosystem, for the same chemicals. Hereditary information is commonly supposed to be stored in DNA in the form of sequences of letters taken from the 4-symbol alphabet. Replication of DNA (and thus of hereditary information) is mediated by a base complentation mechanism (A pairing with T, G pairing with C), and by enzymes which may already be present in the cell, or may be synthesised before replication is scheduled to take place.

The read-out or transmission of hereditary information is generally supposed to take place via a signalling system comprising ribonucleic acid molecules of low molecular weight, the so-called messenger ribonucleic acid, mRNA. (Brenner *et al.*, 1961). Reception of hereditary information occurs at aggregates of small ribonuclear particles, called polysomes, ergosomes, or polyribosomal aggregates. It is here that the hereditary information is used to guide the synthesis of macromolecules (Warner *et al.*, 1963). There is also involved in these processes of replication, transmission and synthesis, a complex network of enzymes and small molecules, *e.g.* allosteric proteins. Many of these protein synthesising systems interact in such a way that the products (protein or metabolic byproduct) may *feedback* to inhibit any further production of new product. Moreover, the products of one system may feedback to inhibit the production of products of other synthesising systems. The dynamical aspects of such interactions, *e.g.* the occurrence and nature of steady-states, are the subject of the science of control, or cybernetics.

The picture that results from contemporary molecular biology, concerning genetic and epigenetic systems in the cell, is that of a *molecular automaton*, highly specific, heterogenous, and stable — in complete accord with the earlier speculations of Schrö-dinger. It would seem therefore that quantum mechanics (which is popularly supposed to underly all mechanics) and cellular biology are not at all inconsistent, and that the behaviour of the organism may well be deducible solely from physics and chemistry. This view is held also by Timofeyev - Resovskiy and Rompe (1959) 'only the quantum theory makes comprehensible the discrete nature of macrophysical structures and phenomena among the infinite multitude of possible combinations of elementary particles, and by the same token, explains the existence of definite, discrete variations and their relative stability'.

This view, which may be termed the mechanistic view, has recently been seriously questioned by a number of eminent physicists and biologists, and is essentially, albeit in a different language, a revival of the old controversy concerning developmental biology, *viz. Preformation vs. Epigenesis*. The idea underlying preformation is that cells contain a complete description of themselves, that is transformed into an adult cell in the development process. In epigenesis, on the other hand, it is held that only an incomplete description is stored, and that in the process of development, additional 'information' appears from somewhere, to complete the adult organism. Contemporary molecular biology tends to reinforce the idea of preformation, *i.e.* the sequence of letters stored in DNA is held to be the description, and there exists a central dogma (Crick, 1959) that in macromolecular synthesis, the flow of information is one-way from DNA to protein, a dogma that certainly underlies the idea of pre-formation. On the other hand developmental biologists, such as Weiss (1962), object to this central dogma, on the grounds that molecular activity may be controlled by *integrative mechanisms* within the cell which operate at a 'higher' level of organisation than that of protein synthesis. Thus 'there must exist certain actions of the (cell) . . . which constrain or restrict the number of degrees of the constituent elements in such a way that the collective product will have a much higher degree of *invariance* than does each individual member of the cell'. This is not at all inconsistent with the experimental evidence that has been found recently concerning molecular control mechanisms (Jacob and Monod, 1961). However, Weiss also considers the specificity and heterogeneity of living systems to be closely connected with these ideas.

Perhaps the most trenchant critiques of the mechanistic hypothesis have been delivered by Elsasser (1958, 1961, 1962) and by Wigner (1960). Elsasser bases his arguments on two premises — concerning the acquisition and degradation of information in organisms.

(1) In the developmental process, organisms are informationally closed — *i.e.* the amount of negative entropy acquired by the organism in development is relatively speaking, negligible compared to that already present in the organism, *i.e.* metabolism plays no part in development.

(2) Organisms do not degrade appreciably, for reasonably long periods of time, *i.e.* the 'relaxation time' for organisms is much greater than the relaxation time for organic components.

The argument then goes as follows. If the mechanistic hypothesis is adopted (*alias* preformationism) then this implies that there exists a 1 : 1 correspondence between the initial and final states of the developing organism — *i.e.* it is state determined. (This is certainly true of isolated physico-chemical systems, (*cf.* Von Bertalanffy, 1950), but not necessarily true of closed systems (these open for energy exchange, but not for matter exchange), and follows from the first premise.) The 1 : 1 correspondence implies that the cell has the character of an automaton (Von Neumann, 1948, see § 3, 4). Elsasser claims that the only known mechanism for ensuring the longevity and stability of organisms is one suggested by Von Neumann (1956, see § 3, 4) which requires the use of statistical ideas, and extremely large numbers of components, so large in fact that organisms could not possibly be constructed that way; ergo the mechanistic assumption must be dropped — or least the idea of *preformation*. Unwilling to give up quantum mechanics however, Elsasser then postulates that while organisms in fact do behave in a manner consistent with quantum mechanics, there exist morphodynamic or biotonic or *epigenetic* laws of organismic behaviour, consistent with quantum mechanics, but which operate so as to prevent the prediction of spatio-temporal events within the organism. As we shall document later (see § 3, 4), Elsasser's arguments need not be taken too seriously, since it has recently been shown that Von Neumann's solution to the problem of preserving organisms, given certain assumptions, is not the only one (*cf.* Winograd and Cowan, 1963), and that these new solutions seem to be consistent with organismic properties. (On the other hand, certain of Elsasser's ideas are well worth studying for other reasons.)

A more serious objection to the mechanistic viewpoint is that raised by Wigner, who examines the possibilities inherent in quantum mechanics for the existence of self-replicating systems, and concludes that such possibilities are effectively zero!

It appears to be the case that quantum mechanics is not consistent with the process of replication, a process which is certainly vital — as far as the preservation of life is concerned. This result of Wigner's is quite contrary to that thesis advanced by Schrödinger concerning the place of quantum theory in biology.

Points of interest made by Wigner are:

(1) The calculation concerns the probability of one organism *surely* replicating, not replicating with some high probability. Wigner notes that such an analysis has been attempted but not concluded.

(2) The result seems to be in conflict with automata theory (Von Neumann, 1948, op. cit.).

(3) The result seems to be in conflict with the Watson-Crick model (op. cit.) for replication via DNA. It is contended that the *reliability* of this model has never been computed, and compared with experience. It is suggested (*cf.* Elsasser) that the virtually absolute reliability of the model must be a consequence of a biotonic law, the contention following from the fact that both quantum mechanical arguments, and Von Neumann's theory of the construction of reliable organisms from unreliable components (Von Neumann, 1956, op. cit.) seem to be at odds with the Watson-Crick model and with the biological evidence.

(4) Wigner finally notes that 'his firm conviction of the existence of biotonic laws stems from the ... phenomenon of consciousness ... living matter being clearly influenced by what it influences: consciousness'. It seems likely that what is meant here is that living systems even at the level of molecular aggregates — are 'intelligent' in the sense of Peirce: 'What is to be accomplished determines what is done'. Using instead non-metaphysical language to describe this phenomenon — it might be that what is intended is that living systems comprise molecular aggregates of a very complex nature, supporting very many cooperative and competitive molecular interactions, that lead macroscopically to a picture of such aggregates as *self-adaptive feedback control systems*. It is to the subject of control mechanisms that we now turn.

2. THE ORGANISM AS A SELF-REGULATING DYNAMICAL SYSTEM

The recent discoveries by Jacob and Monod (1961) concerning induction and repression at genetic loci, and the introduction of the concepts of structural, operator and repressor genes, as well as the discovery of feedback inhibition by small molecules such as *allosteric proteins* (Monod *et al.*, 1963) and by metabolic byproducts, has focussed attention on the properties of molecular control systems, and upon mathematical theories of interacting control.

The science of control or *cybernetics* (Wiener, 1948) received its first modern impetus from Maxwell's mathematical analysis of the governor (Maxwell, 1868), but then remained dormant until the advent of the feedback amplifier (Nyquist, 1932; Bode, 1945). The essential idea was recognised that control, *i.e.* the maintenance of essential variables within certain requisite limits could be effected by the device of *feeding back* signals from the output of a device (or the response of a dynamic system) so as to effect the input to the device (or the driving force exerted on the system). The place of such an idea in biology was recognised by physiologists such as Cannon (1932), and of course the idea of a *reflex arc* as developed by Sherrington and others (Sherrington, 1906) in neurophysiology was recognised as being of primary importance in the study of the integrative properties of neural tissue. Following Nyquist and Bode it was recognised that *negative feedback*, *i.e.* the feedback of signals that oppose

References p. 61

the build-up of further output signals was closely connected with the *stability* of dynamical systems, and it was Bigelow together with Wiener and Rosenblueth who first recognised that it was not the energy in the feedback signal, but the pattern of energy, *i.e. the information* in such a signal that was of supreme importance for control (Rosenblueth *et al.*, 1943; see also Craik, 1943). The first attempt to unite the dynamical theory of control mechanisms developed by Nyquist *et al.* (but see Lyapunov, 1907) with the biological ideas of *adaptation, habituation,* and *homeostasis* developed by Cannon and others, was that made by W. Ross Ashby (1954, *et seq.*). In attempting to apply control ideas to the nervous system, Ashby extended the idea of stability — introducing the concepts of *ultrastability,* and *multistability.* We recall that a dynamical system is in stable equilibrium if under a small perturbation, forces operate successfully within the system so as to restore the equilibrium state. An ultrastable system is one possessing many states of stable equilibrium such that any perturbation from one state produces a disturbance within the system which operates continously until a new state of equilibrium is reached; *i.e.* the ultrastable system *hunts* for stability. The multistable system is a collection of (loosely coupled) ultrastable systems, not all of which are active at any one instant, which has the important property of being able to change the configuration of active subsystems, so as to remove disturbances caused by any impingent stimuli. *I.e.* the multistable system is *adaptive,* and displays as a consequence, the properties of habituation, and of homeostasis.

Although Ashby's analysis is merely qualitative, no mathematical analysis being given for the multistability of complex dynamical systems, several important properties of such systems are deduced:

(a) The system must be loosely coupled, or not all parts active at any one time.

(b) The system must be heterogeneous, *i.e.* not all subsystems must be similar in structure and function, or there must be a certain amount of noise within the system, *e.g.* some randomness of interconnexion, or malfunctions in the outputs of the units comprising the various subsystems (*cf.* § 4 on reliability of automata). *It is important to recognise that essentially the same properties considered to be important for the persistence of living systems, by Schrödinger and Weiss, are essentially those properties of dynamical systems that result in multistability.*

The attempt to obtain quantitative results concerning the stability properties of complex dynamical systems comprising large numbers of interconnected nonlinear devices (as the components of neural tissue, and of macromolecular aggregates seem to be), on the other hand, has not kept pace with the qualitative heuristic ideas developed by Ashby. Dynamical systems containing one feedback path have been studied extensively, and much has been discovered concerning the properties of such systems, be they linear, non-linear, and/or adaptive; but not many advances have been made in the study of multicomponent systems comprising many interacting pathways. There are however two significant exceptions to this — notably the work of Wiener (1958) and others on the application of Gibbsian statistical mechanics, and that of Beurle (1956) and others on the properties of large randomly interconnected networks of highly non-linear devices called switching elements.

Wiener's idea may be described succinctly as follows. In classical Newtonian mechanics a differential equation and a set of initial conditions are all that are required, in principle, for the solution of dynamical problems. Of course in general, it is extremely difficult to obtain solutions to arbitrary differential equations especially if they are non-linear, and numerical integration is the rule. On the other hand if the equation is linear, it is always solvable, by a variety of methods. One particular method, the *operational method*, developed notably by Heaviside (1892) is of special interest. It turns out that the behaviour of a linear system may be completely characterised by its response to a pulse of finite energy (a way of putting in initial conditions) that occupies a vanishingly small time-interval, the so-called *unit impulse function*, or Dirac δ-function, wellknown to physicists. This is not the case for any arbitrary non-linear system however, and corresponds to the fact that different initial conditions may lead to quite distinct modes of response. In the event that the non-linear system has stationary state however, and provided that the system does not dissipate energy, another use of the unit impulse is possible, that corresponds to Gibbsian statistical mechanics, *viz.* an *ensemble* (*i.e.* a collection comprising very many identical copies of the system) is considered rather than one system. Each member of the ensemble reacts to a different unit impulse, and *the response of the ensemble is taken to be the average of all the individual responses of the members* of the ensemble. Under certain conditions (ergodicity, metrical transitivity, etc.) such a response is also the average of the responses of only one system, to a very long train of unit impulses. But a very long train of unit impulses, all distinct, is essentially a random or pseudorandom sequence, having a spectral characteristic (energy density or power density spectrum) that is essentially that of white noise, *i.e.* energy is distributed equally throughout all regions of the frequency spectrum — and so the response is called the *white noise response*. Such a response then characterises the stationary non-dissipative non-linear system, and represents an extension of the use of Heaviside's and Gibbs' methods to engineering (see also Gabor, 1956).

Among the many applications of this theory, one in particular is very relevant to the theme of this paper, and concerns the mechanisms underlying the production of *biological clocks* (see Cold Spring Harbor Symposia on Quantitative Biology, Vol. 25, Biological Clocks, 1961). In considering the power density spectrum of an assembly of coupled non-linear oscillators (having a wide range of fundamental frequencies), Wiener showed that such a spectrum was in general, of the type shown in Fig. 1.

That is, a large amount of oscillatory energy is concentrated in the immediate

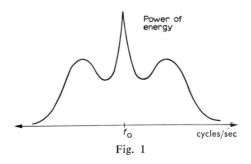

Fig. 1

neighbourhood of the frequency f_0; moreover, there is a 'dip' in the spectrum in the surrounding neighbourhood. This suggests that restoring forces operate within the assembly to stabilise its operating frequency at f_0, and that any perturbations from this are compensated — frequencies $f_0 - \triangle f$ being 'pulled' up to f_0, those at $f_0 + \triangle f$ being pulled down to f_0. In this way then an assembly of interacting non-linear oscillators may have a fundamental oscillatory component which is considerably more stable than the fundamental frequency component of any member of the assembly. This property is clearly an *integrative property* of the assembly, of the type we have already discussed. It is important to note that this integrative property depends critically on the non-linearity of the individual elements of the assembly, thus (Wiener, 1957):

"It is important to observe that if the frequency of an oscillator can be changed by impulses of a different frequency, the mechanism must be non-linear. A linear mechanism acting on an oscillation of a given frequency can produce only oscillations of the same frequency, generally with some change of amplitude. This is not true for non-linear mechanisms, which may produce oscillations of frequencies which are the sums and differences of different orders, of the frequency of the oscillator and the frequency of the imposed disturbance. It is quite possible for such a mechanism to displace a frequency; and in the case which we have considered, this displacement will be of the nature of an attraction. It is not too improbable that this attraction will be long-time or secular phenomenon, and that for short times this system will remain approximately linear."

Wiener's suggestion is that such a mechanism provides a clock in, for example, the central nervous system, whereby the impulses in nerve fibres are *synchronised* so that neural computation (or integration as it is called by neurophysiologists) can take place. It is noted elsewhere (Wiener, 1957) that such a clock is not localised, thus:

"Where is (the) clock? The answer is: everywhere and nowhere ... the system is organized ... so that the question 'where is the time regulating mechanism?' is a meaningless one. It is a *distributed organization*, which nevertheless has a very tight organization from the standpoint of organization itself."

We shall return to this very important question of distributed function in biological systems, in later sections.

Independently of Wiener, a closely similar application of Gibbsian methods has been made to demography, by Kerner (1957, 1959, 1961). This work is a generalisation of the well-known analysis by Volterra (1937) of predator–prey interactions in biological associations. The starting point is a set of Volterra equations for n biological species in interaction, having population numbers $N_1, N_2, \ldots, N_n$.

$$\frac{dN_r}{dt} = \varepsilon_r N_r + \beta_r^{-1} \sum_s a_{sr} N_s N_r \tag{12}$$

ε_r may be positive or negative, and is the constant of self-accretion (*i.e.* the growth or decay constant of the rth species), $a_{rs} = -a_{sr}$ are the interaction coefficients for the rth and s^{th} species, and β_r^{-1} are Volterra's 'equivalent numbers' such that in the binary encounters r,s the ratio of the number of members of the sth species lost (or gained) per sec to the number of members of the rth species gained (or lost) per sec is $\beta_s^{-1} : \beta_r^{-1}$.

It is well known that the case of only binary encounters was solved by Volterra even though the equations are non-linear. He demonstrated the existence of relaxation oscillations in such encounters, *e.g.* the predators would eat the prey and increase, while the prey decreased, until there were too few prey, at which time the predators would decrease, and the prey increase, and so on. (See Fig. 2). N.B. There is no dissipative term or coefficient of self-inhibition.

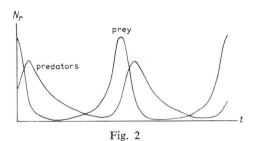

Fig. 2

In the case of *n*-ary encounters however, Volterra's method fails, and statistical mechanics has to be introduced. This is done by considering the stationary states of (eqn. 12), $(N_r)_{\text{stat}} = q_r$, $q_r \neq 0$. Volterra found that for binary interactions, the fluctuations in N_r are bounded between positive limits, and at least some of the species fluctuate without damping out, and that the time average of N_r, $<N_r> = q_r$ independently of any initial conditions. Such stationary states are used to set up the statistical mechanics as follows. A large number of copies of the biological association is considered, each controlled by the same equation (12), but having all variety of initial values of N_r.... the so-called *Gibbs ensemble*. It is shown that for such an ensemble, Liouville's Theorem holds and that the equations (12) in the stationary state can be transformed into an equation (13)

$$\sum_r \tau_r (e^{v_r} - v_r) = G \tag{13}$$

where $\tau_r = \beta_r q_r$, $v_r = \log \dfrac{N_r}{q_r}$, and where G is a constant, in fact, the only general *intergral of motion* of equation (12). The quantity

$$\tau_r(e^{v_r} - v_r) = G_r \tag{14}$$

is used to characterise the rth species. It can thus be shown that

$$v_r = \sum_s \gamma_{sr} \frac{\partial G}{\partial v_s} \tag{15}$$

where $\gamma_{sr} = a_{sr}/\beta_s\beta_r = -\gamma_{sr}$. Equation (15) is (loosely) reminiscent of Hamilton's equations of motion. Thus all the prerequisites for constructing a statistical mechanics of interacting biological associations are satisfied by the equation (12). Since a constant of motion or *invariant* G is available it is possible to define analogues of dynamical quantities such as kinetic energy, and to compute ensemble averages of these quantities, *e.g.* Let

$$T_r = v_r \frac{\partial G}{\partial v_r} \tag{16}$$

Then it can be shown that the ensemble average of T_r, $\overline{T}_r$ is given by a quantity that is independent of r, such that T is equidistributed among all the n species of the association, *i.e.* T *is analogous to kinetic energy, and is equipartitioned throughout the association.* In similar fashion other dynamical properties can be proved, notably what amounts to an ergodic theorem. It can be shown that the ensemble average of N_r itself, *i.e.* $\overline{N}_r$, is equal to q_r.

These properties are obtained from what is essentially the Gibbs' *microcanonical ensemble.* Corresponding properties of thermodynamic-like analogues may be obtained from a consideration of the Gibbs' *canonical ensemble; i.e.* the behaviour of some v of the n associating species is considered. G_v is not now an invariant of the system, although $G = G_v + G_{n-v}$ is an invariant. However corresponding to states of the system having characteristic G_0 in the microcanonical distribution previously considered, are states of the system comprising the vth species, distributed according to the well-known law

$$\varrho_v = e^{\psi - G_v/\theta} \tag{17}$$

where ϱ_v is of course the relative 'density' of such states in the subsystem, and the factor $e^{-\psi/\theta}$ is chosen so as to normalise the 'volume' integral of ϱ_v. Such a distribution is characterised by the constant θ, rather than by G. θ of course is the analogue of temperature, and ψ the analogue of free energy, both equilibrium concepts. Using the canonical ensemble various thermodynamic-like properties and relations can be deduced such as

$$\overline{T}_r = \theta = \frac{\beta_r}{q_r} \overline{(N_r - q_r)^2} \tag{18}$$

demonstrating the relationship between the *average kinetic energy of the subsystem, the temperature, and the mean square deviations of the populations from their stationary-values, and vice-versa.*

An analogue of the *Maxwell-Boltzmann* distribution for gases can be proved that turns out to be exactly that distribution of the 'intrinsic abundance' of a species assumed by Corbet *et al.* (1943) to deduce under certain assumptions the probability that a 'catch' of individuals in time t contains just i individuals.

Similarly, the thermodynamic-like variables, *free energy, internal energy, entropy,* etc. can be related to the quantities defined in (12) *e.g.*

(a) Free energy ψ:

$$\psi = \tau_r \log \frac{\tau_r}{\theta} - \theta \log \Gamma\left(\frac{\tau_r}{\theta}\right) = \sum_r \psi_r \tag{19}$$

(b) Internal energy G:

$$\overline{G}_r = \tau \, \log \frac{\tau_r}{\theta} + \tau_r - \tau_r \varphi\left(\frac{\tau_r}{\theta}\right)$$

$$\overline{G} = \sum_r \overline{G}_r$$

where

$$\varphi(x) = \frac{d}{dx} \log \Gamma(x) \tag{20}$$

(c) Entropy S:

$$\overline{S_r} = \frac{\tau r}{\theta}\left(1 - \varphi\left(\frac{r}{\theta}\right)\right) + \log \Gamma\left(\frac{\tau r}{\theta}\right)$$

$$\overline{S} = \sum_r \overline{S_r} \tag{21}$$

We note that the familiar Gibbs' relation holds for each species

$$\psi_r = \overline{G_r} - \theta\ _r\overline{S} \tag{22}$$

Finally an important application of the canonical ensemble is made, namely the prediction of the horizontal spreads of population curves (the 'wave-form' to be expected from any species). In particular it is shown that the fraction T_-/T of a long time interval T spent by a species, below the average level q_r is, in the limit

$$\frac{T_-}{T} \to \frac{\dfrac{x_r^{x_r} e^{-x_r}}{x_r!}}{\dfrac{\int_-(e^{v_r} - 1)\, dt}{\int_- dt}} \tag{23}$$

where

$$x_r = \frac{\overline{N_r}^2}{(N_r - \overline{N_r})^2} \tag{24}$$

and of course $v_r = \log N_r/q_r$.

Similarly T_+/T the function of T spent above q_r, by the rth species is given by

$$\frac{T_+}{T} \to \frac{\dfrac{x_r^{x_r} e^{-x_r}}{x_r!}}{\dfrac{\int_+(e^{v_r} - 1)\, dt}{\int_+ dt}} \tag{25}$$

It turns out that at low population temperatures, θ small, such wave-forms look as follows (Fig. 3).

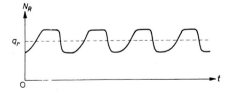

Fig. 3

whereas at high population temperatures, θ large, we obtain the wave-forms shown in Fig. 4:

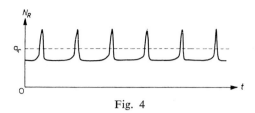

Fig. 4

Recalling equation (18), we see that temperature is a measure of the complexity of interaction of various species, so *the higher the complexity of interaction, the more spike-like do the oscillations become*. Recalling Wiener's work on *synchronization* it seems likely that any complex association of interacting biological species, neuronal assemblies or molecular assemblies, which are describable by non-linear differential equations embeddable into a Gibbsian ensemble will generate synchronous spike-like activity as its basic dynamical characteristic. We shall return to this possibility in later sections.

The application to molecular biology of Gibbsian mechanics, has in fact, already been carried out by Goodwin (1963). The basic system considered is that of a DNA → mRNA → protein system with feedback inhibition from protein to DNA via some intermediary (see Jacob and Monod, *op. cit.*). The following non-linear differential equation is derived for such a system

$$a_r \frac{X_r^2}{2} - \beta_r X_r + b_r Y_r - \frac{a_r}{k_r} n(A_r + k_r Y_r) = G \qquad (26)$$

where X_r, Y_r are the concentrations of mRNA and protein at the rth synthesising system, and where the other parameters are various complex parameters containing rate constants for various chemical interactions taking place — the system being of course in a stationary state. It is shown that such an equation is embeddable into a Gibbsian ensemble, and results similar to Kerner's and Wiener's are obtained, for the various oscillations and so on, to be found in molecular populations.

It should be noted however, that such applications of Gibbsian statistical mechanics, while extremely interesting in themselves, fall somewhat short of the mark in their veridicality as models for neuronal or molecular populations, at any rate. This is because such populations comprise aggregates of very strongly interacting assemblies, not the (essentially) weakly interacting systems considered by the Gibbsian method: the application of statistical mechanics to such systems is very complex, and of relatively recent origin (see for example, Ter Haar, 1957), and little has been achieved other than in applications to physics. However a number of studies of the dynamical. properties of switching networks have been made, which are of immediate interest. Beurle (1956) has given the most comprehensive account of such networks and we shall outline his formulation and solution of the problems. The networks studied comprise elements or cells *assumed to be randomly distributed with a volume density p*. They comprise a density Rp of 'sensitive cells' which have the ability to become active under conditions specified below, and a density $(1 - R)p$ of 'used cells', *i.e.* those which have recently become active. R is a function therefore, of both position in the network, and of time. The expression $\xi(x)$ is used to represent the richness of connexions between cells and is defined as the mean number of connexions from all cells in an infinite plane of unit thickness to a single cell at a distance x. The expression

$$\xi(x) = b\,e^{-|x|/a_0} \qquad (27)$$

is used for such a connexion function, it being derived from empirical data obtained by Sholl (1953) concerning the interconnexions of neurons.

When a sensitive cell (primary cell) becomes active it excites any other sensitive cell to which it is connected (secondary cell). The initial quantity of excitation received by the second cell is evidently proportional to the number of connexions to it, and its response is a function of the integrated input excitation. The following cell properties are assumed:

(a) $X(t)$ the proportion of excitation produced by a primary cell which remains t units after the cell fires (time decrement of excitation) is a rectangular function of duration x.

(b) After firing cells are insensitive for a period r (recovery time).

(c) The integrated excitation input to a cell must exceed q (excitation threshold) for the cell to fire.

(d) The time between excitation at or above threshold, and firing of a cell is τ (delay or synaptic delay).

(e) It is assumed that all activity takes place at multiples of τ only, $i.e.$ length of period of activity is incorporated in $X(t)$.

It is evident that any activity in such a network of cells is of a rather complex form, being essentially *cooperative* in nature, and Beurle considers, not the single unit activity, but the proportion of cells becoming active at any one time. (*cf.* Kerner's N_r). This is denoted by $F(x,y,z,t)$ or simply by F. (In fact only variation in the x direction is considered.)

$F(x,t)\,\xi\,(x-X)\,\mathrm{d}X$ is thus the mean rate of arrival of impulses at single secondary cells in the plane x from cells becoming active at a mean rate F within a plane of thickness $\mathrm{d}X$ at X.

The convolution

$$\int_{-\infty}^{\infty} F(x,\,t)\,\xi\,(x-X)\,\mathrm{d}X$$

therefore represents in terms of x and t, the mean rate of arrival of impulses at cells in the plane x from all other cells.

The convolution

$$\overline{N}(x,\,t) = \int_{-\infty}^{0}\int_{-\infty}^{\infty} F(X,\,T)\,\xi\,(x-X)\,X\,(t-T)\,\mathrm{d}X\,\mathrm{d}T \qquad (28)$$

similarly gives the mean value of integrated excitation, N, for cells in the plane x.

From N and R the proportion can be calculated of cells which have an integrated excitation of $q-1$ and are also sensitive, so that the arrival of one more impulse will trigger them off. How many of these cells that do in fact fire during a short period δt

depends upon the first convolution. Hence the proportion $F(x,t + \tau)$ of cells active at time $t + \tau$ can be computed.

Two forms of activity are considered by Beurle, continuous random activity, and the propagation of plane waves. We shall not be concerned with the latter form of activity (at least in this paper), but shall limit ourselves to the former type of activity.

We consider the case when F is constant and independent of x throughout the cell volume. The first convolution then becomes

$$F \int_{\infty}^{\infty} \xi(x)\, dx = 2\, b\, a_0\, F \tag{29}$$

using (27). Similarly

$$N = 2\, ba_0\, sF \tag{30}$$

A Poisson distribution of actual numbers of impulses is assumed, so that the proportion of cells with a total excitation of $q - 1$ will be

$$P_{(q-1)} = e^{-\overline{N}} \frac{\overline{N}^{q-1}}{(q-1)!} = e^{-2ba_0 sF} \frac{(2ba_0 sF)^{q-1}}{(q-1)!} \tag{31}$$

The proportion of sensitive cells with the above property is then

$$R\, P_{(q-1)}$$

The proportion of cells which actually receive an impulse during δt will be

$$2\, b\, a_0\, F\, \delta t$$

Thus the proportion of cells which are sensitive and attain the threshold during a period δt will be

$$RP_{(q-1)}\, 2\, b\, a_0\, F\, \delta t$$

leading to the equation

$$F(t + \tau) = RP_{(q-1)}\, 2\, b\, a_0\, F(t) \tag{32}$$

or

$$F(t + \tau) - F(t) = (RP_{(q-1)}\, k - 1)\, F(t) \tag{33}$$

where $k = 2\, b\, a_0$,
or equivalently

$$\frac{dF}{dt} = (RP_{(q-1)}\, k - 1)\, F \tag{34}$$

It follows from (31) that $P_{(q-1)}$ is proportional to $F_{(q-1)}$ so for large $F(t)$, $F(t + \tau)$ is greater, for small $F(t)$, $F(t + \tau)$ is less. If $F(t)$ is constant then clearly

$$RP_{(q-1)}\, k = 1 \tag{35}$$

and also the recovery rate should equal the rate at which sensitive cells fire, *i.e.*

$$p - Rp = F\, r\, p \tag{36}$$

Thus

$$P_{(q-1)} (1 - Fr) k = 1$$

or

$$e^{-Fks} \frac{(Fks^{(q-1)})}{(q-1)} \left(k - Fks\frac{r}{s}\right) = 1 \tag{37}$$

It is clear however that such continuous random activity is unstable, any small perturbation leading either to saturation or quiescence in the network. (see Fig. 5).

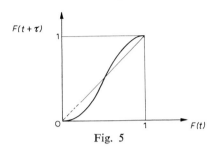

Fig. 5

Thus the only two stable states of such networks are $F(t) = F(t + n\tau) = 0$ or 1.

It was also noted in passing by Beurle, that

"Information about a large number of occurrences is 'stored' in any one network of cells, (and given many networks) . . . information about a particular type of occurrence is stored in a very large number of such units in such a way that it can be extracted for use when necessary. There is thus a multiple diversity effect which would readily account for the fact that damage to a limited region of the (network) does not have any marked effect on the operation of the whole system."

Thus Beurle's concept of a biological organization is that of a large number of networks of randomly interconnected cells having certain properties of stability (and instability) on perturbations and to damage. (It should also be noted that many important biological phenomena, e.g. learning and memory, are displayed by such networks provided suitable additional assumptions are made).

We shall later return to a consideration of damage in networks, but for the moment we now consider more recent work on the stability of randomly interconnected switching nets, notably that of Smith and Davidson (1962).

As we have noted (see Fig. 5) the only two stable states of the networks previously considered are $F(t) = 0$ or 1. This can be shown to derive from the assumption that all interconnexions between cells are excitatory; i.e. impingent impulse always 'excite' a cell, never 'inhibit' it. It was shown by Davidson and Smith (op. cit.) that if such inhibitory connexions are allowed, as well as excitatory ones, then the equilibrium and stationary states may be defined by the following equation:

$$F(t + \tau) = \sum_{i=q}^{sE} \sum_{j=0}^{\min(i-q, sI)} \binom{sE}{i} \binom{sI}{j}$$
$$\times F(t)^{(i+j)} (1 - F(t))^{s(E+I)-(i+j)} \tag{38}$$

where sE are the excitatory inputs, and sI the inhibitory inputs.

It is shown that in addition to the saturated stable states, there may exist intermediate levels of stable activity. (See Fig. 6; wherein a network with two non-zero stable states is shown).

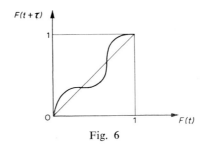

Fig. 6

This result (see also Griffith, 1963a,b) suggests the possibility of using Gibbsian methods to describe the behaviour of strongly interacting switching networks which contain both excitatory and inhibitory interconnexions. The step from continuous non-linear differential equations, to discrete switching networks is perhaps a large one, but certainly seems to be a distinct possibility.

There are however some other results concerning the properties of discrete switching networks arrived at by rather different considerations, which are especially relevant to the problem of replication. These results are to be found in the theory of automata, to which we now turn.

3. THE ORGANISM AS AN AUTOMATON

In § 2 we have considered the organism as a dynamical system, wherein the concepts of their analogues of energy, force, and to a lesser degree, entropy have been primary. The various physical quantities considered have been essentially *continuous*, or if they were discrete, aggregates were considered, which had effectively continuous properties. There is a great deal of evidence that many biological variables are in fact discrete, *e.g.* the all-or-nothing *nerve impulse* (Adrian and Forbes, 1922), the two configurations of the *allosteric protein* (Monod *et al.*, 1963), the macromolecular complexes containing the genetic code (Crick *et al.*, 1961) etc. What seems to matter in such systems is not so much the energy or forces operating, but the pattern of energy or force that results in the persistence of certain configurations of the states of such variables. Quantities such as energy, force etc. are essentially properties of individual or elementary *components* of systems, whereas configurational properties are system properties, although they depend upon the component properties. The former properties are in the domain of physics, chemistry, physiology, etc. whereas the latter properties fall into the domains of automata theory and of information theory. Thus Von Neumann (1948):

"(Living) systems are of enormous complexity and it is clearly necessary to sub-divide the problem that they represent into several parts. One method of sub-division ... is this: The organisms can be viewed as made up of parts which to a certain extent are independent, elementary units. We may, therefore, to this extent, view as the first part of the problem the structure and functioning of such elementary units individually. The second part of the problem consists of understanding how these elements are organized as a whole, and how the functioning of the whole is expressed in terms of the elements. The first part of the problem ... is closely connected with ... organic chemistry and physical chemistry and may in due course be greatly helped by quantum mechanics ... The second part is (connected with logic) . . . (We) remove the first part of the problem by the process of axio-matization, and concentrate on the second one.

The Axiomatic Procedure. Axiomatizing the behaviour of the elements means this: We assume that the elements have certain well-defined, outside functional characteristics; that is, they are to be treated as 'black boxes'. They are viewed as automatisms, the inner structure of which need not be disclosed, but which are assumed to react to certain unambiguously defined stimuli, by certain unambiguously defined responses . . . we may then investigate the larger organisms that can be built up from these elements, their structure, their functioning, the connexions between elements, and the general regularities that may be detectable in the complex synthesis of the organisms in question.'

The theory of automations, or automata, is thus closely connected with those configurations of the states of certain variables of complex organisms, designated as *functional units.* It is also closely connected with modern developments in mathematical logic, and in fact modern notions of automata derive from the formulation of mathematical logic as a deductive science, initiated by Boole (1847), and carried forward by Whitehead and Russell (1910) and by Godel (1931). This work was mainly concerned with the nature of the axiomatization of mathematics, and with theorem-proving and the general processes involved in deduction. Turing (1937) made a very important contribution to the subject by reducing these formulations of theorem-proving to the problem of deciding whether or not a certain computing automaton can 'compute' any given number or formula. The so-called *Turing-machine* is in fact of fundamental importance for the application of automata theory to biology, although not in its original form. (Recent attempts to apply the existing theory of Turing machines to biology (Stahl and Goheen, 1963) do not, in this author's opinion, provide more than a convenient notation for representing biological phenomena.)

The Turing-machine or computing automaton may be formally defined as follows:

An automaton is a 'black-box' having the following attributes:

(a) It possesses a finite number of 'states', $1, 2, \ldots, n$.

(b) Its operating characteristic comprises a description (short-code) of possible state-transitions.

(c) Its 'environment' consists of a (potentially) infinite tape, divided into fields or squares. (*I.e.* the tape is a one dimensional tesselation.) Each field may or may not contain a sign, say, a dot, and it is assumed that it is possible to erase, as well as to write in such a dot. A field marked with a dot is called '1', an unmarked field '0'. The sequence or pattern of '1's and '0's in the tesselation is called a *configuration.*

(d) It is assumed that one field of the tape is under direct inspection by the automaton, and that it has the ability to move the tape forward or backward, one field at a time.

(e) Let the automaton be in the state $i(i = 1, \ldots, n)$, and let it 'see' on the tape an $e (= 0,1)$. It will then print on to the tape an $f(= 0,1)$, move the tape by p fields ($p = 0, + 1, - 1$), and then go over into the state j ($j = 0,1, \ldots, n$). The specification of j, p, and f as functions of i and e comprises the short-code, and is a complete definition of the functioning of such an automaton.

Turing further introduced and analysed the concept of a '*universal automaton*', a concept of great importance, based on the following development: an infinite sequence of digits $e (= 0, 1)$, *i.e.* an infinite configuration in an infinite one dimensional tesselation, is essentially equivalent to the concept of a real number. Turing therefore considered such configurations, and investigated the question as to which automata were able to produce which configurations, *i.e.* given a definition law for the formation of such a configuration (*e.g.* a recursive definition), he inquired as to which automata can be used to 'form' the configuration, according to that law of formation. An automaton is able to form a certain configuration if it is possible to specify a finite length of tape, appropriately marked, so that if this tape is fed to the automaton it will thereupon write the configuration on the remaining (potentially infinite) free portion of the tape. The process of writing the configuration is in general, an indefinitely continuing one, so what is meant is that the automaton will keep running indefinitely, and given a sufficiently long time, will have inscribed any desired (but of course finite) part of the (infinite) configuration. The finite piece of tape constitutes the 'instruction' to the automaton relevant to the given problem. *An automaton is then said to be 'universal' if any configuration that can be produced by any automaton at all can also be produced by this particular automaton.* It might be thought a priori that this is impossible. Turing however, observed that a completely general description of any conceivable automaton can be given in a finite number of words (in the sense of the above definition). Such a description will contain certain empty passages — referring to *j, p, f* in terms of *i, e* — which specify the actual functioning of the automaton. When these empty passages are filled in, a specific automaton is then described. As long as they are left empty however, the schema represents the general definition of the general automaton. It then becomes possible to describe an automaton which when fed these functions (the short-code) thereupon functions like the automaton described. Such an automaton is then the universal computing automaton. To make it duplicate any *operation* that any other automaton can execute, it suffices to furnish it with a description of the automaton in question, and in addition, with the instructions which that device would have required for the operations under consideration.

McCulloch and Pitts (1943) made immediate use of Turing's results to show that any physiological, behaviouristic, or introspective activity of brains, which could be described in a finite number of words, could be realized by a computing automaton, more exactly, by a switching network. This network was composed of elementary functional units called 'formal neurons' (*cf.* Beurle, *op. cit.*), whose properties were minimal abstractions of the known properties of nerve cells and their processes. Kleene (1956) re-derived their results in a more transparent form, of which we shall give a brief outline.

A *formal neuron* or *f*-neuron consists of a device which integrates the excitatory or inhibitory impulses of many impinging inputs, and after a suitable delay (synaptic delay) produces an output (according to certain rules) which can influence other *f*-neurons. At equally separated times each such *f*-neuron is either active or quiescent, and the activity is of the all-or-none variety, *i.e.* an *f*-neuron is active at time *t* if and only if a certain minimal number θ (the *threshold* of the *f*-neuron) of excitatory inputs, and none of the inhibitory inputs to the given *f*-neuron was active at time τ, and the resultant activity is of constant amplitude independently of the particular number of active excitatory inputs. We write $y(t) = 1$ if the *f*-neuron is active at time

t, $y(t) = 0$ if it is quiescent, and assume that no errors occur in the functioning of such devices. Thus formal neurons are ideal synchronous digital switching devices, possessing a threshold θ, and a delay τ.

A *formal neural network* or *f.n.* network is any arrangement of a finite number of *f*-neurons. Such networks may be *cyclic* (*i.e.* containing circles) or *acyclic*. The activity of *f*-neurons is expressed by means of logical formulas taken from the two-valued logic of propositions and propositional functions. For example, the formula $P(t) = y_1(t - 1) \mathbin{\&} y_2(t - 1) \mathbin{\&} \bar{y}_3(t - 1)$ expresses logically the fact that the *f*-neuron fires at time t if, and only if, *f*-neurons 1 and 2 fired at time $t - 1$, and *f*-neuron 3 did not. In a similar way network configurations may be specified by giving these *f*-neurons firing at various times.

A particularly important representation of *f.n.* network activity is the following: The input to such a network over all past time up to a given instant t may be described by a table with columns corresponding to inputs, and rows corresponding to past time instants, *e.g.*

TABLE I

	1	2	3	4	5
t–1	1	1	0	1	0
t–2	1	1	1	0	0
t–3	0	1	1	0	1

Any sub-class of the class of all possible tables describing the input over all past time constitutes an *event*, which occurs when the table describing the actual input belongs to this class. Thus the event corresponding to

$$P(t) = y_1(t - 1) \mathbin{\&} y_2(t - 1) \mathbin{\&} \bar{y}_3(t - 1) \mathbin{\&} \bar{y}_4(t - 1) \mathbin{\&} \bar{y}_5(t - 1) \qquad (39)$$

occurs in Table I. When events are referred to a fixed period of time consisting of some m ($\geqslant 1$) consecutive instants $t - \mathrm{m} + 1$, $t - m + 2, \ldots t - 1$, t they are called *definite events of duration m*. Otherwise they are called *indefinite events*.

The main problem in the McCulloch-Pitts theory is the representation of such events (or, in another language, the recognition of such configurations), and the following theorems are proved:

(1) To each ... definite event there is an acyclic network which represents the event by firing some *f*. neurons in the network at time $t + 2$.

(2) Any event which is representable in an acyclic network by such a firing at time $t + \tau$ ($\tau \geqslant 1$) is definite.

Thus there exists a direct connexion between definite events, and acyclic networks. There exists also a connexion between indefinite events and cyclic networks, requiring the introduction of the concept of a *regular event*. Roughly speaking a regular event is composed of an (in general infinite) number of definite events, and so includes the class of definite events, and some, but not all, members of the class of indefinite events. The following theorem is then proved:

(3) To each regular event, there is a network which represents the event by firing some f-neuron in the network at time $t + 2$, when started with a suitable network configuration at time 1.

References p. 61

A more general concept than a network, the so-called *finite automaton* is then introduced, comprising a finite *f.n.* network with any finite number of states (*i.e.* the *f*-neurons may have more than one active state, but must be discrete). It is then proved that

(4) In any finite automaton started at time 1, in a given state, the event represented by a given state at time *t*, is regular.

The behaviour of finite automata was thus specified in the sense that those configurations eliciting specific network responses were specified, and *vice-versa*. McCulloch and Pitts interpreted these results to be a demonstration of the formal equivalence between Turing machines, and *f*-neural networks, provided such networks possessed auxiliary stores of unbounded capacity, and laid the foundations for much later work on the similarities between the computer and the brain; *cf.* Arbib (1961) for a clear exposition of their work.

Since then, much work has been done on the mathematics of finite automata, Turing machines, and so forth, but little of it of a specifically mathematical character has been usefully applied to the description of biological phenomena. The reason underlying this is that most of such work has been concerned with problems of effective computability or solvability, *i.e.* the existence of algorithms for the solution of general classes of problems, and not with the properties of specific computing systems. Some notable exceptions have been the work of Beurle *et al.* referred to in § 1, and that of Uttley (1954, *et seq.*), Rosenblatt (1962, *et seq.*) and others, on the simulation of intelligence, but since such work is not strictly within the domain of this enquiry, we shall not discuss it.

In the field of molecular biology however, Sugita (1961, *et seq.*) has used essentially the McCulloch-Pitts formulation of automata theory, to describe enzymatic reactions. Instead of considering concentrations (see Goodwin, *op. cit.*) he considers only the presence or absence of metabolites, and so forth, *assuming the system to be always in a stationary state*. It is then possible to describe for example, the scheme for genetic regulation put forward by Jacob and Monod (1961) to which we have already referred. Unfortunately this analysis is purely descriptive as yet, and contains no possibility of real predictive value. The reason for this is similar to the reasons for the basic inapplicability of mathematical logic *per se* to biology — it is not concerned with the unfolding of specified events in specific systems — but with theorem-proving.

A recent approach to finite automata theory (see for example Rhodes and Krohn, 1963) however, may contain possibilities for such a development. The new automata theory is essentially a branch of the theory of groups and of semi-groups, and as such, asks different questions. It is true that hitherto, purely algebraic questions have been exclusively considered (unique factorization theorems, minimization problems, etc.), but previous experience concerning the application of group theory to mechanics, notably quantum mechanics, suggests that a dynamical theory of automata may be more than a remote possibility. Recent work on the dynamics of control systems (Kalman, 1963) seems to indicate, in fact, a deep connexion between the descriptions of linear dynamic systems, at any rate, and the descriptions of finite automata.

There is however one application of automata theory, although not of finite automata, that is of great biological interest, namely *the theory of self-reproducing automata* developed by Von Neumann. Most of Von Neumann's work on this topic, is as yet unpublished. He gave an outline of the theory in 1948 (Von Neumann, 1948, *op cit.*) but did not live to complete and publish any further work on this topic. What he did manage to do will however be published posthumously, (University of Illinois Press, 1965, Ed. A. W. Burks). Burks has given an exposition of this work (Philco Symposium on Memory and the Adaptive System, January, 1962), which we shall briefly outline. The basic problem is essentially to discover the requisite organization, or pre-organization required for self-reproduction. Von Neumann considered initially, a so-called *kinematic model*, *i.e.* a model in which automata were to be constructed from mechano-like parts, but in which the truly mechanical questions concerning force and energy are ignored, attention being focussed on the geometrical-kinematic problems of movement, contact, positioning, fusing, and cutting. The temporal reference frame was discrete: logical and kinematic action taking place instantaneously at discrete times. The following kinds of parts were postulated:

  (i) A rigid member or girder,
  (ii) A fusing organ, and
  (iii) A cutting organ.
  (iv) A stimulus organ, probably a logical 'or' or disjunction.
  (v) A coincidence organ, *i.e.* a logical 'and' and or conjunction, and
  (vi) An inhibitory organ, *i.e.* a logical 'not' or negation.
  (vii) A muscle organ, *i.e.* a normally rigid connexion which constructs effectively to length zero, when stimulated.
(viii) A stimulus producer, *i.e.* a gated reservoir, or perhaps a clock.

The problem of self-reproduction was then posed as follows: Can one build an aggregate out of the above basic elements (or perhaps a slightly larger set) in such a manner that if it is put into a reservoir, in which there floats all these elements in large numbers, it will then begin to construct other aggregates, each of which will at the end turn out to be another automaton exactly like the original one? It turns out that this problem is feasible, and in principle closely related to that of Turning's universal computing automaton — in the sense that a complete description of any automaton can be given in a finite number of words . . . such a description will again contain empty spaces, so that it is general. The following automata are then describable:

(a) A universal constructing automaton, A

That is an automaton which when furnished with a description of any other automaton will construct that entity. The description is not however a configuration of a one-dimensional tessellation, but a configuration of states of the basic structural elements having however all the notational properties of the tessellations. Such a description is called an *instruction* I. The process of construction is then effected in a free-floating reservoir of elementary components, the basic set of these components being assumed sufficient for such a process (*i.e.* sensing, welding, cutting, moving, etc.). It is noted that 'one need not worry about how a fixed automaton . . . can produce others which are larger and more complex than itself . . . the greater size and the higher complexity of the object to be constructed will be reflected in a presumably still greater size of the instructions I that have to be furnished . . . which will themselves be aggregates of elementary parts'.

In all the automata considered, a location will exist where such instructions I can be inserted so that when such automata are being described, the specification for the location is understood to form part of the description. Thus the statement 'inserting a given instruction I into a given automaton A' is meaningful.

(b) A copying automaton, B

Since I is an aggregate of elementary parts, the copying automaton has merely to duplicate any particular aggregate, much as a tape reading machine can reproduce any input tape.

The following procedure then results in self reproduction:

(1) Suppose the automata A and B are combined together with the following control mechanism C: assume A contains the instruction I. Then C causes A to construct the automaton described in I, and then causes B to copy I, and insert it into the automaton constructed by A. By assumption this automaton contains a location for I. Finally C separates the resultant automaton from the aggregate $A + B + C = D$.

(2) The aggregate D must itself contain I, inserted into A. Form I_d which describes D, and insert this into A. Then $A + B + C$ will construct and turn loose another automaton or aggregate $A + B + C$. Call $A + B + C + I_d$ the aggregate E. E is clearly self-reproductive.

Von Neumann notes (at least in 1948) that no paradox exists . . . when the 'formation' of I_d is called for, D exists already, and is not modified by the formation of I_d. However, he later notes (Von Neumann, 1952) 'that logical paradoxes of the Richard type (self-referential paradoxes) are likely to arise if one tries to copy a live machine'.

Von Neumann goes on to make some interesting statements concerning the relationship of his kinematic model to biology, namely:

(a) I_d roughly executes genetic function;
(b) The automaton B performs the fundamental reproductive act, the replication of genetic material;
(c) Arbitrary alterations in the system E, *i.e.* mutations, especially in I_d can affect the reproductive process.

He notes that:

". . . . . the natural gene does probably not contain a complete description of the object whose construction its presence stimulates. It probably contains only general pointers, general clues."

Thus Von Neumann tended to the epigenetic view of natural development, although his actual model is the epitome of pre-formationism! (See also Ashby, 1952).

As a final comment Von Neumann noted that:

'complication' on its lowest levels is probably degenerative, that is, every automaton that can produce other automata will only be able to produce less complicated ones. There is, however, a certain minimum level where this degenerative characteristic ceases to be universal. At this point automata which can reproduce themselves, or even construct higher entities, become possible. This fact, that complication as well as organization, below a certain minimum level is degenerative, and beyond that level can become self-supporting and even increasing, will clearly play an important role in any future theory of the subject."

It seems that beyond this informal level, the kinematic self-reproducing model was never developed in any great detail, (see however Burks, 1959), and Von Neumann turned to a mathematically more tractable model, the so-called *cellular or tessellation model* (Von Neumann, 1964, *op. cit.*).

The tessellation model comprises a two-dimensional tessellation (for terminology and definitions, see Moore, 1962) containing square cells or fields of equal size. In each field there exists a finite automaton possessing only 29 states. At some initial time $t = t_0$ all but a finite number of cells are in a so-called blank or unexcited state U. The problem is to reproduce the initial configuration at any later time t. Von Neumann was motivated by Turing's construction of a universal Turing machine to believe there existed a universal constructing machine. However this turned out to be more than suggestive, and the universal constructing automaton had to be constructed *ab initio* — the result being a monstrous blueprint sprawling over some 40,000 squares of the tessellation. We leave discussion of this paper however, until published details are fully available, and consider instead, a very similar formulation of the reproduction problem, one not aimed at mathematical rigour however, but at providing biological insight, by Barricelli (1957, 1962).

The problem considered by Barricelli is not essentially the problem of self-reproduction, but the problem of *evolution*. In particular the evolution of increasingly complex organisms is considered, *on the assumption that self-reproducing entities already exist*. Such entities however are numerical and exist as different states of the cells of a two dimensional Euclidean tessellation space. The following rules of reproduction and of interaction are then defined:

Let a be the column number in a tessellation, and g the row number corresponding respectively to position and generation of a given numerical entity. Let X_{ag} be the state of a-th cell in the g-th generation. Then the *reproduction rule* is

$$X_{ag} = n \to X_{a+n, \, g+1} = n \tag{40}$$

i.e. the state of the $(a + n)$-th cell in the $(g + 1)$-th generation is equal to the state of a-th cell in the g-th generation. Fig. 7 shows an example of such a process:

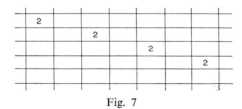

Fig. 7

It is evident that if this is the only process that occurs, no increase of complexity can take place. Accordingly a *rule of interaction* is defined as follows:

$$X_{a,g} = n \,\&\, X_{a,g-1} = m \to X_{a+n, \, g+1} = n \,\& \\ X_{a+m, \, g+1} = n \,\&\, X_{a+m, \, g} = m \tag{41}$$

Examples of this process are shown in Fig. 8.

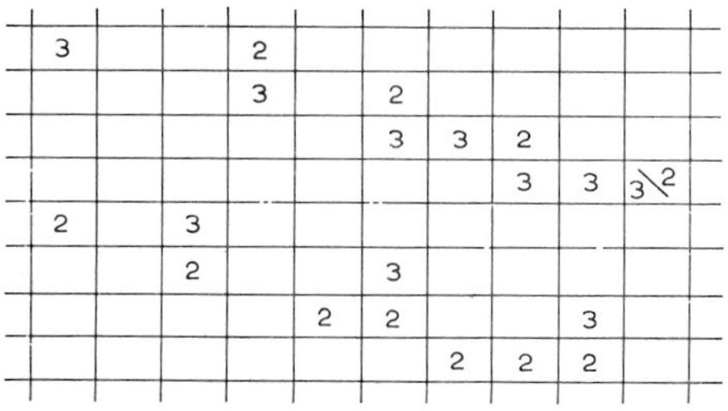

Fig. 8

It is evident that as a result of the interaction, number entities can proliferate in the tessellation.

With many such rules it may sometimes happen that *collisions* occur in the tessellation. To deal with this Barricelli assumed (initially) a rule of consistency, so that number entities in collision were all erased.

$$X_{a,g} = n \ \& \ X_{a,g} = m$$
$$\to X_{a,g} = x \text{ (blank), unless } m = n \tag{42}$$

Such a process is shown in Fig. 9:

Fig. 9

A computer simulation of such a system was then carried out, and various properties were discovered, among them being:

(a) *Self-reproduction* — e.g. in Fig. 10 it is shown how a particular configuration (called a *symbio-organism* by Barricelli) is able to reproduce itself:

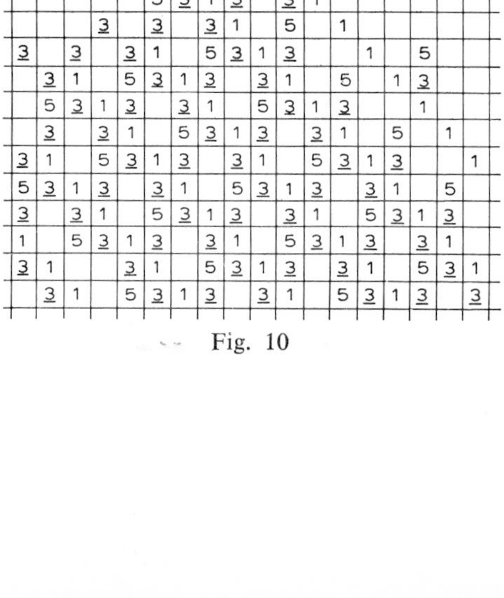

Fig. 10

(b) *Cross-breeding* — it is shown that if two symbio-organisms are placed in the same tessellation, then an exchange of numbers takes place mimicking chromosomal exchange in haploid organisms. *E.g.* the symbio-organism (9, — 11, 1, — 7) and (5, — 11, 1, — 3) can crossbreed to give (5, — 11, 1, — 7) and (9, — 11, 1, — 3) as well as the parent symbio-organisms.

(c) *Great variability* — each symbio-organism may consist of many elements (genes) and each element may have several states (alleles). The number of varieties which can arise is practically unlimited.

(d) *Parasitism* — same symbio-organisms cannot reproduce completely, and degenerate into simpler symbio-organisms (*cf.* Von Neumann), unless they can interact with other symbio-organisms.

(e) *Self-repairing properties* — damage to symbio-organisms is generally repaired after some small number of generations. The process may often be successful even if all the configurations in any one generation are damaged. *The greater the number of cooperating symbio-organisms present, the greater is the probability of survival.* Barricelli notes that this phenomenon is analogous to reactivation by multiple infection with inactivated (for example irradiated) bacteriophages.

It is not however necessary to simulate the above symbio-organisms to deduce these properties, and we give in an appendix, the beginnings of a mathematical analysis aimed at complete prediction of self-reproducing phenomena of the type considered by Barricelli. On the other hand, evolutionary properties do not show up in the above, and a *rule of mutation* has to be introduced instead of the rule of collision (41), making mathematical analysis much more difficult. The following rule is used:

(1) An X which happens to be under an occupied square remains.

(2) An X which happens to be under an empty square or under another X is replaced by a number M, whose absolute value is equal to distance between its nearest neighbours (in the same generation), and whose sign is positive if such neighbours have the same parity, negative if otherwise.

(3) If (1) and (2) do not occur, then X remains. Examples of these rules are shown in Fig. 11.

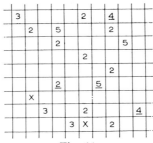

Fig. 11

With such a rule of mutation, the following properties were discovered:

(f) *Spontaneous formation of symbio-organism* — if the numbers 1, — 1 are placed randomly into a tessellation (according to the tossing of an unbiassed coin, say), in subsequent generations, new symbio-organisms comprising numbers other than 1, — 1 arise. Under favourable conditions (lack of competition from existant symbio-organisms) such symbio-organisms tend to be formed quite frequently — *i.e. the spontaneous formation of symbio-organisms, given self-reproducing, cooperative entities, is not a rare event.*

(g) *Evolution* — symbio-organisms may be completely modified, so that their complexity increases drastically, and so that they branch into different species *which are unable to interbreed.* Such evolution leads to a better adaptation to the artificial environmental conditions, and to a greater ability to compete with other symbio-organisms. *Both mutation and the interbreeding or crossing phenomenon previously described, play a central role in the evolution of symbio-organisms.*

It is evident that the symbiotic phenomena described by Barricelli are extremely suggestive of existing biotic phenomena, and he has essentially given a set of minimal conditions for the evolution of complex self-reproducing systems. The fact that mutations play an important role is a vindication of contemporary evolutionary genetics, while the importance of the crossing phenomena has its parallel in the known importance of chromosomal exchange and crossing that takes place in meiosis.

If would seem then that on the basis of Von Neumann's and Barricelli's work on self-reproducing systems, that Wigner's conclusions on the probability of self-reproduction are incorrect. On the other hand, however, even Von Neumann recognised that his automata were idealisations of dynamical systems which might not correspond to macromolecular systems. Thus (Wigner: *op. cit.*)

". . . . . . the model used by Von Neumann . . . can assume only a discrete set of states, whereas all our variables . . . . are continuous. This permits the postulation of an ideal behaviour of the system and the 'tailoring' of what substitutes for equations of motion in such a way that they permit reproduction."

Wigner further notes that the Watson-Crick model of DNA replication (Watson and Crick, 1953) seems at odds with his own analysis, but comments:

'. . . . . . the details of the functioning of the model do not appear to have been worked out completely. Similarly, the reliability of the model, that is the probability of its malfunctioning has not been evaluated and compared with experience. One may incline, therefore, to the view, implicit also in Elsasser's ideas, that the type of reproduction for which the model of Crick and Watson seems to apply, can, as can all similar processes, be described by the known laws of nature, but only approximately. However, the apparently virtually absolute reliability of the functioning of the model is the consequence of a biotonic law."

Wigner's critique of Von Neumann's use of ideal automata as models of living systems is well taken, although he also (in addition to Elsasser) invokes biotonic phenomena as responsible for maintaining the high reliability of biological replication. In the next section, however, we shall discuss how the theory of non-ideal automata may be developed, and later, how some of its results might be applied to the above problems.

4. THE ORGANISM AS AN INFORMATION PROGRESSOR

The theory of automata that we have outlined deals with ideal automata, *i.e.* with automata whose elements are 'noiseless'. A completely different class of problems is met with in connexion with the problem of synthesising reliable automata from noisy elements.

Perhaps the first to consider this problem in detail was Von Neumann (1952), as might have been guessed. Pitts and McCulloch (1947) in attempting to apply the theory of automata to problems concerning auditory and visual perception and cortical functioning, had noted that those *f*-neural networks designed to model such aspects of complex biological systems ought to be constructed so that their function was unaffected by small fluctuations in excitations and inhibitions, in thresholds of *f*-neurons, and in local details of interconnexion between *f*-neurons. Wiener (1948, *op. cit.*) had also considered an aspect of this problem, that of computer malfunctions caused by malfunctions and/or failures of their elements. He had noted that in existing computers the use of majority logic — 'what I tell you three times is true' — coupled with a search procedure for finding new elements, resulted in reliability of computation.

It was with this background in mind that Von Neumann attacked these problems. His principal solution to this problem was obtained in the following manner. The reliable recognition of input configurations is required of some finite automaton, that corresponds say, to the reliable computation of a Boolian function (*cf.* McCulloch and Pitts, 1943, *op. cit.*). It is assumed that *f*-neurons are available for the construction of the automaton in question that compute one of the universal Boolian functions, from aggregates of which every other Boolian function may be constructed. In this particular case the so-called Sheffer-stroke function $P(t) = \bar{y}_1(t-1) \,\&\, \bar{y}_2(t-1)$ was used. Signals are transmitted from *f*-neuron to *f*-neuron via connexions that carry only binary impulses. It is also assumed that *f*-neurons fail to function correctly, with a probability ε, which is independent of the general state of the network, and of the occurrence of other malfunctions.

To minimise the effects of such malfunctions, a network is designed that comprises many more *f*-neurons and connexions than are absolutely necessary to compute the requisite Boolian function, *i.e. redundant* network is designed. Consider for example the finite automaton shown in Fig. 12, which realizes a given definite event in a supposedly non-redundant way. Suppose this is the event to be realised with malfunctioning *f*-neurons. Compute the event with the following automaton: each *f*-neuron of the precursor automaton is replaced by an aggregate of *f*-neurons of the same type, and each connexion is replaced by a bundle of connexions. The organization within each aggregate and bundle is not completely ordered — some microlevel randomness is permitted. However the organization between aggregates follows exactly that of the precursor automaton. Each aggregate processes only that which the single precursor *f*-neuron and connexion did. Thus many *f*-neurons and connexions of the network are redundant, and each aggregate operates on a repeated signal carried by a bundle, and makes a decision only on a majority basis. The details of such a process are as follows: Each bundle comprises n connexions, each carrying binary impulses, so that there are 2^n distinct patterns of excitation, ranging from $(111\ldots.1111)$ to $(000\ldots.0000)$. The number of ones in any pattern is termed F, and a fiduciary level is set, such that

1. $n \geqslant F \geqslant (1 - \triangle)\, n$ signals '1'
2. $0 \leqslant F \leqslant \triangle n$ signals '0'
3. $\triangle n < F < (1 - \triangle)\, n$ signals malfunction.

Each redundant aggregate operates on its input bundles in the following manner. Any input pattern having F greater than some critical value F_c produces an output pattern with an increased number of ones, and any input pattern having F less than F_c produces an output pattern with a decreased number of ones, (see Fig. 12):

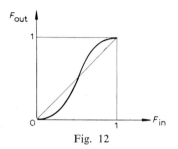

Fig. 12

By suitable iterations, any pattern of ones and zeros can be converted into either all one's or all zero's. Such an assembly was called by von Neumann, a *restoring-organ*, since it effectively restores excitation patterns that have been corrupted by noise. If Fig. 12 is compared with Fig. 5 describing the stable states of Beurle's network of randomly connected f-neurons, (*cf.* § 2), the similarity is striking, and in fact it is clear that Von Neumann's restoring organs are in fact examples of Beurle's networks, in which the steady states, two in number, are designated '1' and '0'. Such a parallel has been noted by many workers (*e.g.* Griffith, 1963a, b, *op. cit.*), but not too much has been made of it. We shall however return to this point in a later section, in a more general context.

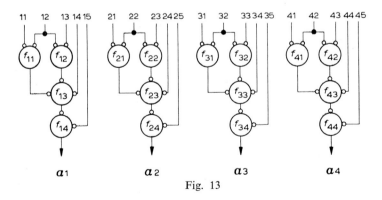

Fig. 13

Fig. 14 shows an example of the resultant redundant automaton obtained from the precursor of Fig. 13, in which each f-neuron is replaced by a redundant aggregate. The redundancy may be defined as

$$N = 3n \tag{43}$$

For given ε, Von Neumann, by varying $\triangle$ and n, was able to show an optimum $\triangle$ existed, so that no malfunctions propagated through the redundant network, *i.e.* all excitation patterns being stabilised at all ones or all zeros. He obtained for the overall probability of malfunction of the automaton, given $\varepsilon = 0.005$ per bit, the function

$$P \cong \frac{6.4}{n} \times 10^{-8n/10000} \tag{44}$$

This expression is such that large values of n (extremely high redundancy) were required to produce reasonably small P's; (see (Table II):

TABLE II

n	p
1 000	2.7×10^{-2}
2 000	2.6×10^{-3}
3 000	2.5×10^{-4}
5 000	4.0×10^{-6}
10 000	1.6×10^{-10}
20 000	2.8×10^{-19}
25 000	1.2×10^{-23}

It is this result which has led Elsasser (*op. cit.*) and to some extent Wigner (*op. cit.*) to postulate the existence of biotonic phenomena as being responsible for the high reliability exhibited by macromolecular systems involved in the maintenance, transmission and read-out of heredity information.

Von Neumann was not satisfied with this result, and voiced the contention that:

".. error should be treated by thermodynamic methods, and be the subject of a thermodynamical theory, as information has been, by the work of L. Szilard and C.E. Shannon."

The beginning of such a development has in fact recently occurred (Winograd and Cowan, *op. cit.*) and it is to this that we now turn.

The starting point of this development is the mathematical theory of communication developed by C. E. Shannon (Shannon, 1948, *op. cit.*) concerning the transmission and coding of information. This theory contains elements already present in statistical theories of matter, but the object of study is not now the properties of matter. Instead it is a highly specific communication system, comprising a *source* of messages, a communication *channel*, and a receiver of messages.

Both source and receiver select symbols from an *alphabet* consisting of a well-defined collection of signs, which is known to both the source and the receiver. The source selects symbols from this alphabet, thus constructing *messages* that are transmitted as *physical signals* through the channel, to the receiver. There the signals control the selection of symbols by the receiver. In such a fashion are messages transmitted and received.

Shannon defined the *information content* of a message to be the *ensemble average*

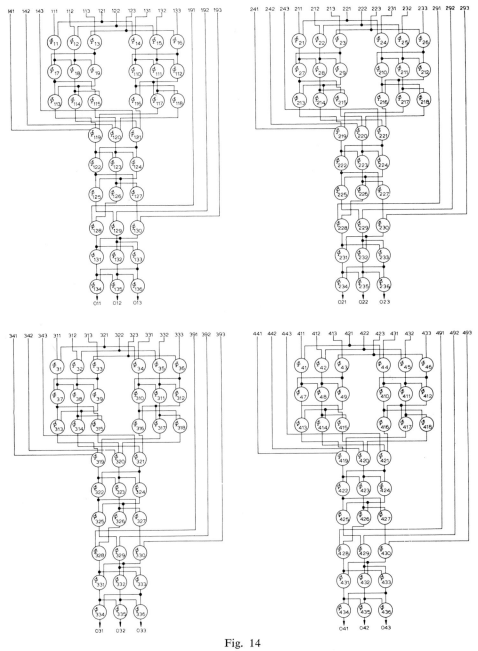

Fig. 14

$$H(X) = -\sum_{i=1}^{k} P(x_i) \log_2 P(x_i) \tag{45}$$

where x_i ($i = 1, 2, \ldots k$) is any symbol selected from the ensemble X: ($x_1, x_2, \ldots x_k$) occurring with probabilities $P(x_i)$ respectively. The logarithmic function was chosen because of its property of transforming multiplicative probabilities into sums of logarithms, thus ensuring that the measure of information was additive for independent symbols.

Shannon in fact called $H(X)$ the *entropy* of the source, since the quantity bears a very close formal resemblance to the Boltzmann-Gibbs entropy function of statistical physics, and proved two important limit theorems which form the real core of information theory. These theorems are connected with so-called *coding operations* that can be performed on messages. The term 'code' denotes any system of symbols, *e.g.* words, arbitrarily used in place of other words, or phrases, to secure brevity or secrecy. In the process of communication, messages, such as printed texts, telegrams, etc. are usually coded into certain standard forms, *e.g.* into sequences of binary digits. This is done for a variety of reasons, one of which is that it costs less to transmit information in coded form. Clearly the fewer binary digits used the better. Shannon's first theorem specifies the average number of binary digits required to code messages selected from a given ensemble. That is: Given an ensemble X of m messages whose information content is $H(X)$, and an alphabet of k symbols, it is possible to encode messages selected from the ensemble into sequences of symbols selected from the given alphabet, so that the average number of symbols per message, $\bar{n}$, satisfies the inequality

$$\frac{H(X)}{\log_2 k} \leqslant \bar{n} < 1 + \frac{H(X)}{\log_2 k} \tag{46}$$

and $\bar{n}$ cannot be smaller than the lower bound.

The relative differences between the upper and lower bounds may be made negligibly small by selecting messages from ensembles containing large amounts of information, *i.e.* if the messages themselves comprise segments of sequences of independent symbols x_i selected from ensembles of information content $H(X_i)$, so that $H(X) = nH(X)$, then in the limit of increasingly long messages:

$$\lim_{n \to \infty} \frac{1}{n} (\log_2 k^{\bar{n}}) = H(X_i) \tag{47}$$

In particular if $k = 2$, *i.e.* the binary alphabet is used, then

$$\lim_{n \to \infty} \bar{n} = H(X) \tag{48}$$

We thus obtain a direct operational meaning for the *information content of an ensemble*, namely it is the (asymptotic) *minimum number of binary digits required on the average to encode a message selected from the ensemble*. We give an example of such a code in Table III.

The second of Shannon's main theorems is concerned with the transmission of coded messages through physical channels, *i.e.* through systems that can transmit or propogate physical signals. Such channels are subject to disturbances called noise by communications engineers, so that in general the messages recovered from the channel are somewhat distorted; (*cf.* Von Neumann, this section). Input messages to the channel may not be uniquely determined by output messages from the channel, and errors may occur if identification is attempted. This situation can be characterised

TABLE III

Message number	Message probability	Binary code-word	$-log_2$ of probability
0	0.25	00	2
1	0.25	01	2
2	0.125	100	3
3	0.125	101	3
4	0.0625	1100	4
5	0.0625	1101	4
6	0.0625	1110	4
7	0.0625	1111	4

by the use of conditional probabilities $P(x_i/y_j)$ specifying the probability that a given output symbol y_j corresponds to a certain transmitted input symbol x_i. The noise is similarly specified by the transition probabilities $P(y_j/x_i)$. These probabilities are related to the information measures, by the formulas

$$H(X/Y) = - \sum_{i,j} P(x_i, y_j) \log P(x_i/y_j)$$

$$H(Y/X) = - \sum_{i,j} P(x_i, y_j) \log P(y_j/x_i)$$

$$(49)$$

$H(X)$ and $H(X/Y)$ are essentially measures of the average uncertainty present in the determination of x symbols before and after transmission, while $H(Y)$ and $H(Y/X)$ refer to the y symbols. The quantity

$$R(X;Y) = H(X) - H(X/Y) \tag{50}$$

is called *rate of transmission of information*, and measures the amount of information acquired per symbol, by the recipient, concerning the X ensemble. This rate is bounded by the effects of channel noise, and it can be shown that there exists an upper limit to it, called the *channel capacity*. One purpose underlying communications engineering design is to make full use of this capacity, subject to a criterion that as few errors as possible are made in the identification of X symbols. Shannon's second theorem is derived at this situation, and its main content is that the probability of occurrence of errors of identification may be made arbitrarily small, under certain circumstances by suitable encoding and decoding of sequences of messages. More exactly: given a discrete source S selecting messages from an ensemble X whose information content is $H(X)$, and a discrete memoryless noisy channel of capacity C, then there exists at least one code with the property that if $H(X) \leqslant C$, then suitably encoded messages may be transmitted over the channel and recovered with an arbitrarily small frequency of identification errors. If $H(X) > C$, then it is possible to encode messages such that $H(X/Y)$ is less than $H(X) - C + \varepsilon$, where ε is arbitrarily small. There is no method of encoding that results in an $H(X/Y)$ less than $H(X) - C$.

The proof of this theorem is somewhat involved and we shall not reproduce it here, suffice it to say that the probability of error of identification P_e, is shown to be given (approximately) by:

$$P_e \cong 2^{-n(C-H(X))} \tag{51}$$

where n is the length of the code words used. It is important to note however, that this error probability is an average. In particular it is an average over all codes that encode only high probability message sequences from S, and since it tends to zero with increasing n, provided $H(X) \leq C$, it follows that *there exists at least one code for which* $P_e \to 0$. Any code approximating to this ideal code would have the property that if any signal is distorted by noise, then the original message can still be recovered, *i.e.* the distortion will not in general cause confusion of signals. This is accomplished by the introduction of redundancy, not in the manner used by Von Neumann (*op. cit.*) but as follows: Messages of length k issuing from a source of information S, are coded into blocks of signal code words of length n, where

$$\frac{k}{n} \leqslant C \tag{52}$$

k/n is in fact identified with the rate of transmission of information per signal digit, through the channel. Such code-words of length n contain k information digits, and $n - k$ additional digits, which can be used for error-correction purposes at the receiver, in various possible ways (*cf.* Petersen, 1961). This occurs because such codes function by 'reserving' sets of output signal sequences for each given input sequencet Such sets comprise all sequences differing in some few digits from the given inpu.

TABLE IV

Input sequences	Reserved sequences
11	11011
	01011
	10011
	11111
	11001
	11010
10	10101
	00101
	11101
	10001
	10111
	10100
01	01110
	11110
	00110
	01010
	01100
	01111
00	00000
	10000
	01000
	00100
	00010
	00001

sequence. Any particular output sequence is then *decoded* according to this classification. For example, a particular code with $k = 1$, $n = 3$, reserves the output sequences $111, 110, 101, 011$, for the input sequence 1, and the sequences $000, 001, 010,$ 100 for the sequence 0, while a certain code with $k = 2$, $n = 5$, reserves the following sequences for the input sequences $11, 10, 01, 00$: (Table IV).

Its is important to note that the encoders and decoders associated with such error-correcting codes, are complicated finite automata (although if arbitrarily small P_e were desired, with $H(X) \cong C$, they would not be finite), and in fact correspond to *definite events*, of the kind already discussed. Thus encoders and decoders may be constructed as *f.n.* networks. *Such networks become more complex as both k and n increase*, and a particular assumption required in the proof of the coding theorem for noisy channels, is that *such networks may be considered to be error-free compared with the channel.*

Turning now to a comparison of formulas (44) and (51), it is evident that ratio n/k is a generalization of the (implicit) ratio $3 n/1$ used to measure *redundancy* in describing Von Neumann's construction of a reliable automaton. A comparison of the two formulas cited (Fig. 15) shows a quite different qualitative character. In (44), P goes to zero with $1/n$, whereas in (51) P goes to zero independently of k/n although both k and n must increase. *I.e.* in Von Neumann's case only a continued increase of redundancy results in high reliability, whereas in Shannon's case, provided a certain minimum redundancy is incorporated high reliability may be obtained with a constant level of redundancy, *provided something else is increased*. What this' something else' is, will become clearer later in this section.

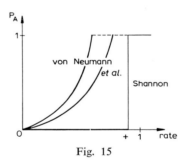

Fig. 15

We now give a short résumé of the extension of Shannon's theorem to computation rather than communication in the presence of noise. We distinguish *computation* from communication as follows: suppose instead of a communication channel (*e.g.* a transmission line, or relay device) we have some finite automaton, or in fact one elementary *f*-neuron that responds uniquely to various input excitation patterns. If given an output pattern from such an automaton, we cannot, even in the absence of noise within the automaton and fluctuations in the excitation pattern uniquely specify the input pattern, then we say the automaton has executed a computation. If, for example, an automaton receives all eight possible input patterns of zero-one triplets, and responds say, as shown in Table V, then we say that computation has been

TABLE V

Input	Output
111	1
110	1
101	1
100	0
011	1
010	0
001	0
000	0

executed, since given an output symbol, the input symbol cannot be uniquely specified at the output. We call the particular mapping of the input patterns on to the set (0,1) the *function* computed by the given unit. The problem of ensuring reliable computation in the presence of noise thus becomes the problem of ensuring that the mapping by a network of input patterns on to output patterns corresponds to the specified function of an automaton, despite errors in the mappings executed by individual elements in the network.

In Winograd and Cowan (*op. cit.*) it is shown how such an automaton may be described by the use of information measures. Thus a generalized computation or information processing system is considered (see Fig. 16) as follows:

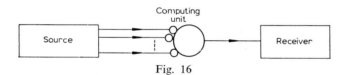

Fig. 16

Assume that at time t each input independently selects one of a possible k symbols from an ensemble X_r ($r = 1, 2, \ldots s$), and that the output is selected at time $(t + 1)$ from an ensemble Y of k_2 symbols. Then the information content of the inputs $x_1, x_2, \ldots x_s$ is given by

$$H(X) = \sum_{r=1}^{S} H(X_r) \tag{53}$$

and the information content of the output y is given by $H(Y)$. The relation between $H(X)$ and $H(Y)$ is determined by the functions from X to Y.

The average uncertainty concerning outputs given an input is then given by $H(Y/X)$ and the following lemma is then proved

$$H(Y/X) \equiv 0 \tag{54}$$

That is, if f is single-valued, then $H(Y/X)$ vanishes identically. This allows a formal distinction to be made (in the noise-free situation) between communication and computation. By virtue of a fundamental identity concerning information measures, namely

$$H(X) - H(X/Y) \equiv H(Y) - H(Y/X) \qquad (55)$$

it follows that

$$H(X) - H(Y) = H(X/Y) \qquad (56)$$

That is, the information content of the input symbols x minus the information content of the output symbols y of an ideal automaton is equal to $H(X/Y)$, the equivocation concerning x given y. Computation is said to occur if $H(X/Y)$ is non-zero, communication if $H(X/Y)$ is zero. (N.B. — all information measures are non-negative.)

We now introduce noise into the system so that the function from inputs to outputs is no longer single-valued, *i.e.* input symbols are selected as before from an ensemble X, but output symbols are now selected from an ensemble Z of noisy output symbols.

We then assume that the noisy automaton can be decomposed into a concatenation of two automata, the first of which represents an ideal automaton that computes the function, while the second represents a noisy automaton that communicates the result of this computation to some receiver.

In effect this assumed decomposition is equivalent to treating all the sources of error in malfunctioning automata or f-neurons, as being 'lumped' together in the outputs of the automata or f-neurons. This cannot always be done exactly, and sometimes the noise in the automaton has to be overestimated in such a way that the decomposition can be effected.

Given such a decomposition however, the following lemmas are then proved:

$$H(Z/X) = H(Z/Y) \qquad (57)$$

$$H(X/Z) = H(X/Y) + H(Y/Z) \qquad (58)$$

The rate of processing information $R_c(X;Z)$ is then defined (*cf.* 50) as

$$\begin{aligned} R_c(X;Z) &= H(X) - H(X/Z) \\ &= H(Z) - H(Z/X) \end{aligned} \qquad (59)$$

and the following theorem is then proved:

$$R_c(X;Z) = R_c(Y;Z) \qquad (60)$$

i.e. the rate of processing information from X to Z is equal to the rate from Y to Z, so that on the average, no more information concerning the inputs x from some source S can be extracted from the outputs z of a noisy automaton computing the function $y = f(x)$, than is provided by the output of a hypothetical noiseless automaton computing the same function.

The *computation capacity* $C_c(X;Z)$ is then defined as the maximum rate of processing information, on the average, by the automaton computing $f(x)$ and it is shown to be equal (in the case when all f's are Boolian functions) to the *communication channel capacity* C of the noisy automaton that 'maps' y into z.

The following generalization of C. E. Shannon's noisy channel coding theorem (*op. cit.*) is then proved:

Given f-neurons which can compute any Boolian function, all with the same computation capacity C_c, for any automaton A that computes a (definite event), and any (rate of information processing, $R_c \leqslant C_c$), an arbitrarily reliable automaton A may be (constructed) that computes the event with a rate R_c' such that $R_c < R_c' \leqslant C_c$.

This theorem is proved, like Shannon's as an existence theorem, but for any given error rate P_A, a reliable system design can be exhibited that achieves such an error rate by using error-correcting codes (*op. cit.*). The theorem thus represents a natural generalization of Shannon's theorem. Several points needing amplification however are discussed below.

(a) Arbitrarily high reliability: An automaton is said to be arbitrarily reliable if its probability of error is arbitrarily close to the probability of malfunction of its output f-neurons. That is, errors are assumed to occur anywhere within the automaton, and hence some can occur in the output f-neurons (*i.e.* those f-neurons that communicate with the automaton's environment, which cannot be corrected within the network. These errors could of course be corrected externally, but there is then raised the problem of who corrects the corrector (Von Neumann, 1948; *op. cit.*). Hence it is considered satisfactory to construct automata that correct all internal errors, and furnish an output perturbed only by errors in their output f-neurons.

(b) The application of error-correcting codes: It is evident from (60) that since all the 'noise' in a noisy automaton is 'lumped' together at the outputs, and any noisy automaton is decomposed into two parts, one comprising an ideal computing automaton feeding into the other part, a noisy communicating automaton or noisy communication channel, that all that need be coded for is the transition from y to z, *i.e. the values of the functions $f(x)$ are to be coded, and not the arguments x*. Thus error-correcting codes are used, just as in the case of communication, but they operate on the outputs of f-neurons, and not on inputs. This principle raises a number of problems however. The model for a communication system usually comprises three functionally distinct parts, a source, a communication channel, and a receiver (see also Fig. 14). The source and receiver (for our purposes) may be replaced by the encoder and decoder respectively of an error-correcting system. Such coders are assumed to be noiseless compared with the channel. It is here that a prime conceptual difficulty lies in straight forwardly applying this model to the case of computation, for in the latter case, one is dealing with an automaton wherein errors are assumed to occur anywhere within the system, and not just in specific locations. The principle is introduced that any assembly within the automaton has its outputs encoded for transmission elsewhere, and decodes all impinging excitation patterns, according to some specified error-correcting code, so that, in general, any f-neuron within the system decodes and then computes an encoded version of its requisite function. Such codes evidently operate on $f(x_a)$ rather than on x_a as required, and the entire technique is called *functional coding*.

(c) Increasing the ensemble: From our previous discussion on error-correcting coding, it is clear that such codes must operate on a 'word' of length k to produce a 'codeword' of length n. In the case of computation such codes must operate not on one automaton, *but on k copies of the automaton, to produce a new automaton comprising*

n/k times as many f-neurons as these k automata, with the various coding constraints built in as specified. The ratio of components in the precursor to that in the encoded automaton is approximately k/n, and its reciprocal n/k is the generalized form of

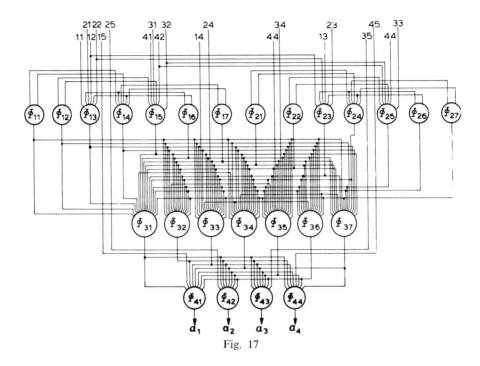

Fig. 17

Von Neumann's *redundancy*, only in this case such redundancy is obtained through functional coding. Fig. 17 shows an encoded version of the precursor of Fig. 13, wherein a (7,4) error-correcting code has been used to obtain increased reliability. Table VI shows the error rates for these two automata:

TABLE VI

Automaton	P_A
Precursor	0.015
(7,4) coded version	0.004

given a probability of *f*-neuron malfunction of 0.005. Note that Von Neumann's construction would require a very high redundancy to obtain this result, but there are certain differences that preclude direct comparison.

(d) F-neuron complexity and noise: One of the reasons for this difficulty should be apparent from a comparison of Figs. 13, 14, and 17. It is evident that whereas in Von Neumann's construction — the so-called *multiplexing method* — only those *f*-neurons are used which are also used in the precursor, whereas in the Winograd-Cowan

construction — using *functional coding* — *more complex f-neurons are required to permit error-correction.* The reason for this is that the ability of (n,k) codes to correct errors depends in general upon their ability to *distribute* information in many places, *i.e.* an (n,k) code essentially takes k independent symbols and produces n interdependent symbols, in the sense that any one of the n symbols is a function of many of these k symbols.

This is achieved by using many channels and thus sending information simultaneously over these channels, before decoding. This in turn requires the use of f-neurons that compute functions of many inputs. In fact it has recently been proved (Winograd, 1963) that if t errors are to be corrected anywhere within the automaton, then the average number of inputs per f-neuron, $\bar{s}$ is bounded by

$$\bar{s} \geqslant \frac{(2t + 1) \cdot k}{n} \tag{61}$$

or equivalently

$$R_c \leqslant \frac{\bar{s}}{2t + 1} \tag{62}$$

Thus if the rate of processing per f-neuron is to remain constant as more and more errors are corrected, the $\bar{s}$ must also increase (since both k and n must both increase, although $k : n$ stays constant). That is, an increase of f-neuron complexity is necessary for increased error-correction at fixed rates of information processing per f-neuron.

It is thus evident that our generalization of Shannon's coding theorem has validity only when the probability of malfunction ε of f-neurons comprising functionally redundant networks is independent of k and n. If such errors increased with k and n, then C_c would be a decreasing function of n and R_c would have to go to zero with P_A as in Von Neumann's case; (see Fig. 15). This assumption that f-neuron malfunction is independent of f-neuron complexity is in fact equivalent to the assumption made in the proof of Shannon's theorem, that encoders and decoders are noiseless compared with communication channels.

(e) Limitations on complexity and noise behaviour. In the event that the requirements so far considered are not satisfied, *i.e.* if only f-neurons of fixed complexity are given, then clearly arbitrarily high reliability cannot be achieved solely by the use of functional coding, and in fact a combination is required of such coding with a generalized version of von Neumann's multiplexing technique (Winograd and Cowan, unpublished work). Several of the mathematical problems involved herein, in obtaining exact formulas for error rates have not yet been solved but approximate bounds can be given. Some typical results are shown in Table VII:

Each f-neuron has an error rate of $\varepsilon = 0.005$. It will be seen that these figures compare very favourably with Von Neumann's results (Table II), *i.e.* much lower redundancies are required to obtain high reliability of computation, given the same elementary components as Von Neumann, when the 'mixed' system design is used. On the other hand, there is now no clear cut definition of a fixed computation capacity which is independent of n, as in Shannon's theorem, or its extension.

(f) Definite vs. indefinite events: There exists a further requirement for the validity

TABLE VII

Number of functionally coded automata (n)	Upper bound to error rate (Q(n))
400	7×10^{-9}
1000	1.4×10^{-18}
10000	1.4×10^{-179}

of this coding theorem, however, concerning the nature of the event which is computed by the given automata. It turns out to be the case that the theorem is valid only if the events computed by such automata are definite, or else are finite portions of indefinite events. It has recently been shown (Rabin, 1963) that automaton which compute indefinite events in a noisy manner cannot be coded to be arbitrarily reliable for the whole event. The meaning of this result is clear: we recall that an indefinite event is one whose representative truth-table is of unbounded length, and that, in general, cyclic networks are required to compute indefinite events. In such networks an uncorrected error may cause all future outputs of the network to be in error, a situation not present in acyclic networks of finite depth, where, as it were, a 'clean sweep' is made for each computation (neglecting the effects of permanent errors or failures — which we shall discuss further on in this section). The restriction to definite events however is in a sense more mathematical than physical, since one is, in practice, interested only in tables of some fixed length, so that any physical automaton in which we are interested may be said to compute a definite event. We thus have the result that automata may be so constructed that they compute with arbitrarily high reliability for some fixed period of time, but thereafter with very high probability they degrade. Such a result implies in a sense a kind of *ageing effect* in automata, and suggests the possible application of such a theory to the natural processes of ageing in living systems.

A further result is proved in Winograd and Cowan (*op. cit.*) which is of interest, namely:

"Let B_p be the blueprint (interconnexion pattern) of a reliable automaton A, operating at a processing rate R_c, and let C_c be the computation capacity of the f-neurons comprising A. If B_p is disregarded with a probability p (such that $-p \log p < C_c - R_c$) (*i.e.* each interconnexion of the automaton may be in error with a probability p, and correct with a probability $1-p$), then with very high probability, A can still be made to function with arbitrarily high reliability."

The meaning of this result is that if a minimum level of reduncancy R_c is used in the design of A ($C_c - R_c$ close to zero), then the interconnexion pattern has to be followed very closely. On the other hand, if more redundancy is used (so that $C_c - R_c$ is larger), a certain sloppiness in the interconnexion pattern becomes tolerable.

The two theorems taken together then imply that computing automata can be so constructed as to exhibit arbitrarily high reliability for finite epochs despite malfunctions of their elements, and despite mistakes in their interconnexion patterns, using not too large levels of redundancy.

We conclude this discussion of Winograd and Cowan's results by noting the following:

We mentioned that a basic principle introduced into reliable system design was that each *f*-neuron of a coded automaton decoded encoded inputs, computed a given function, and then encoded this for transmission elsewhere. The effect of this procedure is that errors are corrected as they occur, and so do not propagate throughout the automaton. A further effect of such a procedure is that conceptually, the separation of an automaton (or set of automata) into computing and coding parts becomes less meaningful, since all such functions are performed everywhere within the automaton. The ultimate reason why redundantly coded automata of this type are effective in controlling malfunctions is that the encoding of functions in the manner outlined, results in a *distribution* of given functions throughout such automata, and a *diversification* of the function of each *f*-neuron in such automata, *i.e.* any one function is computed in many places and any one *f*-neuron is involved in the computation of many functions.

It should also be noted that permanent errors have not been considered, and in a sense the *f*-neurons we have used, are *self-repairing*. In the event that such components are not given, then quite different techniques must be used to extend the lifetime (or increase the reliability) of computing automata. In fact it has been shown that aggregates of selfreproducing automata can be so formed that the aggregate exhibits a self-repairing property which results in extended lifetime (Löfgren, 1961 and 1962). These results however are more closely connected with Von Neumann's techniques than with functional coding, and it is hoped that more extensive results on self-repairing automata than Löfgren's will be obtained by embedding ensembles of self-reproducing automata into an error-correcting scheme. Note that Barricelli's work (3, *op. cit.*) demonstrates the existence of such a possibility, (and in fact genetic mixing and recombination phenomena seem to be closely connected with this process). If such a theory is discovered, then reliable computation in the presence of noise may well become a paradigm for the ability of organisms to survive infection, competition, and so forth, as well as for their ability to exist for extended periods of time. In any case some light is already shed on the question of organismic reliability.

5. A UNIFIED APPROACH TO ORGANISMIC STABILITY

It is evident from § 2-A that there exist on the face of it, a number of quite different approaches to questions concerning the stability or reliability of organismic processes. One might distinguish these differences as the reductionist approach *vs.* the holistic approach, or the mechanistic *vs.* the biotonic, or the preformationistic *vs.* the epigenetic on the one hand; and on the other as the microscopic *vs.* the macroscopic or the unitary *vs.* the systemic; or even as the probabilistic *vs.* the deterministic approach to this problem, which is a major part of that problem which has been called (Wiess, 1957, *op. cit.*), the major biological problem, namely the problem of *biological integration*.

We shall advance the hypothesis, that there is in fact, only one approach, and that all the so-called differences, are not substantive, but are merely linguistic. Moreover, we claim that the key to understanding, is contained in the central theorem of information theory, namely the noisy channel coding theorem, provided that the assumptions underlying this theorem are placed in a new context, namely the quantum theory of matter.

A number of considerations and connexions support such an hypothesis. In § 2 we considered, for example, the behaviour of switching networks as examples of possible neural networks. It is clear that a very close connexion exists between the stationary states of networks comprising only excitatory connexions, and those error-correcting networks designed by Von Neumann (§ 4, *op. cit.*) to further the reliable processing of one bit of 'information'. In the light of Winograd-Cowan's work (§ 4, *op. cit.*) it is also clear that a very close connexion exists between the stationary states of networks comprising both excitatory and inhibitory connexions (Davidson-Smith, § 2, *op. cit.*), and those error-correcting networks designed to process not one bit, but k bits of information.

The nature of this connexion is quite clear. In a switching network with only excitatory connexions, and a moderate degree of refractoriness (see Allanson, 1956), any high level of activity will clearly spread throughout the network, since such activity will tend to excite neighbouring units. Similarly any low level of activity will tend to die out, since each unit is itself a threshold device, and requires a minimal level of activity for excitation. Thus at high levels a cooperative effect operates, at low levels a threshold effect.

In a network with mixed excitatory and inhibitory connexions, however, these effects are somewhat modified. The cooperative effect will not always produce saturation (every unit firing) because the inhibitory connexions will tend to damp the spread of activity and thus to stabilize certain levels of activity. Similarly the threshold effect at low excitation levels need not come into play, since lack of inhibitory activity may result in some raising of the level of activity, and the consequent stabilization of this level at some non-zero value.

In error-correcting networks such differences show up as differences between networks incorporating an $(n,1)$ error-correcting code into their design with limitations on the complexity of the units comprising the network, and networks incorporating an (n,k) error-correcting code into the design with or without limits on unit complexity. Noisy signals within such networks correspond to perturbations from the stationary state in the randomly interconnected switching networks. On the other hand, there do exist certain differences between the two kinds of networks, in that whereas the randomly interconnected switching networks are assumed to comprise ideal elements, the error-correcting automata comprise malfunctioning elements, and there is also a certain degree of randomness in interconnexion. This distinction is not however entirely clear cut, it being complicated by the fact that (Winograd and Cowan, *op. cit.*) errors of interconnexion are to some extent interchangeable with malfunctions. However it does seem to be the case that the effects of noise on the stability of randomly interconnected switching networks have not been completely taken into account. This suggests that there may well exist relationships between the number and complexity of the units comprising a population of switching elements and the statistical aspects of their structure and functioning that may have a parallel not only in information theory (as it obviously does) but in statistical thermodynamics. That is, there may well exist analogues of free and internal energy, and of temperature and entropy derivable from statistical analyses of the behaviour of such switching networks, that generate qualitative (and even quantitative) insights into the properties of such networks.

Obviously the work of Wiener *et al.* (§2, *op. cit.*) is decidedly relevant to such an hypothesis. We assume that non-linear interactions result in spike-like activity, and in synchronization of such spikes, and consider the Gibbsian statistical mechanics of ensembles of assemblies of non-linear components, that have stationary states. As we have seen, such assemblies have integrals of motion (*integral invariants*) that permit the definition of analogues of the thermodynamic quantities previously noted. *E.g.* equations (18)–(21) relate such thermodynamic-like variables to the deviations of levels of populations of interacting biological species, from their stationary values.

To complete the third link in the postulated triadic relation between Gibbsian ensembles, randomly interconnected switching networks, and error-correcting automata, namely the link between the first and last of these objects, we have on the one hand the fact that all three collexions display a multiple diversity of structure and function (*cf.* Wiener on distributed clocks, p. 11, Beurle on brain damage, p. 19; and Winograd-Cowan on efficient error-correction, p. 53), and more importantly, there exists a very intriguing parallel between the quantitative aspects of the noisy channel coding theorem (see Fig. 15), and the quantitative aspects of those aspects of the behaviour of complex physical objects such as crystals, alloys, ferromagnets and so forth, known as order-disorder transitions.

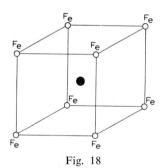

Fig. 18

Order-disorder phenomena belong to the class of cooperative phenomena of considerable physical and mathematical interest and significance, and extensive work has been carried out concerning such phenomena for many years (see the review of Newell and Montroll, 1953). We shall briefly describe the main content of such studies, in a somewhat simplified way.

The order–disorder problem is essentially concerned with the stability or otherwise of configurations of atoms in crystals and alloys, with spin configurations in ferromagnets, and with other more general configurational problems. Two concepts of order are used, *long range order*, and *short range order*. These are defined as follows: consider the structure of the FeAl alloy, the unit cell of which is shown in Fig. 18. This is clearly the unit cell of a body-centred lattice which may be sub-divided into two interpenetrating simple cubic-sub-lattices such that all Fe atoms lie in one and all Al atoms on the other sub-lattice. Evidently the nearest neighbours of any site on one sub-lattice all lie on the other sublattice, *i.e.* in a perfectly ordered FeAl structure, the nearest neighbours of Fe atoms are all Al atoms and *vice-versa*. For all other than the state of perfect order, there will exist some interchange of Fe and Al atoms between the sub-lattices and in the completely disordered state each sub-lattice will be occupied by equal numbers of Fe and Al atoms. This is formalised as follows: suppose there are N lattice points of which $N/2$ are of type a, $N/2$ of type b. The

```
a b a b a b a b a b a b a b a b
b a b a b a b a b a b a b a b a
a b a b a b a b a b a b a b a b
b a b a b a b a b a b a b a b a
```

Fig. 19

nearest neighbours of a sites are b sites and *vice-versa*: (see Fig. 19). Suppose also that there are $N/2$ atoms of type A and $N/2$ of type B. Let $A(a)$ be the number of A atoms on a sites, $A(b)$ be the number of A atoms on b sites, and so forth. Define the long range order parameter to be

$$s = \frac{A(a) - N/4}{N/2 - N/4}$$

$$= \frac{4}{N}(A(a)) - 1 \tag{63}$$

$N/4$ is evidently that $A(a)$ resulting from a completely random distribution, $N/2$ that $A(a)$ corresponding to complete order. It can easily be shown that

$$s = \frac{4}{N}(B(b)) - 1 \tag{64}$$

as might be expected. The limits of s are taken to be 0 and 1, the former corresponding to $A(a) = B(b) = N/4$, the latter to $A(a) = B(b) = N/2$. Intermediate levels of s clearly correspond to states of partial order; s thus provides information concerning the average distribution of atoms on sites. Positive values of s indicate some preference of atoms of given kind for sites of a given kind, such a preferential ordering being called '*long range order*'.

On the other hand even if s is zero, since it is an average, a structure can be 'well-ordered' *e.g.* consider the linear chain of A and B atoms shown in Fig. 20:

The chain as a whole has an s of 0, yet the two halves of the chain considered separately each have an s of 1.

```
......ABABAB BABABA......
......a b a b a b a b a b a b......
```

Fig. 20

If we ignore such anomalies we are still left with an inadequacy in that there may be a tendency for *A* atoms to have *B* atoms as nearest neighbours, and *vice-versa*, even though *s* is small. Such ordering is called local or *short-range ordering*, and an example is shown in Fig. 21: A parameter of short range order σ may be defined similarly to *s*.

$$......ABBBABBAABAAABAABBAB......$$
$$......a\,b\,a\,b\,a\,b\,a\,b\,a\,b\,a\,b\,a\,b\,a\,b\,a\,b\,a\,b\,a\,b......$$

Fig. 21

The parameters *s* and σ are then used to infer various and important features of the configurations or *configurational states* to which they belong, among them being the *configurational energy*. Among important properties of these parameters are their equilibrium values as functions of temperature. The determination of these properties relating order to temperature, configuration energy and so forth, has become known as the order-disorder problem, since it turns out to be the case that in complex structures there frequently occur *critical temperatures* when the properties of such structures change spectacularly. The corresponding problem in *s* and σ is then to determine the singular points of *s* and σ as functions of temperature. Such a problem when posed in its full generality presents many difficulties, and the properties are generally studied of idealised structures — linear chains, planar crystals, etc. Exact solutions to this problem (known to physicists as the Ising problem) have been obtained only for linear and planar structures, but not for structures of three or more dimensions. The results that have been obtained however are of great interest and relevance to our problems.

The method of solution is essentially that of equilibrium statistical mechanics (§ 2, *op. cit.*) with some mathematical refinement; *i.e.* the partition function (corresponding to $e^{-\psi/\theta}$ *cf.* (17) giving the distribution of configurational states corresponding to the free energy ψ is computed, and from this various parameters such as internal energy, entropy etc. and of course long-range and short-range order are computed as functions of the temperature θ. (Of course ψ/θ becomes E_a/kT where E_a is the energy of the quantum state a obtained by solution of the complete Schrödinger equation for the crystal.) Various approximations and assumptions are made concerning the exact evaluation of the partition function, which we must take for granted. The results however are of great interest, and are shown in Fig. 22:

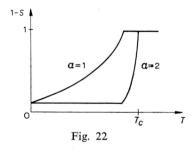

Fig. 22

In the case of the linear chain ($a = 1$) there exists no critical temperature, long range disorder increasing steadily with temperature. In the case of the planar structure, ($a = 2$) long range order persists until a critical temperature is reached, when it suddenly disappears. The reason underlying this is that as the temperature increases, interchanges of A and B atoms tend to facilitate other interchanges, so that eventually a threshold is reached when such interchanges produce very many more, and a *cooperative* effect is said to take place (*cf.* Beurle on the stability of switching networks, § 1). Underlying such a discontinuity is essentially a discontinuity in the energy ψ or E_a which occurs at T_c. The reason for this is as follows: Recalling the Gibbs relation

$$\psi = U - TS \tag{65}$$

it can be shown that in the linear case U (a measure of inter-atomic coupling, and *of the number of nearest neighbours per atom*) is always small compared to TS, whereas in the planar and higher dimensional cases U is initially large compared with TS, and dominates until sufficiently high temperature T_c is reached. Thus there exists a relationship between the stability of configurational states of crystals, etc. and their complexity of unit interactions.

Reference to Fig. 15 concerning the efficiency of error-correcting automata, will show an obvious parallel between this situation and the order-disorder problem. That is:

(1) Channel capacity in information processing appears to be analogous to critical temperature in order–disorder phenomena.

(2) Von Neumann's multiplex technique — minimum complexity encoding — is analogous to the behaviour of a linear atomic chain as far as stability is concerned.

This certainly suggests that there do exist for switching networks analogues of thermodynamic (and dynamic) quantities that might provide real insight into the various relationships between network variables, and that a thermodynamic-like theory of information processing in automata is not implausible.

It should be noted in this connexion, that Cragg and Temperley (1954) have already constructed a model for neuronal assemblies based on an analogy between the cerebral cortex and the ferromagnet, and in fact Temperley (1961) has already suggested that there exists a close connexion between error-correcting automata, and Ising-like structures. What such relationships are of course, remains to be seen, but it does seem that error rates, channel capacity, redundancy etc. have thermodynamic parallels.

It is also possible that there exists a connexion between the dynamical aspects of switching networks (and *a fortiori* the thermodynamic aspects) and the theory of automata currently being developed by Rhodes and Krohn (§ 3, *op. cit.*). It is possible that Symbolic Dynamics (Morse and Hedlund, 1938) may prove to be the link between these disciplines.

We now turn briefly to that other aspect of configurational stability, namely that connected with microdynamics rather than macrodynamics, that is, with the properties of units as stable individuals, rather than with the stability of assemblies. We wish to call attention to an aspect of this problem, connected with information theory and possibly with quantum theory.

As we have noted in § 1, Schrödinger and others have advanced the hypothesis that only the quantum theory makes possible ... the relative stability of elementary particles and atoms. It seems likely that it is this stability which makes possible the configurational stability of crystals, ferromagnets and so forth, *i.e.* the individual units of such structures remain stable in the face of multiple interactions with other units, thus permitting cooperative phenomena to take full hold. This suggests that perhaps the difference between Von Neumann's approach to error-correction in automata, and that of Shannon *et al.* lies in the fact that in the former advantage is not taken, and in the latter is taken, of that increasing stability with size of elementary switching units, that results from the existence of forbidden transitions between the stationary states of microscopic structures, *i.e.* we are postulating that the assumption underlying Shannon's noisy channel coding theorem, and the Winograd-Cowan extension, namely that the error rates of individual units are roughly independent of their complexity, can be justified via quantum theory. (See however, Swanson, 1960; and Landauer, 1961). A great deal of work requires to be done concerning this postulated connexion, as well as that concerning statistical thermodynamics and information theory, but it seems plausible. Perhaps some of the difficulties raised by the work of Wigner and Elsasser (§ 1, *op. cit.*) on biotonic phenomena will turn up here also. In any case it seems to this author, that one important problem concerning the reliability of organisms is closely related to the problem of justifying the assumption underlying the noisy channel coding theorem and its extensions. The solution of this problem would make more valuable any application of information theory to biology. Note also that the establishment of a dynamic basis on which to construct a theory of information processing in biology, would remove that (valid) criticism which is commonly made concerning the biology application of information theory, namely that we do not know what the basic objects of communication and processing are in living systems, let alone their relative frequencies of occurrence, (see Cowan, 1962). That such an application seems necessary however, appears to be a valid proposition. The recent discussions concerning the error-rates of certain living processes (macromolecular synthesis — Pauling, 1957; Orgel, 1963; Jehle, 1963; radiation damage — Quastler, 1958; neural processing — McCulloch, 1960; Cowan, 1963a, b; Verveen, 1959) would certainly be illuminated by the presence of such a theory, as would be certain aspects of gerontology, and of developmental biology.

We conclude this essay with the statement that it represents at best, an outline of a research programme, that the surface has only been scratched of the problem of organismic reliability, that the way ahead from qualitative speculations to quantitative mathematics appears to be long and hard, but that 'what is to be accomplished determines what is done' (Peirce, *op. cit.*), so that we have felt such speculation to be a necessary prolegomena to such an endeavour.

References p. 61

SUMMARY

This paper discusses three seemingly different approaches toward an explanation of the high reliability exhibited by organisms in the performance of vital processes. It is concluded that these three approaches, stemming from mechanics, mathematical logic, and information theory, have many points of contact, and a proposed synthesis is briefly outlined.

ACKNOWLEDGEMENTS

We are indebted to Dr. M. A. Arbib for his comments and criticism of this essay, and to the Office of Naval Research, U.S. Department of the Navy, for support of this work under contract N. 62558–3515.

APPENDIX

A Note on Symbiogenetic Evolutionary Phenomena

(1) N. Barricelli (Acta Biotheor., **16**, I/II, 1962) has devised a very interesting model of an evolutionary process. The model is numeric in a form suitable for digital computer programming. It comprises a *tessellation* space, *i.e.* a 2-dimensional Euclidean space divided into square cells of equal size, so that each size may or may not contain an integer. Let a be the column number (position of a *numeric 'organism'*) and g the row number (generation number of the 'organism'), and let X_{ag} be the content of the ath cell in the gth generation. The following rules of *reproduction* and *interaction* of numeric organisms are defined:

R1
$$X_{a,g} = n \rightarrow X_{a+n,\ g+1} = n$$

R2
$$X_{a,g} = n \ \& \ X_{a,g-1} = m$$
$$\rightarrow X_{a+n,\ g+1} = n \ \& \ X_{a+m,\ g+1} = n \ \& \ X_{a+m,\ g} = m$$

R1 is the *reproduction rule*, and R2 is the interaction or *'capture' rule*.

(2) Evidently a number of different phenomena can occur such as 'capture' of numeric organisms, cooperative activity (multiple capture), collisions, and so forth. It is the purpose of this note to find the numerical prerequisites for such conditions. To do so we consider a *'mutation'-free* situation in which numeric organisms colliding on the same cell are all erased unless they are identical, *i.e.*

R3
$$X_{a,g} = n \ \& \ X_{a,g} = m$$
$$\rightarrow X_{a,g} = X(\text{blank}), \text{ unless } m = n.$$

We call this a *consistency rule*.

(3) To characterise these phenomena, we consider two cells a and b, $a < b$, such that $X_a \geqslant X_b$. We define the 'distance' between a and b to be simply $b–a$, *i.e.*

D1
$$d(a,b) = b–a$$

and the distance between a and b in the gth row to be $d_g(a,b)$. The following basic phenomena are then characterised by $d(a,b)$, X_a and X_b:

P1 $\qquad\qquad d_g(a,b) = r_1(X_a - X_b)$ r_1 any positive integer.

This is obviously *collision*, since

$$d_g(a, b) = r_1(X_a - X_b)$$

$$d_{g+1}(a, b) = r_1 X_a - X_a - r_1 X_a + X_b$$

$$= (r_1 - 1)(X_a - X_b)$$

$$\cdots\cdots$$

$$d_{g+r_1}(a, b) = 0$$

P2 $\qquad\qquad d_g(a, b) = X_a + r_2(X_a - X_b)$ r_2 any positive integer.

Clearly P2 implies

$$d_{g+1}(a, b) = r_2 X_a - (r_2 - 1) X_b$$

$$\cdots\cdots$$

$$d_{g+r_2-1}(a, b) = X_a \qquad (*)$$

This is clearly X_a-capture, since (*) implies

$$X_{a,\ g+r_2} = X_a\ \&\ X_{a,\ g+r_2-1} = X_b$$

which satisfies R2.

P3 $\qquad\qquad d_g(a, b) = -X_b + r_3(X_a - X_b)$ r_3 any positive integer.

Clearly P3 implies

$$d_{g+1}(a, b) = (r_3 - 1) X_a - r_3 X_b$$

$$\cdots\cdots$$

$$d_{g+r_3-1}(a, b) = -X_b \qquad (**)$$

(**) evidently implies $X_{a,\ g+r_3} = X_b\ \&\ X_{a,\ g+r_3-1} = X_a$ which leads to X_b-capture.

P1-P3 exhaust the set of basic or elementary phenomena, and all other numeric conditions result in no interaction.

Let $c(P_i)$ $i = 1, 2, 3$ be the numerical conditions relating to P_i.

(4) In addition to P1 to P3 occurring separately, various combinations may occur. Two categories exist

(a) X_a, X_b of same parity.

(i) Suppose $c(P_2) = c(P_3)$

Then

$$X_a + r_2(X_a - X_b) = -X_b + r_3(X_a - X_b)$$

i.e.

$$\frac{X_a + X_b}{X_a - X_b} = r_3 - r_2 = \lambda$$

λ must be integral, since r_3 and r_2 are integral. Two cases exist:

(α) λ even.

$$\frac{X_a + X_b}{X_a - X_b} = 2r$$

$$\therefore \qquad X_a = -X_b + 2r(X_a - X_b)$$

Set

$$X_a = b - a$$

Thus

$$b - a = -X_a + O(X_a - X_b) \tag{P_2}$$

$$b - a = -X_b + 2r(X_a - X_b) \tag{P_3}$$

It follows that

$$b - a \neq 2r(X_a - X_b) \tag{P_1}$$

i.e. we have proved that

$$c(P_2) = c(P_3) \ (\lambda \text{ even}) \to \overline{P_1} \ \& \ P_2 \ \& \ P_3$$

Thus $c(P_3) = c(P_2)$ $(r_3-r_2$ even) is the numeric condition for double-capture, or cooperative activity, and $X_b : X_a = 2r - 1 : 2r + 1$, where r is any integer.

(β) λ odd.

$$\frac{X_a + X_b}{X_a - X_b} = 2r - 1$$

$$\therefore \qquad X_a + X_b = (2r - 1)(X_a - X_b)$$

$$\therefore \qquad X_a(2r - 2) = X_b(2r)$$

$$X_a(r - 1) = X_b r$$

$$X_a = r(X_a - X_b)$$

Set

$$X_a = b - a$$

$$\therefore \qquad b - a = r(X_a - X_b) \tag{P_1}$$

$$b - a = X_a + O(X_a - X_b) \tag{$\bar{P}_2$}$$

$$b - a \neq -X_b + r(X_a - X_b) \tag{P_3}$$

i.e. $c(P_2) = c(P_3) \ (\lambda \text{ odd}) \to P_1 \ \& \ P_2 \ \& \ P_3$

Thus $c(P_2) = c(P_3)$ $(r_3 - r_2$ odd) is the numeric condition for *collision, X_a surviving,* and $X_b : X_a = r - 1 : r$.

(ii) Evidently $c(P_2) = c(P_3)$ $(r_3 - r_2$ odd) is consistent with $c(P_1) = c(P_2)$, which

can be shown to imply P_1 & P_2 & $\overline{P_3}$

(iii) Suppose $c(P_1) = c(P)_3$

$$r_1(X_a - X_b) = - X_b + r_3(\lambda_a - X_b)$$

$\therefore$
$$X_b = (r_3 - r_1(X_a - X_b)$$

Set $b - a = X_b$

$\therefore$
$$b - a = (r_3 - r_1)(X_a - X_b) \tag{P_1}$$

$$-(b - a) = - X_b + O(X_a - X_b) \tag{x}$$

$$b - a \neq X_a + (r_3 - r_1)(X_a - X_b)$$

$c(P_1) = c(P_3)$ is consistent with P_1, *i.e.* collision, but (x) is not realisable, since it requires reversal of causality (the numberic organisms propagating backwards in generation time).

i.e.
$$c(P_1) = c(P_3) \rightarrow P_1 \ \& \ \overline{P_2} \ \& \ \overline{P_3}$$

(b) X_a, X_b of different parity. Suppose $X_a > 0$, $X_b < 0$;

Denote $- X_b$ by $\underline{X_b}$

(i) $c(P_2) = c(P_3)$

$$X_a + r_2(X_a - \underline{X_b}) = - \underline{X_b} + r_3(X_a - \underline{X_b})$$

$\therefore$
$$\frac{X_a + X_h}{X_a - \underline{X_b}} = r_3 - r_2$$

But

$$\frac{X_a + \underline{X_b}}{X_a - \underline{X_b}} = \frac{X_a - X_b}{X_a + X_b} \text{ so that}$$

$r_3 - r_2$ cannot be integral, unless $r_3 = r_2$.

i.e.
$$X_a + r_2(X_a - \underline{X_b}) = - \underline{X_b} + r_2(X_a - \underline{X_b})$$

i.e.
$$X_a = X_b$$

Thus
$$X_a + r_2(X_a + X_b) = b - a$$

i.e.
$$b - a = (2r_2 + 1)X_a$$

Thus cooperative activity occurs if, and only if, $X_a = X_b$, otherwise no interaction takes place.

$$\text{(ii) } c(P_1) = c(P_2)$$

By similar reasoning, we obtain

$$\frac{X_a}{X_a + X_b} = r_1 - r_2$$

i.e. there are no integral solutions to this unless $r_1 = r_2$, in which case $X_a = 0$ which is meaningless (*i.e.* there must be a numeric organism at cell a).

(iii) $c(P_1) = c(P_3)$ also has no integral solutions, similarly to (b) (ii).

This exhausts all possibilities, but note that the condition for collision in case (b) becomes

$$r_1(X_a - \underline{X_b}) = b - a$$

i.e.
$$r_1(X_a + X_b) = b - a$$

and
$$2r_1(X_a) = b - a \text{ if } X_a = X_b.$$

(5) We give here tables for the activity discussed in (4).

(a) Cooperative activity.

	(1,3)	(2,6)	(3,9)	(4,12)	. . .
(X_b, X_a):	(3,5)	(6,10)	(9,15)	(12,20)	. . .
	(5,7)	(10,14)	(15,21)	(20,28)	. . .
(X_b, X_a):	(1,1)	(2,2)	(3,3)	(4,4)	. . .

(b) Collision and X_a survival.

	(1,2)	(2,4)	(3,6)	(4,8)	. . .
(X_b, X_a):	(2,3)	(4,6)	(6,9)	(8,12)	. . .
	(3,4)	(6,8)	(9,12)	(12,16)	. . .

(6) Examples of the various symbiogenetic phenomena.

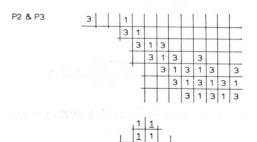

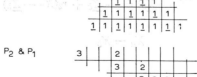

Fig. 23

REFERENCES

ADRIAN, E. D., AND FORBES, A., (1922); The all-or-nothing response of sensory nerve fibres. *J. Physiol. (Lond.)*, **56**, 301–330.

ALLANSON, J. T., (1956); *Information Theory*, E. C. Cherry, Editor. London. Butterworths (pp. 303–313).

ARBIB, M. A., (1961); Turing machines, finite automata and neural nets. *J. Ass.* Computing Machines, **8**, 467–475.

ASHBY, W. R., (1952); *Brit. J. Phil. Sci.*, **3**, 44–57.

ASHBY, W. R., (1954); *Design for a Brain*. London. Chapman and Hall.

BARRICELLI, N. A., (1957); Symbiogenetic evolution processes realized by artificial methods. *Methodos*, **9**, 143–183.

BARRICELLI, N. A., (1962); Numerical testing of evolution theories part I. Theoretical introduction and basic tests. *Acta biotheor. (Leiden)*, **16**, 69–98.

BEURLE, R. L., (1956); Properties of a mass of cells capable of regenerating pulses. *Phil. Trans. B*, **240**, 55–95.

BODE, H. W., (1945); *Network Analysis and Feedback Amplifier Design*. New York. Van Nostrand.

BOOLE, G., (1847); *The Mathematical Analysis of Logic*. Cambridge. University Press.

BORN, M., (1959); Dans quelle mesure la mécanique peut-elle prédire les trajectoires? *J. Phys. Radium (Paris)*, **20**, 43–50.

BRENNER, S., (1961); An unstable intermediate carrying information from series to ribosomes for protein synthesis. *Nature (Lond.)*, **190**, 576–580.

BURKS, A. W., (1959); *Computation, Behavior and Structure in Fixed and Growing Automata*. Techn. Report. University of Michigan.

CANNON, W., (1932); *The Wisdom of the Body*. New York. Norton and Co.

CORBET, A. S., (1943); The relation between the number of species and the number of individuals in a random sample of animal population. *J. Anim. Ecol.*, **12**, 42–58.

COWAN, J. D., (1962); *Training in Biomathematics*. H. L. Lucas, Editor, Washington. N.I.H. (pp. 297–311).

COWAN, J. D., (1963a); The engineering approach to the problem of biological integration. *Nerve, Brain and Memory Models. Progress in Brain Research Vol. 2,* N. Wiener and J. P. Schadé, Editors. Amsterdam–New York. Elsevier (pp. 22–30).

COWAN, J. D., (1963b); Proceedings of the Symposium on Information Processing in the Nervous System. *Excerpta Med. (Amst.)*, in press.

CRAGG, B. G., AND TEMPERLEY, H. N. V., (1954); The organisation of neurones; a cooperative analogy. *Electroenceph. Clin. Neurophysiol.*, **6**, 85–92.

CRAIK, K. W., (1943); *The Nature of Explanation*. Cambridge. University Press.

CRICK, F. H. C., (1959); Brookhaven *Symposium in Biology*, **12**, 35–39.

CRICK, F. H. C., (1961); General nature of the genetic code for proteins. *Nature, (Lond.)*, **192**, 1227–1232.

ELSASSER, W., (1958); *The Physical Foundations of Biology*. New York. Pergamon Press.

ELSASSER, W., (1961); Quanta and the concept of organismic law. *J. Theoret. Biol.*, **1**, 27–58.

ELSASSER, W., (1962); Physical aspects of non-mechanistic biological theory. *J. theoret. Biol.*, **3**, 164–191.

FELLER, W., (1952); *An Introduction to Probability Theory*. New York. John Wiley and Sons.

GABOR, D., (1961); A universal nonlinear filter, predictor and simulator which optimizes itself by a learning process. *Proc. I.E.E.*, **108**, 422–438.

GAMOW, G., (1955); On information transfer from nucleic acids. *Dansk Biol. Medd.*, **22**, 8, 1–7.

GÖDEL, K., (1931); Über formal unentscheidbare Sätze der Principia Mathematica und verwandter Systeme I. *Mschr. Math. Phys.*, **38**, 173–189.

GOODWIN, B. C., (1963); *Temporal Organization in Cells*. New York. Academic Press.

GRIFFITH, J. S., (1963a); A field theory of neural nets I. Derivation of field equations. *Bull. Mathemat. Biophys.*, **25**, 111–120.

GRIFFITH, J. S., (1963b); On the stability of brain-like structures. *Biophys. J.*, **3**, 299–308.

HEAVISIDE, O. W., (1892); *Electromagnetic Theory*. London. The Electrician printing and publishing Comp.

JACOB, F., AND MONOD, J., (1961); Genetic regulatory mechanisms in the synthesis of proteins. *J. Mol. Biol.*, **3**, 318–356.

JEHLE, H., (1963); Intermolecular forces and biological specificity. *P.N.A.S.*, **50**, 516–524.

KALMAN, R. E., (1963); Journal on Control, Ser. A., **1**, 152–192.

KERNER, E. H., (1957); Statistical mechanics of interacting biological species. *Bull. Mathemat. Biophys.*, **19**, 121–146.

KERNER, E. H., (1959); Further considerations on the statistical mechanics of biological associations. *Bull. Mathemat. Biophys.*, **21**, 217–255.

KERNER, E. H., (1961); On the Volterra-Lotta principle. *Bull. Mathemat. Biophys.*, **23**, 141–157.

KLEENE, S. C., (1956); Representation of events in nerve nets and finite automata. *Automata Studies.* C. E. Shannon and J. McCarthy, Editors. Princeton University Press (pp. 3–41).

LANDAUER, R., (1961); Irreversibility and heat generation in the computing process. *IBM J. Res. Develop.*, **5**, 3, 183–191.

LENGYEL, P., (1961); Synthetic polynucleotides and the amino acid code. *P.N.A.S.*, **47**, 1936–1943.

LÖFGREN, L., (1962a); *Principles of Self-Organization*. H. von Foerster and G. Zopf, Editors. New York. Pergamon Press (pp. 181–228).

LÖFGREN, L., (1962b); *Biological Prototypes and Synthetic Systems*. E. Barnard and M. Kare, Editors. New York, Plenum Press (pp. 342–369).

LYAPUNOV, A. A., (1907); *Problème Général de la Stabilité du Mouvement*. Princeton University Press.

MAXWLL, J. C., (1868); On governors. *Proc. roy. Soc. B*, **16**, 270–283.

McCULLOCH, W. S., (1960); The reliability of biological systems. *Self-Organizing Systems*. M. C. Yovitts and S. Cameron, Editors. New York. Pergamon Press (pp. 262–282).

McCULLOCH, W. S., AND PITTS, W. H., (1943); A logical calculus of the ideas immanent in nervous activity. *Bull. Mathernat. Biophys.*, **5**, 115–133.

MONOD, F., (1963); Allosteric proteins and cellular control systems. *J. Mol. Biol.*, **6**, 306–329.

MOORE, E. H., (1962); Proc. Symp. on Math. Problems in Biological Sciences. Editors. New York. American Mathematical Society (pp. 17–34).

MORSE, M., AND HEDLUND, G. A., (1938); Symbolic dynamics. *Amer. J. Maths.*, **60**, 815–866.

NEWELL, F. G., AND MONTROLL, E. W., (1953); On the theory of the ising model of ferromagnetism. *Rev. Mode. Phys.*, **25**, 353–389.

NIHRENBERG, M. W., AND MATTHAI, J. H., (1961); Characteristics and stabilization of DNAase-sensitive protein synthesis in *E. coli* extracts. The dependence of cell-free protein synthesis in *E. coli* upon naturally occurring or synthetic polyribonucleotides. *P.N.A.S.*, **47**, 1580–1602.

NYQUIST, H., (1932); *Bell System Techn. J.*, **11**, 126.

ORGEL, L. E., (1963); The maintenance of the accuracy of protein synthesis and its relevance to ageing. *P.N.A.S.*, **49**, 517–520.

PAULING, L., (1957); The probability of errors in the process of synthesis of protein molecules. Festschrift A. Stoll. Basel. Birkhauser AG. (pp. 597–602).

PEIRCE, C. S., (1935); Materialistic Aspects of Reasoning. Collected Papers. Hartshone and Weiss, Editors. VI. Scientific Metaphysics.

PETERSEN, W. W., (1961); *Error-Correcting Codes*. Cambridge. The M.I.T. Press.

PITTS, W. H., AND McCULLOCH, W. S., (1947); *Bull. Mathemat. Biophys.*, **9**, 127–147.

QUASTLER, H., (1959); Information theory of biological integration. *Amer. Naturalist*, **871**, 245–254.

RABIN, M. O., (1963); Probabilistic Automata. Inf. and Control., **6**, 230–245.

RHODES, J. L., AND KROHN, K. W., (1963); Proc. Symp. on Math. Theory of Automata. Editor. New York. Polytechnic Press/Wiley Press. (pp. 341–384).

ROSENBLATT, F., (1962); *Principles of Neurodynamics*. Washington. Spartan Books Inc.

ROSENBLUETH, A., WIENER, N., AND BIGELOW, J., (1943); Behavior, purpose and teleology. *Philosophy of Science*, **10**, 18–24.

SCHRÖDINGER, E., (1944); *What is Life*. Cambridge. University Press.

SHANNON, C. E., (1948); A mathematical theory of communication. *Bell System Techn. J.*, **27**, 379–423; 623–658.

SHERRINGTON, C. S., (1906); *The Integrative Action of the Nervous System*. New Haven. Yale University Press.

SMITH, D. R., AND DAVIDSON, C. H., (1962); Maintained activity in neural nets. *J. Assoc. Computting Mach.*, **9**, 268–279.

STAHL, W. R., AND GOHEEN, H. E., (1963); Molecular algorithms. *J. Theoret. Biol.*, **5**, 266–287.

SUGITA, M., (1961); Functional analysis of chemical systems in vivo using a logical circuit equivalent. *J. Theoret. Biol.*, **1**, 415–430.

SWANSON, J. A., (1960); Physical versus logical coupling in memory systems. *IBM J. Res. Develop*, **4**, 3, 305–310.

TEMPERLEY, H. N. V., (1961); Personal communication.

TER HAAR, D., (1957); *Introduction to the Physics of Many-Body Problems*. New York. Inter Science.

TIMOFEYEV-RESOVSKIJ, phenomena and the amplification principle in biology. *Probl. Kibernetiki,* **2,** 213–228.

TURING, A. M., (1937); On computable numbers, with an application to the Entscheidungsproblem. *Proc. Lond. Math. Soc. Ser. 2,* **42,** 230–265.

UTTLEY, A. M., (1954); The classification of signals in the nervous system. *Electroenceph. clin. Neurophysiol.,* **6,** 479–494.

VERVEEN, A. A., (1960); On the fluctuation of threshold of the nerve fibre. *Structure and Function of the Cerebral Cortex.* D. B. Tower and J. P. Schadé, Editors. Amsterdam. Elsevier (pp. 282–289).

VOLTERRA, V., (1937); Principe de biologie mathématique. *Acta biotheor. (Leiden),* **3,** 1–36.

VON BERTALANFFY, Z., (1950); The theory of open systems in physics and biology. *Science,* **111,** 23–29.

VON NEUMANN, J., (1951); The general and logical theory of automata. *Cerebral Mechanisms in Behaviour.* L. A. Jeffress, Editor. New York. John Wiley and Sons (pp. 1–41).

VON NEUMANN, J., (1955); *Mathematical Foundations of Quantum Mechanics.* Princeton University Press.

VON NEUMANN, J., (1956); Probabilistic logics and the synthesis of reliable organisms from unreliable components. *Automata Studies.* C. E. Shannon and J. McCarthy, Editors. Princeton University Press. (pp. 43–98).

VON NEUMANN, J., (1963–1964); Theory of Automata: Construction, reproduction and homogeneity. Uncompleted typescript of three chapters (n.d. *circa* 1952) 220 pp. Princeton University Press. In press.

WARNER, J. R., (1963); A multiple ribosomal structure in protein synthesis. *P.N.A.S.,* **49,** 122–129.

WATSON, J. D., AND CRICK, F. H. C., (1953); Molecular structure of nucleic acids. *Nature (Lond.),* **171,** 737–738.

WEISS, P., (1959); Quotation. *Concepts of Biology.* R. Gerard, Editor. Washington. Nat. Acad. Sciences. (pp. 191–192).

WEISS, P., (1962); From cell to molecule. *Symp. on Molecular Control of Cellular Activity.* Editors. New York. John. Wiley and Sons (pp.).

WHITEHEAD, A. N., AND RUSSELL, B. A. W., (1910–1913); *Principia Mathematica.* Cambridge. University Press.

WIENER, N., (1948); *Cybernetics.* New York. John Wiley and Sons.

WIENER, N., (1955); Nonlinear prediction and dynamics. Proc. Third Berkeley Symp. Math. Stat. and Prob., Editor. (pp. 247–252).

WIENER, N., (1957); Proc. Rudolf Virchow Med. Soc., **16,** 109–123.

WIENER, N., (1958); *Non-linear Problems in Random Noise Theory.* Cambridge. M.I.T. Press.

WIGNER, E. P., (1959); *Group Theory.* New York. Academic Press.

WIGNER, E. P., (1960); Festschrift für M. Polanyi. Editor. Cambridge University Press (pp. 231–238).

WINOGRAD, S., (1963); Redundancy and complexity of logical elements. Information and Control,

WINOGRAD, S., AND COWAN, J. D., (1963); *Reliable Computation in the Presence of Noise.* Cambridge. M.I.T. Press.

Zur Theorie der Lateralen Nervösen Inhibition im *Limulus* Komplex-Auge

WERNER REICHARDT

Max-Planck-Institut für Biologie, Tübingen (D.B.R.)

Das Komplexauge von *Limulus* besteht aus etwa 1000 Ommatidien, die durch Pigment optisch voneinander isoliert sind. Der sinnesphysiologische Apparat eines Ommatidiums setzt sich aus acht bis zwanzig Retinulazellen zusammen, deren Rhabdomere den Fortsatz einer bipolaren Zelle umschliessen (Demoll, 1914; Miller, 1957), die auch als exzentrische Zelle bezeichnet wird. Sowohl von den Retinulazellen als auch von der exzentrischen Zelle jedes Ommatidiums geht je ein Axon aus; die Axone bilden zusammen den optischen Nerv. In unmittelbarer Nähe der Ommatidien liegt ein Geflecht von Kollateralen, die Querverbindungen zwischen den Axonen herstellen und vermutlich über Synapsen auf die Impulsbildungsorte einwirken.

Bestrahlt man ein Ommatidium des Auges, so wird in seiner exzentrischen Zelle ein Generatorpotential erzeugt, dessen stationärer Anteil annähernd logarithmisch von der Lichtintensität abhängt. Alle bisherigen Untersuchungen deuten darauf hin, dass von der Lichtstrahlung Nervenimpulse (spikes) nur im Axon der exzentrischen Zelle, dagegen nicht in den Axonen der Retinulazellen ausgelöst werden. Daher ist jedes Ommatidium dieses Komplexauges offenbar als funktionelle Einheit aufzufassen. Unter stationären Bedingungen besteht ein linearer Zusammenhang zwischen dem Generatorpotential einer exzentrischen Zelle und der durch dieses Potential ausgelösten Nervenimpulsfrequenz im entsprechenden Axon des optischen Nervs. Solange nur je ein Ommatidium des Komplexauges gereizt wird, besteht dieser Zusammenhang für alle Axone; werden dagegen zwei oder mehr Ommatidien gereizt, so treten die Erregungen in den Axonen des optischen Nervs über das Kollateralengeflecht miteinander in Wechselwirkung. Diese Interaktion ist ein teillinearer Prozess vom Typ der lateralen '*Rückinhibition*' (Hartline *et al.*, 1956; Hartline and Ratliff, 1957, 1958; Ratliff *et al.*, 1958; Ratliff and Hartline, 1959; Varjú, 1962), deren funktionelle Eigenschaften im folgenden betrachtet werden.

A. AUFSTELLEN DER GLEICHUNGEN

Die Wechselwirkung zwischen zwei Ommatidien i, j im Komplexauge von *Limulus* lässt sich durch ein Paar simultaner teillinearer Gleichungen beschreiben

$$z_i = y_i - \beta_{ij} \, (z_j - z^*_{ij})$$
$$z_j = y_j - \beta_{ji} \, (z_i - z^*_{ji})$$

(1)

In Gl. (1) bedeuten: z_i, z_j die Impulsfrequenzen, die von den aktiven Fasern der Ommatidien i, j bei Erregung gemessen werden können; y_i, y_j die Impulsfrequenzen, die in diesen Fasern erzeugt werden, wenn die hemmende Wechselwirkung im Experiment ausgeschaltet wird; β_{ij}, β_{ji} Koeffizienten, die den Grad der wechselseitigen Inhibition angeben und z^*_{ij}, z^*_{ji} Impulsfrequenz-Schwellenwerte dieses Wechselwirkungsprozesses. Gl. (1) gilt im Bereich

$$z_j \geqq z^*_{ij}, \; z_i \geqq z^*_{ji}, \; y_i \geqq \beta_{ij} (z_j - z^*_{ij}) \text{ und } y_j \geqq \beta_{ji} (z_i - z^*_{ji}),$$

da negative Impulsfrequenzen nicht auftreten können. Im *Limulus*-Auge erstreckt sich die teillineare Wechselwirkung zwischen den Rezeptoren auf grosse Augenbereiche und äussert sich darin, dass jeder Rezeptor von einer Gruppe umgebender Rezeptoren inhibiert wird. Für n Rezeptoren lässt sich dieser Wechselwirkungsprozess durch nachstehende Gleichung beschreiben, von der Gl. (1) ein Spezialfall für zwei Rezeptoren ist.

$$z_i = \begin{cases} \left(y_i - \sum_{\substack{j=1 \\ j=i}}^{n} \beta_{ij} (z_j - z^*_{ij}) \right) & y_i > \sum_{\substack{j=1 \\ j \neq i}}^{n} \beta_{ij} (z_j - z^*_{ij}) \\ \\ 0 & y_i \leqq \sum_{\substack{j=1 \\ j \neq i}}^{n} \beta_{ij} (z_j - z^*_{ij}) \end{cases} \text{ wenn} \tag{2}$$

Für Gl. (2) gelten hinsichtlich der Impulsfrequenzschwellenwerte z^*_{ij} entsprechende Beschränkungen wie für Gl. (1). Vernachlässigt man im folgenden die Impulsfrequenzschwellenwerte, was in guter Näherung erlaubt ist, so folgt aus dem ersten Teil von Gl. (2)

$$y_i = z_i + \sum_{\substack{j=1 \\ j \neq i}}^{n} \beta_{ij} z_j = \sum_{\substack{j=1 \\ j \neq i}}^{n} \beta_{ij} z_j \qquad i = 1,2 \dots n \tag{3A}$$
$$\text{mit } \beta_{ii} = 1$$

Sowohl die z_i als auch β_{ij} sind stets grösser gleich null und somit $y_i \geqq z_i$. Sind einige Grössen y_i grösser null, dann ist für diese diese entweder

$$y_i > \sum_{\substack{j=1 \\ j \neq i}}^{n} \beta_{ij} z_j \tag{3B}$$

sodass die entsprechenden $z_i > 0$ sind; oder aber es ist

$$y_i \leqq \sum_{\substack{j=1 \\ j \neq i}}^{n} \beta_{ij} z_j \tag{3C}$$

wobei

Literatur S. 73

$$\sum_{\substack{j=1 \\ j \neq i}}^{n} \beta_{ij} z_j > 0 \tag{3D}$$

sodass ein oder mehrere der $z_j > 0$, die z_i dagegen nach Gl. (2) gleich null sein müssen.

Zusammenfassend lässt sich sagen: Sind einige der Eingangsgrössen (Impulsfrequenzwerte y_i ohne Einfluss der lateralen Inhibition) grösser null, so ist auch mindestens *eine* der Ausgangsgrössen (Impulsfrequenzwerte z_i unter dem Einfluss der lateralen Inhibition) grösser null. Dagegen, sind einige der Ausgangsgrössen grösser null, so sind es auch die korrespondierenden Eingangsgrössen.

Wird eine Verteilung von Eingangsgrössen vorgegeben, so stellt sich daraufhin eine Verteilung von Ausgangsgrössen z_i ein. Im allgemeinsten Fall sind einige der Ausgangsgrössen grösser null, andere dagegen null. Wir bezeichnen mit S die Mannigfaltigkeit von Ausgangsgrössen, die grösser null, mit $\bar{S}$ die Mannigfaltigkeit, die null ist. Also

$$S = [i \subset n \text{ und } z_i > 0] \tag{4}$$
$$\bar{S} = [i \subset n \text{ und } z_i = 0]$$

Darin sind $S + \bar{S} = n$ und $S > 0$, wenn ein oder einige der $y_i > 0$ sind. Wir definieren nun die vier Spaltenvektoren

$$\begin{array}{cc} \mathfrak{y} = \{y_i\} & , \quad \mathfrak{y} = \{z_i\} \\ i \subset n & i \subset n \\ \mathfrak{y}^* = \{y_i\} & , \quad \mathfrak{y}^* = \{z_i\} \\ i \subset S & i \subset S \end{array} \tag{5}$$

und die Matrix $\mathfrak{B}^* = (\beta_{ij})_{i,j \subset S}$; damit lässt sich die Beziehung zwischen den y_i und z_i abgekürzt wie folgt formulieren:

$$y_i = \sum_{j \subset n} \beta_{ij} z_j = \sum_{j \subset s} \beta_{ij} z_j, \, i < S \text{ oder } \mathfrak{y}^* = \mathfrak{B}^* \, \mathfrak{z}^* \tag{6}$$

Die Umkehrung hierzu ist $\mathfrak{y}^* = \mathfrak{B}^{*-1} \mathfrak{y}^*$, was voraussetzt, dass die det $|\mathfrak{B}^*| \neq 0$ ist; hierin ist $\mathfrak{B}^{*-1}$ die zu $\mathfrak{B}^*$ inverse Matrix. Nun definieren wir ferner die $n \times n$ Matrix $\mathfrak{B} = (\beta_{ij})_{i,j \subset n}$; dann lässt sich $\mathfrak{B}^*$ aus $\mathfrak{B}$ gewinnen, indem man alle Zeilen und Spalten in $\mathfrak{B}$ streicht deren i, j zur Mannigfaltigkeit $\bar{S}$ gehören. Natürlich lässt sich in dieser Weise $\mathfrak{B}^{*-1}$ nicht aus $\mathfrak{B}^{-1}$ bestimmen.

B. STABILITÄT DER LÖSUNGEN

Das Gleichungssystem der lateralen Inhibition besitzt Lösungen, deren Stabilität in hohem Masse von den Koeffizienten β_{ij} und der Verteilung der Eingangsgrössen y_i abhängt (Reichardt, 1961; Reichardt und Mac Ginitie, 1962). Um dies zu zeigen, gehen wir vom Zusammenhang zwischen den y_i und z_i aus

$$z_i = \begin{cases} \left(y_i - \sum_{\substack{j \subset S \\ i=j}} \beta_{ij} z_j \right) \\ 0 \end{cases} \text{wenn} \begin{cases} i \subset S \\ i \subset \bar{S} \end{cases} \tag{7}$$

und prägen den Ausgangsgrössen additiv eine Störung ε_i auf. Dann gehen die z_i in S über in $z_i + \varepsilon_i$; in $\bar{S}$ dagegen seien alle $\varepsilon_i = 0$. Aus Gl. (7) ergibt sich daher im Störungsfall

$$z'_i = \begin{cases} \left(y_i - \sum_{\substack{j \subset S \\ i \neq j}} \beta_{ij} (z_j + \varepsilon_j) \right) \\ 0 \end{cases} \text{wenn} \begin{cases} i \subset S \\ i \subset \bar{S} \end{cases} \tag{8}$$

Die ε_i rufen Änderungen der Ausgangsgrössen hervor, die wir mit $\Delta_i = z'_i - z_i$ bezeichnen und für die man aus Gl. (7) und (8) erhält

$$\Delta_i = \begin{cases} \left(- \sum_{\substack{j \; S \\ i \neq j}} \beta_{ij} \varepsilon_j \right) \\ 0 \end{cases} \text{wenn} \begin{cases} i \subset S \\ i \subset \bar{S} \end{cases} \tag{9}$$

Da nach Voraussetzung $\beta_{ii} = 1$ ist, ergibt sich an Stelle von Gl. (9)

$$\Delta_i = \varepsilon_i - \sum_{j \subset S} \beta_{ij} \varepsilon_j \qquad i \subset S \tag{10}$$

Definieren wir nun zusätzlich die Spaltenvektoren

$$\Delta^* = \{\Delta_i\}_{i \subset S}, \varepsilon^* = \{\varepsilon_i\}_{i \subset S} \tag{11}$$

so lässt sich Gl. (10) abgekürzt schreiben

$$\Delta^* = \varepsilon^* - \mathfrak{B}^* \varepsilon^* \tag{12}$$

Wir ziehen nun die Eigenwerte λ_k und die Eigenvektoren $\mathfrak{q}^*_k$ der Matrix $\mathfrak{B}^*$ hinzu, die sich aus der Bestimmungsgleichung

$$\mathfrak{B}^* \mathfrak{q}^*_k = \lambda_k \mathfrak{q}^*_k \tag{13}$$

ergeben. Berücksichtigt man, dass die wechselseitigen Inhibitionen zwischen je zwei Rezeptoren im Mittel einander gleich sind (Kirschfeld und Reichardt, 1964), also $\beta_{ij} = \beta_{ji}$ und damit die $\mathfrak{B}^*$ Matrix symmetrisch ist, so folgt, dass die Eigenwerte und Eigenvektoren von $\mathfrak{B}^*$ reell sind.

Wählen wir als Störung $\varepsilon^* = \mathfrak{q}^*_k$, so ergibt sich aus Gl. (12)

$$\Delta^* = \mathfrak{q}^*_k - \mathfrak{B}^* \mathfrak{q}^*_k = \mathfrak{q}^*_k - \lambda_k \mathfrak{q}^*_k = (1 - \lambda_k) \mathfrak{q}^*_k = (1 - \lambda_k) \varepsilon^* \tag{14}$$

Wenn $(1 - \lambda_k) < 1$, dann klingt die Störung ab. Es muss also $0 < \lambda_k < 2$ für alle k

sein, damit die Stabilität des Systems garantiert ist. Ist dagegen $(1 - \lambda_k) = 1$, dann wird $\Delta^* = \varepsilon^*$, sodass die Störung unverändert erhalten bleibt. In diesem Fall befindet sich das Inhibitionssystem in einem indifferenten Gleichgewicht. Wenn dagegen $(1 - \lambda_k) > 1$ für irgend ein k ist, wird die Störung vergrössert. Das Inhibitionssystem ist unter diesen Umständen instabil. Damit ist das Stabilitätsproblem auf die Eigenwerte der Matrix $\mathfrak{B}^* = (\beta_{ij})_{i,j \subset S}$ zurückgeführt und wir können zusammenfassen: Das Inhibitions-System ist

$$
\begin{array}{llll}
\text{stabil} & & 0 < \lambda < 2 & \\
\text{indifferent} & \text{wenn} & \lambda = 0 & \quad (15) \\
\text{instabil} & & \lambda < 0 &
\end{array}
$$

ist.

Die Stabilitätsuntersuchung des Inhibitions-Systems läuft also im wesentlichen auf die Bestimmung des kleinsten Eigenwertes der $\mathfrak{B}^*$ Matrix heraus. Diese Bestimmung ist dann nur erforderlich, wenn die β_{ij} die nachfolgend gegebene Abschätzung nicht erfüllen. Bezeichnen wir mit q^k_i die Komponenten des Eigenvektors $\mathfrak{q}^*_k$, also

$$
\mathfrak{q}^*_k = \{q^k_i\}_{i \subset S} \tag{16}
$$

dann folgt aus Gl. (13)

$$
\sum_{j \subset S} \beta_{ij} q^k_j = \lambda_k q^k_i \qquad i \subset S \tag{17}
$$

Da $\beta_{ii} = 1$, erhält man

$$
\sum_{\substack{j \subset S \\ j \neq i}} \beta_{ij} q^k_j = (\lambda_k - 1) q^k_i \qquad i \subset S \tag{18}
$$

Nun ist aber

$$
|\lambda_k - 1| \, |q^k_i| = \left| \sum_{\substack{j \subset S \\ j \neq i}} \beta_{ij} q^k_j \right| \leqq \sum_{\substack{j \subset S \\ j \neq i}} \left| \beta_{ij} q^k_j \right| ; \, i \subset S. \tag{19}
$$

Die β_{ij} sind positive reelle Zahlen, also

$$
\sum_{\substack{j \subset S \\ j \neq i}} |\beta_{ij} q^k_j| = \sum_{\substack{j \subset S \\ j \neq i}} \beta_{ij} |q^k_j| \qquad i \subset S \tag{20}
$$

Es sei $|q^k_i| = \max_j |q^k_j|$, sodass

$$
\sum_{\substack{j \subset S \\ j \neq i}} \beta_{ij} |q^k_j| \leqq \sum_{\substack{j \subset S \\ j \neq i}} \beta_{ij} |q^k_i| = |q^k_i| \sum_{\substack{j \subset S \\ j \neq i}} \beta_{ij}; \qquad i \subset S \tag{21}
$$

Also

$$
|\lambda_k - 1| \, |q^k_i| \leqq |q^k_i| \sum_{\substack{j \subset S \\ j \neq i}} \beta_{ij} \qquad i \subset S \tag{22}
$$

und damit

$$| \lambda_k - 1 | \leq \sum_{\substack{j \subset S \\ j \neq i}} \beta_{ij} \leq \max_{i \subset S} \left\{ \sum_{\substack{j \subset S \\ j \neq i}} \beta_{ij} \right\}. \tag{23}$$

Hieraus folgt in Verbindung mit der Stabilitätsbedingung $(1 - \lambda_k) < 1$: Ist die Summe der Inhibitions-Koeffizienten für alle Rezeptoren in S kleiner eins, dann ist das System stabil. Wird sie dagegen für einen oder mehrere Rezeptoren gleich oder grösser eins, dann *kann* das Inhibitions-System indifferent oder instabil sein. Eine Entscheidung über die Stabilität des Systems erfordert in diesen Fällen die Berechnung des Eigenwertspektrums der $\mathfrak{B}^*$-Matrix.–Kürzlich vorgenommene Untersuchungen (Kirschfeld und Reichardt, 1964) haben zu dem Ergebnis geführt, dass zumindest für Rezeptoren im Zentralbereich des *Limulus*-Auges die Summe der Inhibitions-Koeffizienten grösser eins ist.

Eine weitere Stabilitätseigenschaft des Inhibitions-Systems sei jetzt betrachtet. Es wird behauptet: Kann eine Reizverteilung $\mathfrak{y}^*$ zwei verschiedene Konfigurationen S_1, S_2 auslösen und liegt S_1 in S_2, dann ist die S_2-Konfiguration instabil. Beweis: Die beiden möglichen Konfigurationen seien

$$\left(\mathfrak{z}_1^* \text{ mit } z_i^{(1)} > 0, i \subset S_1; z_i^{(1)} = 0, i \subset \bar{S}_1 \right) \atop \left(\mathfrak{z}_2^* \text{ mit } z_i^{(2)} > 0, i \subset S_2; z_i^{(2)} = 0, i \subset \bar{S}_2 \right) \tag{24}$$

wobei nach Voraussetzung $S_1 < S_2$ und $\mathfrak{z}_2^*$ eine Lösung von

$$z_i^{(2)} = \left\{ \begin{array}{ll} y_i - \sum_{\substack{j \subset n \\ j \neq i}} \beta_{ij} z_j^{(2)} & i \subset S_2 \\[2em] 0 & i \subset \bar{S}_2 \end{array} \right\} \tag{25}$$

ist. Prägt man den Ausgangsgrössen eine Störung ε_i auf, so ruft diese eine Abweichung Δ_i hervor. Es ist also

$$z_i^{(2)} + \Delta_i = \left\{ \begin{array}{ll} y_i - \sum_{\substack{j \subset n \\ j \neq i}} \beta_{ij} (z_j^{(2)} + \varepsilon_j) & i \subset S_2 \\[2em] 0 & i \subset \bar{S}_2 \end{array} \right\} \tag{26}$$

Nun sei $\varepsilon^* = \alpha (\mathfrak{z}_1^* - \mathfrak{z}_2^*)$ und α eine Konstante. Dann erhält man für ε_i

$$\varepsilon_i = \left\{ \begin{array}{ll} \alpha(z_i^{(1)} - z_i^{(2)}) & i \subset S_1 \\ - \alpha z_i^{(2)} & i \subset \bar{S}_1 \cap S_2 \\ 0 & i \subset \bar{S}_2 \end{array} \right\} \tag{27}$$

$\mathfrak{z}_1^*$ ist eine Lösung in S_1 und $\mathfrak{z}_1^* = \mathfrak{z}_2^* + \dfrac{1}{\alpha} \varepsilon^*$, sodass

$$y_i - \sum_{\substack{j \subset n \\ j \neq i}} \beta_{ij} \left(z_j^{(2)} + \frac{1}{\alpha} \varepsilon_j \right) \left\{ \begin{array}{l} = z_i^{(2)} + \dfrac{1}{\alpha} \varepsilon_i, \, i \subset S_1 \\[2em] \leq 0 \qquad\qquad , \, i \subset S_1 \end{array} \right\} \tag{28}$$

und für Δ_i

$$\Delta_i \left\{ \begin{array}{ll} = \varepsilon_i & i \subset S_1 \\ \leqq - \alpha \, z_i^{(2)} = \varepsilon_i & i \subset \bar{S}_1 \wedge S_2 \\ = 0 & i \subset \bar{S}_2 \end{array} \right\} \tag{29}$$

Da $z_i^{(2)} > 0$ für $i \subset S_2$ und $\varepsilon_i < 0$ für i $\subset \bar{S}_1 \cap S_2$, erhält man schliesslich

$$\frac{\Delta_i}{\varepsilon_i} \geqq 1 \text{ für alle } i \subset S_2 \tag{30}$$

Das heisst: Es gibt eine Störung in S_2, die entweder aufrechterhalten oder sogar ständig vergrössert wird. Daher ist die S_2-Konfiguration instabil.

Die bisher angestellten Überlegungen basieren auf den stationären Vorgängen der lateralen Inhibition und berücksichtigen nicht die dynamischen Eigenschaften dieser Wechselwirkungsprozesse. Erste orientierende Versuche schliessen nicht aus, dass auch die dynamischen Vorgänge linearer Natur sind (Hartline *et al.*, 1961). Daher sei der dynamische Fall an Hand zweier Beispiele hier kurz behandelt.

Wird den Ausgangsgrössen eines Inhibitions-Systems mit Dynamik im Zeitpunkt $t = 0$ eine Störung ε_i aufgeprägt, so reagiert es darauf mit Eigenschwingungen. Nehmen wir an, die aufgeprägte Störung löst nur eine der möglichen Eigenschwingungen aus, dann wird

$$\varepsilon_i(t) = \varepsilon_i \, e^{pt} \qquad \text{für } t > 0 \tag{31}$$

Hierin ist p eine komplexe Frequenz. Damit geht Gl. (9) über in

$$\Delta_i(t) = - \sum_{\substack{j \subset S \\ j \neq i}} \beta_{ij}(p) \, \varepsilon_j \, e^{pt} \qquad \text{für } t > 0 \text{ und } i \subset S \tag{32}$$

und entsprechend erhalten wir an Stelle von Gl. (12)

$$\Delta^*(t) = (\varepsilon^* - \mathfrak{B}^*(p) \, \varepsilon^*) e^{pt} \qquad \text{für } t > 0 \tag{33}$$

Das Inhibitions-System ist ein gegengekoppeltes System, sodass $\varepsilon^*(t) = \Delta^*(t)$ und daher Gl. (33) übergeht in

$$\varepsilon^*(t) = \varepsilon^*(t) - \mathfrak{B}^*(p) \, \varepsilon^*(t) \tag{34}$$

Daraus folgt

$$\mathfrak{B}^*(p) \, \varepsilon^*(t) = 0 \tag{35A}$$

oder

$$\det [\mathfrak{B}^*(p)] = 0 \tag{35B}$$

Sind die Realteile aller Wurzeln p_k von Gl. (35B) kleiner null, so ist das Inhibitions-System stabil. Die Eigenschwingungen sind gedämpft. Verschwindet ein oder verschwinden mehrere der Realteile von p_k, so bleiben die Eigenschwingungen ständig erhalten. Das System ist dagegen instabil, wenn Wurzeln auftreten, deren Realteile grösser null sind. Unter diesen Bedingungen nehmen die Amplituden der Eigenschwingungen exponentiell zu.

Die Bestimmung der Wurzeln von Gl. (35B) wird sehr vereinfacht, wenn die dynamischen Eigenschaften aller Inhibitions-Wechselwirkungen einander gleich sind. In diesem Fall ist

$$\beta_{ij}(p) = \begin{cases} A(p)\,\beta_{ij} & \text{für } j \neq i \\ 1 & \text{für } j \neq i \end{cases} \quad \text{mit } A(O) = 1. \tag{36}$$

Definieren wir die Einheitsmatrix

$$\mathfrak{E}^* = \{\delta_{ij}\}_{i,j \subset S} \text{ mit } \delta_{ij} = \begin{cases} 1 & j = i \\ 0 & j \neq i, \end{cases} \tag{37}$$

so erhält man für

$$\beta_{ij}(p) = A(p)\,\{\beta_{ij} - \delta_{ij}\} + \delta_{ij} \tag{38}$$

und

$$\mathfrak{B}^*(p) = A(p)\,[\mathfrak{B}^* - \mathfrak{E}^*] + \mathfrak{E}^*. \tag{39}$$

Zu Gl. (35B) ist $\mathfrak{B}^*(p)\,\mathfrak{q}_k^* = 0$ äquivalent, sodass

$$[A(p)\,(\mathfrak{B}^* - \mathfrak{E}^*) + \mathfrak{E}^*]\,\mathfrak{q}_k^* = 0. \tag{40}$$

Da $A(p)$ ein Skalar und $\mathfrak{q}_k^*$ ein Eigenvektor von $\mathfrak{B}^*$ ist, erhält man $A(p)\,\lambda_k\,\mathfrak{q}_k - A(p)\,\mathfrak{q}_k^* + \mathfrak{q}_k^* = 0$ und

$$A(p)\,\lambda_k - A(p) + 1 = 0 \tag{41}$$

Also

$$A(p) - \frac{1}{1 - \lambda_k} = 0$$

Damit ist die Stabilitätsbetrachtung auf das Kriterium von Nyquist (1932) zurückgeführt. Stabilität ist nur dann vorhanden, wenn die Nullstellen von p in der linken Hälfte der p-Ebene liegen. Zwei Fälle seien betrachtet:

Beispiel 1. Es werde angenommen, dass die hemmende Wirkung jedes Rezeptors auf alle anderen Rezeptoren um Δt Sekunden verzögert ist. Dann ist $A(p) = e^{-p\Delta t}$ und die Stabilitätsbedingung lautet $e^{-p\Delta t} - (1 - \lambda_k)^{-1} = 0$. Umläuft man die rechte Hälfte der p-Ebene entlang der imaginären Achse (von $- i\infty$ bis $+ i\infty$ und entlang eines Halbkreises um $p = 0$ mit dem Radius $R \to \infty$), so rotiert in der $A(p)$-Ebene ein komplexer Zeiger mit dem Radius eins um den Nullpunkt. Hierbei wird die linke Hälfte der p-Ebene auf das Gebiet ausserhalb des beschriebenen Kreises in der $A(p)$-Ebene abgebildet (genauer gesagt, auf ein entsprechendes Gebiet einer vielblättrigen $A(p)$-Ebene), woraus folgt, dass für Stabilität $|\frac{1}{1 - \lambda_k}| > 1$ erforderlich ist. Übersetzt man diese Bedingung in die λ-Ebene, so ergibt sich $|\lambda_k - 1| < 1$ als Stabilitätsbedingung für die Eigenwerte der $\mathfrak{B}^*$-Matrix. Das heisst: Stabilität dieses Inhibitionssystems ist dann nur gesichert, wenn alle Eigenwerte λ_k innerhalb eines

Kreises der λ-Ebene mit dem Radius eins liegen, dessen Mittelpunkt sich auf der reellen Achse im Punkte $+1$ befindet. Dieses Resultat enthält eine tiefere Begründung des in Gl. (15) angeschriebenen Stabilitätskriteriums.

Beispiel 2. Die Dynamik der hemmenden Wirkung jedes Rezeptors auf alle übrigen Rezeptoren korrespondiere zu der Übertragungseigenschaft eines einfachen Tiefpass-filters mit der Zeitkonstanten τ. Dann wird $A(p) = \dfrac{1}{1 + \dfrac{\tau}{2\pi} p}$. Umläuft man

wiederum die rechte Hälfte der p-Ebene, so wird die linke Hälfte dieser Ebene auf ein Gebiet der $A(p)$-Ebene abgebildet, das ausserhalb eines Kreises mit dem Radius $1/2$ liegt, dessen Mittelpunkt sich im Punkte $1/2$ auf der reellen Achse befindet. Die Stabilitätsbedingung lautet daher in diesem Fall $\left| \dfrac{1}{1 - \lambda_k} - \tfrac{1}{2} \right| > \tfrac{1}{2}$ oder Realteil $(\lambda_k) > 0$. Liegen die Realteile aller Eigenwerte der $\mathfrak{B}^*$-Matrix in der rechten Hälfte der λ-Ebene, dann ist das betrachtete Inhibitionssystem stabil.

C. EINDEUTIGKEIT DER ZUORDNUNG ZWISCHEN DEN y_i UND z_i

Das Inhibitionssystem im Lateralauge von *Limulus* ist stabil. Daraus folgt, dass die Eigenwerte der Matrix $\mathfrak{B}^*$ der Inhibitions-Koeffizienten grösser null sind. Für Erregungsverteilungen, die im Gültigkeitsbereich von Gl. (3A) liegen ist damit gezeigt, dass die durch das Inhibitionssystem bewirkte Zuordnung zwischen den y_i und z_i eine umkehrbar eindeutige ist. Denn die notwendige und hinreichende Bedingung für die eindeutige Auflösbarkeit von Gl. (3A) ist, dass die Determinante der β_{ij} verschieden von null ist. Für symmetrische Matrizen ist diese Determinante jedoch durch das Produkt der reellen Eigenwerte der Matrix gegeben, also

$$\det | \beta_{ij} | = \lambda_1 \lambda_2 \dots \lambda_n \tag{42}$$

Es ist daher $\det | \beta_{ij} | \neq 0$.

Das Inhibitionssystem des *Limulus*-Auges bewirkt daher eine eindeutige Zuordnung zwischen räumlichen Reizverteilungen auf dem Rezeptorenraster und dem von ihnen ausglösten Erregungsverteilungen im Querschnitt des optischen Nervs.

SUMMARY

A mathematical model of lateral nervous inhibition in the complex eye of the horse-shoecrab *Limulus* is considered here, with account on the changes in the effective structure of the nerve network resulting from the forced inactivity of fibers whose inhibition exceeds their excitation. The stability of the network model as a function of the inhibition coefficients is studied and two theorems regarding the stability are proven. One of the consequences of the stability of the inhibition system is that a one to one correspondence exists between stationary retinal patterns on the receptor mosaic and their associated excitation patterns in the cross-section of the optic nerve.

LITERATUR

DEMOLL, R., (1914); Die Augen von *Limulus*. *Zool. Jb.*, **38**, 443.

HARTLINE, H. K., AND RATLIFF, F., (1957); Inhibitory interaction of receptor units in the eye of *Limulus*. *J. gen. Physiol.*, **40**, 357.

HARTLINE, H. K., AND RATLIFF, F., (1958); Spatial summation of inhibitory influences in the eye of *Limulus*, and the Mutual interaction of receptor units. *J. gen. Physiol.*, **41**, 1049.

HARTLINE, H. K., RATLIFF, F., AND MILLER, W. H., (1961); Inhibitory interaction in the retina and its significance in vision. *Nervous Inhibition*. New York, Pergamon Press.

HARTLINE, H. K., WAGNER, H., AND RATLIFF, F., (1956); Inhibition in the eye of *Limulus*. *J. gen. Physiol.*, **39**, 651.

KIRSCHFELD, K., UND REICHARDT, W., (1964); Die Verarbeitung stationärer optischer Nachrichten im Komplexauge von *Limulus*. *Kybernetik*. **2**, 43.

MILLER, W. H., (1957); Morphology of the Ommatidia of the compound eye of *Limulus*. *J. biophys. biochem. Cytol.*, **3**, 421–428.

NYQUIST, M., (1932); Regeneration theory. *Bell System Tech. J.*, **11**, 126.

RATLIFF, F., AND HARTLINE, H. K., (1959); The responses of *Limulus* optic nerve fibers to patterns of illumination on the receptor mosaic. *J. gen. Physiol.*, **42**, 1241.

RATLIFF, F., MILLER, W. H., AND HARTLINE, H. K., (1958); Neural interaction in the eye and the integration of receptor activity. *Ann. N. Y. Acad. Sci.*, **74**, 210.

RATLIFF, F., MILLER, W. H., AND HARTLINE, H. K., (1958); Neural interaction in the eye and the integration of receptor activity. *Ann. N. Y. Acad. Sci.*, **74**, 210.

REICHARDT, W., (1961); Über das optische Auflösungsvermögen der Facettenaugen von *Limulus Kybernetik*, **1**, 57.

REICHARDT, W., UND MACGINITIE, G., (1962); Zur Theorie der lateralen Inhibition. *Kybernetik*, **1**, 155.

VARJÚ, D., (1962); Vergleich zweier Modelle für laterale Inhibition *Kybernetik*, **1**, 200.

Über Nichtlineare Analogschaltungen zur Simulierung Biologischer Adaptationsvorgänge

DEZSÖ VARJÚ

Max-Planck-Institut für Biologie in Tübingen, Abt. Reichardt (D.B.R.)

I. DIE GESETZE VON WEBER UND FECHNER

Die auf unseren Organismus einwirkenden Reize variieren in Bereichen, welche bei manchen Reizmodalitäten mehrere Zehnerpotenzen umfassen. Die Sinnesorgane erfüllen ihren Zweck in diesen weiten Bereichen der Reizgrössen und informieren den Organismus über Zustand und Änderung der Umwelt. Der Messtechniker löst entsprechende Aufgaben durch die Anwendung mehrer, gleichartiger Messinstrumente, deren Empfindlichkeit an Teilbereiche der zu messenden Grösse angepasst ist. Innerhalb eines Teilbereiches ist der Zusammenhang zwischen dem Zeigerausschlag und der Messgrösse meistens linear. Die Sinnesorgane bewältigen die Aufgabe durch die kontinuierliche Anpassung ihrer Empfindlichkeit an den jeweiligen Wert der Reizgrösse (Adaptation). Jede kleine Änderung in der Intensität des Reizes zieht eine entsprechende Änderung im Organismus nach sich. Der Zusammenhang zwischen der Reizgrösse und deren Wirkung (Reaktion) ist dadurch oft nichtlinear.

Die Anpassungsfähigkeit der Sinnesorgane wurde bereits von E. H. Weber quantitativ untersucht. Er stellte fest, dass die Unterschieds-Schwelle ΔS, — die eben noch bemerkbare Differenz, — beim Vergleichen von Gewichten mit den Händen dem Bezugsgewicht S proportional ist:

$$\Delta S/S = k \qquad (1)$$

Für die Konstante k ergaben seine Untersuchungen einen Wert von $k = 1/40$. Der gleiche Zusammenhang wurde für eine Anzahl anderer Reizmodalitäten gefunden, wobei Werte für k von 0.003 bis 0.350 gemessen wurden.

Der gefundene Zusammenhang zwischen ΔS und S (Webersches Gesetz) ist ein formelmässiger Ausdruck der Tatsache, dass die Empfindlichkeit der Sinnesorgane bei der Wahrnehmung von *Unterschieden* der Reizintensität der jeweiligen Bezugsgrösse angepasst ist.

Gl. (1) sagt nichts über die zeitlichen Vorgänge aus, welche sich erfahrungsgemäss abspielen, während sich die Empfindlichkeit nach einer Änderung des Bezugsreizes der neuen Reizgrösse anpasst. Diese zeitlichen Ereignisse werden *Kinetik der Adaptation* genannt. Welchen Einfluss die Zeit auf die Messergebnisse ausübt, hängt von den jeweiligen experimentellen Gegebenheiten ab. Man unterscheidet gewöhnlich zwischen der *simultanen* und der *sukzessiven* Unterschiedsschwelle. Die simultane Unterschiedsschwelle wird untersucht, indem der eben noch bemerkbare Unterschied zweier, gleichzeitig dargebotener Reize gleicher Modalität gemessen wird. (So z.B. der Helligkeitsunterschied zweier unterschiedlich beleuchteter Flächen, der Temperaturunterschied zweier Körper, usw.). Durch geeignete Vorkehrungen im Experiment lässt sich der Einfluss der Zeit auf die simultane Schwelle leicht beseitigen. Bei der Untersuchung der sukzessiven Unterschiedsschwelle werden unterschiedlich starke Reize gleicher Modalität zeitlich nacheinander dargeboten. Das Ergebnis eines Experiments hängt in diesem Fall davon ab, wie weit die Änderung der Empfindlichkeit fortgeschritten ist, während die Wirkung des neuen Reizes durch Messung ermittelt wird. Sogar die Gültigkeit des Weberschen Gesetzes kann davon abhängen, in welchem Zeitpunkt die Wirkung des Reizes untersucht wird. Eine genaue Aussage hierüber kann nur bei Kenntnis der Kinetik der Adaptation erfolgen. Im zweiten Teil dieser Arbeit wird hierzu ein Beispiel diskutiert. Das Webersche Gesetz gibt auch darüber keine Auskunft, welcher Zusammenhang zwischen einem überschwelligen Reizunterschied und dessen Wirkung besteht. Um einen eindeutigen Zusammenhang zwischen dem Reiz S und der Reaktion R zu erhalten, hat G. Th. Fechner hypothetisch angenommen, dass ein kleiner Reizzuwachs ΔS stets einen Reaktionszuwachs ΔR nach sich zieht. Er setzte für die Konstante k in Gl. (1) den Reaktionszuwachs ΔR ein und erhielt somit die Beziehung

$$\Delta R = c \, \frac{\Delta S}{S}.$$

c bedeutet hier eine Proportionalitätskonstante. Zu dem Zusammenhang zwischen dem Reiz S und der Reaktion R gelangt man durch die Integration der Gl. (2a).

Gl. (2a) ist sinngemäss ein Spezialfall der allgemeinen Beziehung

$$\Delta R = \Delta S \, E_s \, (S), \tag{2b}$$

worin $E_s \, (S)$ die vom Reiz S abhängige Schwellenempfindlichkeit bedeutet. Gl. (2b$^)$ stellt Webers Befund dann dar, wenn $E_s \, (S) = 1/S$ ist.

Um die Integration der Gl. (2b) durchzuführen, benötigt man ebenfalls Kenntnisse über die Kinetik der Adaptation. Anhand zweier Extremfälle lässt sich diese Aussage veranschaulichen. Der eine Fall liegt dann vor, wenn die Wirkung des veränderten Reizes bereits gemessen werden kann, bevor die Empfindlichkeit sich massgebend verändert. Stellt man die Gültigkeit des Weberschen Gesetzes fest, (Schwellenempfindlichkeit = 1/S), so liefert die Integration der Gl. (2b) die Beziehung zwischen der Reaktion R und dem Reiz S:

$$R = a + c \, \frac{S}{S_0}. \tag{3}$$

Hierin ist a eine Integrationskonstante. Der Reiz wurde von S_0 auf S verändert. Die Integration der Gl. (2a) liefert in diesem Fall einen linearen Zusammenhang zwischen dem Reiz S und der Reaktion R.

Häufig ist jedoch der andere Extremfall in Experimenten leichter zu verwirklichen. Er tritt dann auf, wenn die Empfindlichkeit nach einer Reizänderung ihren neuen, stationären Wert zur Zeit der Messung bereits erreicht hat. Die Gültigkeit des Weber-schen Gesetzes vorausgesetzt liefert dann die Integration der Gl. (2b):

$$R = a + c \log S \qquad (4)$$

a ist auch hier eine Integrationskonstante.

Fechner hat den Zusammenhang (4) zwischen dem Reiz *S* und der Reaktion *R* auf-gestellt. Die Beziehung (4) hat in der Psychophysik unter der Bezeichnung 'Fechner-sches Gesetz' eine sehr bedeutende Rolle gespielt. Sowohl das Webersche wie auch das Fechnersche Gesetz erwiesen sich nur in beschränkten Intensitätsbereichen verschie-dener Reizmodalitäten als gute Approximationen psychophysikalischer Reiz–Reak-tions-Zusammenhänge. Mit dieser Einschränkung wurden jedoch beide Gesetze durch ein Jahrhundert akzeptiert. In jüngster Zeit hat Stevens (1961) gezeigt, dass die psycho-physikalischen Reiz–Reaktions-Zusammenhänge vielfach eher durch eine Potenz-Funktion, als durch eine logarithmische Beziehung beschrieben werden. Er stellte für eine Reihe verschiedener Reizmodalitäten den Zusammenhang $R = k(S - S_0)^n$ zwischen dem Reiz *S* und dessen Wirkung *R* fest. *k* und *n* sind konstante, deren Werte für verschiedene Reizmodalitäten verschieden sind. Für *n* hat Stevens Werte zwischen 0.33 und 3.5 gefunden. S_0 ist der absolute Schwellenreiz.

Stevens' Befund lässt sich aber — zumindest im Fall des visuellen Systems des Menschen — auch folgendermassen interpretieren: Da in seinen einschlägigen Experimenten (Stevens, 1963) der veränderte Lichtreiz nur eine Sekunde lang der Versuchsperson dargeboten wurde, hängt das Ergebnis der Messung auch von der Kinetik der Adaptation ab. Interessanterweise wird das Ergebnis eines Experiments bei kurzen Lichtreizen von deren Dauer nicht wesentlich beeinflusst (Stevens, 1963, p. 375). Erst bei sehr langen Lichtreizen macht sich die Wirkung der Kinetik bemerkbar und führt dazu, dass — im stationären Zustand — nicht mehr eine Potenz, sondern eine logarithmische Funktion den Zusammenhang zwischen der subjektiven Helligkeit und der Lichtintensität beschreibt (Stevens, 1963, p. 381). Aufgrund des vorher Gesagten kann man nun die Auffassung vertreten, dass das 'power law' auf das im stationären Fall gültige Fechnersche Gesetz *und* die Kinetik der Adaptation zurück-zuführen ist.

Aus den vorangegangenen Ausführungen kann man zusammenfassend folgende Schlüsse ziehen: Die Gültigkeit des Weberschen Gesetzes hat uneingeschränkt nur für stationäre Reize die Gültigkeit des Fechnerschen Gesetzes zur Folge. Spielt auch die Kinetik der Adaptation bei den Untersuchungen eine Rolle, so ist es im Prinzip möglich, dass die Abhängigkeit des Schwellenreizes von dem Bezugsreiz durch das Webersche Gesetz beschrieben wird, während die Wirkung überschwelliger Reize dem Fechnerschen Gesetz nicht folgt (vgl. Gl. 3). Im Allgemeinen muss man aber die Kinetik der Adaptation kennen, um über die Gültigkeit der beiden Gesetze entschei-den zu können.

Im folgenden Teil dieser Arbeit soll ein Beispiel für das Studium der Kinetik eines Adaptationsvorganges diskutiert werden. Die Analyse wurde von Delbrück und

Reichardt (1956) durchgeführt und später in verschiedenen Arbeiten diskutiert. (Reichardt und Varjú, 1958; Reichardt, 1959 und 1963). Die Zusammenfassung der Ergebnisse erfolgt in Anlehnung an diese Arbeiten.

II. DIE KINETIK DER ADAPTATION VON *Phycomyces*

Das Objekt der Untersuchungen war der einzellige Pilz *Phycomyces blakesleanus*. Er ist auf einer Reihe natürlicher und künstlicher Nährböden leicht zu züchten. Einige Tage nach dem Aussäen der Sporen wachsen zylindrische Sporangienträger aus dem Mycelium heran, etwa 0.05 mm im Durchmesser. Nach Bildung des Sporangiums gelangen die Sporangienträger in ein Stadium nahezu stationären Wachstums. Das Wachstum ist auf eine etwa 2 mm lange Zone (Wachstumszone, WZ) unmittelbar unterhalb des Sporangiums beschränkt. Die Wachstumsgeschwindigkeit beträgt in diesem Stadium 2–3 mm in der Stunde, wenn die Umwelthelligkeit konstant gehalten wird. Abb. 1 zeigt den Sporangienträger schematisch und veranschaulicht die Verhältnisse während des Wachstums.

Wird die Umwelthelligkeit plötzlich verändert, so tritt eine vorübergehende Änderung in der Wachstumsgeschwindigkeit auf, welche sowohl von dem Ausmass der

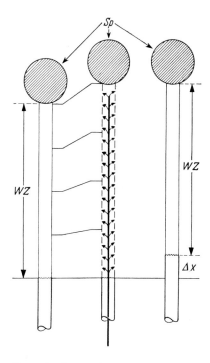

Abb. 1. Schematische Darstellung des Sporangienträgers von *Phycomyces* und Veranschaulichung der Verhältnisse während des Wachstums. Die Wachstumszone (*WZ*) streckt sich und nimmt neues Zellwandmaterial auf. Eine entsprechende Länge *Δ*x, um die sich die *WZ* in der Zeiteinheit streckt, verwandelt sich an ihrer Basis in nichtwachsende Zellwand um. *Sp*: Sporangium. (Nach Delbrück und Reichardt, 1956, verändert).

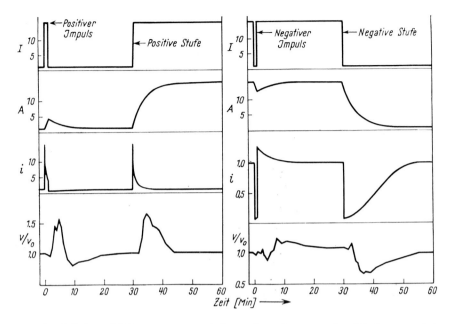

Abb. 2. Vier einfache Reizlichtprogramme und die von ihnen hervorgerufene Wachstumsreaktionen.
I: Lichtintensität als Funktion der Zeit. (Obere Reihe). v: Wachstumsgeschwindigkeit, auf die statio-
näre Wachstumsgeschwindigkeit v_0 bezogen und als Funktion der Zeit aufgetragen. (Untere Reihe).
Die zweite und die dritte Reihe zeigen den Verlauf der theoretisch ermittelten Grössen *A* und *i* (vgl.
S. 81–82). Die Einheit der *i* (*t*)-Skala auf der rechten Seite ist um einen Faktor 20 gegenüber der
auf der linken Seite gestreckt (nach Reichardt, 1961).

Intensitätsänderung, wie auch von der vorherigen stationären Beleuchtungsstärke
abhängt. Eine eingehende, experimentelle Untersuchung der Zusammenhänge wird
dadurch begünstigt, dass die WZ für die Anwendung verschiedener Reizlichtprogramme gut zugänglich, und die relativ hohe Wachstumsgeschwindigkeit und deren
Änderung unter dem Binokular leicht zu messen sind. Da die WZ auch phototropisch
reagiert, — sie wächst bei seitlicher Beleuchtung in Richtung des einfallenden Lichtes
— muss dafür Sorge getragen werden, dass die Intensität des einfallenden Lichtes
azimutal symmetrisch verteilt und geändert wird, um den störenden Effekt der
Abbiegung des Sporangienträgers während der Wachstumsreaktion zu vermeiden.

Abb. 2 zeigt die Wachstumsreaktion auf einige Lichtreizprogramme. Folgende
qualitative Eigenschaften der Wachstumsreaktion lassen sich aus den dargestellten
Reaktionskurven ablesen:

1. Ein positiver Lichtimpuls verursacht zunächst, — nach einer Latenzzeit von
etwa 2.5 Minuten — eine Phase schnelleren Wachstums. Nach einigen Minuten nimmt
die Wachstumsgeschwindigkeit wieder ab, unterschreitet vorübergehend den stationären Wert und erreicht ihn wieder etwa 15 Minuten nach der Reizgebung. Ein Netto-
wachstum ist dabei nicht zu verzeichnen; die Erhöhung und die Erniedrigung der
Wachstumsgeschwindigkeit kompensieren sich im Zeitmittel.

2. Die WZ beantwortet eine positive Intensitätsstufe mit einer vorübergehend
erhöhten Wachstumsgeschwindigkeit.

3. Ändert man das Vorzeichen des Impulsreizes oder des Stufenreizes, so erfolgt auch die Änderung der Wachstumsgeschwindigkeit in entgegengesetztem Sinn.

Zum quantitativen Studium der Vorgänge wurde die Reaktion auf positive Lichtimpulse gewählt. Folgende Bezeichnungen wurden eingeführt: I_1: Stationäre Beleuchtungsstärke vor der Reizgebung (Adaptationslicht). I_2: Beleuchtungsstärke während der Dauer des Reizimpulses. $S = I_2 \Delta t$: Reizgrösse. Δt: Dauer des Lichtimpulses. Es wurde festgestellt:

1. Die Form der Reaktionskurven sowie die Latenzzeit werden von der Reizgrösse nicht beeinflusst. Als Mass für die Reaktion R wurde deshalb die mittlere Wachstumsgeschwindigkeit $\bar{v}$ zwischen den Zeitpunkten $t = 2.5$ und 5 Minuten nach Reizgebung eingeführt, bezogen auf die stationäre Wachstumsgeschwindigkeit v_0 unmittelbar vor der Reaktion.

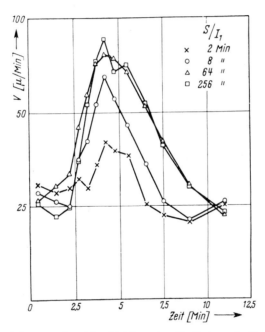

Abb. 3. Wachstumsreaktionen auf positive Lichtimpulse. Variiert wurde die Reizstärke S bei konstanter Adaptationsintensität I_1. (Nach Delbrück und Reichardt, 1956).

2. Die Reaktion ist eine graduierte Funktion des Reizes. [Zu 1. und 2. vgl. Abb. 3].

3. Die Reaktion wird nur von dem Produkt $I_2 \Delta t$ bestimmt, solange Δt nicht grösser als etwa 1 Minute ist. Sie folgt somit dem Bunsen–Roscoe-Gesetz der Photochemie (Abb. 4). Δt betrug in den Experimenten gewöhnlich 15 Sek.

Die Reaktion R wurde bei zwei unterschiedlichen Adaptationsintensitäten I_1 als Funktion von S gemessen. Die Ergebnisse sind in Abb. 5 wiedergegeben. S und I_1 sind in relativen logarithmischen Einheiten zur Basis 2 angeben. In dieser Darstellung sind die Reaktionskurven an der $\log_2 S$-Achse um die logarithmische Differenz der beiden Adaptationsintensitäten gegeneinander verschoben. Für die kleinsten gemessenen Reaktionen gilt dies sehr genau und auch für grössere Reaktionen in guter Näherung*.

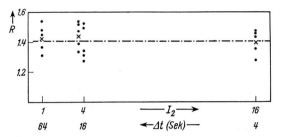

Abb. 4. Reziprozität zwischen Zeit und Lichtintensität. Das Produkt $I_2 \Delta t$ betrug stets 64. Die × stellen Mittelwerte der Einzelmessungen (·) dar. Die horizontale Linie ist der Mittelwert aller Messungen. (Nach Delbrück und Reichardt, 1956, Bezeichnungen verändert).

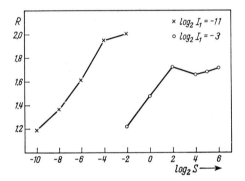

Abb. 5. Das Reaktionsmass R als Funktion der Reizgrösse S bei zwei unterschiedlichen Adaptationsintensitäten $I_1 = 2^{-11}$ und $I_1 = 2^{-3}$. Die Reaktionskurven sind an der $\log_2 S$-Achse um die logarithmische Differenz der beiden Adaptationsintensitäten voneindnder entfernt. (Nach Delbruck und Reichardt, 1956).

Anhand dieses Befundes kann festgestellt werden, in welcher Weise der Schwellenreiz von dem Bezugsreiz abhängt. Da die Reaktion eine graduierte Funktion des Reizes ist, muss derjenige Reiz als Schwellenreiz angesehen werden, welcher eine eben noch messbare Reaktion verursacht. Die Ergebnisse in der Abb. 5 besagen, dass der so definierte Schwellenreiz dem Bezugsreiz proportional ist. Das ist der quantitative Inhalt des Weberschen Gesetzes. Die Gültigkeit des Gesetzes ist jedoch auf einen bestimmten Zeitbereich nach der Reizgebung beschränkt, da eine Änderung der Lichtintensität nur eine vorübergehende Änderung der Wachstumsgeschwindigkeit

---

* Der nahezu horizontale Verlauf der Reaktionskurve für grosse Reize bei der höheren Adaptationsintensität (Kurve rechts in Abb. 5) war nach Delbrück und Reichardt die Eigenschaft des benutzten Sporangienträgers. Sie ist für die angewandte Adaptationsintensität nicht charakteristisch.
* Bei sehr hohen und sehr niedrigen Adaptationsintensitäten weicht der Verlauf der Reaktionskurven von dem gezeigten ab. Die Analyse der Wachstumreaktion wurde im sogenannten 'Normalbereich' der Lichtintensität durchgeführt. Er enhält keine extrem grossen und kleinen Adaptionsintensitäten.

nach sich zieht; es liegt hier ein adaptierendes System vor, für welches die Kinetik der Adaptation die Gültigkeit des Weberschen Gesetzes wesentlich mitbestimmt.

Zur Analyse der Kinetik wurde eine innere Grösse A ('Adaptationszustand') eingeführt, welche in jedem Zeitpunkt die Empfindlichkeit der WZ charakterisieren soll. Um den Verhältnissen im stationären Zustand Rechnung zu tragen, wurde eine direkte Proportionalität zwischen A und I_1 — der stationären Adaptationsintensität — postuliert. Der Proportionalitätsfaktor zwischen A und I_1 kann dabei willkürlich zu Eins gewählt werden, wenn nur die Änderung von A als Funktion der Zeit zu ermitteln ist. Mit der in Abschnitt I eingeführten Terminologie entspricht A der reziproken Empfindlichkeit.

Es galt nunmehr A als Funktion der Zeit zu bestimmen, wenn die Beleuchtungsstärke in der Zeit variiert. Hierzu wurde jeweils diejenige Reizgrösse S bestimmt, welche im gegebenen Zeitpunkt eine Standardreaktion von der Stärke $R = 1.4$ verursachte. Die so ermittelte Reizstärke ist ein direktes Mass für den Adaptationszustand.

Die Zeitabhängigkeit des Adaptationszustandes wurde in zweierlei Experimenten gemessen. In einer Serie von Messungen wurde die WZ 30 min lang verschiedenen Adaptationsintensitäten ausgesetzt. Während dieser Zeit erreicht A seinen endgültigen, der jeweiligen Beleuchtungsstärke I_1 entsprechenden stationären Wert. Die Änderung von A nach Abschalten des Adaptationslichtes zeigt Abb. 6a. Im zweiten Experiment wurde der WZ nur ein kurzer Lichtreiz der Stärke S dargeboten. Die Kurven in Abb. 6b zeigen A als Funktion der Zeit nach dem Impulsreiz. Unabhängig davon, wie hoch sein ursprünglicher Wert gewesen ist, und in welcher Weise er erreicht wurde, nimmt A zunächst stets exponentiell ab. Die Abnahme verlangsamt sich später.

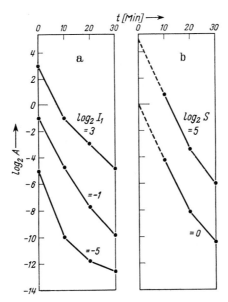

Abb. 6. Die Änderung des Adaptationszustandes als Funktion der Zeit, (a) nach 30 Minuten Beleuchtung mit I_1, und (b) nach Darbietung des Reizes von der Stärke S. (Nach Delbrück und Reichardt, 1956).

Über 30 Minuten hinaus wurden keine Messungen durchgeführt. Mann muss bedenken, dass die WZ bei einer Gesamtlänge von etwa 2 mm in der Stunde durchschnittlich 2–3 mm wächst. In 30 Minuten wird in dieser Weise etwa die Hälfte der WZ erneuert. Die Auswertung von Messergebnissen, welche in grossem Zeitabstand vom Beginn der Messung gewonnen werden, wird dadurch sehr problematisch.

Die Daten der Abb. 6 lassen sich als eine Lösung der Differentialgleichung erster Ordnung mit konstanten Koeffizienten

$$b \frac{dA}{dt} + A = I \tag{5a}$$

interpretieren. Die allgemeine Lösung dieser Gleichung

$$A(t) = A(o)e^{-t/b} + (1/b) \int_0^t I(t')e^{-(t-t')/b} \, dt' \tag{5b}$$

liefert den Zusammenhang zwischen einem beliebigen Lichtprogramm $I(t)$ und dem Adaptationszustand $A(t)$. Die Zeitkonstante b wurde aus Abb. 6 zu 3.8 Minuten bestimmt. Es ist zu erwarten, dass die Wachstumsgeschwindigkeit $v(t)$ auf beliebige Lichtprogramme dem Quotienten $i(t) = I(t)/A(t)$ proportional ist. $i(t)$ wurde 'subjektive Intensität' genannt. In Abb. 2 sind neben $v(t)$ auch der errechnete Verlauf von $A(t)$ und $i(t)$ auf die in der ersten Reihe dargestellten Lichtprogramme aufgetragen. Obwohl der Verlauf von $i(t)$ die gleichen Phasen aufweist, wie der von $v(t)$, besteht eine direkte Proportionalität zwischen den beiden Grössen nur im trivialen Fall der stationären Beleuchtung. Delbrück und Reichardt postulierten deshalb, dass die Transformation von $i(t)$ in $v(t)$ durch eine Instanz erfolgt, welche die Eigenschaften eines linearen Tiefpassfilters besitzt. Mit diesem Zusatz ergibt sich die in Abb. 7

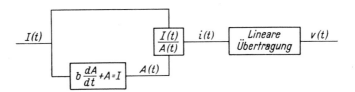

Abb. 7. Funktionsstruktur der Wachstumsreaktion (im Normalbereich der Beleuchtungsstärke). Der Lichteingang $I(t)$ steuert den Adaptationszustand $A(t)$. Der Zusammenhang zwischen $I(t)$ und $A(t)$ ist durch eine lineare Differentialgleichung erster Ordnung mit konstanten Koeffizienten gegeben. $i(t)$ steuert über ein lineares träges Übertragungselement die Wachstumsgeschwindigkeit $v(t)$. Im stationären Fall sind $i(t)$ und $v(t)$ von $I(t)$ unabhängig. (Nach Reichardt und Varjú, 1958, verändert).

dargestellte Funktionsstruktur der Wachstumreaktion. Die Gewichtsfunktion $W(t)$ des zusätzlichen Tiefpassfilters wurde nicht bestimmt. Durch Superpositionsexperimente haben jedoch Delbrück und Reichardt gezeigt, dass der Zusammenhang zwischen $i(t)$ und $v(t)$ *linear* ist.

Mit Hilfe dieser Funktionsstruktur und der Gl. (5b) haben Delbrück und Reichardt berechnet, welcher Zusammenhang zwischen einem kurzen, beliebig starken rechteckförmigen Impulsreiz S und der entsprechenden Reaktion R bei einer gegebenen Adaptationsintensität I_1 zu erwarten ist. Sie erhielten den Zusammenhang

$$R = Kb \log (1 + S/bI_1), \tag{6}$$

worin K eine Proportionalitätskonstante bedeutet. Für kleine Werte von S lässt sich die rechte Seite der Gl. (6) in eine Potenzreihe entwickeln, worin die Glieder mit höheren Exponenten vernachlässigt werden können. Für kleine Reize ergibt sich in dieser Weise die Beziehung

$$R = K \, S/I_1. \tag{7a}$$

Gl. (7a) entspricht genau dem Zusammenhang in Gl. (3), welcher *eine* mögliche Integration der Weberschen Gleichung (2a) darstellt. Für starke Reize ist dagegen 1 neben S/bI_1 in Gl. (6) zu vernachlässigen. Man erhält dadurch die Beziehung

$$R = - KbI_1 + Kb \log S. \tag{7b}$$

R nimmt in Gl. (7b) logarithmisch mit S zu. Dies entspricht dem experimentell festgestellten logarithmischen Zusammenhang zwischen der Reaktion R und dem Reiz S (vgl. Abb. 5). Formal entspricht Gl. (7b) ausserdem dem Fechnerschen Zusammenhang in Gl. (4). Während aber Gl. (4) unter der Voraussetzung eines stationären Reiz–Reaktions-Zusammenhanges abgeleitet wurde, bezieht sich Gl. (7b) auf dynamische Vorgänge. Sie ist die Folge der Kinetik der Adaptation und kann nur in Kenntniss des zeitlichen Verlaufs des Adaptationsvorganges abgeleitet werden.

Obwohl die gefundene Funktionsstruktur wesentlich zum Verständnis des Reiz–Reaktions-Zusammenhanges beiträgt, stellt sie nur eine formale Analyse dar. Um die den Grössen A und i zugrunde liegenden chemischen Reaktionen zu erfassen, benötigt man chemische Modelle. Delbrück und Reichardt haben gezeigt, dass das dynamische Verhalten der WZ nur dann auf der Basis eines chemischen Modells verstanden werden kann, wenn die antagonistische Wirkung von mindestens zwei Enzymen angenommen wird, deren Aktivität vom Licht gesteuert wird. Einzelheiten hierzu sind in der zitierten Literatur besprochen*.

III. EINE VERALLGEMEINERUNG DER FUNKTIONSSTRUKTUR DER WACHSTUMSREAKTION VON *Phycomyces*

Die Ergebnisse des vorangegangenen Kapitels zeigen, dass Funktionsstrukturen gefunden werden können, welche biologische Reiz–Reaktions-Systeme vollständig und quantitativ zu beschreiben vermögen. Es wäre jedoch unbegründeter Optimismus, gleiche Erfolge auch bei höheren Organismen zu erhoffen, besonders im Bezug auf Vollständigkeit. Ich zitiere Shropshire (1963): 'In man and other higher animals, the problem approaches infinite complexity, primarily because of the multicellular nature of these organisms, the neural networks of the systems evaluating stimuli, and the spatial separation of the perceiving, integrating and responding structures. Thus, intuitively, one is led to the naive hypothesis, that perhaps a unicellular organism

---

* Hassenstein (1960) schlug ein weiteres chemisches Modell auf der Basis des Massenwirkungsgesetzes vor.

Literatur S. 100

which possesses many of the functional properties of the more complex stimulus–response systems would be more profitable for study. If the mechanics of transduction of stimuli can be mapped out in fine detail for such a relatively simple unicellular system, our confidence will increase that such an approach is, in fact, possible and we can then begin to extrapolate cautiously to more complex systems.'

Im folgenden Teil dieser Arbeit soll die vorsichtige Extrapolation gewagt und die Frage untersucht werden, ob und in welcher Weise sich die Funktionsstruktur der Wachstumsreaktion von Phycomyces erweitern liesse, um andere Reiz–Reaktions-Zusammenhänge mindestens teilweise zu beschreiben.

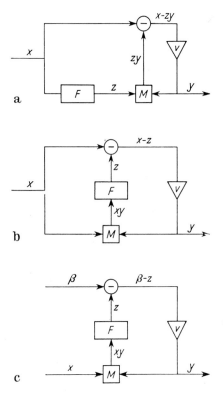

Abb. 8. (a) Elektronische Analogschaltung der Funktionsstruktur der Wachstumsreaktion nach Abb. 7. F: Lineares Übertragungselement. M: Multiplikator. V: Operationsverstärker mit dem Verstärkungsfaktor V. Die Schaltung ist der Funktionsstruktur der Wachstumsreaktion gleichwertig, wenn der Verstärkungsfaktor $V \to \infty$. Für endliche Werte von V ist die Ausgangsgrösse y auch im stationären Fall eine eindeutig umkehrbare Funktion der Eingangsgrösse x. (b) und (c): Modifikationen von (a). Im stationären Fall sind die Schaltungen a, b, und c gleichwertig. In c ist β eine konstante Referenzgrösse.

Da in den meisten Fällen die Reaktion auch von einem stationären Reiz abhängt, möchte ich zunächst zeigen, dass die Funktionsstruktur der Wachstumsreaktion für stationäre Reize den Grenzfall eines eindeutig umkehrbaren Reiz–Reaktions-Zusammenhanges darstellt. Konstruiert man das elektrische Analogschaltbild der Funktionsstruktur in Abb. 7, so wird der Divisionsvorgang durch die bei Analogrechnern übliche multiplikative Rückkoppelung ersetzt, wie sie in Abb. 8a schematisch gezeigt ist. V ist der Verstärkungsfaktor eines Operationsverstärkers. M bedeutet Multiplikation. F ist ein lineares Übertragungselement, welches entweder durch die Gewichtsfunktion $W(t)$, oder durch die Übertragungsfunktion $G(s)$ charakterisiert wird. s ist die Laplace-Variabel. Lineare Übertragungselemente, die auf y wirken, sind in Abb. 8 nicht mehr gezeigt. x, y und z sind Funktionen der Zeit, zwischen denen folgende Zusammenhänge bestehen:

$$y = V(x - yz);\qquad(8a)$$

$$z(t) = \int_{0}^{t} W(t')\,x(t - t')dt',\qquad(9a)$$

oder

$$z(s) = G(s)\,x(s).\qquad(9b)$$

Aus Gl. (8a) ergibt sich für y:

$$y = \frac{Vx}{1 + Vz}\qquad(8b)$$

Entspricht x der Beleuchtungsstärke $I(t)$, y dem subjektiven Reiz, $i(t)$ und z dem Adaptationszustand $A(t)$, so drückt Gl. (8b) den für Phycomyces gefundenen Zusammenhang zwischen der Beleuchtungsstärke $I(t)$ und dem subjektiven Reiz $i(t)$ aus, *wenn nur der Verstärkungsfaktor V so gross ist, dass 1 im Nenner neben Vz vernachlässigt werden darf.* Bezeichnet man die stationären Werte von x, y und z mit x_0, y_0, und z_0, so erhält man für den stationären Fall:

$$y_0 = \frac{Vx_0}{1 + qVx_0},\qquad(8c)$$

da im stationären Zustand $z_0 = qx_0$ ist. q bedeutet hier einen konstanten Faktor. Für grosse Werte von V ist $y_0 = 1/q$ und somit unabhängig von x_0.

Für kleinere Werte von V stellt dagegen Gl. (8c) einen eindeutig umkehrbaren Zusammenhang zwischen einem stationären Reiz (x_0) und y_0 (Reaktion, oder eine der Reaktion proportionaler Grösse) dar, welcher in einem Bereich von etwa 2 Zehnerpotenzen eine gute Approximation des Fechnerschen Gesetzes ist (Abb. 9). So gross ist aber der Bereich, in welchem die subjektive Helligkeit in psychophysikalischen

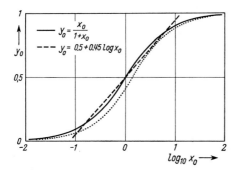

Abb. 9. Ausgezogene Kurve: Ausgangsgrösse y der Schaltungen in Abb. 8 als Funktion der stationären Eingangsgrösse x. y stellt in einem Bereich von etwa 2 Zehnerpotenzen der Eingangsgrösse ein gute Approximation des Fechnerschen Gesetzes dar. (Gestrichelte Gerade). Punktierte Kurve: Siehe Text, Seite 97.

Literatur S. 100

Experimenten in guter Näherung dem Fechnerschen Gesetz entsprechend von der Beleuchtungsstärke abhängt.

Grössere Abweichungen von dem Fechnerschen Zusammenhang treten im Modell lediglich für sehr kleine und sehr grosse Werte von x_0 auf. Eine gleichsinnige Abweichung findet man aber auch experimentell für die meisten Reiz–Reaktions-Zusammenhänge. Diese Feststellungen legen die Untersuchung der dynamischen Eigenschaften der Schaltung in Abb. 8a nahe. Besonders für das visuelle System des Menschen ist die Analyse vielversprechend, da Bouman *et al.* (1963) die Formel in Gl. (8c) bereits mit Erfolg benutzt haben, um Adaptationserscheinungen des menschlichen Auges im Weber- Fechner-Bereich zu beschreiben.

Ich möchte zunächst darauf hinweisen, dass die stationären Eigenschaften der Schaltung in Abb. 8a nicht nur von einer Änderung der Gewichtsfunktion $W(t)$ bzw. der Übertragungsfunktion $G(s)$, sondern auch von bestimmten strukturellen Änderungen unbeeinflusst bleiben. Abb. 8b und 8c zeigen hierzu zwei Beispiele. In Abb. 8b befindet sich das lineare Übertragungselement F nicht mehr vor, sondern nach dem Multiplikator M, also in dem Kreis der multiplikativen Rückkoppelung. In Abb. 8c ist ausserdem die eine Eingangsgrösse der Subtraktionsinstanz nicht mehr die Variable x, sondern eine konstante Referenzgrösse β. Die Zusammenhänge zwischen x, y und z sind:

$$y = V(x - z) \qquad \text{für Abb. 8b, und} \tag{10a}$$

$$y = V(\beta - z) \qquad \text{für Abb. 8c, sowie} \tag{10b}$$

$$z(t) = \int_{-\infty}^{t} W(t')\, x(t - t')\, y(t - t')\, dt', \tag{11a}$$

oder

$$z(s) = G(s)\, [x(s)\, y(s)] \tag{11b}$$

sowohl für Abb. 8b wie auch für Abb. 8c. Im stationären Fall ist hier $z_0 = q x_0 y_0$. Setzt man diesen Wert in Gl. (10a) ein, so ergibt sich für y_0 wieder der Zusammenhang (8c). In der gleichen Weise erhält man für die Schaltung in Abb. 8c:

$$y_0 = \frac{\beta V}{1 + q V x_0}, \tag{12a}$$

beziehungsweise

$$x_0\, y_0 = \frac{z_0}{q} = \frac{\beta V x_0}{1 + q V x_0} \tag{12b}$$

Gl. (12b) ist bis auf den Faktor β mit Gl. (8c) identisch, wenn nur die Rolle der Funktion y_0 in Gl. (8c) dem Produkt $x_0 y_0$ oder der Grösse z_0/q zugeschrieben wird. Entsprach etwa die Funktion y_0 der stationären Reaktion in den Schaltungen nach Abb. 8a und 8b, so muss $x_0 y_0$ oder z_0/q in der Schaltung nach Abb. 8c als Reaktion angesehen werden*. Unterschiede können lediglich im dynamischen Verhalten der

---

*Die Schaltung nach Abb. 8c wurde von Wenking (unveröffentlicht) aus dem Modell nach Abb. 7 abgeleitet und in einem lichtelektrischen Messgerät als Adaptations-Regler angewandt.

drei Schaltungen auftreten, da die Gln. (9) und (11) in wesentlichen qualitativen Merkmalen voneinander abweichen.

In dieser Arbeit soll nur die Schaltung nach Abb. 8a daraufhin untersucht werden, ob sie ein Modell für dynamische Eigenschaften des visuellen Systems der Menschen darstellt. Das Übertragungselement F soll auch hier linear sein. x sei stets der retinalen Beleuchtungsstärke proportional, y — eventuell nach weiterer linearer Filterung — der Reaktion. Das Modell soll nur *zeitliche* und keine *räumlichen* Zusammenhänge im visuellen System beschreiben*. Zum Vergleich mit experimentellen Daten werden nur solche Experimente herangezogen, in welchen die retinale Beleuchtungsstärke sinusförmig moduliert wurde. Die Eingangsfunktion $x(t)$ habe also stets die Form:

$$x(t) = x_0 (1 + m \sin \omega t). \tag{13}$$

x_0 ist hier die Gleichkomponente von $x(t)$, m der Modulationsgrad, $(0 \leq m \leq 1)$, und $\omega = 2\pi \nu$ die Kreisfrequenz. Gl. (13) schliesst mit $m = 0$ auch den stationären Fall ein.

Lichtreize von periodisch varriierender Stärke wurden seit langer Zeit gerne angewandt, um Eigenschaften des visuellen Systems zu studieren. Die Modulation der retinalen Beleuchtungsstärke erfolgte in früheren Experimenten sehrt oft rechteckförmig. Die wichtigsten Untersuchungen wurden jedoch zum grössten Teil auch mit sinusförmig modulierten Lichtreizen wiederholt, meist, um eine mathematische Analyse des Reiz–Reaktions-Zusammenhanges zu erleichtern. An dieser Stelle sollen diejenigen experimentellen Ergebnisse kurz besprochen werden, welche durch das vorgeschlagene Modell zu beschreiben wären.

In einer Reihe von Experimenten wurde untersucht, wie die periodische Modulation der retinalen Beleuchtungsstärke die subjektive Helligkeit beeinflusst. Bereits Brücke (1864) hat nachgewiesen, dass die subjektive Helligkeit intermittierender Lichtreize in Abhängigkeit von der Flimmerfrequenz erhöht wird, selbst wenn die mittlere Beleuchtungsstärke konstant gehalten wird. Er führte die Experimente mit Hilfe von rotierenden Scheiben aus, die aus hellen und dunklen Sektoren zusammengesetzt waren. Um einen eventuell vorliegenden Einfluss der Bewegung der Sektoren auf die Wahrnehmung auszuschalten, wurde dieses Experiment später mit periodisch beleuchteten stehenden Flächen wiederholt. Verschiedene quantitative Aspekte dieser Erscheinung wurden von Bartley (1961 und die dort zitierte Literatur) untersucht. Man bezeichnet dieses Phänomen seither auch als Bartley-Effekt.

Zur Ermittlung der Abhängigkeit der subjektiven Helligkeit von der Flimmerfrequenz werden in der Regel zwei beleuchtete Flächen miteinander verglichen. Die eine Fläche wird mit intermittierendem Licht konstanter mittlerer Intensität beleuchtet. Die Helligkeit der anderen, stationär beleuchteten Fläche kann von einer Versuchsperson (VP) kontrolliert werden. Die Aufgabe der VP besteht darin, die Helligkeit der Kontrollfläche so einzustellen, dass beide Flächen gleich hell erscheinen. Der Frequenzbereich, in welchem die Messungen durchgeführt und die Ergebnisse repro-

---

* Kelly (1961b) bezeichnete ein solches Modell mit dem Ausdruck 'Ein-Kanal-Modell'. Die Bezeichnung 'Ein-Rezeptor-Modell' ist nach ihm nicht zutreffend, da nicht jeder Rezeptor notwendigerweise eine visuelle Einheit ist.

Literatur S. 100

duziert werden können, ist zu niedrigen Modulationsfrequenzen hin begrenzt; bei
zu niedrigen Frequenzen kann die VP die Helligkeit der Test- und Kontrollfläche
nicht mehr vergleichen. Für rechteckförmige Modulation lag in eigenen Experimenten
die untere Grenzfrequenz für eine VP z.B. bei 1.5 Hz, für sinusförmige Modulation
etwas niedriger, bei ca. 0.5 Hz (Varjú, 1964).

Die Messergebnisse verschiedener Autoren weichen voneinander zum Teil erheblich
ab. Während alle Ergebnisse darin übereinstimmen, dass eine Modulation des
Reizlichtes die subjektive Helligkeit in der Nähe der Flimmer-Fusions-Frequenz und
bei noch höheren Frequenzen nicht mehr beeinflusst, wurde eine maximale Erhöhung
im Frequenzbereich von 2–20 Hz gefunden.

In früheren Experimenten von Bartley lag das Maximum der subjektiven Helligkeit
bei etwa 10 Hz; einer Frequenz, die mit dem α-Rhythmus des EEG's gut übereinstimmt.
Bartley zog deshalb die Möglichkeit in Betracht, dass bei diesen Frequenzen für die
Erhöhung der subjektiven Helligkeit corticale Vorgänge verantwortlich sein könnten.
Die Ansicht setzt sich jedoch mehr und mehr durch, dass der Brücke-Effekt bereits
durch eine frequenzabhängige Erhöhung des retinalen Signalflusses zustande kommt.
Reidemeister und Grüsser (1959) haben die mittlere Entladungsfrequenz der Neurone
in der Katzenretina gemessen und deren Abhängigkeit von der Flimmerfrequenz
nachgewiesen. Dieser Befund legte nahe, dass die neurophysiologischen Grundlagen
des Brücke-Effekts bereits in der Retina zu finden sind. Rabello und Grüsser (1961)
haben ausserdem gefunden, dass die Lage der maximalen Erhöhung der subjektiven
Helligkeit unter den von ihnen angewandten Bedingungen je nach mittlerer Beleuchtungsstärke und Grösse der beleuchteten Fläche zwischen 2 und 8 Lichtreizen
pro Sekunde lag. Auch in diesem Befund sahen die Autoren einen Hinweis für den
retinalen Ursprung des Brücke-Effekts.

In den Experimenten von Rabello und Grüsser wurde die Beleuchtungsstärke
rechteckförmig moduliert. In eigenen Experimenten, die mit sinusförmig moduliertem
Licht durchgeführt wurden, konnte ein Effekt der mittleren Beleuchtungsstärke auf
die Lage der maximalen subjektiven Helligkeit auf der Frequenzachse nicht mit
Sicherheit festgestellt werden. Es wurde jedoch gezeigt, dass der Unterschied in den
Ergebnissen nicht von dem Unterschied in der Art der Modulation herrührt.

Die Wirkung modulierter Lichtreize auf das visuelle System kann auch unter dem
Gesichtspunkt der Reizschwelle betrachtet werden. Es war das Ziel zahlreicher Untersuchungen, die eben noch merkbare Modulation der Umwelthelligkeit zu ermitteln.
Wäre das Webersche Gesetz für das visuelle System des Menschen uneingeschränkt
gültig, so müsste die Schwellenmodulation des Reizlichtes von der mittleren Beleuchtungsstärke unabhängig sein. Bei rechteckförmiger Modulation z.B. ist die Änderung
des Reizes $\Delta m = 2 S_0 m$, woraus für die sukzessive Schwelle nach Gl. (1) $\Delta S/S =
S_0 m/S_0 = m_s = k$ folgt. m_s bezeichnet die Schwellenmodulation. m_s dürfte lediglich
von der Modulationsfrequenz abhängen, da bei der sukzessiven Schwelle auch die
Dynamik der Adaptation eine Rolle spielt. Bie einer gegebenen Modulationsfrequenz
müsste aber m_s von der mittleren Beleuchtungsstärke S_0 unabhängig sein. Auch bei
einer sinusförmigen Modulation der Beleuchtungsstärke müsste man mit der gleichen
Gesetzmässigkeit rechnen. Die Untersuchungen haben jedoch gezeigt, dass die Schwel-

lenmodulation m_s mit wachsender mittlerer Beleuchtungsstärke von sehr niedrigen Modulationsfrequenzen abgesehen zunächst stark abnimmt und erst bei sehr starken Reizen konstant bleibt. Wie zu erwarten hängt sie ausserdem von der Modulationsfrequenz ab. Ihr Kehrwert m^{-1} — die Empfindlichkeit gegenüber Flickerlicht — ist bei etwa 15 Hz maximal, wenn die mittlere Beleuchtungsstärke sehr hoch ist. Das Maximum wird mit abnehmender mittlerer Beleuchtungsstärke nicht nur kleiner, sondern verlagert sich auch zu niedrigeren Modulationsfrequenzen (siehe z.B. Kelly, 1961a).

Bezüglich der Eigenschaften des Filters F sollen im Modell zunächst keine speziellen Annahmen gemacht werden. Aus der Linearität folgt lediglich, dass $z(t)$ von der Form

$$z(t) = x_0 \left[1 + Q_\omega m \sin(\omega t - \varphi_\omega) \right] \tag{14}$$

sein muss. Hierin sind Q_ω ein Amplituden-Faktor, φ_ω ein Phasenwinkel. Q_ω und φ_ω sind Funktionen der Modulationsfrequenz. (Bei minimalphasigen Filtern besteht weiterhin ein eindeutiger Zusammenhang zwischen Q_ω und φ_ω. Vgl. z.B. Kaufmann, 1959.) Ermittelt man die Eigenschaften der Ausgangsgrösse $y(t)$ als Funktion von Q_ω und φ_ω, so lässt sich auch die Wirkung von speziellen Übertragungsfiltern schnell erkennen. Die Ausgangsgrösse $y(t)$ ergibt sich aus den Gln. (8b), (13) und (14) zu

$$y(t) = \frac{x_0 (1 + m \sin \omega t)}{1 + x_0 \left[1 + Q_\omega m \sin(\omega t - \varphi_\omega) \right]} \tag{15}$$

Der Verstärkungsfaktor V, sowie sonstige Proportionalitätsfaktoren wurden aus Gründen der Einfachheit Eins gesetzt.

Die Wirkung der Parameter Q_ω, φ_ω, x_0 und m auf den Verlauf von y lässt sich zum Teil aus Abb. 10, zum Teil unmittelbar aus Gl. (15) feststellen. Abb. 10a zeigt $y(t)$ mit verschiedenen Gleichwerten x_0 der Eingangsgrösse als Parameter. In allen drei angeführten Beispielen sind $Q_\omega = m = 1$, $\varphi = 0$. Die Kurven stellen etwa logarithmisch verzerrte Sinusfunktionen dar. Je grösser x_0, umso stärker die Verzerrung. Da die Ausgangsfunktion $y(t)$ durch Spiegelung der sinusförmigen Eingangsfunktion an der nichtlinearen Kennlinie in Abb. 9 (ausgezogene Kurve), entsteht, wird ihre Verzerrung bei einem beliebigen Gleichwert x_0 umso kleiner, je kleiner der Modulationsgrad m. Ähnlich wirkt auch die Verminderung des Amplitudenfaktors Q_m. Während aber im Grenzfall $m = 0$ $y(t)$ den stationären Ausgang für $x(t) = x_0$ darstellt, erhält man für $Q_\omega = 0$ aus Gl. (15) am Ausgang die Funktion

$$y(t) = \frac{x_0}{1 + x_0} (1 + m \sin \omega t), \tag{16}$$

welche der Eingangsfunktion proportional ist. Den Einfluss des Phasenwinkels φ auf $y(t)$ zeigt Abb. 10b. Sowohl die Amplitude wie auch der Mittelwert von $y(t)$ nehmen mit zunehmendem Phasenwinkel φ zu, und erreichen ein Maximum bei $\varphi = \pi$.

Während die Amplitude von $y(t)$ durch nachgeschaltete lineare Übertragungs-

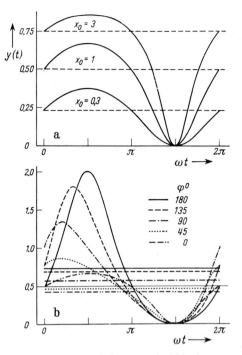

Abb. 10. Die Ausgangsgrösse $y(t)$ der Schaltung nach Abb. 8a, wenn die Eingangsgrösse $x(t)$ sinusförmig moduliert wird. In a) wurde die Gleichkomponente x_0 der Eingangsgrösse als Parameter variiert. Die gestrichelten, horizontalen Linien stellen die entsprechende stationäre Ausgangsgrösse y_0 dar. In b) dient der Phasenwinkel π zwischen den Grössen x und z als Parameter und besitzt die angegebenen Werte. Die dünn ausgezogene horizontale Linie ist die entsprechende stationäre Ausgangsgrösse y_0. Die anderen horizontalen Linien stellen den jeweiligen Mittelwert $\bar{y}$ der Ausgangsgrösse y dar.

elemente weiter beeinflusst werden kann, erscheint die einmal erfolgte Änderung des Mittelwertes auch nach linearer Filterung am Ende der Reiz–Reaktions-Kette. Mit Hinblick auf die vermutete Zuordnung des Brücke-Effekts zu retinalen Prozessen ist der Mittelwert der Ausgangsfunktion $y(t)$ von Interesse. Aus Gl. (15) ist

$$\bar{y} = \frac{1}{T} \int_{t_0}^{t_0 + T} \frac{x_0 \left(1 + m \sin \omega t\right)}{1 + x_0 \left[1 + Q_\omega m \sin \left(\omega t - \varphi_\omega\right)\right]} \, dt \tag{17}$$

T ist die Periodenlänge der sinusförmig modulierten Eingangsgrösse $x(t)$. Die in Gl. (17) vorkommenden Integrale können Integraltafeln entnommen werden. Nach Einsetzen der Integralgrenzen und nach kurzer Zwischenrechnung erhält man:

$$\bar{y} = \frac{x_0}{\sqrt{(1 + x_0)^2 - x_0^2 \; x_0^2 \; Q_\omega^2 \; m^2}} + \left[1 - \frac{1 + x_0}{\sqrt{(1 + x_0)^2 - x_0^2 \; Q_\omega^2 \; m^2}}\right] \frac{\cos \varphi_\omega}{Q_\omega} \tag{18}$$

$\bar{y}$ in Gl. (18) hängt durch Q_ω und φ_ω von den Übertragungseigenschaften des Filters F in Abb. 8a, und somit von der Modulationsfrequenz ν ab.

Die Abhängigkeit der subjektiven Helligkeit von der Modulationsfrequenz des Reizlichtes wird dann durch $\bar{y}$ qualitativ beschrieben, wenn $\bar{y}$ mit steigender ω erst zu-, dann wieder abnimmt und schliesslich den stationären Wert nach Gl. (8c) mit

$V = 1$, $q = 1$, erreicht. Es zeigte sich, dass ein mathematisch sehr einfaches Übertragungselement F mit der Übertragungsfunktion

$$G(s) = \frac{1 - \tau_1 S}{1 + \tau_1 S} \cdot \frac{1}{1 + \tau_2 S} \qquad (19)$$

zu diesem Ziel führt. $G(s)$ in Gl. (19) setzt sich aus der Übertragungsfunktion eines Allpassfilters mit der Zeitkonstanten τ_1 und der eines Tiefpassfilters mit der Zeitkonstanten τ_2 multiplikativ zusammen. Dies bedeutet, dass in einer Analogschaltung die beiden Filter hintereinander geschaltet werden müssen. Die Abhängigkeit des Amplitudenfaktors Q_ω und des Phasenwinkels φ_ω ist durch folgende Gleichungen gegeben:

$$\left.\begin{array}{l} Q_\omega = 1 \\ \varphi_\omega = 2 \text{ arc tg } \omega\tau_1 \end{array}\right\} \text{Allpassfilter} \qquad \begin{array}{l} (20a) \\ (20b) \end{array}$$

$$\left.\begin{array}{l} Q_\omega = 1/\sqrt{1 + \omega^2\tau_2^2} \\ \varphi_\omega = \text{arc tg } \omega\tau_2 \end{array}\right\} \text{Tiefpassfilter} \qquad \begin{array}{l} (21a) \\ (21b) \end{array}$$

Ist $\tau_1 \gg \tau_2$, so steigt zunächst φ mit wachsendem ω von 0 bis π an, während Q_ω unverändert 1 bleibt. Dies hat einen Anstieg von $\bar{y}$ von dem kleinsten bis zum höchstmöglichen Wert zur Folge. Wird nun die Modulationsfrequenz weiter erhöht, so wirkt auch das Tiefpassfilter auf die Eingangsgrösse x: Der Amplitudenfaktor Q_ω wird der Gl. von π auf $3\pi/2$ erhöht. Sowohl die Abnahme von Q_ω, wie auch die weitere Zunahme von φ_ω bewirkt ein schnelles Absinken von $\bar{y}$, bis zum stationären Endwert $x_0/(1 + x_0)$. Abb. 11a und b stellen die Verhältnisse graphisch dar. Da τ_1 und τ_2

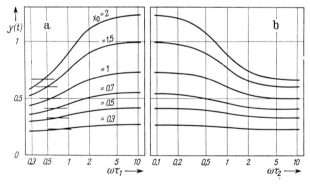

Abb. 11. Der Mittelwert $\overline{y(t)}$ der Ausgangsgrösse $y(t)$ der Schaltung in Abb. 8a, wenn die Eingangsgrösse $x(t)$ sinusförmig moduliert wird und das lineare Übertragungselement F (a) ein Allpassfilter mit der Zeitkonstanten τ_1, (b) ein Tiefpassfilter mit der Zeitkonstanten τ_2 ist. In b ist ein zusätzlicher Phasenwinkel π zu der Phasenverschiebung des Tiefpassfilters addiert. Als Parameter wurde der Mittelwert x_0 der Eingangsgrösse x variiert. Der Modulationsgrad m beträgt für alle Kurven Eins. In a bezeichnen die horizontalen Striche die entsprechenden Werte der stationären Ausgangsgrösse.

zunächst noch unbestimmt sind, wurden $\omega\tau_1$ und $\omega\tau_2$ als Abszisse aufgetragen. x_0 wurde als Parameter variiert, $m = 1$ gesetzt.

Die Eigenschaften der Kurven in Abb. 11a und b repräsentieren qualitativ den Brücke-Effekt. Es muss noch untersucht werden, ob durch geeignete Wahl der

Parameter τ_1, τ_2 und x_0 auch eine quantitative Übereinstimmung erzielt werden kann. Die experimentell gewonnenen Daten sind in Form des Verhältnisses der Leucht-dichte des Vergleichsfeldes während der Modulation des Testlichtes (x_{01}) und un-mittelbar davor (x_0) gegeben. x_{01} wird als wirkungsgleiche stationäre Leuchtdichte bezeichnet. Wenn man Gl. (8c) auf die Leuchtdichte des Vergleichsfeldes anwendet, ist $\bar{y} = x_{01}/(1 - x_{01})$, woraus sich x_{01} zu

$$x_{01} = \frac{\bar{y}}{1 - y} \text{ errechnen lässt.} \qquad (22)$$

Zu bemerken ist, dass x_{0l} in Gl. (22) unendlich gross wird, wenn $\bar{y}$ den Wert 1 erreicht. Dieser Wert ergibt sich für $\bar{y}$ aus Gl. (18) z.B., wenn $x_0 = 1.5$ und $Q_\omega = m = 1$, $\varphi = \pi$ sind. Dieser Umstand bedeutet für die Theorie zunächst nur, dass der geeignete Wert von x_0 mit Sicherheit kleiner als 1.5 sein wird.

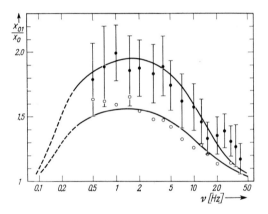

Abb. 12. Punkte und Kreise: Relative Erhöhung der subjektiven Helligkeit als Funktion der Modul-ations-Frequenz der sinusförmig modulierten Beleuchtungsstärke, für eine Versuchsperson. Die mittlere Beleuchtungsstärke war für die Punkte 10mal so gross, als für die Kreise. Der Modulations-grad m betrug in beiden Fällen 1. (Nach Varjú, 1964). Ausgezogene Kurven: Theoretisch ermittelte Werte.

Ermittelt man das Verhältnis x_{01}/x_0 mit Hilfe der Gln. (18), (19) und (22), so kann die Frequenzabhängigkeit der experimentell gewonnenen Daten (in Abb. 12) durch die Theorie auch quantitativ gut beschrieben werden, wenn die Parameter τ_1, τ_2 und x_0 folgende Werte besitzen: $\tau_1 = 0.127$ sec; $\tau_2 = 0.00955$ sec; $x_0 = 0.8$ für die obere Kurve und $x_0 = 0.6$ für die untere Kurve. Die Zahlenwerte wurden durch nach Augenmass erfolgte Anpassung der berechneten Kurven an die Messwerte ermittelt. Der Wert von τ_1 ist wenig gesichert, da im entsprechenden Frequenzbereich nur wenige Messwerte gewonnen werden konnten.

Die Daten der unteren Kurve in Abb. 12 wurden im Experiment mit 10mal kleinerer mittlerer Leuchtdichte gewonnen, als die der oberen Kurve. Die theoretisch ermittelten Werte von x_0 stehen aber in einem Verhältnis wie 8/6 zueinander. Man könnte nun untersuchen, ob mit Hilfe anderer linearer Filter die Abhängigkeit der subjektiven Helligkeit sowohl von der Modulationsfrequenz wie auch von der mittleren Leuchtdichte richtig wiedergegeben wird. Es kann zunächst gezeigt werden, dass andere Werte der Konstanten V und q in Gl. (8c) nicht zum Ziel führen. Auch für einige, mathematisch noch leicht zu berechnende, lineare Filter kann einfach gezeigt werden, dass sie kein befriedigendes Ergebnis liefern. Es wurde nicht angestrebt, alle Möglichkeiten zu erschöpfen oder einen Existenzbeweis zu finden, da eine geringfügige strukturelle Änderung des Modells in Abb. 8a das gewünschte Resultat bringt. Die benötigte Änderung besteht in der Einführung eines zweiten linearen Filters parallel

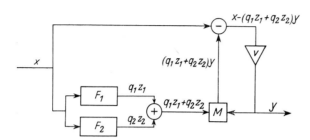

Abb. 13 Modifikation der Schaltung nach Abb. 8a. Das lineare Übertragungselement F_1 ist sehr träge im Vergleich zu F_2. q_1 und q_2 sind konstante Faktoren. Näheres im Text.

zu F, deren Ausgänge vor dem Multiplikator addiert werden (Abb. 13). Sind die zwei Filter F_1 und F_2, die entsprechenden Ausgangsfunktionen $q_1 z_1$ und $q_2 z_2$, so ist

$$z = q_1 z_1 + q_2 z_2, \tag{23}$$

worin q_1 und q_2 konstante Faktoren sind. Der Zusammenhang zwischen x, y und z ist jetzt

$$y = V [x - (q_1 z_1 + q_2 z_2) y], \tag{24a}$$

und

$$z_1 (s) = G_1 (s) x (s) \tag{25a}$$

$$z_2 (s) = G_2 (s) x (s), \tag{25b}$$

wenn $G_1 (s)$ und $G_2 (s)$ die Übertragungsfunktionen von F_1 und F_2 bezeichnen. Aus (24a) ergibt sich weiterhin:

$$y = \frac{Vx}{1 + V (q_1 z_1 + q_2 z_2)} \tag{24b}$$

Die Forderungen an die Theorie werden erfüllt, wenn das eine Übertragungselement, z.B. F_2, die bereits ermittelten Eigenschaften des Filters F in Abb. 8a (Gl. 19) beibehält, das andere, F_1, im Vergleich zu F_2 eine sehr träge Übertragung repräsentiert, und die Konstanten q_1 und q_2 geeignete Zahlenwerte besitzen. Die Eigenschaften des Filters F_1 lassen sich weiter präzisieren: Es muss so träge sein, dass für z_1 während die Helligkeit des Vergleichsfeldes von der VP eingestellt wird, in guter Näherung $z_1 = x_0$ besteht, und zwar sowohl für das Test-, wie auch für das Vergleichsfeld. Unter dieser Bedingung brauchen seine Übertragungseigenschaften und seine Zeitkennwerte nicht näher bestimmt zu werden. Durch diese Massnahme treten zwei, ebenfalls nichtlineare Kennlinien anstelle der ausgezogenen Kurve in Abb. 9. Die eine Kennlinie beschreibt die relativ schnellen, die andere dagegen sehr langsame Ereignisse. Anders ausgedrückt wird die Ausgangsgrösse nach einer schnellen Änderung der Eingangsgrösse zunächst der einen, schnelleren, später der anderen, langsameren Kennlinie proportional. Da im stationären Fall $z_1 = x_1$ und $z_2 = x_2$ sind, ergibt sich aus Gl. (24b) für die langsame Kennlinie

$$y_0 = \frac{x_0}{1 + (q_1 + q_2)\, x_0}, \tag{26a}$$

und für die schnelle Kennlinie

$$y_0{}^* = \frac{x_0}{1 + q_1\, x_0{}^* + q_2\, x_0}. \tag{26b}$$

Nach einer Änderung von x_0 bleibt $q_1\, x_0{}^*$ zunächst in guter Näherung konstant und dient für $y_0{}^*$ als Parameter. y_0 und $y_0{}^*$ sind in Abb. 14 gezeigt. q_1 und q_2 wurden beide zu 0.5 gewählt. Als Parameter für die schnelle Kennlinie dienten $x_0{}^* = 1$; 10 und 100.

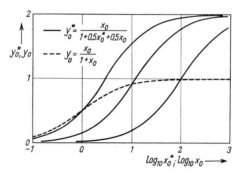

Abb. 14. Schnelle und langsame Kennlinie der Schaltung nach Abb. 13. Näheres im Text.

Ist die Eingangsfunktion sinusförmig moduliert, so ist $y^*(t)$ in Analogie zu Gl. (15):

$$y^*(t) = \frac{x_0\, (1 + m \sin \omega t)}{(1 + q_1\, x_0{}^*) + q_2\, x_0\, [1 + Q_\omega\, m \sin(\omega t - \varphi_\omega)]}. \tag{27}$$

Der Mittelwert $\bar{y}^*$ lässt sich in ähnlicher Weise wie in Gl. (18) zu

$$\bar{y}^* = \frac{x_0}{\sqrt{[1 + (q_1 + q_2)\, x_0]^2 - q_2{}^2\, x_0{}^2\, Q_\omega{}^2\, m^2}} + \tag{28a}$$

$$+ \frac{1}{q_2}\left[1 - \frac{1 + (q_1 + q_2)\, x_0}{\sqrt{[1 + (q_1 + q_2)\, x_0]^2 - q_1{}^2\, x_0{}^2\, Q_\omega{}^2\, m^2}}\right] \frac{\cos \varphi_\omega}{Q_\omega}$$

errechnen. Die zur Verfügung stehenden Daten reichen nur aus, um das Verhältnis der Konstanten q_1 und q_2, nicht aber ihren Wert zu bestimmen. Um die Formel (28a) weiter zu vereinfachen, konnte deshalb die Summe $q_1 + q_2$ willkürlich zu 1 gewählt werden. Setzt man q für q_2 und $1 - q$ für q_1, so ist

$$\overline{y^*} = \frac{x_0}{\sqrt{(1 + x_0)^2 - q^2 \, x_0^2 \, Q_\omega^2 \, m^2}} + \tag{28b}$$

$$+ \frac{1}{q} \left[1 - \frac{1 + x_0}{\sqrt{(1 + x_0)^2 - q^2 \, x^2 \, Q_\omega^2 \, m^2}} \right] \frac{\cos \varphi_\omega}{Q_\omega}$$

Die wirkungsgleiche stationäre Eingangsgrösse x_{01} is jetzt aus Gl. (26b):

$$x_{01} = \frac{[1 + (1 - q) \, x_0^*] \, \overline{y^*}}{1 - q \, y^*} \tag{29}$$

Die theoretischen Kurven in Abb. 12 erhält man mit Hilfe des modifizierten Modells, wenn $q = 0{,}453$, $x_0^* = 47{,}6$ (obere Kurve), bzw. $x_0^* = 4.7$ (untere Kurve) sind. Das Verhältnis der beiden Gleichkomponenten der Eingangsgrösse stimmt jetzt mit dem Verhältnis der mittleren Beleuchtungsstärken überein.

Obwohl der Einführung zweier, parallel geschalteter linearer Übertragungselemente eine rein theoretische Notwendigkeit zugrunde lag, gibt es auch experimentelle Hinweise, welche diese Annahme berechtigen. Es wurde eine schnelle bzw. eine langsame Phase des Adaptationsvorganges beobachtet. (α — bzw. β — Adaptation, vgl. z.B. Rabello und Grüsser, 1961). Allerdings bleibt es fraglich, ob die für die Trägheit des Filters F_1 gestellte Bedingung in den Experimenten erfüllt werden kann. Die Schwierigkeit liegt darin, dass die VP von Fall zu Fall unterschiedliche Zeitspannen benötigt, um die Leuchtdichte des Vergleichsfeldes einzustellen. Daher gibt es keine Garantie dafür, dass die Feststellung des Vergleichswertes gerade dann erfolgt, wenn die schnelle Phase der Adaptation bereits abgeklungen, die langsame noch nicht wesentlich fortgeschritten ist. In eigenen Experimenten zeigte der Vergleichswert stets eine messbare Abhängigkeit von der Einstellzeit (Varjú, 1964).

Im weiteren soll noch kurz untersucht werden, ob das Modell neben dem Brücke-Effekt auch die Abhängigkeit der Flimmerlicht-Schwelle von der mittleren Beleuchtungsstärke zu beschreiben vermag. Hierzu muss die Amplitude der Ausgangsfunktion y^* (t) in Gl. (27) bei einer gegebenen Modulationsfrequenz ν als Funktion der mittleren Beleuchtungsstärke x_0 und des Modulationsgrades m untersucht werden. Mit dem üblichen Postulat, dass die Schwellen-Amplitude von y^* (t) stets einen konstanten Wert k besitzen muss, lässt sich dann die entsprechende Schwellenmodulation m_s der Umwelthelligkeit, oder ihrt Kehrwert $1/m_s$ als Funktion der mittleren Beleuchtungsstärke x_0 aus dem Zusammenhang

$$p \, (\omega) \, m_{ys} = f \, (m_s, \, x_0, \, \omega) = k \tag{30}$$

errechnen. m_{ys} bezeichnet hier die Schwellenmodulation der 'Reaktion' y, m_s die zu ermittelnde Schwellenmodulation des Reizes. ω tritt im Argument der Funktion f auf, da die Amplitude der Ausgangsfunktion $y^*(t)$ in Gl. (27) auch vom Amplitudenfaktor Q_ω und dem Phasenwinkel φ_ω abhängt (vgl. Abb. 10b). Der Faktor $p(\omega)$ trägt der Möglichkeit Rechnung, dass die Amplitude von $y^*(t)$ durch weitere, dem Modell nachgeschaltete lineare Übertragungselemente beeinflusst werden kann. Als Schwellen-Amplitude der Reaktion muss aber dann $p \, (\omega) \, m_{ys}$ angesehen werden.

Literatur S. 100

Die Annahme solcher Übertragungselemente ist sogar zwingend. Für höhere Modulationsfrequenzen wird der Amplitudenfaktor Q_ω in Gl. (27) zu Null. Gl. (27) geht dann mit $q_1 + q_2 = 1$ in Gl. (16) über, und somit wird die Amplitude von $y(t)$ von der Modulationsfrequenz unabhängig. Die Modulation der Umwelthelligkeit wird aber — je nach mittlerer Beleuchtungsstärke — auch mit $m = 1$ nur bis zu einer bestimmten Höchstfrequenz, der Flimmer–Fusions-Frequenz, gesehen. Träge lineare Filter können diesem Befund Rechnung tragen. Ihre Eigenschaften wurden u.a. von Kelly (1961b) und von Levinson und Harmon (1961) im einzelnen untersucht. Im vorliegenden Fall bedeutet $p(\omega)$ jedoch nur einen frequenzabhängigen Normierungsfaktor, dessen Wert bei der Anpassung der theoretischen Kurven an die Messwerte von Fall zu Fall ermittelt werden kann.

Diese Berechnung der Amplitude von $y*(t)$ in Gl. (27) wird sehr langwierig, sobald der Phasenwinkel φ bei einem endlichen Amplitudenfaktor Q andere Werte als 0 oder π besitzt. Die nachfolgende Überlegung ermöglicht eine einfache und genügend genaue Abschätzung der Verhältnisse: Der Frequenzbereich, in welchem die einschlägigen Messungen durchgeführt wurden, erstreckt sich gewöhnlich von etwa 1 Hz bis zur jeweiligen Flimmer–Fusions-Frequenz. Letztere hängt von der mittleren Beleuchtungsstärke ab und liegt je nach mittlerer Beleuchtungsstärke zwischen 20 und 60 Hz. Am Anfang des Frequenzbereiches ist $\varphi_\omega = \pi$, $Q_\omega = 1$, und am Ende $\varphi_\omega \to 3\pi/2$ und $Q_\omega \to 0$. (Vgl. Abb. 12). Ermittelt man den Verlauf von $1/m_s$ aus Gl. (30) für diese Extremfälle, so müssten alle Werte von $1/m_s$ im Inneren des Frequenzbereiches für eine beliebige mittlere Beleuchtungsstärke zwischen den Extremwerten liegen, da die Amplitude von $y*(t)$ sich monoton ändert, wenn φ von π auf $3\pi/2$ erhöht und Q_ω von 1 auf 0 erniedrigt wird. (Vgl. Abb. 10b und Gl. 16). $f(m_s, x_0, \omega)$ in Gl. (30) lässt sich aber für diese Extremfälle leicht errechnen. Für den Fall $Q_\omega \to 0$, $\varphi_\omega \to 3\pi/2$ erhält man aus Gl. (27) mit $q_1 + q_2 = 1$ den bereits abgeleiteten Zusammenhang (16), woraus sich unmittelbar die Beziehung

$$f(m_s, x_0, \omega) = m_s \frac{x_0}{1 + x_0} \tag{31}$$

ergibt.

Im anderen Extremfall muss berücksichtigt werden, dass $y*(t)$ in Gl. (27) vom sinusförmigen Verlauf abweichen kann, da $\varphi_\omega = \pi$ ist. (Vgl. Abb. 10b). Als Schwellenmodulation kommen aber in diesem Frequenzbereich nur kleine Werte von m in Betracht, und somit verzerrt die nichtlineare Kennlinie (Abb. 9) die sinusförmige Eingangsfunktion nur geringfügig. Die halbe Differenz der Extremwerte von $y*(t)$ in Gl. (27) kann deshalb als Amplitude angesehen werden. Sie lässt sich zu

$$f(m_s, x_0, \omega) = m_s \frac{x_0(1 + x_0) + qx_0^2}{(1 + x_0)^2 - q^2 m^2 x_0^2} = \frac{1}{2}\left[y*_{\max} - y*_{\min}\right] \tag{32a}$$

errechnen, wenn $q_1 + q_2 = 1$, $q_2 = q$ in Gl. (27) eingesetzt wird.

Zu Gl. (32a) gelangt man mit Hilfe der herkömmlichen Methoden der Infinitesimalrechnung. Die einzelnen Schritte sollen hier deshalb nicht dargestellt werden.

Da für kleine Werte von m in Gl. (32a) $q^2 m^2 x_0^2$ neben $(1 + x_0)^2$ vernachlässigt werden kann, erhält man schliesslich für den Fall $\varphi_\omega = \pi$, $Q_\omega = 1$:

$$(m_s, x_0, \omega) = m_s \left[\frac{x_0}{1 + x_0} + q \frac{x_0^2}{(1 + x_0)^2} \right] \qquad (32b)$$

Setzt man die Gln. (31) und (32b) in Gl. (30), so ergibt sich nach Umformung:

$$\frac{1}{m_s} = \frac{p(\omega)}{k} \frac{x_0}{1 + x_0}; \text{ wenn } Q_\omega \to 0; \; \varphi_\omega \to 3\pi/2, \qquad (33)$$

$$\frac{1}{m_s} = \frac{p(\omega)}{k} \left[\frac{x_0}{1 + x_0} + q \frac{x_0^2}{(+ x_0)^2} \right]; \text{ wenn } Q_\omega = 1; \; \varphi_\omega = \pi. \quad (34)$$

Vergleichen kann man nur den *Verlauf* der Funktionen (33) und (34), da der Faktor $p(\omega)/k$ unbestimmt ist und im Gültigkeitsbereich des jeweiligen Zusammenhanges verschiedene Werte annehmen darf. Die normierten Werte von $1/m_s$ sind in Abb. 9 aufgetragen. Die ausgezogene Kurve zeigt $1/m_s$ als Funktion von x_0 nach Gl. (33). Die punktierte Kurve gibt $1/m_s$ nach Gl. (34) wieder, mit dem für den Brücke-Effekt ermittelten Wert von q.

Zwischen den beiden Kurven besteht kein nennenswerter Unterschied. Da sie die zwei extremen Möglichkeiten darstellen, kann eine von beiden für jede Modulationsfrequenz benutzt werden, um sie mit experimentell gewonnenen Daten zu vergleichen. Ich zog die einfachere Formel nach Gl. (33) heran. Die theoretischen Kurven in Abb. 15 wurden nach Augenmass den Messdaten von Kelly (1961a) angepasst. Es wurde

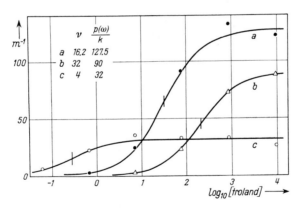

Abb. 15. Empfindlichkeit gegenüber Flimmerlicht als Funktion der mittleren Beleuchtungsstärke. Parameter: Modulationsfrequenz. Messpunkte nach Kelly (1961a). Ausgezogene Kurven: Berechnete Werte.

zunächst für alle drei Modulationsfrequenzen der geeignete Wert von $p(\omega)/k$ bestimmt, und die theoretischen Kurven als Funktion von $\log x_0$ aufgetragen. Danach wurden die Kurven entlang der log [troland]-Achse so verschoben, dass eine gute Übereinstimmung zwischen den Messwerten und der jeweiligen Kurve entstand. Es hat sich gezeigt, dass die relative Lage der log x_0-Achse gegenüber der log [troland]-Achse für alle drei Frequenzen unterschiedlich gewählt werden musste. Dies zeigen die senkrechten Striche an den einzelnen Kurven, welche den Wert $x_0 = 1$ an der log x_0-Achse markieren. Im übrigen entsprechen die berechneten Kurven den gemessenen Daten.

Der Leistungsfähigkeit der durchgeführten Formalanalyse scheint mit dieser Feststellung eine Grenze gesetzt zu sein, obwohl die Möglichkeiten keinesfalls vollständig erschöpft sind. Die Eigenschaften des linearen Übertragungselements F in Abb. 8a wurden bestimmt, um eine quantitative Beschreibung des Brücke-Effektes zu erzielen. Dies ist mit sehr einfachen Annahmen gelungen. Gleichzeitig konnte auch die Abhängigkeit der Flimmerlicht-Schwelle von der mittleren Beleuchtungsstärke bei einer gegebenen Modulationsfrequenz quantitativ beschrieben werden. Dem Einfluss der Modulationsfrequenz auf die Flimmerlicht-Schwelle trägt das Modell dagegen keine Rechnung. Man könnte versuchen, die Schaltung in Abb. 8a weiter auszubauen, oder die Schaltungen in Abb. 8b und 8c heranzuziehen, um ein auch in dieser Hinsicht befriedigendes Modell zu entwickeln. Hierzu sei jedoch folgendes bemerkt: In den diskutierten Experimenten konnten durch Messungen nur Anfang und Ende einer sehr komplexen Reiz–Reaktions-Kette erfasst werden. Zwischen der kontrollierbaren Umwelthelligkeit und der Reaktion einer VP liegt ausser der Aktivierung des nervösen Substrats noch eine Reihe nervöser Wechselwirkungen. Von dem vorgeschlagenen Modell wird aber nur erwartet, dass es die retinale Adaptation beschreibt, sowie solche Ereignisse des Reiz–Reaktions-Zusammenhanges, welche ausschliesslich auf retinale Adaptationsvorgänge zurückzuführen sind. Wie es an entsprechender Stelle besprochen wurde, kann dies für den Brücke-Effekt mit grosser Wahrscheinlichkeit behauptet werden, nicht zuletzt aufgrund elektrophysiologischer Untersuchungen. Solange keine Anhaltspunkte vorliegen, welche auch für die Flimmerlicht-Schwelle ausschliesslich retinale Ursachen vermuten lassen, ist eine entsprechende Weiterentwicklung des Modells nicht ausreichend begründet.

Von einer Formalanalyse wird üblicherweise nicht mehr verlangt, als eine quantitative Beschreibung des Reiz–Reaktions-Zusammenhanges. Es kann gewöhnlich nicht entschieden werden, ob das Modell tatsächlichen Ereignissen chemischer oder neurophysiologischer Natur entspricht. Dies liegt nicht zuletzt daran, dass sicht oft mehrere Möglichkeiten anbieten, um eine gute Approximation experimentell ermittelter Daten zu erzielen. Ein gewähltes Schema besitzt meistens eine sehr grosse Anzahl von Freiheitsgraden, welche neben einem Vergleich mit experimentell gewonnenen Daten unter dem Gesichtspunkt mathematischer Einfachheit, einer möglichst kleinen Anzahl von Konstanten u.a.m. eingeengt wird. Das gleiche gilt auch für das hier diskutierte Modell, sofern die Eigenschaften des linearen Übertragungselements F betrachtet werden. Es besteht jedoch wenig Möglichkeit, die stationäre Kennlinie in Abb. 9 durch Änderung bestimmter Konstanten zu beeinflussen. Man kann lediglich die gesamte Funktion mit einem Normierungsfaktor multiplizieren oder entlang der log x-Achse verschieben, *nicht aber ihre Form ändern*. Zwei Punkte, welche bestimmte Bruchteile des maximalen Wertes repräsentieren, sind auf der Abszisse stets um den gleichen logarithmischen Abstand voneinander entfernt. Deshalb ist es besonders bemerkenswert, dass eine gute Übereinstimmung zwischen den berechneten und den experimentell ermittelten Daten in Abb. 12, ja sogar in Abb. 15 erzielt werden konnte.

Angesichts dieser Tatsache erscheint die Hoffnung nicht unbegründet, dass die Prinzipien der durchgeführten Formalanalyse retinale Prozesse isomorf abbilden.

In dieser Beziehung wäre es von grossem Interesse, auch die Form der Ausgangsfunktion des Modells mit experimentellen Ergebnissen zu vergleichen. Charakteristisch ist für die Schaltungen nach Abb. 8 die frequenzabhängige Verzerrung der Ausgangsfunktion bei sinusförmig modulierter Eingangsgrösse. Während bei niedrigen Modulationsfrequenzen eine Asymmetrie nur in Ordinatenrichtung entsteht, wird die Symmetrie bei höheren Frequenzen auch in Abszissenrichtung zerstört. (Im Gegensatz zu Modellen, welche eine nichtlineare Kennlinie und dynamische Übertragungselemente nur hintereinandergeschaltet enthalten). Der Grund hierfür ist sehr anschaulich: Die Ausgangsfunktion y (t) in Gl. (15) entsteht als Produkt der Eingangsfunktion x_0 $(1 + m \sin \omega t)$ und der von der Eingangsfunktion abhängigen Empfindlichkeit $1/ \{1 + x_0 [1 + Q_\omega \, m \sin (\omega t - \varphi_\omega)]\}$. Mit wachsender Modulationsfrequenz folgt die Änderung der Empfindlichkeit der Änderung der Eingangsfunktion mit ständig zunehmender Phasenverschiebung φ_ω, Die bei niedrigen Frequenzen logarithmisch verzerrte Ausgangsfunktion nimmt dadurch eine Form an, welche einer Sägezahn-Funktion ähnlich ist (vgl. Abb. 10b, $\varphi = 90°$).

Die Durchführung entsprechender Experimente ist an der menschlichen Retina wohl kaum möglich. Die Untersuchungen am Komplexauge von Käfern (Kirschfeld, 1961) haben dagegen gezeigt, dass die Verzerrung des Elektroretinogramms eine ähnliche Frequenzabhängigkeit aufweist, wie die Ausgangsfunktion y (t) des Modells. Nicht nur Retinae, sondern auch andere adaptierende Systeme können mit gleichen Eigenschaften gefunden werden. C. v. Campenhausen (1963) hat die mechanische Spannung des lichtempfindlichen Irismuskels einer Kröte (*Discoglossus pictus*) untersucht und bei sinusförmiger Modulation der Beleuchtungsstärke eine Verzerrung der Messgrösse gefunden, welche qualitativ den Kurven der Abb. 10 entspricht. Will man jedoch die Kurven der Abb. 10 mit experimentell gewonnenen Daten quantitativ vergleichen, so muss man die Möglichkeit im Auge behalten, dass nachgeschaltete lineare Übertragungselemente die Form der Ausgangsfunktion y (t) zustäzlich verändern können.

Die beiden zuletzt genannten Beispiele weisen darauf hin, dass die modifizierte Funktionsstruktur der Wachstumsreaktion von *Phycomyces* geeignet erscheint die Kinetik mehrerer biologischer Adaptationsvorgänge zu beschreiben.

ZUSAMMENFASSUNG

Die Empfindlichkeit vieler biologischer Reiz–Reaktions-Systeme wird an die jeweilige Reizstärke angepasst. Die Änderung der Empfindlichkeit erfolgt häufig langsamer als die Änderung der Reizstärke. Die Reiz–Reaktions-Ereignisse können daher oft nur bei Kenntnis der Kinetik der Adaptation verstanden werden. Im ersten Teil der Arbeit sind die Gesetze von Weber und Fechner unter diesem Gesichtspunkt diskutiert. Im weiteren wird die Licht–Wachstumsreaktion des Pilzes *Phycomyces* eingehend besprochen. Die von Delbrück und Reichardt durchgeführte Analyse ergibt ein mathematisches Modell für die Adaptations-Kinetik von *Phycomyces*. Das Modell

Literatur S. 100

lässt sich weiter entwickeln, um bestimmte Eigenschaften des visuellen Systems des Menschen zu beschreiben. Die Abhängigkeit der subjektiven Helligkeit von der Modulationsfrequenz einer sinusförmig modulierten retinalen Beleuchtungsstärke (Brücke-Effekt) kann hierdurch formal dargestellt werden. Der Einfluss der mittleren Beleuchtungsstärke auf die Schwellenmodulation lässt sich vom Modell ebenfalls beschreiben.

SUMMARY

Most of the biological stimulus-response systems show adaptation: The sensitivity of a system changes with stimulus intensity. The change of the sensitivity does not follow the change of the stimulus intensity immediately. Thus, the kinetics of the adaptation must also be studied in order to understand stimulus-response events. The applicability of the laws of Weber and Fechner are discussed in this paper. The adaptation of the fungus *Phycomyces* to light is described in detail. The analysis, carried out by Delbrück and Reichardt, resulted in a mathematical model which accounts for the kinetics of the light adaptation. Based on the results obtained with *Phycomyces* a model was developed to describe certain properties of the human visual system. This attempt succeeded in describing the dependence of the subjective brightness upon the modulation frequency of the sinusoidally modulated retinal illumination (Brücke effect). The model also accounts for the influence of the average brightness upon the amplitude threshold at a given modulation frequency.

LITERATUR

BARTLEY, S. H., (1961); A clarification of some of the procedures and concepts involved in dealing with the optic pathway. In *Neurophysiologie und Psychophysik des visuellen Systems*. R. Jung und H. Kornhuber, Editors. Berlin, Springer (pp. 386–400).

BOUMAN, M. A., VOS, J. J., AND WALRAWEN, P. L., (1963); Fluctuation Theory of Luminance and Chromaticity Discrimination. *J. Optical Soc. America*, **53**, 121–128.

BRÜCKE, E., (1864); Über den Nutzeffekt intermittierender Netzhautreizung. *S.-B. K. Akad. Wiss., Wien, math.-nat. Kl.* **49** (II), 128–153. (Zitat nach Rabello und Grüsser, 1961).

CAMPENHAUSEN, C. V., (1963); Quantitative Beziehungen zwischen Lichtreiz und Kontraktion des Musculus sphincter pupillae vom Scheibenzüngler (*Discoglossus pictus*). *Kybernetik*, **1**, 249–267.

DELBRÜCK, M., AND REICHARDT, W., (1956); System Analysis for the light growth reactions of phycomyces. In: *Cellular Mechanism in Differentiation and Growth*. Dorothea Rudnick, Editor. Princeton University Press. (pp. 3–44).

GRÜSSER, O.-J., UND REIDEMEISTER, CH., (1959); Flimmerlichtuntersuchungen an der Katzenretina II. *Z. Biol.*, **111**, 254–270.

HASSENSTEIN, B., (1960); Die bisherige Rolle der Kybernetik in der biologischen Forschung. *Naturwissenschaftliche Rundschau*, *Jg.* **13**, 373–382.

KAUFMANN, H., (1959); *Dynamische Vorgänge in linearen Systemen der Nachrichten- und Regelungstechnik*. München. R. Oldenbourg Verlag.

KELLY, D. H., (1961a); Visual Responses to Time-Dependent Stimuli. I. Amplitude Sensitivity Measurements. *J. Optical Soc. America*, **51**, 422–429.

KELLY, D. H., (1961b); Visual Responses to Time-Dependent Stimuli. II. Single-Channel Model of the Photopic Visual System. *J. Optical Soc. America*, **51**, 747–754.

KIRSCHFELD, K., (1961); Quantitative Beziehungen zwischen Lichtreiz und monophasischem Elektroretinogramm bei Rüsselkäfern. *Z. vergl. Physiol.*, **44**, 371–413.

LEVINSON, J., AND HARMON, L. D., (1961); Studies with Artificial Neurons, III: Mechanism of Flicker-Fusion. *Kybernetik*, **1**, 107–117.

RABELLO, CARMEN UND GRÜSSER, O.-J., (1961); Die Abhängigkeit der subjektiven Helligkeit intermittierender Lichtreize von der Flimmerfrequenz. *Physiol., Forsch.*, **26**, 299–312.

REICHARDT, W. UND VARJÚ, D., (1958); Eine Inversionsphase der phototropischen Reaktion. *Z. Physik. Chemie, Neue Folge*, **15**, 297–320.

REICHARDT, W., (1959); Analysis of a Nonlinear Biological Filter. *Nuovo Cimento, Suppl. Vol.* **13**, Serie X, 608–616.

REICHARDT, W., (1961); Die Lichtreaktionen von *Phycomyces. Kybernetik*, **1**, 6–21.

REIDEMEISTER, CH. UND GRÜSSER, O.-J., (1959); Flimmerlichtuntersuchungen an der Katzenretina I. *Z. Biol.*, **111**, 241–253.

SHROPSHIRE, W., FR., (1963); Photoresponses of the Fungus, *Phycomyces. Physiol. Revs.*, **43**, 38–67.

STEVENS, S. S., (1961); To Honor Fechner and Repeal His Law. *Science*, **133**, 80–86.

STEVENS, S. S., (1963); Brightness Function: Effects of Adaptation. *J. Optical Soc. America*, **53**, 375–385.

VARJÚ, D., (1964); Der Einfluss sinusförmiger Leuchtdichteänderungen auf die mittlere Pupillenweite und auf die subjektive Helligkeit, *Kybernetik*, **2**, 33–43.

WENKING, H., (Unveröffentlicht); Adaptation von Photoelektronenvervielfacher. (Persönliche Mitteilung).

Some Problems in Artificial Intelligence

J. R. ULLMANN

National Physical Laboratory, Autonomics Division, Teddington, Middlesex (Great Britain)

PART I

To test behaviourally a brain model which learns goal-attaining responses to a number of stimuli and then predicts goal-attaining responses to stimuli which have never occurred before, one must show that the model can make all the predictions which the modelled brain can *possibly* make. The more predictions a model can possibly make, the less we say is *built into* the model. It is generally impracticable to find experimentally all the predictions which an intelligent animal can *possibly* make, and therefore it is difficult to know how much to build into a predictive brain model.

But when, as in the following pages, very little is built in, the model becomes astronomically big; and therefore, if this model can make all the predictions the brain can possibly make, some as yet unknown technique must be employed in the design of the brain. One cannot at present make plausible detailed physiological hypotheses to test the suggestion that very little is built into the brain; and a purpose of the present work is to contribute to the theory of logical design so that it will eventually be *possible* to make such hypotheses.

Another motive for seeking plausible designs for simple predictive machines with very little built in is the possibility of relevance to practical problems in which not enough knowledge (or perhaps programming effort) is available for conventional techniques to be applied. The problems formulated in the following pages are so difficult that there is much to be said for considering these before facing even more formidable problems which may have commercial application.

For example, a formidable prediction problem arises in the domain of automatic process control (*e.g.* the optimal control of a distillation column): after many optimisations using a sophisticated trial and error strategy it would be desirable to predict the optimal path from a new starting point rather than always optimising by trial and error with no benefit from experience gained on previous runs. This is a more clearly predictive problem than that of mechanical translation where the machine must continually give translations of new sentences, or information retrieval where documents are specified by newly worded requests, or character recognition where the correct classification is required for new variants of characters. In Turing's test (Turing, 1950) the interrogator is always liable to say something new to the machine.

An obvious danger of working on simple models is that the chosen simplifications may lead to irrelevant or intractable problems. To reduce this danger we deal with the problem of designing a machine which is recognisably animal-like in that its stimuli are retinal patterns, its responses are configurations of a many jointed limb and its goals are attained by placing the tip of the limb on appropriate objects in the visual field. This limb pointing system is now described in more detail before a number of logical design problems arising from it are introduced.

The artificial retina is an array of binary light receptors and is kept in a fixed position so that it is unnecessary to consider variations in size and perspective of retinal images of objects, which would be an unduly complicated problem at this stage. Patterns on a row of binary motor units electromechanically control the hinges of the many jointed limb or *linkage*. All the configurations of the linkage are confined to a single fixed plane, and the base of the linkage is permanently fixed in position and orientation.

The objects to which the linkage points are two dimensional and are confined to an object plane parallel and very close to the linkage plane. Close behind the object plane is a parallel plane containing the fixed unchanging background pattern. Part of these three planes is illuminated and constitutes the field of view of the retina: the retina is parallel to these planes.

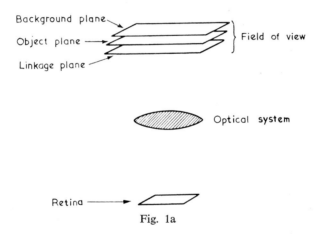

Fig. 1a

The optical system which focusses the field of view onto the retina is such that the image of a given object, whatever its position in the visual field, does not vary in size or shape. The objects are not noisy – *i.e.* their retinal images are not subject to deformations and mutilations.

Different goals are attained by appropriately placing the linkage tip on different objects, and only one object associated with a given goal is present in the field of view at one time. A binary pattern is externally written on a goal requirement indicating array (Fig. 1b) to determine which goal (if any) the machine is required to achieve, and only one goal is indicated at any given time. The linkage tip contains a binary goal attainment sensor. When the goal requirement is externally changed it is also externally arranged that the goal attainment sensor is only activated if the

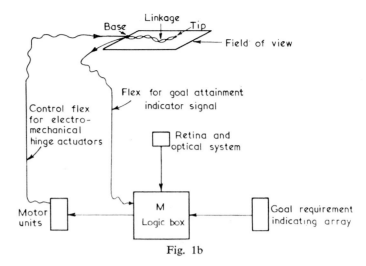

Fig. 1b

linkage touches the appropriate part of the appropriate object in the field of view.

At a given time there may be many objects in the field of view, but not all of these need be associated with a goal. Objects in the object plane do not overlap each other, and may turn up in any position (but not orientation). The choice of objects in the field of view is made externally and changed at regular intervals.

We are concerned with the problem of designing the logic box M given that

(a) M is to set the linkage in a goal attaining configuration corresponding to any given retinal pattern and goal requirement indication.

(b) The following information is not available to the designer of M:

(i) What objects will be included in the visual field.

(ii) The background pattern.

(iii) What goal if any is associated with which point on which object.

(iv) Which pattern of activity in the motor units sets the linkage in which configuration.

(v) How many hinges there are in the linkage, nor what linkage images look like.

(c) The total number of trials which M may make in the course of trial and error is strictly limited so that the correct response for each retinal pattern that occurs cannot be found in turn by trial and error, and prediction is therefore necessary in view of (b) above.

(d) The number of different objects which ever actually occur in the field of view is striclty limited, so that very many fewer than all possible retinal patterns ever actually occur.

(e) When the retina comprises many (e.g. 10^6) photocells the number of logical units in M must not be astronomical (e.g. must not be greater than 10^{10}).

In Part III below a design for M is given in terms of machines specified (but not designed) in Part II. Part II contains a sequence of detailed logical design problems and Parts I and III provide a background against which the choice of problems in Part II can be understood. In Part II it is convenient to use elementary set-theoretical terminology, and the correspondence between the ordered sets of locations with which Part II is concerned and the retina and motor units of the limb-pointing system is explained in Part III.

Instead of discussing the literature of artificial intelligence we refer to the surveys by Minsky (1961), Hawkins (1961) and Uttley (1962). The topic of concept learning is broadly treated in Hunt (1962) and the study of the practical intelligence of animals in Viaud (1960) is highly pertinent to the present work.

PART II

Problem 1

We consider two ordered sets S and T of N elements which we call *locations*, and (generally different) *partitions* of these sets into j subjets $S_1, S_2, \ldots S_j$, and $T_1, T_2, \ldots T_j$; *i.e.* such that each element of S belongs to exactly one of these subsets of S and each element of T belongs to exactly one of these subsets of T.

We consider *patterns on* S_0 defined as ordered sets of binary digits (0 or 1) in one to one correspondence with a subset S_0 of S (possibly S itself). Patterns *on* T_0 are similarly defined. Clearly a partition of S induces a partition of any pattern on S.

Suppose we have chosen from the j subsets of S and T, for each i from 1 to j, k pairs of *corresponding* patterns $(s_{i1}, t_{i1}), \ldots \ldots \ldots (s_{ik}, t_{ik})$ on the pair of *corresponding* subsets (S_i, T_i), such that no two patterns on S_i are the same, and likewise for T_i. (It is clearly necessary that k does not exceed 2^n, where n is the size of the smallest S_i, T_i). We say that a pattern on T *corresponds* to a pattern on S if the constituent patterns on the subsets $T_1, T_2, \ldots \ldots T_j$ correspond to the patterns on $S_1, S_2 \ldots \ldots S_j$.

The problem is, given that k^j is very much less than 2^N, to design a plausibly economical machine which, if fed in turn (in any given order) with different pairs of corresponding patterns on S and T, will ultimately predict the pattern on T corresponding to the pattern on S. The machine is not provided with the values of j or k, nor an indication of the chosen partitions of S and T, and it must succeed in prediction whatever the chosen partitions, patterns, and values of j and k.

For example, suppose $k = 2$, $j = 3$ and that the pairs of corresponding patterns on (S_i, T_i) are as shown in Fig. 2a; *e.g.* the top row in Fig. 2a shows a pair of corresponding patterns on the subsets (S_1, T_1) and neither 1 nor 0 is written in locations not included in (S_1, T_1). The first row in Fig. 2b comprises one of the two chosen patterns on (S_1, T_1), one of the two chosen patterns on (S_2, T_2) and one of the two chosen patterns on (S_3, T_3). The eight rows in Fig. 2b are obtained by choosing in turn all possible combinations of patterns on (S_1, T_1); (S_2, T_2); (S_3, T_3) to make up patterns on S and T. The rows are written in Fig. 2b in a randomly chosen order.

After being fed with, say, the first six pairs of corresponding patterns on S and T, the machine is required to predict the seventh on T given the seventh on S, and the eighth on T given the eighth on S.

(We are exploring the following approach to this problem. The predicting machine M (Fig. 3a) is replaced by a machine M_0 (Fig. 3b) comprising a number of predicting

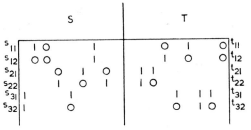

Fig. 2a

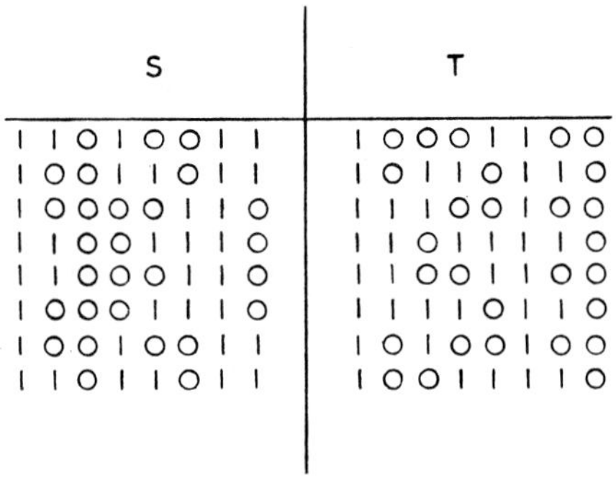

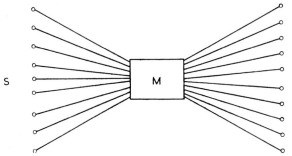

Fig. 2b

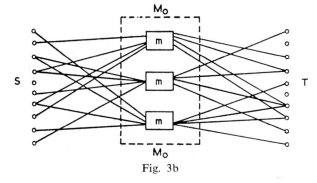

Fig. 3a

Fig. 3b

machines m which are fed with patterns on subsets of the sets of locations constituting S and T. For these sample patterns a machine m behaves exactly like an M, but of course the m is very much smaller than a similarly designed M.

Computer simulation of M_0 in the trivial limiting case of the present problem in which S is partitioned into only one subset and no prediction is possible (Ullmann, 1962) has formed part of a preliminary investigation of an iterative technique by which the outputs from the m's are fitted together in M_0.)

Problem 2

In this problem it is convenient to think of the N locations in the set S arranged spatially in the form of a ring. A subset of S may be translated, or cyclically shifted, to any of N positions in the ring. S and T are partitioned into j subsets of adjacent locations, and, as in problem 1, k pairs of corresponding patterns on the subsets (S_i, T_i) are chosen for all i from 1 to j. But in making up corresponding pairs of patterns on S and T, the subsets $S_1, S_2, \ldots . S_j$ may now be permuted in any way, and translated any distance round S, provided they always constitute a partition of S. The chosen subsets of T, however, are rigidly fixed in position as in problem 1.

The problem is, given that k^j is very much less than 2^N, to design a plausibly economical machine which eventually predicts patterns on T corresponding to patterns on S, just as in problem 1.

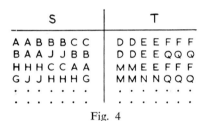

S	T
A A B B B C C	D D E E F F F
B A A J J B B	D D E E Q Q Q
H H H C C A A	M M E E F F F
G J J H H H G	M M N N Q Q Q
. . . .	. . . .
. . . .	. . . .

Fig. 4

For example, representing every digit in a pattern on the same subset by the same letter, corresponding patterns on S and T in this problem could be as in Fig. 4 (since chosen subsets now contain only adjacent digits, ABABBCC is not a possible pattern on S).

Problem 3

Patterns on a subset S_i are sequences of 0's and 1's written in the ordered set of locations which constitutes S_i. We now consider *pattern chains*, such that a pattern on a chain on S_i is a sequence of patterns written on an ordered set of subsets S_{i1}, $S_{i2}, \ldots . S_{ip}$ which constitute a partition of S_i. Fixing the position of one subset S_{ii} of S_i imposes a specified restriction on the position of the next subset $S_{i(i+1)}$. Problem 3 in fact deals only with pattern chains in which the postion of $S_{i(i+1)}$ is uniquely determined by the position of S_{ii} and q different patterns on each subset $S_{i1} \ldots . . S_{ip}$ are chosen so there are q^p possible different patterns on a chain in this problem. The subset T_i corresponding to S_i is partitioned into p subsets, and for each pattern on a subset of S_i we choose a unique corresponding pattern on the corresponding subset of T_i.

Problem 3 differs from problem 2 only in that $S_{i1}, S_{i2} \ldots \ldots S_{ip}$ may not be translated or permuted within S_i, although S_i may be translated within S and permuted with the other subsets of S. For example, representing patterns on the chosen subsets

S	T
A A B B B α α β β γ γ γ	D D E E δ δ δ ε ε η η
B A A α α β β ν ν ν B B	D D E E δ δ δ ψ ψ η η
H H λ λ μ μ γ γ γ A A H	M M E E φ φ φ ε ε ω ω
β β γ γ γ H H H G G λ λ	M M N N δ δ δ ε ε ω ω
· · · · · · · · · · · ·	· · · · · · · · · · ·
· · · · · · · · · · · ·	· · · · · · · · · · ·

Fig. 5

of S_i by Greek letters, corresponding patterns on S and T could be as in Fig. 5. (There is no T pattern corresponding to patterns AABB $\alpha\alpha\gamma\gamma\beta\beta$ or AA$\alpha\alpha$ BB$\beta\beta\beta\gamma\gamma\gamma$ on S, because $\alpha\alpha$, $\beta\beta$, $\gamma\gamma\gamma$ may only occur in the fixed relative positions $\alpha\alpha\beta\beta\gamma\gamma\gamma$).

Problem 4

We say that a pattern P_i on a subset S_i is *superimposed* on a pattern P on S when the least possible change is made in P so that P_i is included in the new pattern on S, and a *background* on S is a chosen pattern on S upon which smaller patterns may be superimposed.

Problem 4 is the same as problem 2 except that the union of the chosen disjunct subsets $S_1, S_2 \ldots \ldots S_j$ is generally not S. Moreover the choice of elements of S not included in these subsets is continually changing, and herein lies the difference between problems 2 and 4. For example, representing background digits by X, corresponding patterns on S and T in problem 4 could be as in Fig. 6.

S	T
X A A X B B B X C C X X X	D D E E F F F
B A A X J J X X X X X B B	D D E E Q Q Q
X X H H H X C C X X A A X	M M E E F F F
G X X J J X X X X H H H G	M M N N Q Q Q
· · · · · · · · · · · · ·	· · · · · · ·
· · · · · · · · · · · · ·	· · · · · · ·

Fig. 6

Problem 5

Here the patterns on S are as in problem 4, and the patterns on T are identical to those on S except that a small pattern π is superimposed on the T pattern adjacent to one of the subsets $T_1, T_2 \ldots \ldots T_j$, the choice of this subset being determined by the pattern on a new set R. Thus the pattern on T is determined jointly by the patterns on R and S. The problem is to design a machine which after being fed with a number of corresponding patterns on R, S, and T, will ultimately predict corresponding T

patterns. The stipulation that the machine is to be plausibly economical (even when there are 10^6 elements in S and T) and that many fewer than 2^N patterns will actually occur on S or T applies to all the problems of Part II, (although, loosely speaking, the machines do not know in advance which patterns will actually occur on S and T).

In problem 5 corresponding patterns on R, S and T could be as in Fig. 7:

R	S	T
R_1	A X X B X C X D E X X	A X X ππ C X D E X X
R_1	X A X D E B X X X Č X	X A X D E B X ππ C X
R_2	A X X B X C X D E X X	A X X B X C ππ E X X
	. . . .	. . . .
	. . . .	. . . .

Fig. 7

We do not discuss the set R again below until the goal requirement indicating array in the limb pointing system is considered in Part III.

Problem 6

Problem 3 was concerned with pattern chains in which fixing the position of S_{ii} rigidly fixed that of $S_{i(i+1)}$, but in which there were a number of alternative patterns on each S_{ii}, $S_{i(i+1)}$. Problem 6 is concerned with pattern chains in which fixing the position of S_{ii} imposes a specified restriction on the possible positions of $S_{i(i+1)}$, but in which there is only one chosen pattern on each of the $(p + 1)$ subsets S_{i1}, S_{i2}, ... $S_{i(p+1)}$. In problem 6 the elements of S are arranged to form a two dimensional array.

To be specific, we say that there are q possible (*i.e.* chosen) relative positions of any pair of consecutive subsets in the chain, and therefore q^p possible patterns on the chain. T is partitioned into p subsets and one subset on T is chosen to correspond to each of the p pairs of consecutive subsets in the chain on S, and a pattern on each chosen subset of T is chosen to correspond to each relative position of the corresponding consecutive subsets on S, so that there are altogether q^p possible patterns on T. As usual the problem is to design a machine which ultimately predicts the pattern on T given the pattern on S.

For example, if $p = 3$ and $q = 3$, corresponding patterns on S and T in problem 6 could be as in Fig. 8.

Problem 7(a)

This problem is concerned with pattern chains in which fixing the position of a subset S_{ii} imposes a specified restriction on the position and orientation of $S_{i(i+1)}$. We stipulate that each of the subsets S_{ii} includes so many elements that the deformation of the boundary of S_{ii} when S_{ii} is rotated is negligible.

In problem 7(a) the pattern on S includes a pattern chain as, for example, in Fig. 9. The pattern on T includes single patterns on two small subsets of T whose position in T is uniquely determined by the positions of the first and last subsets in the chain on S.

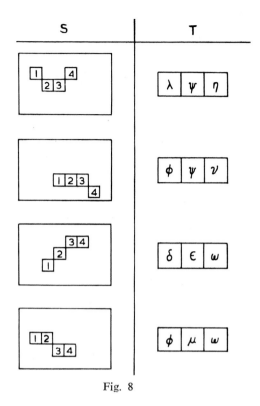

Fig. 8

Thus in problem 7(a) the position of the first and last subsets in a pattern chain on S are abstracted onto T. The machine is required ultimately to predict patterns on T corresponding to patterns on S.

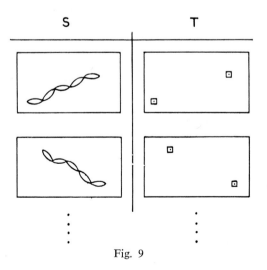

Fig. 9

Problem 7(b)

To formulate this problem we say that the elements of S and T are locations in which 1, or 0, or '1 and 0', or 'neither 1 nor 0' may be written ('neither 1 nor 0' is not necessary in problem 7(b) but the notion of a *blank* background on S, meaning that all the elements on S are in state 'neither 1 nor 0', is useful in Part III). We say that two patterns are written *simultaneously* on S when each location in S, in which 1 would be written for one pattern and 0 for the other, has written in it '1 and 0'. Suppose for example that S comprises five locations and that 10110 and 11010 are written on S simultaneously: then S has in its five locations 1, '1 and 0', '1 and 0', 1, 0. (We say that as a result of writing only 10110 and 11010 on S simultaneously, 10010 and 11110 are written on S *accidentally*).

Problem 7(b) is essentially a back-to-front version of problem 7(a). Patterns on S contain single patterns on two small subsets of S, and the corresponding patterns on T include a pattern chain in which the positions of the first and last subsets are uniquely determined by the positions of the two small subsets in S.

The problem is to design a machine which after being fed a number of corresponding patterns on S and T, will eventually write on T simultaneously all the patterns on the chain which have their first and last subsets in positions uniquely determined

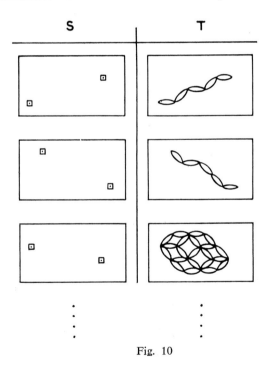

Fig. 10

by the positions of the two small patterns on S. In Fig. 10 the first two pairs of S and T patterns are examples of corresponding patterns with which the machine might be fed, and the third pair illustrates a predicted T pattern corresponding to an S pattern.

References p. 117

If the shapes of the subsets in the chain and the number of possible angles between successive subsets are appropriately restricted, no pattern on the chain will ever be accidentally written in a predicted T pattern.

8. *Generator Machines*

Part III offers a design for the limb pointing system in terms of machines specified in Part II. The two main building blocks of this design are introduced below in sections 9 and 10. When the complete system is described, in section 11, the functional significance of the arrays S and T will become clear. In the following sections it is convenient to use the notions of 'generator machines', 'pattern gates' and 'pattern comparators' and we now introduce these by applying them to problem 1.

We consider a generator machine G which is programmed in accordance with the formulation of problem 1 in Part II so that G generates corresponding patterns on S and T. G derives its random choices from a source of noise, and writes corresponding patterns on S and T at regular intervals.

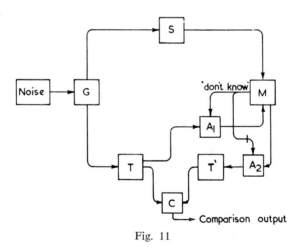

Fig. 11

If M fails to make any prediction when fed with a pattern on S it emits a binary 'don't know' signal which opens gate A_1 and closes gate A_2. (In Fig. 13 the horizontal bar just before the arrowhead signifies that the 'don't know' signal closes gate A_2). Immediately after emitting the 'don't known' signal M stores the corresponding patterns on S and T and M then ceases to emit the 'don't know' signal. Eventually M succeeds in making a prediction of the pattern on T, and the comparison output from the comparator C indicates the accuracy of the prediction by M.

The other problems of Part II could be similarly discussed, but to facilitate analysis of the limb pointing system it is convenient at this stage to discuss different arrangements of M and G as applied to problems 5 and 7(b) for trial and error learning and problem 6 for using proprioceptive feedback in learning.

9. Trial and Error Learning

(a) The Image of the Linkage. – In the limb pointing system for simplicity we stipulate that each hinge in the linkage can be set only to q different angles, and there are p hinges in the linkage. The retinal image of a linkage configuration is a pattern on a pattern chain. It is convenient to stipulate that the value of q and the shape of the linkage is such that when images of all possible linkage configurations which have their base in the same place and tip in the same place are written on T simultaneously, no configuration is written on T accidentally. As in Part I the base of the linkage, *i.e.*, the first subset in the chain, is permanently fixed in position and orientation.

(b) Combining Problems 5 and 7(b). – In the combined problem patterns on R indicate what goal the machine is required to achieve (analogous to autonomic indications of hunger, thirst, etc.), and there is one pattern which when written on R indicates that the machine is not required to attain any goal at that time. In the combined problem the position of the base of the linkage and the target point on the target subset correspond to the positions of the two small patterns on S in problem 7(b) and the linkage tip corresponds to π in problem 5. S now includes a number of patterns on a background as in problem 4, and corresponding patterns on R, S *and* T could be, for example, as in Fig. 12.

(c) Trial and Error Learning. The generator G in Fig. 13 periodically writes corresponding patterns (as in 9(b) above) on R, S and T.

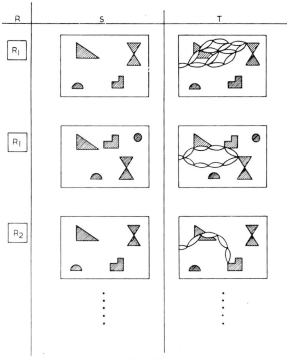

Fig. 12

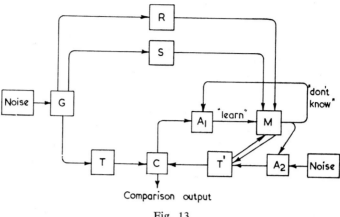

Fig. 13

If unable to predict the T pattern corresponding to the patterns on R and S, M emits a 'don't know' signal which opens gates A_1 and A_2 causing random patterns to be written on T' : T' is an ordered array of locations in one to one correspondence with T. Eventually there is an instant when the T and T' patterns are identical and the comparator C sends a signal *via* the gate A_1 instructing M to store (or 'learn') the patterns on R, S and T'. Ultimately M succeeds in predicting T patterns and the comparison output from C may be used in assessing the performance of M. Trial and error testing of patterns on T' would of course generally take a very long time, but in the actual limb pointing system only possible linkage images are tried out, rather than purely random patterns on T'.

10. Proprioceptive Feedback in Learning

Here problem 6 is modified so that the patterns on S consist of linkage images on a blank background: patterns on T correspond to patterns on the chain (*i.e.* linkage configurations) just as in problem 6. In Fig. 14 instead of periodically writing corre-

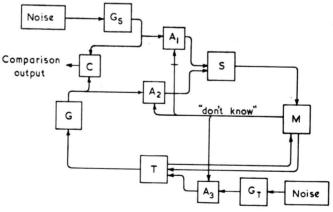

Fig. 14

sponding patterns on S and T, G functions as follows. Patterns are written by some other means on T, and if the pattern on T is identical with one of the chosen T patterns in G, G writes on S the corresponding S pattern. (T corresponds to the motor units in the limb pointing system and the generator G writes on S the retinal image of the linkage which corresponds to any given T pattern: G represents a proprioceptive feedback path).

Suppose that the list of all corresponding S and T patterns in G is copied into two lists one containing only S patterns and the other only T patterns and that the entries in these lists are shuffled so that the ith entry on the T list is a pattern which does not correspond to the ith pattern on the S list. The S list is written into a generator G_S and the T list into a generator G_T such that G_S and G_T periodically and synchronously emit S and T patterns which do not correspond.

If for a pattern from G_S M fails to predict a corresponding T pattern, M emits a 'don't know' signal which closes the gate A_1 and opens the gates A_2 and A_3; thus G_T writes a pattern in T and G writes the corresponding pattern in S. M now stores the corresponding S and T patterns and ceases to emit the 'don't know' signal. G_S writes another pattern in S and so on until eventually M succeeds in predicting corresponding T patterns.

(Turning again to the limb pointing system, the generation of patterns by G_T corresponds to a random choice of limb configurations during the exploratory period while the machine learns what motor pattern corresponds to which linkage configuration, $c.f.$ Ullmann, 1963.)

11. Limb Pointing System

In Fig. 15, G_1, R, S_1, T_1, M_1 are the same as G, R, S, T, M in section 9 above (Fig. 13). G_2, S_2, T_2 and G_T are the same as G, S, T, and G_T in section 10 above (Fig. 14). M_2 differs only from M of section 10 in that the background of the pattern chain on T_1' is not blank: the pattern chain in S_2 is superimposed on the S_1 pattern in S_3.

G_1 writes corresponding patterns in R, S_1 and T_1 at a frequency f_1, and the S_3

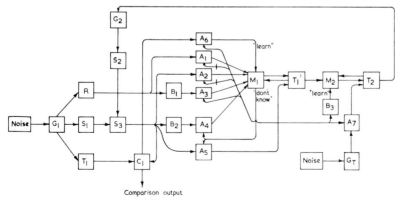

Fig. 15

and R patterns are fed to M_1 *via* gates A_1 and A_2. M emits a 'don't know' signal if it fails to predict a T pattern, thus closing gates A_1 and A_2, opening all other gates, and sending a 'learn' signal to M_2 *via* a short delay B_3. G_T writes patterns in T_2 at a frequency f_T. For each T_2 pattern G_2 gives the corresponding S_2 pattern, and M_2 attempts to predict the T_2 pattern corresponding to the T_1' pattern. If it fails and at the same time receives a 'learn' signal from B_3, M_2 learns the corresponding T_1' and T_2 patterns. When it succeeds in making a prediction, M_2 does not learn.

During these trials when G_T emits T_2 patterns in random order, it is possible that by chance the linkage image configuration in S_3 will be in one of the configurations on T_1, and the comparator C_1 is designed to detect this (goal attainment) situation and send a signal via A_6 to M_1 instructing M_1 to learn the R and S_3 patterns available *via* A_3 and A_4 from the delays B_1 and B_2, and the pattern in T_1', and then cease to emit the 'don't know' signal.

To be specific, we say that B_1 and B_2 both delay patterns for the same time b, and

$$f_T = \frac{2}{b} = 10^3 \times f_1$$

which makes negligible the chance that C_1 will emit the 'learn' signal less than b time units after G_1 changes the R, S_1 and T_1 patterns. Before reaching the predicting stage M_2 learns corresponding patterns at a frequency f_T whereas M_1 only learns when G_T generates a goal-achieving configuration: it is therefore reasonable to assume that if M_1 succeeds in predicting a T_1' pattern, M_2 will by then be able to predict the corresponding T_2 pattern.

As in section 9 above, T_1' patterns predicted by M_1 contain simultaneously all goal-achieving configurations, and it is therefore necessary to modify M_2 so that it

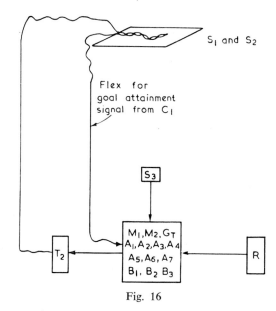

Fig. 16

makes an arbitrary choice of one of these configurations, *e.g.*, by a development of the technique used for this purpose in the appendix to Ullmann (1963).

By way of a comparison of Fig. 15 with the specification of the limb pointing system given in Part I, in Fig. 16 Fig. 1,B is relabelled in the terms of Fig. 15. B_1 and B_2 might be regarded as a short term memory.

12. Concluding remarks

An obvious sequel to this research would be to design a three dimensional limb pointing system, which used two retinae, and could cope with variations in size and perspective of images of objects, and learn to point to objects in a three dimensional field. One would wish the system to recognise objects in spite of limited deformation or mutilation; and preferably trial and error during the learning phase would be governed by a sophisticated strategy.

Before asking the question 'what is the logical design of the brain?' surely one should answer the question 'what could possibly be the logical design of the brain?'

ACKNOWLEDGEMENTS

A number of valuable suggestions concerning the presentation of this paper were made by Mr. P. H. Hammond, Mr. M. J. Woodger and Dr. N. Rees. This paper is published by permission of the Director of the National Physical Laboratory.

SUMMARY

A succession of logical design problems are formulated in which a machine learns the goal attaining responses to a number of stimuli and then predicts goal-attaining responses to stimuli which have never occurred before.

REFERENCES

HAWKINS, J. K., (1961); Self-organising systems–A review and a commentary. *Proc. Inst. Radio Engineers*, **49**, 31–48.
HUNT, E. G., (1962); *Concept Learning*. New York and London. John Wiley and Sons.
MINSKY, M., (1961); Steps toward artificial intelligence. *Proc. Inst. Radio Engineers*, **49**, 8–30.
TURING, A. M., (1950); Computing Machinery and Intelligence. *Mind*, **59**, 96–119.
ULLMANN, J. R., (1962); A Consistency Technique for Pattern Association. *Trans. Inst. Radio Engineers Information Theory IT-8*, 74–81.
ULLMANN, J. R., (1963); Cybernetic Models Which Learn Sensory-Motor Connections. *Med. Electronics Biol. Eng.*, **1**, 91–99.
UTTLEY, A. M., (1962); Properties of Plastic Networks. *Biophys. J.*, **2**, Suppl., 169–188.
VIAUD, G., (1960); *Intelligence: Its Evolution and Forms*. Arrow Science Books.

On Cybernetics, Information Processing, and Thinking

M. E. MARON*

The RAND Corporation, Santa Monica, Calif. (U.S.A.)

INTRODUCTION

Norbert Wiener's great intellectual capacities erupted at an early age to make him a child prodigy, but unlike many child prodigies, especially those with a flair for mathematics, Wiener's intellectual powers neither faded nor froze and he emerged as one of our great applied mathematicians. We honor not only an outstanding mathematician, but also the herald of a revolution in technology and science, the influence of which has been felt in such areas as automation, education, and economics, with possible reverberations shaking the structure of society itself. However, the full impact and implications of the revolution of cybernetics, with which his name is associated, will not be recognized properly for some years to come, which is the way with most intellectual revolutions. Norbert Wiener has changed our way of looking at and grappling with problems. What is especially significant is that the scope of his revolution includes some of man's basic problems, perhaps the most important of which is the problem of the brain, how men think, and how to understand the activity of *knowing*.

1. ORIGINS AND SCOPE OF CYBERNETICS

The background

What is cybernetics? Perhaps the best answer has been provided by Norbert Wiener himself in the introduction to *Cybernetics* (Wiener, 1948), his classic work on the subject. Wiener relates how the ideas for cybernetics grew out of a seminar at Harvard on the methodology of science. The participants in the seminar were researchers from diverse fields, whose participation reflected their common belief that new and exciting areas for scientific exploration lay in the borderlands between established fields – in those areas where the problems could be attacked successfully only by an interdisciplinary group of scientists representing different fields of specialization.

* The views expressed in this paper are those of the author. They should not be interpreted as reflecting the views of The RAND Corporation or the official opinion or policy of any of its governmental or private research sponsors.

With the onset of World War II, Prof. Wiener found himself involved in just such a multidisciplinary problem, *viz.*, the problem of designing an automatic system to feed aircraft-tracking radar data into a computing machine which, in turn, would predict the future course of the aircraft being tracked and then generate and transmit control signals to aim the guns at the moving target. Thus, Prof. Wiener, together with Julian Bigelow, became immersed in a set of new and complex problems relating to the theory of prediction and the design of machines that could embody the theory. In the course of this study they came to the very important realization of the critical role of feedback in voluntary human motor activity. Prof. Wiener and Julian Bigelow conjectured that the human mechanisms which control motor activity could suffer from improper feedback and show the same 'symptoms' as known mechanical systems, and that the mechanisms for manipulating feedback information in automatic machines are similar to those in that part of the brain where motor activity is controlled.* If this were so, both systems should malfunction in similar ways, and apparently they did.

With this insight came the recognition that the problems of communication and of control are intricately bound together. An analysis of control problems involves analysis of the underlying communication problems, and the latter, in turn, center around the fundamental concept of the *message*. With the problem of analyzing messages comes the problem of noise, and this led Wiener to questions of the relationship between amount of information and entropy, and their roles as measures of degree of organization and disorganization of a system.

For the historian of cybernetics, the following is a key passage:

". . . as far back as four years ago, the group of scientists about Dr. Rosenblueth and myself had already become aware of the essential unity of the set of problems centering about communication, control, and statistical mechanics, whether in the machine or in living tissue. On the other hand, we were seriously hampered by the lack of unity of the literature concerning these problems, and by the absence of any common terminology, or even of a single name for the field. After much consideration, we have come to the conclusion that all of the existing terminology has too heavy a bias to one side or another to serve the future development of the field as well as it should; and as happens so often to scientists, we have been forced to coin at least one artificial neo-Greek expression to fill the gap. We have decided to call the entire field of control and communication theory, whether by machine or in the animal, by the name *Cybernetics*. . . ." (Wiener, 1948, p. 19).

In that splendid personal account describing the circumstances which gave rise to cybernetics, Prof. Wiener goes on to describe the relationships of other subjects to the broad field of cybernetics, *e.g.* neurophysiology and information processing in the cerebral cortex, mathematical logic and its application to the analysis of neural switching circuits, computers and their use in constructing models of brain mech-

---

* A joint paper discussing feedback and purposeful behavior was published in 1943 (Rosenblueth *et al.*, 1943).

References p. 136

anisms, etc. Thus, we find in his book the groundwork and beginnings of a broad interdisciplinary study of all phases of information processing and control systems and of the implications and ramifications of this for such subjects as the psychology of perception, psychiatry and memory disorders, linguistics, and sociology. Since cybernetics erupted on the scientific scene in 1948, much work has been carried out in the field. Let us look briefly at some of those more recent developments which are relevant to an information-flow study of brain mechanisms and of artificial mechanisms designed to exhibit intelligent behavior.

Subsequent developments

Theory of information

If cybernetics is concerned with those sciences, studies, techniques, and mechanisms which relate to communication and control, the concept of information must play a central role. What sort of a commodity is information? What are its properties and what would we expect to find in a *theory* of information? Messages, of course, have many properties — their information may be precise, complex, redundant, timely, improbable, effective, etc. It is reasonable to assume that we need a different measure for determining the 'amount' of each different property in a message. In 1948, Claude Shannon, a mathematician and former student of Prof. Wiener, published a theory of communication (Shannon, 1948; Shannon and Weaver, 1949), which for the first time quantitatively explicated one of these measures. Shannon's theory allows one to define precisely the notion of the *capacity* of a communication channel, as well as the capacity of an information store, so that it is possible to answer the question: How much more information can be conveyed over one communication system than over another? Shannon's theory provides a means of determining the *amount* of information generated by an information source, real or artificial. The important notion of a code for conveying messages is treated in a formal way so that one can talk of the *efficiency* of a given coding system. And one can decide whether or not a given coding system (relative to a given information source) is the best possible one. Shannon's theory clarified the key concept of *noise* and showed how *redundancy* can be introduced in coding schemes so as to combat the destructive effects of noise on messages. And finally, he showed some very interesting and surprising relationships between noise, redundancy, channel capacity, and error-free transmission of messages.

Computer technology and applications

Since the digital computer is a mechanism for the physical (and logical) processing of information, computer theory and technology occupy a sizable part of the cybernetic stage. The computer field includes not only digital technology and theory of computer design and organization, but also includes the facets of computer applications. Following World War II, and beginning just before the publication of *Cybernetics* and Shannon's *Mathematical Theory of Communication*, there started an almost explosive development of digital computer technology. Some early digital machines were developed secretly during the war, but once the general knowledge of computers and their components and their potentials became known, there was a race to develop new switching components and circuitry and new types of information storage media. More recently, we have seen the development and refinement of very-high-speed circuits and switching components and comparable gains have been made in the perfection of high-density, rapid-access memory media. Finally, associated with these developments, there has appeared a host of sophisticated input–output (and analog–digital conversion) equipment to aid in the task of communicating to and from a computer.

While the component and systems engineers were pushing rapidly ahead, their more theoretically oriented colleagues were working at the corresponding theory of information machines — including automata theory and the theory of Turing machines. The theory of machines includes switching theory and what might be called the *art* of computer design and organization. These theoretical probings have led to the beginnings of a theory of reliability dealing with the question of how best to organize a large number of unreliable switching components to do a particular job so that the system as a whole is extremely reliable. Other theoretical aspects of computer organization have to do with programming theory, development of new computer languages, and the theory of algorithms.

Whereas initially the computer was looked on primarily as a machine designed to execute complex mathematical computations at high speed, we have since come to recognize the universality and flexibility of computers as information machines. It is this great universality that makes the modern computer a general-purpose research vehicle — a tool giving scientists the ability to perform arbitrary experiments at high speed. One of the more significant uses of computers now, and increasingly so in the future, lies in the fact that experiments can be executed by machines through simulation. Subsequently, we shall describe how a computer can be used to aid both psychologists and neurophysiologists by simulating aspects of the structure of the brain and the behavior of human beings. A clarification of the use of computing machines in these types of applications reveals the impact of cybernetics not only on psychology and neurophysiology, but also on the *theory* of knowledge itself.

2. INFORMATION PROCESSING IN ARTIFICIAL AND NATURAL SYSTEMS

The brain as a computing machine

Since the publication of Wiener's *Cybernetics*, comparisons have been made between the human brain and electronic computing machines on at least three different levels: components, coding and logical organization, and information processing. As the concepts of information theory, the computer, automata, and control theory have become developed and refined, attempts have been made to apply these notions to describe and interpret information processing in biological systems (McCulloch, 1949; Ashby, 1952; Sluckin, 1954; Von Neumann, 1958; Wooldridge, 1963).

When making such comparisons, the brain is viewed as an information transforming device which accepts data from the external world, interprets and operates on these data, and produces control information. In the jargon of the computer engineer, the brain is a black box which receives input signals *via* the receptors from the various sensory organs, and operates on these signals to generate other output signals which finally go to effectors causing appropriate muscles and glands to function. The information loop is closed *via* the external world and thus the brain is interpreted as a complex automatic regulating device which allows its owner to react so as to maintain a certain stability of success in his interaction with the local environment. Given this representation of the brain as a complex computer, attempts have been made to describe the information-flow paths and the logical organization of its major sub-systems.

In the brain the neuron is usually considered as *the* basic information processing unit. One of the first formal models of a neuron was described by McCulloch and Pitts in 1943 (McCulloch and Pitts, 1943), when they argued that the all-or-none principle of neuronal activity allowed one to interpret the behavior of a nerve cell in terms of truth-functional logic. Thus, just as Shannon in 1938 had applied truth-functional logic to the analysis and synthesis of switching circuits (Shannon, 1938), McCulloch and Pitts interpreted the behavior of neurons as two-state switching devices. We now know that the behavior of nerve cells is more complex than that implied by the early McCulloch–Pitts model, and even the most elaborate of recent models suggested by computer technology for neurons account for only a fraction of the richness and complexity of actual neuronal behavior.

One of the major simplifying assumptions of the McCulloch–Pitts model was that the pulses in a neural net are synchronized — *i.e.* that the action spikes generated and propagated by individual nerve cells correspond to those in a binary computer where each gate is pulsed by a signal from the central timing clock. This means that the neuron can fire (if at all) only at regular discrete intervals, and this interpretation leads to a so-called 'binary quantized' coding system. However, other coding schemes have been suggested, *e.g.* pulse interval modulation. Using different coding schemes (MacKay and McCulloch, 1952) one can compare the theoretical channel capacity of biological 'cables'. The problem of discovering the coding schemes used by the various sensory channels has attracted attention, and with information analyses of sensory and other channels there has been work on interpreting the various biological input–output and conversion mechanisms in terms of computer counterparts.

There is also the question of memory and how past events are coded and recorded in the brain. Estimates have been made by Von Neumann (Von Neumann, 1958) and others as to the total information capacity of the brain. Various types of experiments (for example, Penfield, 1958) suggest that a very large proportion of our experiences are coded, recorded, and under certain conditions can be subject to recall. It has been proposed that information may be stored by means of many different kinds of mechanisms ranging from circulating loops, analogous to the delay-line memories of computer technology, to variable thresholds, modifiable synaptic weights (Maron, 1961), variable time delay mechanisms (MacKay, 1962a), DNA memory mechanisms, and neural glia (Schmitt, 1962). Each of these has its own properties of permanence and access speed. We have no lack of proposals for biological memory mechanisms, but we have yet to see an adequate theory of recall—on the mechanism level. Other organizationaⅼ comparisons have been made (Von Neumann, 1956, 1958), showing how the brain might embody redundancy in the form of circuits and codes, how computing in the nervous system is organized so as to balance precision, logical depth, reliability, etc. Finally, numerous feedback and control mechanisms have been suggested as models to account for the automatic internal control of breathing, heart action, kidney function, blood sugar concentration, body temperature control, appetite, etc.

Thus, on the level of components, codes, and logical organization of underlying structure, the concepts and language of information theory and cybernetics have been used by some in an attempt to analyze brain mechanisms in terms of artificial information processing mechanisms. But, at this level of comparison between the brain and the computer, the notions have yet to suggest any really deep neurophysiological hypotheses. It is one thing to understand the logic of neural firing, the coding of basic cortical messages, or the mechanisms of storage and recall in the brain, and quite another problem to relate these mechanisms to complex intelligent behavior.

The other level of comparison between the brain and a computer relates to their *functional* similarities. Both are information transforming mechanisms which accept input data and, as a function of previously stored data, derive output conclusions. They both process information *in order to* derive outputs of a certain kind. There is a rationale to the input–output relation in both the brain of a normal person and a computer with a meaningful program. This functional similarity suggests that the logic of information processing and automata theory applied at first solely to computers might be applied also to the analysis of biological information machines and that it might help to bridge the gap between the psychology of behavior and the physiology of those mechanisms which produce it. MacKay has described this conceptual bridge as follows:

> "Now the language of information and control, in which the theory of automata is framed, is conceptually intermediate between those of psychology and physiology. It belongs in a sense to both fields, inasmuch as questions of information transfer arise in both.
>
> It seems possible therefore that the theory of an automaton, specifically designed to be a research model of the human organism considered as an information-flow system might provide a common meeting-ground and a common language in which hypotheses might be framed and tested and progressively refined with the help of clues from both sides." (MacKay, 1956, p. 31).

What is the logic of the relationship between behavior and the information processing mechanism which produces it?

The logic of information processing

There are three separate but related problems that must be clarified in order to understand the sense in which brain–computer comparisons are not merely interesting, but potentially valuable. On the one hand, one may look inside the brain, so to speak, and compare its structure and the organization of its structure with that of a computing machine. On the other hand, it is possible to treat each as a black box which cannot be opened, and compare the kinds of input–output relationships that are possible in the brain and a computer. Finally, there is the question of how to relate input and output behavior with the internal mechanisms which produce them.

In the case of a human we ordinarily talk of observing his behavior — *i.e.* the relationship between stimuli and responses — but we might equally well move upstream and consider the input and output signal patterns which correspond to stimuli and responses. We can consider signal patterns in an abstract way as expressions of a logical language. And we will find it most convenient to clarify the relationships between input and output expressions if we assume that they belong to the language of elementary truth–functional logic.

In what ways might input and output expressions be related? Consider the case where we know the truth relationships between input and output for all possible values. That is, for every allowable truth value of the input expression, we know the corresponding truth value of the outputs. It is now possible to formulate a description of this relationship in terms of a complex sentence of truth–functional logic. We emphasize that there is a mechanical procedure for describing the truth relationship in terms of the grammar represented by the logical connectives, such as negation, conjunction, disjunction, etc. In fact, it is possible to translate any expression into an equivalent one which contains only occurrences of a single type of connective, *viz.*, the Sheffer stroke function or the Peirce function, both of which are *universal*.

Turing first pointed out (Turing, 1938) that it is convenient to clarify problems in logic by talking in terms of the mechanisms for implementing logical operations. We know that if we can construct the physical counterpart of the elementary operations of truth–functional logic in the form of, say, electrical switching circuits, then it is possible to build the physical counterpart of the logical expression which describes the truth relationship between input and output expressions. (Note that one may wish to base the truth value of a conclusion not only on current premises, but on past history as well. There are concepts in automata theory (see, for example, McNaughton, 1961), such as the *state* of an automaton, which permit past input history to be dealt with in a precise way so that the output is a function not only of current input values but also of the state.)

We have traced the transition from the statement of an input–output relationship to its description as an expression in truth–functional logic, and to its physical implementation as an automaton. This automaton may, in turn, be thought of as a special-purpose computer tailored to solve automatically the particular problem in question. But, all problems that are solved by the use of any special-purpose computer can also be solved on a universal general-purpose, stored-program, digital computer, whose essential characteristic is that it is able to interpret and execute a set of stored instructions (which are themselves reducible to elementary logical operations) and modify its course of computations during the execution of a problem. These remarks are intended to explain and justify the following statement of Ashby: "Name the behavior, and the logic of mechanisms leads inexorably to a program that with the machine forms a whole mechanism that will show the behavior" (Ashby, 1962, p. 306). If one can give a complete and unambiguous description of behavior, this description is, in a sense, equivalent to a blueprint of an information processing mechanism (a computer program) for producing it. This is one aspect of the relationship between behavior and the underlying mechanisms for generating it. But it leads us to ask the following questions:

(a) To what extent can complex behavior be specified in complete and unambiguous detail, eventually in the language of logic?

(b) If there exist the equivalent of stored computer programs in the brain (Wooldridge, 1963, p. 62) which control complex purposeful behavior, how do they originate? How does the logical chain (*i.e.* the program) get modified and corrected with experience? How do we account for learning *via* feedback from the environment?

(c) What is the logic, if any, of this process of discovery and could it be embodied in an artifact which could exhibit learning and intelligent behavior?

This final question takes us away from neurophysiology to the problem of artificial intelligence.

3. THE PROBLEM OF ARTIFICIAL INTELLIGENCE

Initial characterization

The goal of artificial intelligence is to find design principles for an intelligent, thinking artifact — *i.e.* an artificially constructed entity which can solve new and different problems, learn from experience, respond appropriately under a variety of different circumstances, and, thus, behave in ways that justify our calling it intelligent. This initial, rough statement of the problem of artificial intelligence appears to encompass all that is relevant to the problem of knowledge itself: how we think and plan, value and behave. This being the case, how does one distinguish between psychology, neurophysiology, artificial intelligence, and related disciplines?

Psychology is alleged to be the study of how we think and learn and behave, and its subject matter is different from that of artificial intelligence in that psychology deals with the behavior of the *actual* biological artifact and not with all possible intelligent entities. Also, its subject is more limited in that most psychologists would argue that it deals with behavior and not with the underlying mechanisms which mediate between perception and behavior.

Neurophysiology, of course, is the study of those underlying signal processing mechanisms (*viz.*, the brain, the nervous system, etc.) which enable intelligent behavior. And since its subject matter concerns the actual biological system, neurophysiology is indeed relevant to artificial intelligence but, of course, not identical with it. We might put the relationship between these two pursuits in the following way: If one had a complete neurophysiological theory that spelled out in detail how the human brain is organized to process information so as to allow its owner to think and act intelligently, then, in principle, one could use that theory to design an intelligent artifact composed of artificial (non-protein) components, assuming, of course, that whatever, if anything, is informationally relevant about protein could be embodied in the artificial counterpart. Notice, however, the converse relationship: If we did have design principles for an intelligent artifact, these principles might be radically different from those incorporated in the human mechanism. Therefore, neurophysiology and artificial intelligence are distinct studies, but are related in the sense that an understanding of the functioning of the former contributes to that of the latter, although the converse does not necessarily hold. It is because the study of artificial intelligence is not unrelated to either psychology or neurophysiology that workers have looked to these and other traditional disciplines for insights into the problem of designing an intelligent artifact.

Methods of attack

How might one proceed to construct a device whose behavior would resemble that of a thinking human? What clues might guide efforts to simulate human problem solving behavior, learning, etc.? At least two different *kinds* of approach are possible; the difference between them becomes more clear in terms of a distinction, made by Donald MacKay (MacKay, 1963b), between the forging of a product and the forging of its generator. The product corresponds to human behavior and its generator corresponds to the information-flow mechanisms which causally determine behavior. If one wanted to imitate the sound of a motor engine, for example, he could observe in minute detail the pressure waveform of the sound, and seek to reproduce it by means of some form of curve-following device driving a hi-fi loudspeaker. He might continue to observe and correct his imitation by matching it against the genuine output and altering details of the curve being followed so as to approximate more and more closely to the original. However, he might proceed in a quite different way, by trying to build a model of the engine which would become a generator of the desired output product. This difference in approach is exemplified in the research conducted so far in artificial intelligence.

Although the work of Newell, Shaw, and Simon was motivated primarily by an interest in the development of a psychological theory, their early work on the Logic Theorist (Newell *et al.*, 1957) represented a step in the direction of artificial intelligence. They attempted to simulate one type of human problem solving behavior by programming a digital computer to derive theorems of elementary logic. Although there is a decision procedure for truth–functional logic, they ignored that procedure and programmed the computer to use methods allegedly similar to those used by humans. They gave the computer the Whitehead–Russell axioms for truth–functional logic, a set of transformation rules (such as *modus ponens*, substitution, etc.), and a set of techniques, called 'heuristics', on how to sequence transformation rules to obtain a proof of a given expression. The heuristics or advice was to correspond with the set of tricks and techniques, not always conscious or explicit, such as working backwards, using a reductio-type proof, knowing when to give up on one line of approach and seek out an alternative, etc., which a human apparently uses. Newell, Shaw, and Simon attempted to clarify and elaborate these techniques and advice so as to make them more precise in the form of a routine which the machine could interpret and execute. Such a computer routine, called a 'heuristic program', would differ from conventional programs in that it might never solve a given problem. Instead it would (hopefully) simulate the problem solving behavior of a human in the sense that it would employ similar sorts of problem solving techniques and methods. It would grope, use trial and error, set up goals and sub-goals, etc.

The adequacy of a problem solving program is tested by matching it against a human subject in the following way: As the human solves a problem he is asked to describe his 'thoughts' as he gropes toward the solution. This report is tape-recorded and typed out for visual inspection. Likewise, the machine is programmed to print out periodically intermediate steps as it proceeds to solve the same problem. Then, these two reports are matched against one another to determine how closely they agree. Where they do not agree, an attempt is made to modify the computer program so that on subsequent problems the outputs will more closely approximate the method employed by the human. Here then is one example of the several attempts to get a machine to simulate human problem solving behavior by *forging the product*.

If one were to take the other approach, he would attempt to forge the generator by modeling the informationally relevant aspects of the brain and nervous system. And, in fact, during the past decade, several groups have been studying so-called 'brain models' by simulating on digital computers various aspects of biological information-flow mechanisms. The strategy has been to ignore some aspects of neuronal behavior*, simplify other aspects, and then introduce assumptions or hypotheses about how cells are modified with 'experience'. The goal is to examine the consequences of these assumptions to see whether or not they can account for pattern recognition, learning, etc. It turns out that if one tries to analyze assumptions about large numbers of interconnected neuron-like elements, the complexity of the situation makes any kind of an analytic understanding practically impossible. Complexity rules out the usual use of standard logical and mathematical tools of analysis. One needs to see the model in action, so to speak, and the large-scale computer is just the research instrument which allows it to be so examined. The description of a neural network can be translated into a computer routine which allows the machine to simulate the behavior of the network in question. Computer simulation allows the researcher to modify his assumptions by merely changing the values of certain parameters in the routine, which in turn cause the simulated network to exhibit different behavior. Thus, the researcher can formulate and examine a variety of hypotheses about neurons and try to find rules which will enable networks to generate interesting behavioral properties. Here then are two different ways of studying the problem of artificial intelligence, both of which depend heavily on the digital computer in its role as a general-purpose simulator.

---

* It should be pointed out, of course, that the so-called neuron doctrine which asserts that information processing is executed exclusively by nerve cells, action spikes, etc., is not free from controversy. See, for example, Bullock, 1959; Galambos, 1961; and Hydén, 1962.

References p. 136

Thinking vs. brain activity

In what sense does the simulation of complex neuron-like nets constitute a reasonable attempt to forge the *generator* of human behavior? The actual brain mechanism of the human is, of course, exceedingly more complex than any net so far simulated, not only in terms of the numbers of elements but also in terms of the behavioral richness of the individual cells. But even more crucial than these differences is the fact that network studies start with the behavior of cell-like elements and proceed to synthesize nets of such elements which display interesting properties, whereas a more fundamental approach would be to look first at the necessary information-flow requirements for any mechanism which is to underlie the intelligent behavior. It is to this question of the logical organization of a generator that we shall return subsequently. For now we ask the following question about those other attempts — such as automatic theorem proving, game playing (Newell and Simon, 1961), etc. — which allege that the computer simulates human thinking: In what sense is it legitimate to say that automatic problem solving on a computer corresponds to human thinking? Is it even sensible (as opposed to true or false) to assert that the machine is thinking when it executes its stored program and subsequently prints out the correct results (along with the methods used in obtaining those results)? Does it not seem, on the surface at least, that what goes on in the 'mind' of a thinking human is not even remotely similar to what goes on in a digital computer when it sequentially interprets and executes those routines which lead from problem to solution?

These questions, of course, bring up the age-old problem of the relationship between the brain and the mind: the problem of relating mechanical, physical processes, such as nerve signals on axons, cell firing, etc., to such mental activities as having ideas, thoughts, sensations, feelings, etc. The mystery of the relationship between the mind and the brain has been expressed by Sherrington as follows:

> "When I turn my gaze skyward I see the flattened dome of the sky and the sun's brilliant disc and a hundred other visible things underneath it. What are the steps which bring this about? A pencil of light from the sun enters the eye and is focused there on the retina. It gives rise to a change, which in turn travels to the nerve-layer at the top of the brain. The whole chain of these events, from the sun to the top of my brain, is physical. Each step is an electrical reaction. But now there succeeds a change wholly unlike any which led up to it, and wholly inexplicable by us. A visual scene presents itself to the mind; I see the dome of sky and the sun in it, and a hundred other visual things beside. In fact, I perceive a picture of the world around me. When this visual scene appears I ought, I suppose, to feel startled; but I am too accustomed to feel even surprised." (Sherrington, 1950, p. 3).

Implicit in this description is what Ryle (Ryle, 1949, Chap. 1) calls the official doctrine about the nature and place of minds. Briefly, this doctrine asserts that every normal person has a body (including his brain) and also a mind. Bodies and brains have mass, occupy space, obey the physical (natural) laws of mechanics, chemistry, etc., and their behavior is, in principle, public and can be studied by qualified observers. Minds, on the other hand, are not physical entities, do not occupy space, are not subject to mechanical laws, and their 'workings' can be observed only by the person whose mind it is. Given this characterization of the two entities, 'minds' and 'brain-bodies', the question is how can these influence one another. Ryle states:

> "What the mind wills, the legs, arms and tongue execute; what affects the ear and the eye has something to do with what the mind perceives; grimaces and smiles betray the mind's moods and bodily castigations lead, it is hoped, to moral improvement. But the actual transactions between the episodes of the private history and those of the public history remain mysterious, since by definition they can belong to neither series. They could not be reported among the happenings described in some one else's biography of that person's overt career. They can be inspected neither by introspection nor by laboratory experiment. They are theoretical shuttlecocks which are forever being bandied from the physiologists back to the psychologist and from the psychologist back to the physiologist." (Ryle, 1949, p. 12).

We cannot consider here the classic paradoxes and difficulties surrounding the mind–brain problem. The literature on this subject is enormous* and its roots can be traced back to the writings of Plato, although Ryle credits Descartes with the 'official' view described above. Attempts to come to grips with the problem of the relationship between the body and the mind have been made by physicists (see, for example, Schrodinger, 1958) and physiologists** as well as philosophers. And the concepts of cybernetics, which have renewed and stimulated analysis of the prospect of designing an intelligent artifact, have also aroused considerable interest in the mind–brain problem.

The notion of complementary descriptions

Perhaps, the difficulty in explaining the mind–brain interaction problem arises from an inadequacy in our *theory* of explanation. Perhaps, our experiences concerning thinking and brain activity cannot be integrated into a single, complete, unified description formulated in a single language. This is not to say that there are two kinds of reality, but rather that there are (at least) two kinds of descriptions of the one reality. Niels Bohr (1958), and others, have suggested that a solution to the mind–brain problem has its analogue in quantum mechanics where the impossibility of deciding between a particle or wave theory of matter has led to the notion of complementary descriptions. Arguing from what might be considered a more general notion of complementarity, Donald MacKay (1958), has suggested that one can, in principle, describe the activities of knowing in two quite different, but complementary, languages: one language expresses the process from the standpoint of the 'actor' who is doing the thinking — having the mental experiences; the other language expresses the

---

* For an indication of some fairly recent discussions see, for example, Hook, 1960, and Scher, 1962.
** See Eccles, 1953; also see the discussions by Adrian, Le Gros Clark, Zuckerman, Slater, Brain, and Penfield in Laslett, 1950.

situation from the standpoint of the 'spectator' — *i.e.* the external observer who can make behavioral observations and who, in principle, has evidence concerning the underlying neurophysiological events, for example, *via* implanted micro-electrodes, etc. The important point is that descriptions formulated in these two different languages are not in conflict. Neither is necessarily incomplete in its own terms but at the same time neither is exclusive of the other. MacKay has written:

> "The false dualism which used to be expressed in the question 'how can matter produce mind' would now seem to have its origin in the genuine dualism of conceptual frames of reference, defined respectively for the viewpoint of actor and spectator." (MacKay, 1951, p. 118).

Let us clarify briefly the implications of this way of looking at brain activity and thought processes. People, real or artificial, who think, feel, have sensations, etc., can describe these activities in actor language. Correlated with the actor's description of knowing, there are the physical and behavioral indications which can be studied by an external observer and formulated in spectator language. This implies that the designer of an intelligent artifact need not worry about how to bring in some 'extra mind-stuff' in order to carry out his job. Rather, his task is first to characterize the *behavioral indications* of thinking, knowing, perceiving, understanding, etc. then to determine the logical organization of the information-flow mechanisms in an artifact which could generate the behavior in question, not *ad hoc*, but as a natural consequence of the identity of the logical organization.

The generator as a prediction machine

How must an artifact be internally organized, from an information-flow point of view, in order to generate the type of behavior which would be compatible with an 'outsider's' description of an intelligent, thinking artifact? What are the essential, logical (information processing) ingredients required in the design of a generator of intelligent behavior? We would argue that a key characteristic of intelligent, understanding-like behavior is the ability to make reasonable predictions. The intelligent person and the intelligent artifact must be able to predict in order to behave appropriately. The predictions in question cover the range of the activities of the artifact from games and mathematics to conversation, and they relate not only to expectations but also to preparations for action. The intelligent artifact must predict what to expect and how to respond, and the predictions must be not only for the present and immediate future, but for more distant futures as well. It is because the ability to predict (linguistically, to make inferences) is presupposed by intelligent behavior that we may characterize the generator of intelligent behavior as a prediction (or inference) machine (Maron, 1963).

What is prediction and what are the logical grounds for making predictions? A prediction, which has grounds for its assertion, is the logical consequence of an empirical hypothesis. It is the hypothesis which gives the prediction its logical grounds. The linguistic form of an hypothesis is a conditional statement of the type: 'If A, then B, with probability p'. In order to obtain hypotheses from which useful predictions can be deduced, it is desirable to have the value of the corresponding probabilities be moved as close to 1 or to 0 as possible. To do this one must find relevant items of information and include reference to these in the antecedent of the hypothesis. As a result, the corresponding conditional statement often has a complex antecedent describing a complex state of affairs which must be satisfied in order for the consequent to hold with the probability p. Given the initial conditions (*i.e.* the antecedent is satisfied), a prediction is the assertion of the consequent of an hypothesis of the type described above. Again, predictions of the type we are considering are logical consequences of hypotheses, which themselves may describe complex relationships between events.

This brings us to the question, what is the logic of hypothesis formation? How are empirical hypotheses formed, modified, corrected, etc.? Are there rules of logic which prescribe how to synthesize hypotheses — how to make the logical leap from evidence to hypothesis? We know, of course, that there is no strict logic of discovery in this sense which gives rules that guarantee how to discover hypotheses. Although there are no such rules of logic now — nor can there ever be — we do have a methodology of empirical science. The instrument for forming and improving hypotheses is provided by the scientific method itself.

Roughly speaking, this methodology advises that in order to improve hypotheses one must test their logical consequences against the relevant facts and, depending on the outcome (*i.e.* whether and how the prediction in question was disconfirmed), modify the hypothesis. Then the cycle of deduction, prediction, testing, and modification continues. Hopefully, the process converges in the sense that the probability of the hypothesis in question can be pushed ever closer to 1 or 0 unless, of course, we are talking about hypotheses describing statistical processes.

The methodology of hypothesis forming, testing, and modifying can be described in the language of feedback and control. Consider the schematization in Fig. 1, which

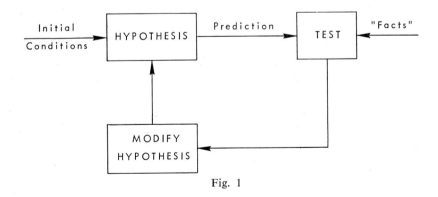

Fig. 1

suggests that a switching circuit with feedback from its environment can be considered as the implementation of a self-correcting technique of the type described above. Needless to say, of course, the schematic representation is grossly oversimplified and we have offered no details of the 'box' which modifies the hypothesis in the most probable direction. However, to the extent that there are heuristics concerning how to filter and use relevant evidence, how to make cross inductions, to appraise and improve inductions, etc., it can be done (Reichenbach, 1949).

Two questions may be raised: Is this information processing logic which we have outlined actually implemented in the brain? Can one construct an artifact along these rough guidelines which will be able to learn to interact successfully with its environment and exhibit intelligent behavior?

Models and the notion of an internal representation

One sense of 'model' is a logical representation or set of hypotheses which, when suitably interpreted, correctly describe some empirical events and their relationships. In order to correctly and consistently predict, one must have a model of those features of the environment in question. The notion that our brain (the generator of intelligent behavior) physically embodies a model of the environment was first suggested by Craik as early as 1943. In his book *The Nature of Explanation* he wrote:

> "My hypothesis then is that thought models, or parallels, reality — that its essential feature is not 'the mind', 'the self', 'sense data', nor propositions but symbolism, and that this symbolism is largely of the same kind as that which is familiar to us in mechanical devices which aid thought and calculation." (Craik, 1952, p. 57).

And again:

> "If the organism carries a 'small scale model' of external reality and of its own possible actions within its head, it is able to try out various alternatives, conclude which is best of them, react to future situations before they arise, utilize the knowledge of past events in dealing with the present and future, and in every way to react in a much fuller, and more competent manner to the emergencies which face it." (p. 61).

The question of how an artifact might most economically embody a model of its world has been discussed with clarity and depth by MacKay (1951, 1952, 1954, 1956, and 1963a). He has argued that since awareness of external events or features implies a 'conditional readiness' to take them into account in the organization of any relevant action, the organizing structure which maintains or controls this conditional readiness can itself serve as an internal representation of the world. For this to be possible, signals received *via* sense organs must be able to 'irritate' the organizing structure, which in turn must be equipped to 'match' or back them off by an adaptive response which can *ipso facto* represent the events or features of the world giving rise to them*. That is, the artifact knows about things and events to the extent that it is prepared to react adaptively to them; and to be prepared to react correctly (*i.e.* to be in a correct state of expectation) means, in a sense, that incoming signals will not put the artifact

---

* MacKay has pointed out that the more stable the environment, the more redundant will be the signal-pattern to which adaptive reaction is required, and the more economical it becomes to develop an internal generator system to match it and organize an appropriate conditional readiness.

'off balance'. Stated differently, this means that its current predictions will not be falsified. The key point here is that the predictions can be thought of as internally generated signal patterns which will *match* those signals generated by the external events being predicted. Thus, external events (objects, etc.) are *represented* internally by those signal patterns which are internally generated to match those generated by the corresponding external events.

> "The point of special relevance here is that insofar as an adaptive response is successful, the automatic movements of the goal-directed control centre will in quite a precise sense *mirror* the current state of affairs, or rather those features of the state of affairs to which it is responding adaptively. The state of the control-centre is in effect a *representation* of those features of the state of affairs, just as much as a code-pattern of binary symbols could be." (MacKay, 1954, p. 191).

In a changing environment, what determines how the internal signal patterns should be generated? The answer, of course, is that there is an hierarchical structure to the logical organization of the model which an intelligent artifact embodies, just as there is an hierarchical structure in science itself. This means that whereas there are signal sequences generated on a first level corresponding to predictions about events, other signal sequences, which in turn control the lower-level sequence generators, correspond to predictions about hypotheses. Thus, the generator of intelligent behavior in an artifact is constantly producing those signal sequences which correspond to its expectations. The internally generated signal patterns are continually being matched against the received externally generated signals. The mismatch information is fed back to modify the way in which the patterns are internally produced (*i.e.* hypotheses are modified). The feedback data modify the 'organizers' or internally generated signals, and so on up the hierarchy. It is along lines such as these that one may begin to outline the logical organization of the 'brain mechanism' of an intelligent entity.

4. CYBERNETICS, NEUROPHYSIOLOGY, AND EPISTEMOLOGY

Cybernetics and neurophysiology

The publication of Prof. Wiener's book on cybernetics (1948) was followed by the growing awareness on the part of engineers and physiologists that both the computing machine and the nervous system can be analyzed and described in the language of communication and control, because both are, in fact, information processing systems. There was a rush on the part of some computer engineers to find out about biological switching components, and the circuit organization of the brain. Were there clues from neurophysiology which could be taken wholesale and used by designers of intelligent artifacts? It turned out that at least two different kinds of problems prevented the engineers from picking up gold nuggets *gratis*. In the first place, there are linguistic and philosophical obstacles blocking the road to a clear discussion of thinking and brain activity. In the second place, the problem of the brain is enormously difficult, involving as it does, one of the most complex systems that we may ever encounter. We have only the first glimmerings of how the brain is organized so as to allow its owner to know the world.

An interesting facet of this relationship however, is that circumstances have caused the coin to be reversed, in the following sense: The cyberneticist who is concerned with the problem of artificial intelligence and the logic of information processing may be able to suggest general hypotheses for the neurophysiologist. And the cyberneticist's way of looking at things may provide a fruitful framework within which the neurophysiologist may gain a better understanding of natural brain mechanisms and hence guide the selection and interpretation of his data. (It is one thing to study the transport of a chemical substance across a cell membrane strictly in terms of the relevant biochemistry, and it is quite different to interpret the same process as the transmission of a message whose function it is to modify information storage. Compare, by analogy, the way in which a computer might be described on the one hand by a physicist, and on the other hand by a computer engineer or programmer.)

In order to describe and analyze an intelligent entity, one is forced to use such concepts as perception, recognition, knowing, thinking, learning, understanding, etc. These concepts, in a sense, fall completely outside the province of neurophysiology, which is concerned with events 'in the small', *i.e.* the signal processing mechanisms. However, as we have said, an analysis of the information-flow organization of the generator of intelligent behavior provides the logical timbers needed to bridge the gap between signal processing and behavioral indications of knowing, etc.

The brain mechanism of an intelligent artifact embodies a model of its world. Things and events are represented internally as signal patterns which generate adaptive responses to the things in question. The artifact gains information about its world when its model is updated and modified, *i.e.* when its states of readiness for adaptive behavior are modified. This is a form of learning. Thinking has its correlate on the information-flow level, in that activity whereby the internal model is driven faster than real time so that the probable future may be examined and alternative behavioral responses evaluated. This activity is part of intelligent planning. And the activity of self-awareness has its correlate in the internal activity of the hierarchical information system whereby one part of the system embodies a model of another part (MacKay, 1952). If the brain mechanism of an artificial agent were organized along the lines outlined above, then it would behave in ways which an external observer would describe as indicative of thinking, perceiving, understanding, etc.*

Cybernetics and epistemology

We have said that intelligent behavior can be characterized in terms of *knowing how* to carry out a wide variety of tasks ranging from solving mathematical problems and games, to conducting sensible conversation. An intelligent artifact must be designed

---

* For a penetrating analysis of how personal language might be applied in talking about an artifact which did, in fact, exhibit all of the appropriate behavior expected of an intelligent person (see MacKay, 1962b).

to execute the activity of *knowing*. If we put the matter this way, what is the impact of artificial intelligence on epistemology? And, are there concepts which have emerged from cybernetics which are relevant for epistemology? The answer to the question is 'yes', but before we go into it a bit more, let us clarify the nature of epistemology.

First of all we must make the important distinction, which is often confounded, between psychology and epistemology. Whereas both have as their subjects the problems of knowledge and how thinking and knowing take place, the psychologist is concerned only with the *actual* processes. The epistemologist, on the other hand, is concerned with how knowing *should* take place so that its outcome will be logically justified. The best place to study the thinking process so as to provide its rational reconstruction as sought by epistemology is in scientific knowledge — the processes of going from observed data to theories which, in turn, are subjected to tests, are falsified, modified, etc., eventually giving rise to knowledge which has good grounds for belief. Reichenbach has said: "Analysis of science comprehends all the basic problems of traditional epistemology; it is therefore in the foreground of consideration when we speak of epistemology" (Reichenbach, 1938, p. 8). So we see that epistemology has as its task an inquiry into the foundations of empirical knowledge and a study and justification of the methods of empirical science, the instrument for predictive knowledge.

To return to artificial intelligence we remember our characterization of the generator of intelligent behavior as a prediction machine; a mechanism which embodies the methodology of science in order to form, test, appraise, modify hypotheses so as to improve its role as a predictor. This suggests immediately that there are at least two points of contact between artificial intelligence and epistemology. Firstly, of course, any methods for discovery and pursuit of knowledge taken from the epistemologist may be valuable to the designer of intelligent artifacts if he can implement them in 'hardware'. Secondly, there are certain concepts from the theory of information which are useful for the development and refinement of not only epistemology but also the theory of intelligent machines. We refer, of course, to the key concepts of uncertainty and amount of information. We can stop only to sketch the outlines.

We can analyze the prediction machine as an information system which at any given time is in a state of uncertainty since, of course, it does not have secure knowledge of expected events, *i.e.* the probabilities associated with its expectations and subsequent responses are not unity. In principle, the state of uncertainty (of at least part) of the system could be measured. The prediction machine *via* its feedback connections with its environment, seeks to reduce the amount of its uncertainty. In fact, certain data if obtained by the artifact would provide more information at least in the sense that they would probably reduce a greater amount of uncertainty than other data. The information system could thus be organized to determine which kinds of data contain more information (in this sense), etc. Thus, we are talking about an epistemological problem having to do with the weight of evidence relative to various theories and the development of measures to determine the kinds and amounts of evidence which confirm or shake theories to a greater or lesser extent. What are efficient ways to remove uncertainty, to test and confirm theories, for gaining information etc.? We are not suggesting that the present theory of information has such measures, nor are we stating that they exist in the literature of contemporary philosophy of science. But it seems clear that both the epistemologist and the cyberneticist are concerned with some of the same problems.

ACKNOWLEDGMENTS

It is a pleasure to acknowledge the help I received, on two counts, from Prof. Donald MacKay. First, his ideas have influenced my thinking and provided the impetus to cast this paper in its present form. Second, I thank him for his kindness in reading an earlier draft and suggesting several changes which served to clarify the discussion. However, I alone stand responsible for the paper as it now appears.

I am pleased to acknowledge the help of my wife Dorothy for her skill in suggesting more graceful and precise ways of expressing myself. Also, I am happy to thank Wade Holland of RAND for many editorial suggestions which have improved the form of the paper.

Finally, I am grateful to the management of The RAND Corporation for providing the environment and encouragement to write this paper.

SUMMARY

It is the purpose of this paper to examine the origins, development, and present status of those key cybernetic notions that provide an information-flow framework within which to attack one aspect of the question of how a person *thinks*; *i.e.* the question of the information mechanisms and processes which underlie and are correlated with thinking.

After an introductory survey of the scope and ramifications of the information sciences, the cybernetic way of looking at information processing in the nervous system is examined so as to see in what sense it provides new and sharp tools of analysis for the neurophysiologist. With this as background, the problem of artificial intelligence is considered and with that the logical and linguistic difficulties in talking about the relationship between thinking and brain activity. An information-flow model of an artificial brain mechanism is described whose activity, it is argued, is the correlate to activity such as perceiving, learning, thinking, knowing, etc.

This leads finally to a consideration of the impact of these notions on theoretical neurophysiology and its attempt to frame suitable hypotheses, and on epistemology which is concerned with the logical analysis of measures, methods, and techniques which can justify the activity of knowing.

REFERENCES

ASHBY, W. R., (1952); *Design for a Brain*. New York. John Wiley and Sons.
ASHBY, W. R., (1962); What is mind? Objective and subjective aspects in cybernetics. *Theories of the Mind*. J. M. Scher, Editor. New York. The Free Press of Glencoe.
BOHR, N., (1958); *Atomic Physics and Human Knowledge*. New York. John Wiley and Sons.

BULLOCK, T. H., (1959); Neuron doctrine and electrophysiology. *Science*, **129**, 997–1002.

CRAIK, K. J. W., (1952); *The Nature of Explanation*. Cambridge. University Press.

ECCLES, J. C., (1952); *The Neurophysiological Basis of Mind*. Oxford. Clarendon Press.

GALAMBOS, R., (1961); A glia-neural theory of brain function. *Proc. Nat. Acad. Sci.*, **47**, 129–136.

HOOK, S., (1961); *Dimensions of Mind*. New York. Collier Books.

HYDÉN, H., (1962); The neuron and its glia–A biochemical and functional unit. *Endeavour*, **21**, 144–155.

LASLETT, P., Editor, (1950); *The Physical Basis of Mind*. New York. MacMillan Company.

MACKAY, D. M., (1951); Mind-like behavior in artefacts. *Brit. J. Phil. Sci.*, **2**, 105–121.

MACKAY, D. M., (1952); Mentality in machines. *Proc. Aristotelian Soc.*, Suppl. **26**, 61–86.

MACKAY, D. M., (1954); Operational aspects of some fundamental concepts of human communication. *Synthese*, **9**, 182–198.

MACKAY, D. M., (1956); Towards an information-flow model of human behavior. *Brit. J. Psychol.*, **47**, 30–43.

MACKAY, D. M., (1962a); Self-organization in the time domain. *Self-Organizing Systems*. Yovits, M. C., *et al.*, Editors. Proceedings of the Conference on Self-Organizing Systems, May 22–24, 1962, Chicago, Ill.

MACKAY, D. M., (1962b); The use of behavioural language to refer to mechanical processes. *Brit. J. Phil. Sci.*, **13**, 89–103.

MACKAY, D. M., (1963a); Internal representation of the external world. Paper presented at *Avionics Panel Symposium on Natural and Artificial Logic Processors, July 15–19, 1963*.

MACKAY, D. M., (1963b); *Discussion during a seminar on computers and comprehension*. The RAND Corporation, Summer 1963.

MACKAY, D. M., AND MCCULLOCH, W. S., (1952); The limiting informational capacity of a neuronal link. *Bull. Mathemat. Biophys.*, **14**, 127–135.

MCCULLOCH, W. S., (1949); The brain as a computing machine. *Electr. Engin.*, **68**.

MCCULLOCH, W. S., AND PITTS, W., (1943); A logical calculus of the ideas imminent in nervous activity. *Bull. Mathemat. Biophys.*, **5**, 115–133.

MCNAUGHTON, R., (1961); The theory of automata: A survey. *Advances in Computers*. Vol. 2. Franz Alt, Editor. New York. Academic Press.

MARON, M. E., (1961); Design principles for an intelligent machine. *IRE Trans. Information Theory*, **IT-8**, 179–185.

MARON, M. E., (1963); *Artificial Intelligence and Brain Mechanisms*. The RAND Corporation, Santa Monica, Calif. RM-3522-PR.

NEWELL, A., SHAW, J. C., AND SIMON, H., (1957); Empirical exploration of the logic theory machine: A case study in heuristics. *Proc. 1957 Western Joint Computer Conf.*, (p. 218–230).

NEWELL, A., AND SIMON, H., (1961); Computer simulation of human thinking. *Science*, **134**, 2011–2017.

PENFIELD, W., (1958); Some mechanisms of consciousness discovered during electrical stimulation of the brain. *Proc. Nat. Acad. Sci.*, **44**, 58–66.

REICHENBACH, H., (1938); *Experience and Prediction*. Chicago. University of Chicago Press.

REICHENBACH, H., (1949); *The Theory of Probability*. Berkeley. University of California Press.

ROSENBLUETH, A., WIENER, N., AND BIGELOW, J., (1943): Behavior, purpose and teleology. *Phil. Sci.*, **10**, 18–24.

RYLE, G., (1949); *The Concept of Mind*. New York. Barnes and Noble.

SCHMITT, F. O., (1962); *Macromolecular Specificity and Biological Memory*. Cambridge, Massachusetts. M.I.T. Press.

SCHRODINGER, ERWIN, (1958); *Mind and Matter*. Cambridge. University Press.

SHANNON, C. E., (1938); A symbolic analysis of relay and switching circuits. *Electr. Engin. Trans.*, Suppl. **57**, 713–723.

SHANNON, C. E., (1948); The mathematical theory of communication. *Bell System Techn. J.*, **27**, 379, 623.

SHANNON, C. E., AND WEAVER, W., (1949); *The Mathematical Theory of Communication*. Urbana, Ill. University of Illinois Press.

SHERRINGTON, C., (1950); Introductory. *The Physical Basis of Mind*. P. Laslett, Editor. New York. MacMillan Company.

SLUCKIN, W., (1954); *Minds and Machines*. London. Penguin Books.

TURING, A. M., (1963); On computable numbers, with an application to the *Entscheidungsproblem*. *Proc. Lond. Mathemat. Soc.*, **42**, 230–265.

VON NEUMANN, J., (1956); Probabilistic logics. *Automata Studies.* C. E. Shannon and J. McCarthy, Editors. Princeton, N.J. Princeton University Press.

VON NEUMANN, J., (1958); *The Computer and the Brain.* New Haven. Yale University Press.

WIENER, N., (1948); *Cybernetics: Or Control and Communication in the Animal and the Machine.* New York. John Wiley and Sons.

WOOLDRIDGE, D. E., (1963); *The Machinery of the Brain.* New York. McGraw-Hill Book Company.

Information and Psychic Activity

J. ZEMAN

Philosophical Institute, Czechoslovak Academy of Sciences, Praha (Czechoslovakia)

1. PRINCIPLE OF TRANSFORMATION IN BRAIN ACTIVITY

The human brain is adapted to receive, process and transmit information. It is in fact an information channel with input and output. A complicated system of noises and transformations acts on information at psychic processes.

The philosopher Gorgias maintained that nothing exists and if something were to exist it would not be known and if it were to be known it could not be communicated. This, of course, is sophism but it conveys the difficulties of the psychic transformation of the human subject and it refers to three groups of problems: reality, knowledge and expression. A closer inspection of the transformation process in the brain reveals three levels of activity. On the first level objective reality is transformed into subjective reflex. The actual basis of the human reflex – second level – is the transfer of brain, physiological processes into conscious psychic contents. At the third level conscious content is transmitted into forms of expression. Richards-Ogden in their book *The Meaning of Meaning* speak of a triangle of references: The first apex indicates the subject, the second the concept – symbol – and the third the character of concept – sign. The relationship between the subject and the concept is gnoseological, between the concept and the sign semantical and between the sign and subject there is a signal relationship.

A similar triangle of relationship could be designed also for the gnoseological fact and for the psychic fact of the brain. The vertices of the gnoseological triangle are: objective reality, subject (= man), expression, and their relationship: reception of in-

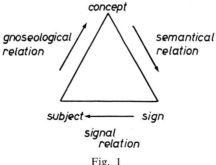

Fig. 1

formation, information processing, information transmission. In a triangle of psychological relationships the first vertex would indicate the physiological substrate – brain –,
the second psychic content – consciousness – and the third vertex expression of the
content – speech. Relationship could be classed as: psychophysical, pre-laryngeal,
post-laryngeal.

The transformation of physiological processes into conscious experience, into
psychic content, into actual conscious information takes place in the brain. This
conscious information is transformed from conceptual thinking (prelaryngeal) into
verbal expression (postlaryngeal). This verbal expression again influences somehow
brain processes (by means of the auditory analyzer at hearing, the motor analyzer at
writing, the visual analyzer at reading or only by the medium of memory in case of
inner speech). In fact it is a transformation of one code into another, a presentation
of one alphabet by another alphabet.

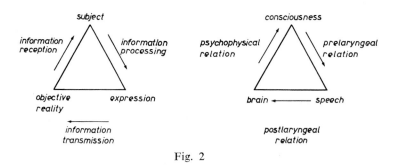

Fig. 2

Psychic activity, the psychic fact actually means the transformation of selective,
'technical', non-semantic information into semantic information in the process of
which at the brain channel output the message is determined, the brain code decoded,
the meaning of the message interpreted and perhaps its further utilisation decided.
In the conscious process a variety of memory contents participate, the brain always
combines information received with information already stored, perception with
experience. Memory recollection in fact means the transformation of potential 'dead'
information into actual 'live' information by means of re-energisation, *i.e.* the revival
of certain neurophysiological structures by some neurophysiological dynamic. The
psychic fact is a complicated process of transformation whose laws and principles
require a closer explanation.

The laws of psychic transformation can be studied on the gnoseological, neurophysiological, psychological and linguistic level. The following four principles could
be postulated:

1. The principle of totality division.
2. The principle of variety reduction.
3. The principle of entropy production.
4. The principle of capacity limitation.

The principle of totality division means that a certain entity is divided into two
asymmetrical components, *i.e.* contrasts. In the gnoseological sense it is a division

into object and subject, into an objective component (reflected) and a subjective component (reflecting) and further into information received (reflected) and information lost (not reflected). The information of the human brain does not reflect the totality of world information, *i.e.* objective reality is larger than knowledge. At the same time, however, human information, human knowledge does not mean only the difference 'all real facts minus the real facts not included' but is of a holistic character, *i.e.* it informs roughly on reality as a whole and not only of some part, similarly, as if I survey some town from a hill I do not see let us say one tenth of it exactly and the other nine tenths of the town not at all but I see the town as a whole in its general approximate shape. In the neurophysiological sense the question with respect to the psychic fact is that of a division of neurophysiological totality into an excited and into an inhibited part. With this corresponds in the psychological sense the division into a distinct shape (perception and thinking) and into a vague up to indistinct background; this in fact is related with a division into central facts, conscious and into peripheral facts, unconscious or subconscious. On the linguistic level the division would be into a reporting component and a reported, *i.e.* also into a basis which is to be defined and into definition which characterises it more closely; whereby the reported and the defining correspond here to information and the participation of the reporting subject and that to which the report relates remain in fact the undefined component, they are in the background, in the 'shadow'. With this phenomenon are connected problems like metaspeech, the paradox, the problem of full formalization, *etc.*

The principle of variety reduction links up on the principle of division. From the total variety of objective reality the human subject effects his selection. In the brain there is no sort of white noise or some Brown's movement but some centers hold in contrast to others a dominating position and certain processes have a closer structure and probability dependence than others. The differentiation process which starts already at neurons and synapses, continues at the higher level of brain centers up to the level of consciousness. Some centers are inhibited, others reinforced and the conscious is actually a sphere of optimal excitability which is the macroexpression and culminating unification of all subordinated lower processes and microprocesses. Here the transformation of the physiological into the psychic takes place which in fact is founded on the principle of variety limitation (only what takes place on the level of optimal neurophysiological events crosses the threshold of consciousness, *i.e.* subcortical and subconscious dynamic manifests itself as a conscious form). In other words in the brain a sort of 'natural selection', a competitive struggle takes place which ensures the optimal quality of psychic contents. (In fact the principle of Maxwell's demon operates here.) This process takes place at every psychic process and thus also at thought and speech.

The psychic fact also includes the principle of entropy production. In the gnoseological sense the consequence of totality division and variety limitation is a certain production of information entropy which manifests itself as incomplete knowledge, as a principle of uncertainty in physical observation, etc. The total of excitable energy or psychic dynamic is divided in the brain into an effective and ineffective part; only

part of excitable energy (dynamic) is transmitted into the shape of conscious information – similarly not all the supplied energy is transmitted in work with thermal
machines, or a certain redundancy at transmission in the noise channel. Perhaps
it could be said that whereas in the machine part of the energy is expended on cooling
in the brain part of the energy is expended on inhibition – and that in the neurophysiological sense (inhibition of weak processes and focei) as well as in the psychological sense (suppression of undesired processes and contents into the unconscious
by means of censorship); without this inhibition the brain would be 'overheated'
with a resulting total excitation essentially as in the case of epileptic convulsions or
ecstasy. With respect to the brain the problem is not the law of adding-up energy but
the law of contrast, of the mutual induction of excitation and inhibition. In the brain
there is apart from information and thermodynamic entropy production also a
production of semantic entropy particularly in verbal expression. Every statement,
even the most comprehensive, means a certain semantic loss because it is always
linked with selection and thus with the negation of other (true and untrue) statements
and with the mentioned division and limitation of variety. The statement 'All mammals
have mammary glands' conveys no information on, for instance, lizards; statement
'The world exists' includes, true enough, a large area but says of it little, is poor of
information; apart from that in these and other similar statements it is not told in
which system of speech these statements are made and what is their source. No
statement, not even a complex of statements can be total.

Another principle of the psychic fact is the principle of capacity limitation. Not
even the master brain is without limitation. Even the biggest genius is essentially
limited by the range of existing human knowledge. He may acquire its substantial
part, by producing his own information he may even get ahead by a few years,
decades or perhaps even centuries but he cannot altogether cross the boundary.
Capacity limitation applies also to the actual knowledge of the human race. The
brain has in the neurophysiological sense a certain flowing through capacity. This
capacity depends on the powerfulness of its dynamic and structure.

The rate of information transmittance is given by Shannon's formula

$$K = H(x) - H_y(x),$$

where $H(x)$ is input entropy and $H_y(x)$ is conditioned entropy showing that at receiving information y information x was transmitted. The output signal E is a function
of the transmitted signal S and noise N:

$$E = f(S,N)$$

The signal E is only then a mere function of signal S when entropy input equals
entropy output (that is in a noiseless channel):

$$H(y) = H(x)$$

The maximal capacity of the noise channel is given as a difference of entropy input
and conditioned entropy output:

$$C = max\ [H(x) - H_y(x)]$$

This information capacity may be determined also as

$$C = M/T,$$

in which M is the rate of space load of transmission given by the quantity of transmitted information and T is the time length of transmission. The volume of signals must not exceed channel capacity. The flow route of information is then determined by the number of decisions at transmission per time unit, which is expressed as

$$J = I/T,$$

I being information and T timelength of transmission. The more the flow exceeds capacity proportionally a greater quantity of information is lost. The ratio of dependence of channel capacity on noise is expressed by Shannon

$$C = W \operatorname{ld} \frac{P + N}{N}$$

where W is the width of the frequency band, P the medium performance of signal and N the medium performance of noise. The noise level must not exceed the signal level if this is to carry some more information.

In the psychological sense the limited capacity of the brain is given as a socalled 'straits' of the conscious. The conscious is capable of taking-in within a defined time unit only a certain number of elementary contents. This has been quite exactly established in the psychology of perception or in Ebbinghaus' and Jost's memory tests. The actual conscious has thus a certain space extent. At the same time the 'straits' of consciousness and the laws of memory are linked with certain time characteristics. Events in time are perceived by consciousness in a manner that a certain portion is felt as being of the present and another portion as already of the past. Consciousness is thus capable of comprehending a given number of elementary contents in a given time, it is a channel with a limited capacity. The same applies to the process of thinking and the process of speech. The mental solution of some problem has also its limitation with respect to extent and time; the mathematician for instance can calculate a certain amount of equations within a certain time. And so it is with reading, lecturing, talk. Naturally the basis for this are neurophysiological characteristics, the flowing-through capacity of the brain. The question here, however, is not only the transmission of information at an external stimulus, for instance, perception, but also the dynamic of transforming physiological processes into psychic ones. Brain capacity here is given by the power of excitable dynamic whose source is primarily the subcortical system and the powerfulness of structure whose basis is primarily the organised system of memory trace. A water dam or a hydro power station whose capacity is determined by the volume of water flow and turbin output serve as analogy. The dam is simultaneously the analogy for the character and height of consciousness threshold and censorship. Dynamic must not exceed structure capacity and contrary at a weak dynamic the structure is not fully used. An order for information given to the brain may be considered as input. The control mechanism activates from memory certain information centers in the brain and releases a certain dynamic. The information used is input information. The operation mechanism effects the operation and at the output above consciousness threshold the processed output information appears. Information as well as thermodynamic entropy production play their part in the process. Noise are those factors which resist the rapid and exact solution of the task. The creativeness of the human subject and the human brain leads to the phenomenon that during the information process apart from entropy production also negative entropy is produced – new information emerges. Thus at the information process in the brain it is not only the difference between entropy input and entropy output as for instance at a telephone wire. At all principles influencing and determining the psychic fact there are apart from negative aspects (loss of information) also positive aspects – on the one hand the possibility of brain activity on the basis of these principles, on the other hand the production of new information.

For a mathematical expression of the flowing-through capacity of the brain (particularly the transformation of physiological events into psychic information) it would be necessary: (1) to carry out measurements with a view to establishing the approximate average amount of the brain dynamic (excitable energy) and structure (this applies to the organisation and power of brain centers, focei, memory traces, *etc.*); (2) to model this dynamic and structure and to model the transformation of the physiological into the psychic (preferably in physical form); (3) for expressing the flowing-through capacity to employ completed Shannon's equations (define exactly what is input information, output information and noise and to keep in mind that the brain itself is the source of new information).

2. SEMANTIC FIELDS AND BRAIN STRUCTURE

In the brain there exist or are formed complexes which could be termed excitable fields. These excitable fields have their dynamic and structure, they are of a combined and discreet nature and have always a certain center (nucleus) and periphery (environment). They are of a diverse character and the relation between the center and periphery is also varied. The periphery of the field has as a rule a weaker dynamic and a less defined structure. The fields are connected with certain focei but they are not quite firm formations, they can change, newly form or extinguish. They have some resemblance with physical fields such as magnetic or gravitation fields. In connection with 'Gestalt' psychology Koffka and Köhler used the term field and Lewin in his topological psychology transferred the term field from the sphere of pure psychophysiology into the sphere of behaviour.

Excitable fields are the basis of psychic fields, *i.e.* of conscious fields and – if combined with thinking and speech processes – of semantic fields. That means that certain brain complexes and brain centers are connected with certain semantic contents, they characterise and model reality, the external world. The brain is a model, a map of the world. Semantic fields are in a certain mutual relation. It may be presumed that certain centers of excitation fields correspond to certain centers of semantic fields. Semantic fields could be described 'geographically' as stratas. The historical emergence of certain semantic fields could correspond to the 'geology' of the brain.

Semantic fields could in model-form also be described by certain specters, wave analysis, *etc.* In the formation and action of semantic fields apparently some physical principles apply, such as Huyghens' principle of wave spreading, and so on.

The word (also sentence, communication, concept and thought) is on the surface in the formal sense unequivocal, exactly defined and limited. But not so with its content, meaning. Semantically it forms a field, which has a certain dispersion, probability distribution and entropy. It has a rich semantic context, is linked with associations, is not isolated and its meaning is bound with these associations. It is in fact only a certain relatively firm nucleus of its field and when connected into higher formations changes semantically. The ambiguity of the word is more apparent where for some reason strict rationality is weakened (in the speech of primitives, children, poets, the mentally ill). The uncertainty of its meaning is related with the mentioned principles of psychic transformation, with the limitation of knowledge and with the creative character of the psyche. The thinking and speech process means the formation of categories that have a probability character. The meaning of the word and the content of concepts is not precisely defined. This is instanced in primitive tongues. In the language of the Arants the word 'patta' means mountain, crowd of people, pap. New semantic groups formed from fragments of meaningful words can be found in the poems of the poet Morgenstern. Once can also form words without a meaning or rather without a meaningful nucleus (for instance the German word 'babig' according to Carnap). For the analysis of real semantic fields in the brain theoretical models may be employed in which entropy of the formal aspects of vowels, words and sentences is determined and after that the entropy of concept and thought contents. Thus for instance entropy in English four-letter words could be established. Each letter could be replaced by all letters of the alphabet, but only some of the words would have a meaning. If I choose the English word 'pile' I could replace for instance the third letter and obtain new words with a meaning, like 'pile' 'pike', 'pine', 'pipe' whereas words like 'pime', 'pioe' and others would make no sense. Similarly if I replaced the first letter the word 'bile' would have a meaning. Thus I could create an artificial semantic field in the center of which would be the word 'pile', in another region would be meaningful words obtained by replacing one letter such as 'pike', 'pine', 'pile', 'bile' a.o.; in a further association region would be words of meaning produced by replacing two letters, *etc.* I could create in the same way a field which would be concerned not only with the auditory, formal aspect of the word but with the meaning, the content of the concept.

Semantic fields in the brain are of a similar pattern and are formed in a similar way; they have their ambiguity and uncertainty. This ambiguity and uncertainty is of course hidden and its source is genetic relationship, unity of all concepts and the laws of psychic transformation. The differentiation of the body of an adult animal may serve as analogue which, however, developed through the gradual differentiation of a considerably homogeneous one-cell egg.

Owing to the genetic nature of the psychic, the psychic and the brain as its material substrate assume the character of a certain non-absolute exactness, *i.e.* they are composed of fields that have a certain ambiguity, semantic entropy, and this psychic has an historical stratiform structure. This has been referred to particularly by psycho-analysis and especially by C. G. Jung. Jung bases his theory on the concept of psychic totality and psychic dynamic. According to him all psychic spheres and events must be comprehended in unity, in interdependence and as dynamic-energetic facts. Consciousness is underlaid with a large sphere of genetic unconscious which is personal as well as collective. J. Jacobi demonstrates the structure of psychic by concentric circles in which the outer indicates consciousness (K), below is personal unconscious-ness (L), then collective unconsciousness (M) and in the center of it is an area which cannot be brought into consciousness al all (N). This is total, complete unconscious which is also according to Jung the actual creative dynamic source of psychic phenom-ena. Collective unconsciousness is the embryonic sphere which unites humanity in space and time, it is the hereditary substance of human development which regene-rates in every individual psychic structure.

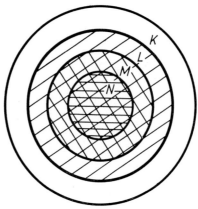

Fig. 3

The psychic phylogenesis is reflected in the structure of the individual soul which is composed of a sort of geological layers connecting the individual with increasingly larger units as shown by J. Jacobi's diagram.

Here A indicates the individual, B the family, C the tribe, D the nation, E the national group, F human ancestors, G animal ancestors, H the central creative force of the bottom layer of collective unconsciousness.

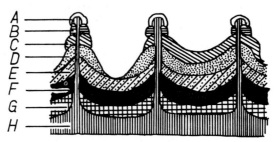

Fig. 4

In the soul there is constant tension, conflict which causes energetic gradient, motion, flow. The focei of mental activity are, according to Jung, complexes. These complexes have their unconscious semantic nucleus and in blocking mental flow they produce tension concentrated in force fields. Such fields are in the first place archetypes – primary ideas, models of behaviour associated with the structure of soul and brain. They are hidden dynamic dispositions produced as historical sediments. They reveal themselves in images, symbols and ideas common to the human race, they penetrate into consciousness and are the foundation of mental and cultural creations. These concepts are indeed noteworthy though much in Jung's theory is speculative. It appears that these concepts of the psychic dynamic and structure together with the concepts of semantic fields could be combined with neurophysiological research and the theory of information in a very fertile system.

3. EVOLUTIONAL POSSIBILITIES IN HUMAN THINKING

With development human knowledge and information of the human brain advances. Past generations hand over to future generations an increasing quantity of obtained and processed information. In the principles of psychic transformation a change of relationship takes place: the negated part of totality at division decreases, variety limitation assumes more and more the character of a deeper understanding of the fundamental, information grows and entropy declines, capacity limitation of knowledge and of the brain decreases. The development of knowledge is towards an asymptote approach the limit of which is complete cancellation of the mentioned principles; at the same time, however, these principles are the substance of human knowledge. What then are the developmental perspectives of the human brain? Will it grow indefinitely or will there be a stop at a certain line? In the latter case – will the curve decline towards degradation, or will it stop or will there be a qualitative change on a new higher level?

If we express the relationship between information growth and time then it is a question of a slow-down or speed-up of this growth. Information may grow either to a certain maximum or to an indefinite value. The relationship between information growth I and time t can be expressed as the relation of two different scales. Time flows evenly, its intervals are equally long, but information increment either decreases or increases in geometrical order. If it is a slowed-down growth the relation may be expressed by the equation

$$I = I_{max} \left(1 - e^{-\frac{t}{\tau}} \right)$$

where I_{max} is some maximum information, e is the basis of natural logarithms and τ is time constant.

The curve corresponds with Ebbinghaus' memoration curve, Backman's curve of organism growth, Du Noüy's curve of wound healing according to age and with ontogenesis generally (gradual decline of vitality, decline of learning capacity, *etc.*).

A speedier growth of information, however, would be more in line with the phylo-

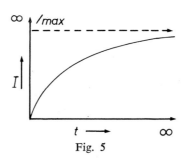

Fig. 5

genesis of society. It can be expressed by an equation

$$I = I_{max}\left(1 - e^{-\frac{t}{\tau}}\right)$$

where t_{max} is time when an infinite quantity of information would be attained. For logarithmic purposes information may be expressed as

$$I = -\tau \ln\left(1 - \frac{t}{t_{max}}\right)$$

The curve resembles Lorentz's curve of transformation equations for time, mass and length in the relativity theory.

It could be said that the above curves describe the mutual relation of the forces of life and death. The first curve shows how the tendency towards information growth is resisted, vitality gradually hampered as if there would operate some system with an opposite tendency. In the second case, however, not entropy but on the contrary

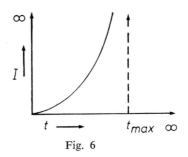

Fig. 6

information grows. It appears that the world is composed of two asymmetric systems with opposite tendencies which the old religion described as the struggle of two gods – Vishna and Shiva, Ormusd and Ariman, Taanit and Moloch, *etc.* who symbolised the principles of creation and destruction, of good and evil, of life and death. However, the growth curve of capacity of the human society may be affected by the growth curve of capacity of automates or also by moral or other catastrophies. Morale, too, has its physical laws, one may speak of a growth or decline of moral entropy and self-denial or temptation could be modelled just as a water dam can be modelled. Man lives in a certain transformation system and is subject to its principles. For instance, transformation of the future into the past. As a consequence of memory growth the extensiveness of our presence (also the extent of our penetration into macrocosmos and microcosmos) increases, *i.e.* from the future and the past an ever greater share is at our disposal. Then there is the transformation of the objective into the subjective and the physiological into the psychic. An exact determination of principles could lead us to establishing a transformation equation of the human brain and to answering the question whether a more perfect information system than this brain is possible and what would be its principles. In answering such questions it would be necessary to consider that the world must apparently be regarded as being composed of two asymmetrical systems with opposing tendencies and that the source of human information is the external objective reality as well as the creative subject itself. The question whether the development of the human brain is limited, whether thinking has its boundaries, remains open. But today we are closer to an answer than were our predecessors and perhaps we shall be able to tell whether the advocates of a limitation in thinking whom Cusanus saw in 'docta ignorantia' and 'coincidentia oppositorum', Kant in the antinomies of pure reason, Spencer in the unthinkable, Wittgenstein in the unspeakable, were right. Perhaps we shall decipher whether the boundary of the brain is a sphere of paradox and whether the brain is a catalogue of all catalogues which do not contain themselves and which cannot and can be included among catalogues containing themselves and among catalogues not containing themselves as is the case in the known Russell paradox. Let us hope that our present 'Ignoramus' will receive another predicate and that this will not be 'Ignorabimus' if the research in cybernetics, psychology, neurophysiology and linguistics will be combined in an efficient manner.

ZUSAMMENFASSUNG

Das menschliche Gehirn kann man als einen spezifischen Transformationskanal fassen. Bei der Gehirntätigkeit werden die äusseren Gegenstände in Begriffe und die Begriffe weiter in die sprachlichen Zeichen transformiert (resp. die physiologischen Prozesse werden in die Bewusstseinsprozesse und diese in die Sprachprozesse überführt). Die psychische Transformation kann man in der erkenntnistheoretischen, neurophysiologischen, psychologischen und linguistischen Ebene untersuchen. Es kommen bei ihr die Prinzipien der Totalitätsspaltung, der Varietätsreduktion, der Entropieproduktion und der Kapazitätseinschränkung zur Geltung. Bei der Uebertragung und bei der Transformation der Information im Gehirn kann man die Shannonsche Formel für die Informationskapazität, für den Informationsfluss usw. anwenden. Ausser der Gehirnsdynamik kann man auch die Gehirnstruktur untersuchen. Es können hier die Gesetzmässigkeiten der sogenannten semantischen Felder und der Tiefenpsychologie angewendet werden. Die Information des menschlichen Gehirns wächst in der Abhängigkeit von der gesellschaftlichen Entwicklung und der Zeit auf. Die ganze Entwicklung kann man als einen Negentropieaufwuchs, resp. Gedächtnisaufwuchs (im breiteren Sinne des Wortes) fassen, dessen Gesetze man auch mathematisch feststellen kann.

References p. 150

REFERENCES

JACOBI, J., (1940); *Die Psychologie von C. G. Jung.* Zürich.

RICHARDS, I. A., AND OGDEN, C. K., (1949); *The meaning of meaning.* London.

SHANNON, C. E., AND WEAVER, W., (1949); *The mathematical theory of communication.* Urbana.

WIENER, N., (1948); *Cybernetics.* Wiley. New York.

ZEMAN, J., (1962); Kybernetik und das psychophysische Problem. *Proc. 1st Intern. Congress Cybernetic Med.*, Naples, 1960. S.I.M.C. (pp. 619–627).

ZEMAN, J., (1962); *Knowledge and Information.* Praha.

ZEMAN, J., (1963); *Information and the Brain. Nerve, Brain and Memory Models.* Progress in Brain Research, Vol. 2. N. Wiener and J. P. Schadé, Editors. Amsterdam-New York, Elsevier (pp. 70–79).

ZEMAN, J., (1965); *Semantic Fields. Cybernetics in Social Sciences.* Praha.

The Kybernetics of Cyclothymia

D. STANLEY-JONES

Buckshead, Hayle, Cornwall (Great Britain)

A new age is dawning upon the industrial history of the world: the Age of Automation. It is currently held by thinkers in high places that those who survive the next 50 years will see a change in the pattern of our daily living, a change besides which even those wrought by the Industrial Revolution and the two World Wars will become but memories of history. The new age may well usher in a series of changes as far-reaching as those of the Neolithic Revolution from which has arisen our common stock of civilizations the world over.

In this momentous passage from era to era, the highest honours should be awarded to the work of Norbert Wiener. His writings and researches on Cybernetics, and the new realm of knowledge that these have brought into being, bear the same relation to the intellectual climate of the New Age as those of Luther to the Reformation, of Bellarmine to the Counter-reformation, of Voltaire, Diderot and the Encyclopaedists to the Age of Revolutions, and of Marx and Engels to the uprising of the proletariat in the East. His are the ideas which are destined to guide the thoughts of men in the reshaping of their habits of living during the years, and possibly in the centuries, that lie immediately ahead.

What is to be the academic status of this new discipline of thought? In what Faculty of our Universities will its professors be chaired? Is it to be a descriptive and speculative branch of economics or engineering, or an exact science akin to mathematics? Or is it a creative art of the nature of architecture, which will serve those who plot out the wiring-diagrams of mechanical brains as architects in the past have served the builders of our cathedrals? The claim of Cybernetics to be numbered among the fundamental sciences would be strengthened if, like relativity and other branches of physics and astronomy, the structure of its reasoning and the primary axioms upon which that structure is erected were sufficiently rigid or logically coherent to be used as a basis for the making of significant predictions. It is, accordingly, with the purpose of making a specific prediction that this essay has been written.

Within the province of psychological medicine, there is no problem which scientifically is more baffling than that of the nature and origin of cyclothymia. Cyclothymia is a disease of the emotions or affects, a form of insanity known also as affective psychosis; it is characterized by alternating periods of mania and depression. Several methods of treatment have been applied, including therapy by electrically induced convulsions, and chemotherapy by synthetic drugs acting in an unknown manner upon unknown regions of the brain; for extreme and intractable cases there has been employed that irrevocably damaging assault upon the personality known as pre-frontal leucotomy. The success of these treatments, and of the many variants and recombinations that have been given their clinical trials, is not lessened by the fact that, in the majority of patients suffering from manic-depressive psychosis, spontaneous remission brings the illness at least to a temporary cure.

For all these empirical and often highly satisfactory treatments, there is not the first beginnings of a rational explanation. The anatomical targets of those drugs which have proved most rewarding is almost entirely a matter of speculation; and the neuro-physiology of the deeper layers of the nervous system, and of the areas of superficial cortex which are isolated by leucotomy, is in its relation to psychosis and the emotions virtually an unexplored terrain. The structure and phasing of the cyclical process in mania and depression are completely unknown, and not even the rudiments of an explanatory theory have yet been put forward. Treatment is still wholly experimental; and unfortunately from neither its successes nor its failures has any light has been thrown upon the abnormal processes that are being treated.

Two faint clues, however, have been detected amid the mass of unsorted clinical detail, and it has been inferred that the substantia nigra of the midbrain is involved both as a relay-station on the pathway of emotional expression, and as a possible site of action of certain drugs acting on the emotions. The substantia nigra, in other words, is concerned in a twofold way with the emotions: is it concerned also with cyclothymia which is a disease of the emotions? Chlorpromazine (a tranquillizer) is used to relieve anxiety, and has a place in the therapy of cyclothymia; its use may be followed by oculogyric crises (eye-rolling spasms), and this is a strong indication that the actual target of this tranquillizer is the substantia nigra. These oculogyric crises are transient 'runaways' (in the kybernetic sense), and they are caused probably by interference with the feedback circuits of the oculomotor nerve as it passes through the substantia nigra (Stanley-Jones, 1958).

Another group of drugs, recently named normothymotics or mood normalizers (Schou, 1963), has been claimed as specific for affective disorders such as cyclothymia. The use of these drugs is occasionally followed by severe tremor without other evidence of neurological disorder, a tremor which comes on within a day or so of first using the drug and disappears when the treatment is discontinued (Hartigan, 1963). Now tremor is an indication of extra-pyramidal disease, and it is a prominent feature of parkinsonism; this disease is associated with almost complete blockage of the usual channels of emotional expression, and the substantia nigra is often the seat of gross neural damage (Stanley-Jones, 1955, 1956b).

The substantia nigra, therefore, is a possible target of action of tranquillizers which have a steadying influence on the emotions in cyclothymia; it is the site of damage in certain forms of parkinsonism in which emotional blockade and muscular tremors are prominent features; and tremor occasionally appears in cyclothymic patients under treatment with normothymotic drugs. The clues are indeed faint, and it is only a tentative inference that cyclothymia may be related to a dysfunction of the substantia nigra; but there are literally no other anatomical or physiological data which can link cyclothymia to a possible dysfunction of any other part of the brain.

Cyclothymia, as its name implies, is a periodic psychosis. It is a regularly alternating change of thymos or mood. Mathematically its structure is an oscillation, and as such it presents a challenge to kybernetics, which has much to say upon the subject of oscillation. Can the oscillations of cyclothymia be made to yield their hitherto inscrutable secret to the powerful new methods of kybernetic analysis?

Only a small proportion of manics and depressives show the characteristic rhythm which gives its name to their disease. A typically cyclothymic patient, therefore, is the exception and not the rule. Some interesting figures on periodicity in mental disease were published by Clouston in 1882: in a year's admissions to Morningside Hospital, Edinburgh, 54% of the manics and 39% of the depressives showed alternate or contrasting phases of sanity and insanity, or other form of periodicity; not more than 2%, however, presented that regular and continuous reversal of phase, the circular rhythm of plus into minus, which is the essential feature of the concept of cyclothymia, albeit rare as a clinical percept (Clouston, 1882).

In spite of its rarity, however, the regular periodicity of true cyclothymia is so outstanding a feature that it compels attention as a fundamental problem. Clouston reported several such cases. One female inmate who was under his care for many years 'has had regularly recurring short attacks of acute mania lasting from a week to four weeks usually. This is succeeded by a few days of dementia with a little depression, and then she becomes practically sane for a period of from a fortnight to four weeks. Her circle takes from four to eight weeks to complete. We have a wonderfully complete record of her symptoms all these 35 years. It shows that over 200 of such attacks may not destroy the mental power of the brain and produce complete and permanent dementia'.

Another case (still quoting Clouston) 'who was for 10 years in the Asylum took attacks of excitement lasting about a fortnight alternating with periods of depression for a week. The depression immediately preceded the excitement, and the periods of sanity were of about three weeks' duration. The regular alternations recurred up to the age of 78, when she died'. A male patient exhibited regular mania every four weeks, almost to a day, for 26 years. These forgotten cases have an historical as well as a clinical interest, for Clouston brought them together 12 years before Kraepelin announced his views.

More recently, Klein and Nunn (1945) have published the details of a man who showed regular weekly cycles of depression (5 days) and mania (2 days). Another of Klein's cases (1950) was observed for 21 cycles, in which the manic period averaged 18 days (ranging from 7 to 35 days), the depressed period 13 days (range 6 to 24). 'Transition from depression into mania was always sudden, and occurred regularly at night. Failure to sleep was invariably the first sign of the change; in the course of the night he became restless, talkative and irritable, and it was difficult to keep him in bed or restrain him. From then on he was from four to six days at the height of his manic phase' (Klein, 1950).

Other cases of periodic psychosis have been collected and reviewed by Crammer (1959). Several new features, hitherto unnoticed, have been described. Periodicity *per se* seems to confer upon the psychosis a specific imprint: the attacks are nearly always biphasic, with an over-active and an under-active phase sharply distinguished, almost like mirror-images above and below the phase of normality; not only does the cycle maintain its rhythm often with remarkable regularity, but also the succession of phases within each half of the cycle follows in a well-ordered sequence that is repeated in detail at every cycle. 'Each attack is often a complex sequence of events. This sequence is true for the physical phenomena as well as for the mental. These phenomena, if they occur, may only do so for a certain time within the whole sequence of the attack, and recur every attack only at the same relative time, peculiar to that case. The total psychotic attack is elaborately orchestrated' (Crammer, 1959).

There are good reasons for thinking that every oscillatory system must of necessity involve a circuit with negative feedback: otherwise it could not oscillate, it could not return regularly to its zero or median position. It is at this point that kybernetic analysis enters into the discussion, and asks the question: where in the human body are to be found the negative feedbacks which are responsible for the oscillations of truly periodic cyclothymia?

Cyclothymia is essentially a disease of the emotions. It is known that emotions are dependent upon the autonomic nervous system, and that 'feelings' of rage, fear, and lust (postulated as the three primary emotions) are conscious because they are mediated by neural activity in the cortex of the brain. This activity is dominated by deeply seated and therefore unconscious physiological events whose controlling headquarters reside in the hypothalamus. The hypothalamic centres are responsible for co-ordinating the actions of the autonomic system, and for relaying information to the higher centres in the cortex. Of the two parts of the autonomic, the orthosympathetic is controlled by the posterior end of the hypothalamus, the parasympathetic by the anterior end.

Rage and fear are orthosympathetic emotions which accompany the fight-or-flight reactions both of humans and of animals. The muscular expression of these emotions is co-ordinated in the rage-centres of the posterior hypothalamus. Rage and fear are primarily based upon alimentary or nutritional responses, for animals of differing species rarely pursue or attack each other unless the attacker is hungry. Rage (the motive-force of aggression) is the emotion proper to the idea 'I am going to eat *you*'; fear (the motive of flight) is the defensive reaction 'You are going to eat *me*'. The vasomotor reactions of the human stomach, namely blushing in rage and pallor in fear, are consonant only with this physiological autonomic explanation of the emotions. Rage and fear are mediated by the orthosympathetic, and they employ the same physiological mechanisms that are used in the defences against cold; of these mechanisms, the chief ingredients are constriction of the blood-vessels, acceleration of the rate of the heart, and raising of the blood-pressure (Stanley-Jones 1957a–d, 1964).

Lust is mediated by the parasympathetic whose headquarters reside in the anterior hypothalamus. Peripherally, it seeks outlet at the genital level (through the nerv i erigentes or nerves of genital erection, the sacral parasympathetic) involving dilatation of the blood-vessels as an essential component. The parasympathetic in general is the vehicle for the defences against over-heating. It works in conjunction with the nerves controlling sweating and vasodilatation which, although anatomically grouped with the orthosympathetic, are cholinergic and therefore physiologically to be regarded as parasympathetic: vasodilatation (Uvnäs, 1960) and sweating are controlled by the parasympathetic anterior half of the hypothalamus.

The alimentary responses of fight and flight, therefore, with the emotions of rage and fear by which they are dominated, and the reproductive emotion of lust, are respectively associated with activity of the orthosympathetic and the parasympathetic moieties of the autonomic. This, in extreme brevity, is the basic tenet of *Structural Psychology* (Stanley-Jones, 1957d).

A further development of this viewpoint is that the three major responses concerned in the mediation of the emotions are (1) the vascular reflexes of vasoconstriction and vasodilatation, (2) alteration in the rate of the heart, and (3) regulation of the blood-pressure against which the heart has to work. These cardiovascular responses are primarily thermostatic in purpose: for the chief contributor to the heat-production of the resting body is the muscular tissue of the heart; and the principal factor which regulates this thermal output is the blood-pressure which quantitatively determines the work performed, and therefore the oxygen consumed and the heat generated, by each individual beat of the heart.

The hypothalamic responses of lust and rage enter consciousness as the emotions of love and hate. They exhibit a polarity or balanced antagonism, of which the direct cause or immediate physiological substrate is the polarity of the two halves of the autonomic. This autonomic polarity is itself the evolutionary response of a warm-blooded animal to the thermal demands of its environment (for some aspects of this polarity are reversed in cold-blooded vertebrates). Emotion as it is consciously experienced in the cortex of the brain is thus linked, through the hypothalamus with its ancillary autonomic and the component vascular and cardiac reflexes, to the rate and force of the heart-beat which is the main source of the thermal output of the body (Stanley-Jones, 1964). The Greeks, little though they knew it, have the support of the unassailable findings of physiology for their belief that the heart was the seat of the emotions.

The crux of the argument, which leads it directly back to the problem under discussion, is that the rate of the heart, and the blood-pressure against which it has to perform its work, are controlled by reflexes which are patterned on negative or stabilizing refection. Is it possible therefore that these cardiovascular reflexes and their negative feedbacks may be responsible not only for the thermostatic control of the mammalian body, but also for the homoeostatic control of the human mind, and for that emotional tranquillity whose balanced polarity is periodically upset in the rhythmic oscillations of cyclothymia?

The two sides of the autonomic nervous system present contrasting patterns also in their kybernetic structure. The orthosympathetic is concerned not only with the

References p. 167

primary emotions of rage and fear, but also with their muscular or somatic outlets as aggression, agitation, anxiety, and with the sensations of visceral pain. These emotions and sensations are uniformly characterized by having a positive feedback into the orthosympathetic, which is potentiated at the chemical level by the secretion of adrenalin into the blood-stream; they carry therefore an ever-present liability to break down into a runaway such as an anxiety-attack, a declaration of war, a bodily convulsion or an intestinal colic. Each of these situations is precipitated by the failure of monitoring refection to control the positive feedback from which it draws its dynamic; and each is accompanied by the release of orthosympathetic emotion. Positive refection (feedback) is restricted to the orthosympathetic half of the autonomic.

The parasympathetic half of the autonomic is in this matter, as in so many other ways, the direct opposite to the orthosympathetic. It is, however, a balanced opposition, a co-operative antagonism, which secures the harmonious co-ordination of the bodily services whose outcome is homoeostasis. The feedbacks or refectory circuits of the parasympathetic are, without exception, in a negative direction: they work to restore the equilibrium of the body, to conserve its resources after their dissipation in fight or flight, to maintain the *status quo* of peaceful good health.

By way of interim summary, the three stages in the argument may be re-stated as follows:

(1) Cyclothymia is a disease of the emotions; and because emotions are mediated by the autonomic, cyclothymia may be a disease of the autonomic.

(2) Cyclothymia in pure form is *par excellence* a periodic phenomenon; it must (from kybernetic principles) necessarily involve physiological mechanisms which are patterned upon negative refection.

(3) Negative refection, in the autonomic system, is associated especially with the parasympathetic.

The hypothesis is put forward, therefore, that cyclothymia is a functional disturbance of the parasympathetic.

The suggestion that cyclothymia is a disease of the autonomic system is not new. It was put forward in 1937 by Singer, and endorsed in 1943 by Sherman and Broder, and again in 1953 by Campbell. Singer believed that the manic and depressive phases were caused by a vegetative upset which influenced the higher centres only consequentially. Sherman and Broder regarded a typical manic–depressive psychosis as 'a periodic autonomic imbalance'. Campbell concluded that the autonomic and emotional disturbances are primary and parallel, while the mental symptoms occur only secondarily: the cyclothymic process is not basically a mental disorder. All these writers were on the right track, their opinions are correct as far as they go; but they lacked the powerful methods of kybernetic analysis with which to develop their viewpoints to a logical conclusion.

The further question arises: from where does the parasympathetic obtain its supplies of neural dynamic? If these neural impulses could be cut off at their source, instead of being interrupted by leucotomy as they traverse the frontal pole of the cerebrum, it is conceivable that an operation could be devised, equivalent to leucotomy in its therapeutic efficacy, which yet would be without the disastrous effects on the personality that restrict its use to all but desperate cases.

The kybernetic or quantitative theory of neural dynamics is relatively new to physiology (Stanley-Jones, 1960). Its main thesis is that no vertebrate nerve-cell has the power of originating or creating *de novo* a neural impulse, but only of transmitting it. All neural impulses arise from sensory receptors lying outside the nervous system, and particularly from those sensory receptors which maintain a constant output of neural impulses in response to a constant stimulus; that is, from receptors which do not adapt themselves to a constant stimulus by reducing their output.

The contrary view is supported by the majority of neurophysiologists. This is only to be expected; for if a single nerve-cell has no power of spontaneous discharge, if it cannot create a neural impulse, how can the brain create its own thoughts? The new theory of the quantitative aspect of neural dynamics, that the whole of the human CNS is dependent upon outside stimulation for its proper functioning, cannot expect to find a ready acceptance, not only because of its novelty but also on account of its philosophical implications.

Belief in the spontaneous generation of neural impulses by nerve-cells rests almost entirely upon experimental work involving the use of intracellular electrodes. In these conditions, a nerve-cell when isolated as far as possible from all incoming afferents continues its rhythmic activity, and maintains a continued emission of neural impulses which are picked up by an electrode within its substance. These experiments, however, cannot be adduced as evidence of spontaneous activity; the graphs from intracellular recording could equally well bear the legends: 'Response of a single neuron to the trauma of insertion of an electrode'. This indeed is almost certainly the true explanation.

Nerve-cells are extremely sensitive to the slightest alteration in their environment. The regularity of discharge of a small group of cells may be altered by the passage of a current much less than a micro-ampere. *A fortiori*, how much more may a cell be affected by the trauma of puncture by an intracellular electrode, by which alone all evidence of spontaneous activity has been collected?

The essence of the problem, from the experimental side, can be found in the alleged spontaneity of the respiratory centre when isolated from all incoming afferents. The neural structure of the respiratory centre is similar to that of the spinal motor centres, in that a sustained and unchanging input can be transformed into a rhythmically alternating output, distributed phase by phase of the cycle to the several muscle-groups concerned: this is the neural substrate of reciprocal innervation, and of the 'perpetual motion reflexes' such as reflex stepping in a spinal dog and ceaseless swimming in a spinal dogfish (Stanley-Jones, 1956a, b).

A needle-electrode inserted into an isolated respiratory centre is sufficient by its mere presence to supply, by the stimulus of local trauma, the sustained input upon which the respiratory centre can operate. A continuous output of rhythmic discharges, in these experiments, is not evidence of spontaneous activity.

Under these conditions (it must be conceded) evidence of spontaneous activity is well nigh impossible to obtain. Let the onus of proof, therefore, be placed on those who seek to disprove the accepted theory by experiment. The essence of the experiment must be that a group of nerve-cells (such as the respiratory centre) must be isolated from all incoming stimuli except one, and its neural output be recorded; removal of the one remaining source of input should be followed by a cessation of output; and output should return with the return of input.

Such an experiment, fulfilling exactly these rigorous conditions, was reported in 1952 by Von Euler and Söderberg. The respiratory centres in a series of cats were isolated by severance of the brain-stem both above and below the medulla, and by section of the vagus nerves; needle-electrodes inserted in the appropriate location of the respiratory centre recorded, even in this completely de-afferented medulla, rhythmic bursts of neural discharges. These and many similar experiments in other hands have been adduced as evidence of the ultimate spontaneity of the respiratory centres, of their implied ability to *create* neural impulses as distinct from their known ability to *transmit*.

In the experiments of Von Euler and Söderberg, however, the possibility of chemical stimulation of nerve cells was investigated. Administration of carbon dioxide resulted in an increased output of impulses from this otherwise completely isolated medulla, thus establishing that the stimulus or input might be chemical rather than neural.

When pure oxygen was given in replacement of carbon dioxide the output ceased entirely, proving that the cells even of the respiratory centre do not possess the power of spontaneous discharge; for when the chemical stimulus was withdrawn the neural output fell to zero. Re-administration of carbon dioxide was followed by a renewed output of neural impulses, proving that their temporary cessation, when deprived of chemical stimulus, was not due to fatigue or to death.

The reasonableness of this new theory of neural dynamics is supported by a consideration of what would happen if the contrary were true: can any nerve-cell be permitted the privilege of spontaneous activity? Nervous tissue in general possesses the power of almost unlimited multiplication and distribution of neural impulses. A single rogue cell in this vast network, were it to start to discharge on its own, that is independently of any outside stimulus or of any neural impulse from a contiguous cell, would throw the whole system into chaos. A similar state of chaos would arise in an electronic computer, were but one element only to usurp the privilege of making decisions 'Yes or No' independently of the input programmed by the operator.

The kybernetic theory of neural dynamic is relevant to the problem of cyclothymia. If the parasympathetic is like all other nervous tissue, it is unable (according to this theory) to generate its own neural impulses. Its neural dynamic must arise from outside. If the source of these impulses could be traced, and if the supply could be interrupted at its origin, it is possible that the ceaseless rhythm of intractable cyclothymia might be brought to a standstill.

It is almost certain that the neural dynamic for the skeletal muscles of posture arises from the stretch-receptors of the antigravity muscles and from the otoliths (Stanley-Jones, 1960). Stretch-receptors are almost alone among the sensory elements to give a sustained output of neural impulses under the stimulus of a sustained unchanging environment. The most probable source of the neural dynamic of the parasympathetic is the stretch-receptors of the aortic arch and of the carotid sinus. These stretch receptors have many of the properties of the stretch-receptors of skeletal muscles: their neural output is quantitatively proportional to the amount of stretching, and (under experimental conditions) it is a sustained, non-adapting output which alone can satisfy the requirements of the nervous system for a completely reliable and unchanging source of input.

The natural, physiological stimulus which activates these stretch receptors in the aortic arch and in the carotid sinus is the pressure of the circulating blood. This distends the arterial wall, and stimulates a continuous neural output which is in proportion to the degree of stretching, hence to the blood-pressure. The output rises to a peak with the passage of the systolic pulse from the heart, and falls to a trough during the phase of diastole. If the arterial wall is mechanically constrained so that it does not stretch, the neural output continues at a constant rate and does not register the fluctuations of the pulse-pressure.

A typical output for a single receptor would be one impulse every thirtieth of a second during systole, slowing to one impulse every twentieth of a second during diastole (Bronk and Stella, 1935). The summated output of these arterial receptors feed into the parasympathetic the neural dynamic which, it is postulated on kybernetic grounds, is essential for the maintenance of its function.

Not all the receptors in the carotid sinus are non-adapting. Some of them adapt rapidly, that is they reduce their output in face of an input or stimulus which (under experimental conditions) is maintained at a constant level. Under natural conditions, however, when subject to fluctuating pressure, these adapting receptors are sensitive in one direction only, namely that of increasing pressure. This unidirectional sensitivity of rapidly adapting receptors appears to be determined by the laws of thermodynamics (Clynes, 1961). Because of this unidirectional sensitivity, the sharp fall in pressure following immediately upon the aortic pulse does not produce an abrupt diminution of output; this further tends to maintain the constancy of neural input into the parasympathetic.

The output of neural impulses from the arterial stretch-receptors serves not only as the sustaining dynamic for the homoeostatic reflexes of the parasympapthetic; it is also linked by negative refection to the physiological output of those reflexes, namely the rate and force of the heart-beat and thus to the thermal output of the heart itself. With every rise of blood-pressure, no matter how transient, an augmented neural input is fed into the parasympathetic centres of the brain-stem, which reflexly activates the parasympathetic (the depressor reflex), and brings about a slowing of the heart and a lowering of the general blood-pressure. Thus there is inbuilt in the physiological structure of the body a kybernetic circuit patterned on negative refection: raising of the blood pressure automatically raises the neural output of the stretch-receptors which respond to the blood-pressure, and reflexly depresses the action of the heart and reduces the blood-pressure by which the neural output was evoked. Although on the effector side there is some adjuvant help on the part of the orthosympathetic, in both the afferent and efferent limbs of this reflex the kybernetic circuits lie wholly within the province of the parasympathetic.

References p. 167

The emerging concept of the parasympathetic as an inhibitory and stabilizing system may now be generalized. The experimental evidence for this is unequivocal. Not only is it the principal inhibitor of the cardiovascular reflexes; it is also the neural substrate for the thermostatic defences of the body against the perils of over-heating. Heat production is reduced by slowing of the rate of the heart and by reduction of the blood pressure against which it has to work, and heat loss is increased by peripheral vasodilatation and by sweating (both of which are mediated by cholinergic nerves under the control of the anterior hypothalamus). The parasympathetic, furthermore, has a profoundly inhibitory effect upon the general musculature of the body, when under experimental conditions it is subject to grossly unnatural over-stimulation.

When the whole trunk of the vagus nerve is stimulated, there is a massive delivery of ascending impulses into the neural centres which normally are receptors of sensory messages from the several branches of the nerve. There immediately ensues an inhibition of all the bodily functions. Under varying conditions of experiment, this inhibition has been shown to abolish the knee-jerk, to control the unconscious movements under light anaesthesia, and to reduce even the convulsions of strychnine poisoning (Schweitzer and Wright, 1937).

Distension of the carotid sinus by perfusion, in a fully conscious dog, brings about the immediate onset of sleep. There is a general relaxation of all the muscles of the body and the cessation of all movements; the head and tail hang limply, the eyelids are partially closed, the pupils constrict, and to painful stimuli only feeble responses can be obtained. On lowering the pressure in the carotid sinus the animal wakes up suddenly (Koch, 1932).

If the postulate is correct that cyclothymia is a functional disease of the parasympathetic, it follows that the opposing syndromes of depression and mania must be related in some way to over-activity and under-activity of the parasympathetic: depression to over-activity, and mania to under-activity. Depression is due to over-activity of the inhibitory role of the parasympathetic.

Clearly the problem is by no means straightforward. Were the polar phases of depression and mania merely the results of over-activity and under-activity of the parasympathetic, such a simple relation of cause and effect would long ago have been noted. Many signs of depression, however, are seemingly those of under-activity of the parasympathetic: loss of salivation, of lachrymation, of gastric secretion, of libido, and many other physical signs betoken reduction of parasympathetic tonus. The most suggestive but by no means constant sign is a slowing of the pulse (due to vagal over-activity) in depression, and a quickening in mania.

The only generalization which it is possible to infer from the multiplicity of autonomic disturbances in cyclothymia is that there is strong evidence of dysfunction of the parasympathetic. This dysfunction canalizes itself as over-activity or under-activity, not so much in its outgoing descending somatic effects (for these are notoriously labile), but rather in its ascending influence upon the higher centres, and especially upon the cerebral cortex. This concept allows a rational physiological explanation of prefrontal leucotomy in the treatment of depression.

Parasympathetic afferents ascend *via* the vagus and glossopharyngeal nuclei and reach the anterior hypothalamus, whence they are relayed ultimately to reach the orbital cortex (area 13) of the frontal lobe. This area is now regarded as the cortical projection area of the vagus (Bailey and Bremer, 1938). The operation of leucotomy interrupts this projection by undercutting the white fibres converging onto the orbital cortex. The clinical relief of intractable depression may be explained as the result of the severance of the parasympathetic (vagal) fibres on their ascent to the orbital cortex, or possibly as they relay from the orbital cortex to adjacent areas. The cortex is released from the generalized inhibitory influence that is mediated by the parasympathetic, and the mind is thereby (it is reasonable to presume) released from its depression.

The mental status of patients who have undergone prefrontal leucotomy is fully in accord with this hypothesis. These patients, while relieved of their depressions, often exhibit a hypomanic state, a group of symptoms known as Rylander's triad: extraversion, elevation of mood, and over-activity. This syndrome has indeed been recognized as a surgically produced homologue of true mania.

Among the many facets of this impoverished personality may be mentioned a lack of social responsibility and moral sense, a failure to adapt to situations calling for a certain propriety of behaviour, garrulousness and grandiloquence, jocularity and facetiousness which may be out of keeping with the company around, and a general over-activity of body and mind which lacks the restraining guidance of a balanced and well-integrated personality. The patient after leucotomy is in the position of the owner of a car who, on finding that he has burnt out his brakes by driving with them on, decides to have the offending brakes repaired in such a way that he cannot put them on at all — and continues to drive.

The hyper-motility of post-leucotomy patients has been related especially to the loss of area 13, the cortical projection of the vagus (Ruch and Shenkin, 1943). This accords with the view that mania is due to under-activity of the inhibitory role of the parasympathetic.

The dominant emotion in the depressive phase of the cyclothymic rhythm is that of guilt. The outstanding feature by which the true manic, or his post-leucotomy imitator, is distinguished from his normal fellows is the absence of guilt. Guilt serves as the restraining inhibitor of the mind, as the parasympathetic serves as the restraining inhibitor of the body. It is a tenet of *Structural Psychology* that the emotion of guilt is mediated by the parasympathetic.

Guilt in psychology usually implies sexual guilt. Its overt manifestation is the blush of shame. Blushing is a dilatation of the cutaneous vessels of the face; and although the relative balance of orthosympathetic and parasympathetic in this phenomenon is far from clear (Fox *et al.*, 1960), it is known that facial vasodilatation in general is closely linked to activity of the cranial parasympathetic.

At the other end of the body, the sacral parasympathetic flows out as the nervi erigentes, and conveys the vasodilator impulses that bring about a genital erection. There appears to be a reciprocity or see–saw action between the two ends (cranial and sacral) of the parasympathetic, not only in the direction of their vasomotor impulses but also in the emotions that accompany them. It is a matter of human experience rather than of physiological experiment that it is impossible to sustain a parasympathetic vasodilator discharge at both ends at one and the same time: a blush of guilt effectively quells the appearance of a phallic erection, and in appropriate circumstances a phallic erection abolishes all sense of guilt. The quantitative aspects of this see–saw effect, this either–or distribution of vasomotor impulses, accords well with the quantitative theory of neural dynamic.

Another instance of a similar quantitative effect is seen after section of the vagus nerve for relief of gastric ulcer. The nerve is cut below the diaphragm, and a major outlet of parasympathetic activity is thereby blocked. Before the operation, many patients complain that an emotional upset would exacerbate the symptoms of their ulcer; this indeed is the rationale of the operation, for the parasympathetic discharge activated by the emotion increases gastric acidity and thus inflames the ulcer.

After vagotomy, emotional tension has to find its outlet in other somatic or visceral disturbances, such as salivation, palpitations, diarrhoea, sweating (Rees, 1953). The neural dynamic engendered by the emotional tension, which formerly found its release down the vagus nerve to the stomach, has to seek a new outlet after vagotomy; it is distributed either to other outlets within the parasympathetic (such as salivation) or more widely as a general disturbance of the autonomic. The accepted psychological explanation of these post-vagotomy symptoms is that the patient's neurosis which originally caused the ulcer now has to seek another bodily outlet to relieve his emotional tension. This explanation in no way conflicts with the new theory of redistribution of neural dynamic from one part of the autonomic to another.

Pertinent at this juncture is a remark attributed to Cushing, that after an injury of the spinal cord 'all men become philosophers': deprivation of libidinal discharge compels a redistribution of neural dynamic within the parasympathetic, a dynamic which is still potentiated at the chemical level by its full quantum of gonadins (thereby distinguishing the paraplegic from the eunuch); this enforces a 'sublimation of libido' into creative activity of the mind.

The reciprocity or mutual exclusiveness of lust and guilt, and the fact that they are mediated by vasodilatation as an essential somatic component, supports the teaching that both emotions are of parasympathetic origin. Guilt is a secondary or derived emotion, having its basis in the primary emotion of lust: guilt appears only when lust has been aroused and its physical expression is blocked. The cause of the block is usually orthosympathetic anxiety.

The kybernetic viewpoint offers also an explanation of Kraepelin's classification of mental illness into manic–depressive insanity which tends towards recovery, and dementia praecox which invariably destroys. This teaching has remained unchallenged for over sixty years, albeit unexplained. It still holds the field because it is based on clinical evidence, but it has never yet fitted into any rational scheme of psychology.

Mania and depression are dysfunctions of the parasympathetic. Their intimate relation to negative feedback or stabilizing refection explains their tendency to spontaneous return to normality: every system that is thrown into unwonted vibration returns to its median position of stability when the disturbing influence is withdrawn, and this is as true of cyclothymia as of every other oscillating system.

Periodicity when fully established seems to confer a certain stability on a psychosis: it acts as a stabilizing influence. Patients have been known to pass through their regular cycles for thirty years or more, yet throughout their illness there has been very little change in the character of the individual attacks. This appears to be a significant feature of the periodic psychoses, for once the periodicity is fully established the details of the attacks remain invariant; the patient does not develop fresh signs and symptoms, and his general condition does not deteriorate (Crammer, 1959). This seems to be true even when there are evident schizophrenic features in the manic and depressive phases. The schizophrenic process is held in check by its association with periodicity and stabilizing refection.

Schizophrenia is patterned on positive feedback. The polarity of its phases, over-active and under-active, are related as runaway-to-maximum and runaway-to-zero. Schizophrenic mania, katatonic frenzy, endogenous fury, hyperkinesis, all are the result of unmonitored positive refection, which in every system in which it develops enlarges its influence in a vicious circle or expanding spiral until it has reached the limits of physical expression, and ceases only with destruction of the system or exhaustion at the chemical level. Schizophrenic melancholia, katalepsy, stupor, mutism, katatonic akinesis, all are the evidence of mental and bodily paralysis brought about by runaway-to-zero. Both aspects of schizophrenia are the *predictable* results of positive refection.

Herein lies the essential differentness between benign (cyclothymic) and malignant (schizophrenic) melancholia and mania. In cyclothymia, the polar phases of melancholia and mania are due to over-activity and under-activity of the parasympathetic with its monitoring or stabilizing refection. The same two symptoms in schizophrenia, seemingly akin to the former in their polarity, are primarily orthosympathetic and are due to the influence of positive refection. The melancholic phase of schizophrenia, unlike that of cyclothymia, is rarely dominated by guilt.

In cyclothymia, negative refection determines the alternation of the phases and their mutual exclusiveness: the rhythm is either–or, and there is no physiological break-up of the personality because there are no intolerable stresses. In schizophrenia, positive refection allows both extremes to appear together, regardless of their clinical incompatibility.

The suggestion is now put forward that the oscillations of true cyclothymia could be interrupted by a section of those branches of the parasympathetic that convey the output of the stretch-receptors in the aortic wall and the carotid sinus. The main afferent nerve from the carotid sinus is a branch of the glossopharyngeal nerve (Hering, 1924); it is remarkably constant in a wide range of animals (Ask-Upmark, 1935), indicating its significance for the fundamental processes of the body over a long era of evolutionary time. Its anatomy has been studied by Boyd (1937) and Sheehan (1941). The great majority of the carotid-sinus parasympathetic afferents join

References p. 167

the glossopharyngeal nerve close to the skull, leaving only the chemical receptors of the orthosympathetic to transmit their impulses by other paths.

Intracranial section of the glossopharyngeal has many times been performed, for glossopharyngeal neuralgia and for the relief of the carotid-sinus syndrome (Ray and Stewart, 1948). The unilateral operation leaves little in the way of physical disability: there is a transient rise in blood-pressure and pulse-rate, from interruption of the depressor impulses, but they return to normal within three days, presumably from compensatory activity of the intact carotid sinus. A series of thirty cases was reported in which the patients were left with no noticeable ill-effects, though careful testing disclosed a loss of taste at the back of the tongue and a loss of sensation in the naso-pharynx (Herbert and Echlin, 1942).

Bilateral denervation of the carotid sinus has been performed on dogs, and it does not impair their ability for normal exercise (Leusen and Lacroix, 1961).

Other stretch-receptors which contribute to the depressor reflex are found in the aortic arch, in the pulmonary arteries (Coleridge and Kidd, 1960) and around the origin of the thyroid arteries (Gann and Bartter, 1959). The latter group are intimately related to those around the carotid sinus; those from the larger vessels discharge into the vagus. Complete denervation of these stretch-receptors would involve there-fore a severance of the relevant arterial branches of the vagus.

There is no reason to believe that cyclothymia is due simply to over-activity of the carotid-sinus reflex; for this is the cause of a well-defined syndrome in man, which has no psychological implications. The physiological basis for cyclothymia resides probably in the anterior (parasympathetic) part of the hypothalamus. Section of the parasympathetic afferents from the stretch-receptors of the carotid body and aortic arch aims at depriving these dysfunctioning hypothalamic centres of a major source of their neural dynamic. It is possible that this would lessen the further upward relay, from the hypothalamus to the prefrontal cortex, of ascending parasympathetic impulses, which are known to project onto area 13. Isolation of area 13 is a factor in the surgical relief of depression; and severance of its connexions by leucotomy has been practised for many years. The somewhat drastic surgical procedure of intra-cranial section of the glossopharyngeal nerves on both sides, together with deafferen-ting the large vessels of the thorax, is relatively safe, and it would be entirely free of the undesirable sequels of leucotomy with its irreparable damage to the moral personality of the patient.

It cannot be assumed that depression *per se*, or mania *per se*, would be relieved by the proposed 'de-buffering' operation. It is postulated only that the hypothalamic centres responsible for the periodicity of the disease would be deprived of their neural dynamic, and by this means the endless cycle of mania and depression would be brought to a standstill. There is no foretelling whether the cyclical process would come to rest at its zero position of normality. It is conceivable that when the negative refection from the parasympathetic reflexes was cut off, a stabilizing influence would be removed and the disease process might deteriorate. This is a risk especially when there is a schizophrenic quality in the psychosis.

Apart from the kybernetic arguments which have led up to the suggested surgical treatment of kyclothymia, there are certain clinical indications that support this somewhat revolutionary proposal. Vagotomy has been practised for the cure of gastric ulcer for many years. Concerning its efficacy for the permanent cure of ulcer there is some doubt, but little of interest to psychology. It is the extraordinary mental changes which may follow this operation on a silent nerve to the stomach which challenge both physiologist and psychiatrist for an explanation.

Many patients after recovery from vagotomy exhibit mental or neurotic symptoms. Often these are a re-emergence or exacerbation of defences which had been employed by the patient some time in his past (Szasz, 1949a). A careful study of the mental history of these ulcer-patients has disclosed a relation between the postoperative symptoms and the preoperative structure of the personality in terms of psychodynamics. Only one explanation can fit these unexpected facts: section of the vagus nerves, by cutting off a potential source of parasympathetic inhibition, releases bygone patterns of behaviour which hitherto have been subject to that inhibition. This reappearance of old, neurotic symptoms by cutting of vagal afferents is to be distinguished from the emergence of new symptoms, mostly somatic, due to cutting of vagal efferents. These vagal efferents, it is believed, had provided an avenue of escape or channel of discharge into the nerves of the stomach, with production of gastric ulcer; with this safety-valve cut off, nervous tension has to find another outlet.

In a few cases, the repressed material has been a phobia, and the patient's personality had the structure, prior to his operation, of a psychoneurosis, that is a latent psychosis which is masked and defended by a manifest neurosis. The parasympathetic afferents from the stomach here contributed, it would seem, to the maintenance of sanity; and when their stabilizing influence was removed by vagotomy the patient's mental balance broke down into a phobia or localized insanity.

In a series of 40 cases described by Rees, 12 patients, despite improvement in ulcer symptoms, had increased difficulties in adjustment at home, at work and in interpersonal relations in general. 'The difficulties were related to changes in emotional disposition and to the development of neurotic symptoms and attitudes. These patients became more anxious and irritable and complained of becoming fatigued easily' (Rees, 1953). Again it appears that prior to operation these people could maintain their adjustments only with the help of their parasympathetic inhibitions. When the stabilizing influence of this negative refection was removed by section of the vagi, the personality reverted to a less mature and less stable pattern of adjustment.

Ocassionally the operation of vagotomy has been followed by depression. 'Moderately severe depressions started very soon after vagotomy and cleared spontaneously in the course of a few months' (Szasz, 1949a). This is a paradoxial result of an operation which, in another form, is proposed as a cure for depression. It is noteworthy, however, that there *is* a relation between vagotomy and depression, a relation for which no explanation has previously been suggested. The onset of depression in these post-vagotomy patients can best be explained as a transitory phase of irritation of the nerve-fibres that have been cut. The truth of this suggested explanation is supported by the fact that 'phantom ulcers' are sometimes experienced by patients during their convalescence.

References p. 167

Phantom ulcers, like phantom limbs after amputations, are sensations experienced by the patient, real sensations of things that are non-existent—of an ulcer that has healed, of a limb that is no longer there. Phantom ulcers have been described as one of the clearcut sequels of vagotomy. 'Immediately after the operation the pain of the ulcer was relieved and the lesion healed. Then, usually within a few weeks, the pre-operative abdominal symptoms returned' (Szasz, 1949b). By analogy with phantom limbs, the sensation of phantom ulcer is probably due to irritation of an afferent nerve that has been cut and caught up in scar-tissue. If this explanation is accepted, then by further analogy, this time with phantom ulcer, the depressions that follow operations could be due to irritation of an afferent nerve in one of the severed vagi. A transient over-activity of the parasympathetic input, it is believed, is the cause of post-vagotomy depression.

These psychiatric sequelae of a surgical operation are highly relevant to the matter under discussion, in spite of the difference between subdiaphragmatic vagotomy and the proposed 'de-buffering operation' which is much more extensive. The vagus afferents from the stomach are not nearly so numerous as the efferents, they have little or no tonic influence or function, and their input in quantitative terms is relatively insignificant when compared with the unceasing discharge that flows from the stretch-receptors in the carotid sinus.

If the interruption of this relatively insignificant quantum of neural dynamic, ascending into the parasympathetic centres of the hypothalamus, can have such a notable effect in certain neurotic patients whose mental outlook is unstable, *a fortiori* may not the surgical interruption of a vastly greater output of neural impulses, unceasing throughout the day and night, have an effect upon the mental instability of cyclothymics?

SUMMARY

The kybernetic analysis of cyclothymia starts with the premises that mania and depression are diseases of the emotions, and that emotions are mediated by the autonomic: cyclothymia is a disease of the autonomic.

True cyclothymia is a periodic psychosis, a species of abnormal oscillation. All oscillations involve negative refection (feedback). Negative refection in the autonomic is limited to the parasympathetic. Cyclothymia may therefore be a kybernetic dysfunction of the parasympathetic.

The quantitative theory of neural dynamics demands that the parasympathetic draws its supplies of neural energy (without which its refectory circuits cannot function) from the stretch-receptors in the carotid sinus and the aortic arch. This neural dynamic ascends via the 9th and 10th nuclei and the anterior hypothalamus to area 13 of the orbital cortex. The success of leucotomy depends on the interruption of this neural relay.

If this neural input could be cut off at source instead of in the frontal pole, the disastrous moral effects of leucotomy could perhaps be avoided. The surgical procedure suggested is bilateral section of the glossopharyngeal nerves (carrying afferents from the carotid sinus), and of those branches of the vagus which arise on the aortic arch.

REFERENCES

ASK-UPMARK, E., (1935); Carotid sinus and cerebral circulation. *Acta psychiat. (Kbh.)*, Suppl. **6**, 1–374.

BAILEY, P., AND BREMER, F., (1938); A sensory cortical representation of the vagus nerve. *J. Neurophysiol.*, **1**, 405–412.

BOYD, J. D., (1937); Human carotid sinus and its nerve supply. *Anat. Anz.*, **84**, 386–399.

BRONK, D. W., AND STELLA, G., (1935); Response of single end organs in isolated carotid sinus. *Amer. J. Physiol.*, **110**, 708–714.

CAMPBELL, J. D., (1953); *Manic–Depressive Disease*. Pennsylvania, Lippincott.

CLOUSTON, T. S., (1882); Alternation, periodicity, and relapse in mental disease. *Edinb. med. J.*, **28**, 13–33.

CLYNES, M., (1961); Unidirectional rate sensitivity: a biocybernetic law. *Ann. N. Y. Acad. Sci.*, **92**, 946–969.

COLERIDGE, J. C. G., AND KIDD, C., (1960); Baroreceptors in the pulmonary artery of the dog. *J. Physiol.*, **150**, 319–331.

CRAMMER, J. L., (1959); Periodic psychoses. *Brit. med. J.*, **1**, 545–549.

FOX, R. H., GOLDSMITH, R., AND KIDD, D. J., (1960); Cutaneous vasomotor control in human nose, lip and chin. *J. Physiol.*, **150**, 22P.

GANN, D. S., AND BARTTER, F. C., (1959); Buffer function of nerves at thyrocarotid arterial junction. *Amer. J. Physiol.*, **197**, 1229–1232.

HARTIGAN, G. P., (1963); Lithium salts in affective disorders. *J. ment. Sci.*, **109**, 810–814.

HERBERT, C., AND ECHLIN, F., (1942); Intracranial section of the glossopharyngeal nerve. *Trans. Amer. neurol. Ass.*, **68**, 29.

HERING, H. E., (1924); Carotid pressure reflexes. *Münch. med. Wschr.*, **71**, 1265–1266.

KLEIN, R., (1950); A manic–depressive with short cycles. *J. ment. Sci.*, **96**, 293–297.

KLEIN, R., AND NUNN, R. F., (1945); A case of manic–depressive psychosis showing regular weekly cycles. *J. ment. Sci.*, **91**, 79–88.

KOCH, E., (1932); *Z. Kreisl.-Forsch.*, **24**, 251.

LEUSEN, I., AND LACROIX, E., (1961); Cardiac output and role of arterial pressoreceptors. *Arch. int. Pharmacodyn.*, **130**, 470–472.

RAY, B. S., AND STEWART, H. J., (1948); Glossopharyngeal nerve in carotid sinus reflex. *Surgery*, **23**, 411–424.

REES, L., (1953); Psychosomatic aspects of vagotomy. *J. ment. Sci.*, **99**, 505–512.

RUCH, T. G., AND SHENKIN, H. A., (1943); The relation of area 13 to hyperactivity in monkeys. *J. Neurophysiol.*, **6**, 349–360.

RYLANDER, G., (1939); *Personality Changes after Operations on the Frontal Lobes*. Copenhagen, Munksgaard.

SCHOU, M., (1963); Normothymotics, mood-normalizers: Are lithium and the imipramine drugs specific for affective disorders? *Brit. J. Psychiat.*, **109**, 803–809.

SCHWEITZER, A., AND WRIGHT, S., (1937); Stimulation of the central end of the vagus. *J. Physiol.*, **88**, 459–475.

SHEEHAN, D., MULHOLLAND, J. H., AND SHAFIROFF, B., (1941); Surgical anatomy of the carotid sinus nerve. *Anat. Rec.*, **8**, 431–442.

SHERMAN, I. C., AND BRODER, S. B., (1943); Dr. H. Douglas Singer's concept of the psychoses. *Arch. Neurol. Psychiat.*, **49**, 732.

STANLEY-JONES, D., (1955); Physiology of tremor and nystagmus: A kybernetic analysis. *J. nerv. ment. Dis.*, **122**, 518–523.

STANLEY-JONES, D., (1956a); Physiology of hemiplegia and athetosis. *J. nerv. ment. Dis.*, **123**, 452–456.

STANLEY-JONES, D., (1956b); Anatomy of rigidity and tremor. *J. nerv. ment. Dis.*, **124**, 163–166.

STANLEY-JONES, D., (1957a); The structure of emotion: Lust and rage. *Psychoanal. Rev.*, **44**, 289–297.

STANLEY-JONES, D., (1957b); The physical basis of anxiety. *J. nerv. ment. Dis.*, **125**, 247–258.

STANLEY-JONES, D., (1957c); The physiology of the Œdipus complex. *J. nerv. ment. Dis.*, **125**, 259–272.

STANLEY-JONES, D., AND K., (1957d); *Structural Psychology*. Bristol, John Wright.

STANLEY-JONES, D., (1958); The kybernetics of ocular movement. *Brit. J. Ophthal.*, **42**, 595–604.

STANLEY-JONES, D., AND K., (1960); *The Kybernetics of Natural Systems*. Oxford, Pergamon. Paris, Gauthier-Villars (*La Cybernétique des Êtres Vivants*).

STANLEY-JONES, D., (1964); The thermostatic theory of emotion (awaiting publication).

SZASZ, T. S., (1949a); Psychiatric aspects of vagotomy. *Psychosom. Med.*, **11**, 187–199.

SZASZ, T. S., (1949b); Phantom ulcer pain. *Arch. Neurol. Psychiat.*, **62**, 728–733.

UVNÄS, B., (1960); Sympathetic vasodilator system. *Physiol. Rev.*, **40**, Suppl., **4**, 69–80.

VON EULER, C., AND SÖDERBERG, U., (1952); Medullary chemosensitive receptors. *J. Physiol.*, **118**, 545–554.

Possibilités d'une Prothèse Sensorielle Acoustique par Stimulation Tactile*

J. M. SAMSÓ DIES

Vila Badó et Torres Gassó, Barcelona (Espagne)

CONSIDÉRATIONS NEUROPHYSIOLOGIQUES

Nous allons considérer schématiquement le cerveau, sous le point de vue de son fonctionnalisme opérationnel, comme un 'effecteur' disposant de certains éléments d'information, soit des 'entrées' et de quelques possibilités d' 'effets' ou de 'sorties' (constitués en dernier ressort, sous le point de vue objectif, par motricité).

L'intégration cérébrale supérieure est constituée sur cette boucle fondamentale sensorielle motrice, qui apporterait la plus simple possibilité de réponse déterminée ou automatique.

La quantité énorme de possibilités de réponse que le cerveau peut donner en face de cette réactivité élémentaire, nous a fourni l'existence des systèmes 'opérationnels, analytiques, intégrateurs', là où le renseignement sensoriel se rapporte d'une manière corrélative aux mécanismes de magasinage ou de mémorisation qui ont été réalisés et qui le sont à nouvelle reprise par l'information sensorielle. Ces mécanismes proviennent non seulement des événements 'effecteurs', mais aussi du résultat même de son 'effet' (possibilités de correction et d'apprentissage). Ainsi on peut prévoir la meilleure adéquation de la réponse à travers l'échelle temporelle.

Le but de l'ensemble est d'obtenir un nouveau équilibre ou sa persistance au dedans du système, vis à vis l'invertissement transitoire, en raison d'une nouvelle stimulation sensorielle.

Les systèmes auditifs et tactiles constituent des systèmes sensoriels extéroceptifs (le système tactile constitue aussi d'un système sensoriel intéroceptif), qui rendent information à l'effecteur, notamment le cerveau, pour le tactile, avec rapport à des événements physiques et physico-chimiques, auxquels ils se trouvent adaptés. Ces événements, tant qu'ils provoquent des réponses sensorielles, constituent des 'stimulations'.

Nous définissons comme éléments sensoriels les éléments organiques exerçant les fonctions de récepteurs sélectifs de qualités spécifiques d'énergie physique ou physico-chimique, en les transformant en impulsions nerveuses. Les éléments sensoriels

---

* Experimentation s'y référant.

auditifs ont été constitués des cellules de Corti, tandis que les éléments sensoriels tactiles ont été constitués des corpuscules de Meissner, ceux de Pacini et de Golgi, les petites terminaisons neurales ramifiées, les fuseaux neuromusculaires, etc.

La quantité minimum d'énergie du stimulant nécessaire à la réponse de l'élément sensoriel avec une impulsion nerveuse (la loi du 'tout ou rien' s'imposant à sa présence) constitue de l'énergie de seuil. Pour le système auditif, cette quantité minimum est comprise, à ce qu'il paraît, dans la valeur d'un cent millième d'Erg/cm² (à la fréquence la plus sensible, 2000 c/s). Pour le système tactile, elle se trouve comprise, semble-t-il, dans la valeur d'une centième à une millième d'Erg/cm².

Le pouvoir discriminatoire entre les deux sens, l'acoustique et le tactile, est très dissemblable. Dans l'acoustique peuvent être discernés plus de 1300 différenciations entre les 500 et les 1300 c/s (réponses à variation de 0,3 c/s), quoi qu'aux bouts extrêmes des échelles d'audition, ce pouvoir discriminatoire diminue nettement et dans celles-là 15–20 singularités entre les 500 c/s sont seulement différencielles.

Dans le tactile, le pouvoir discriminatoire est très variable, selon les secteurs de la peau et la concentration existante des éléments sensoriels, mais aux points les plus sensibles, p.e. aux doigts, on observe des variations de 3 à 4 dixièmes de la valeur de stimulation, tandis qu'aux régions peu sensibles, on a besoin de 4 à 5 fois de l'intensité de stimulation pour être à même de discriminer. Selon l'entraînement ces valeurs discriminatoires peuvent varier entre certaines limites, aussi bien dans le système auditif que dans le système tactile.

Les parcours nerveux sont intégrés par un axon d'un neurone bipolaire, situé dans le ganglion de Corti pour la sensibilité auditive et en T pour la sensibilité tactile dans les ganglions pinaux. La fibre efférente forme une connexion avec un neurone médullaire ou bulbaire, se trouvant en connexion avec un troisième neurone thalamique, par les deux voies, avant la projection des fibres sur ses aires corticales de réception primaire.

Toutes les deux voies sont formées par des fibres myéliniques (conduction rapide). A bloc et en tâche, le temps de réaction pour les deux sensibilités est pratiquement le même, notamment 1/10 sec. Les délais logiques se présentant dans la stimulation tactile, dûs au besoin de parcourir l'appel nerveux un chemin plus prolongé, semblent être compensés par le temps de réaction tari dans l'ouïe moyenne.

L'information nerveuse des deux voies comporte, en fait de données élémentaires: (a) une qualité (dépendante des éléments sensoriels d'où elles proviennent); (b) une durée temporale; (c) une intensité modulée en fonction des fréquences ou en nombre des éléments recrutés, et (d) une localisation spatiale.

Dès le dernier neurone thalamique, les fibres s'orientent par les voies auditives vers l'aire ecto-sylvienne et par les voies tactiles, vers la circonvolution pariétale ascendante. Il y a une représentation spatiale dans l'aire réceptive auditive primaire, en rapport avec les fréquences, et il y a une représentation spatiale dans l'aire réceptive tactile primaire, en rapport avec la topographie de distribution sur la surface corporelle des éléments tactiles ou somatotopiques.

Une représentation spatiale plus simple apparaît aussi pour les deux voies au niveau du relais neuronal thalamique.

L'aire réceptive auditive primaire reçoit l'information bilatérale. L'aire réceptive tactile primaire reçoit l'information latéralisée.

Les deux aires sont mises en rapport avec une seconde aire réceptive corticale dont l'information tactile est déjà de provenance bilatérale, et une troisième aire polysensorielle cérébrale a été détectée, par réceptivité provenant des voies auditives, des voies tactiles, et d'autres voies sensorielles.

La sensation unitaire du tacte est la résultante intégrée au cerveau des informations provenant des différents éléments sensoriels tactiles actifs. Tous ces éléments peuvent être excités par l'électricité.

Les deux voies sensorielles émettent des collatérales vers les formations réticulaires, étant à soupçonner dans l'imbrication de ces parcours une action identique ou similaire à l'égard de sa réaction alerte et de sa réaction inhibitoire.

De toutes ces considérations neurophysiologiques, quoique développées d'une façon schématique, il convient de faire ressortir quelques points singuliers, qui deviendront utiles à l'exposition de notre problème.

(1) Il y a une similarité entre le sens auditif et le sens tactile, quant au temps de réaction.

(2) Il y a une disparité en face des quantités d'énergie nécessaires pour provoquer la réactivité au milieu des éléments sensoriels.

(3) Il y une disparité quant au pouvoir de discrimination, moins accusée aux bouts extrêmes de la bande de fréquences audibles.

(4) Il y a une habituation dissemblable, moins accusée, alors que la stimulation tactile s'est réalisée par des impulsions électriques.

(5) Pour les deux sens une représentation spatiale dans les aires réceptives corticales primaires est similaire; pour l'acoustique à l'égard des tonalités; pour le tactile à l'égard de la somato-topographie des éléments sensoriels. L'organe de Corti a une localisation spatiale pour les tons.

Vu ces singularités, nous avons proposé d'étudier les possibilités qui peuvent s'offrir à une tentative de transposition sensorielle moyennant une prothèse électronique. En exerçant les fonctions analogues au système de Corti, cela transformerait les stimulations auditives en stimulations électriques pour agir sur le système tactile et de façon à transformer les stimulations tactiles en une variabilité de localisation spatiale et en une intensité dépendante d'une certaine manière des stimulations auditives et à étudier sur une préparation animale la conduite objective et relative, en face de cette transposition.

TRAVAIL EXPÉRIMENTAL FONDAMENTAL

Un chien sourd, auquel il a été appliqué un microphone avec un petit amplificateur, dont l'émission de courant de faible intensité est connectée, moyennant une électrode située sur la région de la peau, sourcilière, au cas où la provision d'aliments soit associée à une stimulation auditive, donc ce chien répondra avec une réaction d'alertation et de déplacement, en face d'une stimulation auditive malgré sa surdité.

Donné ce montage, le chien ne dispose d'aucune possibilité de discrimination, soit de manifester son comportement. Il répondra à un son quelconque, tant qu'il sera d'une intensité suffisante pour eveiller une pareille stimulation tactile. L'amplification employée agit comme un linteau du système utilisé.

Guidés par l'intention de donner à l'animal les possibilités pour discriminer les variations de la stimulation auditive et de manifester aussi le comportement y afférent, on a constitué un montage électronique d'alimentation indépendante (piles), d'un poids très léger et d'une dépense réduite, pour permettre ainsi une suffisante autonomie d'emploi, ainsi que la motilité volontaire de l'animal. Les amplificateurs transistorisés sont alimentés par des microphones de réplique ajustée. Un système de fixation garde les amplificateurs sur le dos, et les microphones sur la tête de l'animal (Fig. 1).

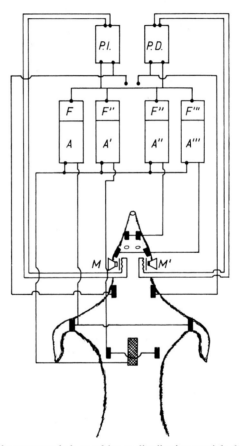

Fig. 1. Schéma général du montage de la prothèse et distribution spatiale du courant stimulateur sur la peau du chien.

Chaque microphone alimente, de manière indépendante, un élément préamplifi-cateur, duquel émergent deux sorties de signal: l'une s'adresse vers une électrode qu'on doit accommoder sur une région latérale de l'animal, homologue au côté correspondant au microphone alimenteur. Ces deux sorties sont unies par un circuit de contrôle de volume négatif, fonctionnant d'une telle manière que, tant qu'un

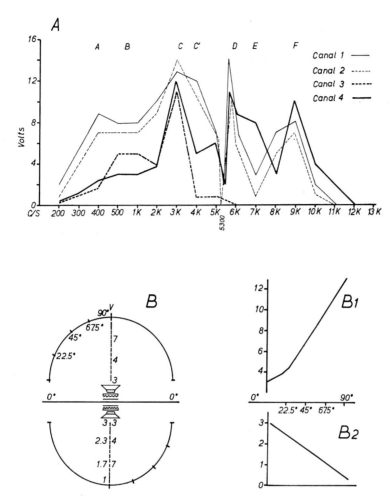

Fig. 2. Gain de la sortie (volts), au déplacement de la source sonore jusqu' à 90° (B₁), et (B₂), décrément de la sortie (volts) du microphone contralatéral avec le même déplacement de la source sonore. Disposition des sorties pour les électrodes latérales pour faciliter les réactions d'alerte et d'orientation du chien en rapport avec la situation spatiale de la source sonore.
(A) Degrés d'intensité d'issue des amplificateurs en relation avec les fréquences (même intensité d'entrée). a, b, c, c', d, e et f, points singuliers dans lesquels aux fréquences correspondantes de stimulation, le chien fait apprentissage des conduites différenciées avec différenciation ou discrimination des sons stimulants.

microphone présente une plus grande intensité de signal, le courant de sortie diminue aussi, ou bien empêche la sortie du signal de l'autre préamplificateur contrelatéral (Fig. 2 B). On a essayé de douer l'animal d'une stimulation tactile différentielle, pour ménager le sens d'orientation, puisque le même stimulant qu'agit latéralement avec des impacts d'intensités differentes dans un microphone ayant égard à l'autre, rendra un signal plus fort ou unique sur une zone de la peau latéralisée, avec une homologie relative à la situation spatiale de la source sonore, en rapport avec l'axe longitudinal de l'animal. Quand la source auditive se trouvera située dans un point proche ou bien sur la prolongation de l'axe longitudinal de l'animal, l'intensité de sortie du signal électrique sur les deux électrodes latéralisées, sera aussi la même.

L'autre sortie des préamplificateurs interconnectés, mêle le signal de deux microphones et alimente quatre amplificateurs de bande roulante, ainsi que des systèmes de filtration, qui peuvent, adaptés aux caractéristiques des microphones, couper un haut pourcentage des fréquences supérieures aux 500, 1.500 et 3.000 c/s, en laissant passer, sur un autre amplificateur des fréquences supérieures à ces dernières.

Sur un autre montage on a laissé des valeurs dissemblables sur chaque bande roulante de fréquences, et une fois obtenues les courbes y référentes, on a cherché des points singuliers convenables, pour y adapter les sons de stimulation (Fig. 2 A).

Les sorties correspondantes à chaque amplificateur aboutissent à des paires d'électrodes qu'on place sur des endroits homologues, mais topographiquement bien différenciés, sur la peau de l'animal (Fig. 1).

Or, chaque paire d'électrodes produit du courant, donc une stimulation tactile en rapport avec les fréquences du son; il s'ensuit que ce son a une certaine distribution spatiale à l'égard de la peau de l'animal et en fonction des fréquences y intégrées.

Les degrés d'intensité d'issue des amplificateurs suivent à peu près une fonction logarithmique en relation avec l'incrément d'intensité du signal au microphone. Avec la même intensité que la source auditive, l'intensité de sortie des amplificateurs suit aussi une fonction logarithmique en relation avec la distance de cette source. On ne doit passer des intensités nociceptives.

L'intensité de sortie des amplificateurs vis-à-vis d'une intensité du signal —10 db (signal auditif) ou bien 0.5 V, appliqué avec entrée directe (réponse au maximum), est de 30 mA à 20 V.

La réponse du courant sorti des préamplificateurs (alimentateurs des électrodes pour l'orientation spatiale) a une fréquence unique de 400 c/s avec morphologie de pointes peu aiguës et les réponses de sortie sont de 30 mA, 20 V au maximum.

La morphologie des signaux qui sortent des amplificateurs correspond à des crêtes très aiguës dans une phase et à des petites pointes arrondies dans l'autre phase. Par rapport à des entrées de signal de 0.5 V à 2 V, elles maintiennent les sorties au maximum d'intensité. Un voltage supérieur à l'entrée qui actionne avec saturation des amplificateurs, maintient la même intensité à maxima de sortie, mais avec une haute distorsion.

Dans l'équipe qui vient d'être décrite, les impédances de sortie des amplificateurs et des préamplificateurs pour la connexion des électrodes, ont une valeur de 100 Ω.

TRAITEMENT EXPÉRIMENTAL

Il y a deux espèces d'animaux qui sont employées pour cette expérimentation: (a) des chiens qui par operation préalable ont subi la coagulation des organes de Corti bilatéraux et qui, en conséquence, sont affectés d'une surdité absolue, (b) des chiens avec l'ouïe normale, lesquels, après les avoir faits la prothèse susdite, seront intervenus à l'objet de les provoquer une complète surdité.

Le contrôle de la surdité provoquée par l'intervention, se réalise durant le méme acte opératoire et pendant l'anesthésie au moyen de s'assurer sur le défaut des complexes K dans l'EEG du chien devant la stimulation auditive.

Après une période post-opératoire assez prolongée, nécessaire pour adapter l'animal à sa nouvelle condition sensorielle déficitaire, on lui applique la prothèse susdite et on réalise un traitement d'apprentissage uniquement conditionné à la stimulation tactile, laquelle, par le mécanisme de la prothèse, est dépendante des signaux auditifs.

Le comportement primaire de l'animal consiste à localiser les endroits stimulants

Fig. 3. Réaction d'alerte d'un chien sourd par appel acoustique avec la prothèse décrite.

References p. 178

et elle tâche de s'en délivrer au moyen de gratter, de lécher ou de mordre. Une fois cette période finie, l'animal, en apprenant un son, subit une réaction de mise en alerte, car toujours il y a eu une association entre un bruit et une ingestion d'aliments (Fig. 3).

Durant des expériences postérieures accomplies dans des lieux qui ne sont pas sonores, on stimule les chiens avec des sons purs dont la génération est produite par des appareils oscillatoires de basses fréquences, en combinant des fréquences simultanées de stimulation que forment des points bien différenciés dans les courbes de réponse, avec des fréquences des canaux de stimulation employés. De cette façon, l'animal arrive à différencier des conduites diverses.

Dans un autre protocole expérimental, lequel est encore en voie d'exécution, la prothèse électronique s'applique initialement à l'animal avec l'ouïe normale. Chaque stimulant auditif significatif produit simultanément une stimulation physiologique auditive et une stimulation tactile dépendante de cette stimulation physiologique, moyennant l'emploi de la prothèse; de cette façon on tâche de faciliter l'apprentissage avec l'association, pendant quelque temps, de deux voies stimulées, et on tâche également de faire un transfert de l'information auditive à l'information tactile au moyen de leur simultanéité répétée, en donnant la même signification aux stimulants, dans le but d'observer après, lorsque le chien sera devenu tout à fait sourd, si les patterns de conduite persistent, déchaînés uniquement par la voie tactile laquelle restera dépendante de celle qui est auditive à travers de la prothèse.

Encore en voie de réalisation, nous pouvons tirer de cette expérimentation, les considérations suivantes: (1) Aucun problème ne 'sest présenté en relation avec les temps de réaction, fait déjà prévu, car dans le bref aperçu neurophysiologique on a déjà dit que, pour les voies auditives, c'était la même chose que pour les voies sensitives et aucun retard appréciable n'a été remarqué par l'emploi de la prothèse; (2) On peut présumer qu'une représentation spatiale corticale par fonction des fréquences, propre de l'aire réceptive auditive primaire, s'accomplisse aussi, quoique fragmentairement, dans l'aire réceptive primaire somato-esthétique, puisque chaque groupement de fréquences avec quelque différenciation parmi elles, au moyen de la prothèse, a sa correspondance de stimulations d'ordre préférable sur certaines aires de la peau, d'une manière bilatérale et homologue à l'aire où l'on a placé les électrodes. En faisant de la stimulation tactile de façon bilatérale et sur des zones homologues, on a essayé de compenser le déficit de la représentation corticale tactile, laquelle est unilatérale, en opposition avec la représentation corticale auditive, laquelle est bilatérale; (3) Aucun problème ne s'est présenté en relation avec les différences des énergies liminaires nécessaires pour la stimulation auditive et tactile. L'amplification qu'on a employée compense la différence physiologique et même elle peut l'augmenter; (4) Devant le problème de la disparité énorme de la faculté de discernement des différences de stimulus qu'on trouve entre le sens auditif et le sens tactile (car il faut se rendre compte qu'avec ces expérimentations on n'a pas obtenu autre chose, jusqu'au moment présent, qu'un nombre très réduit de comportements différents), la seule voie qu'on peut envisager pour des nouvelles expériences est la possibilité de rendre plus complexe le dispositif électronique au moyen de nouveaux canaux que fourniraient le plus grand nombre possible de bandes de fréquences différenciées et, par conséquent, avec

la possibilité de stimuler aussi un plus grand nombre d'aires tactiles également différenciées; (5) Etant donné que l'accroissement d'intensité du stimulant auditif, quand
il arrive aux microphones du prothèse, est suivi à travers des amplificateurs par un
accroissement jusqu'à un certain point logarithmique des intensités de stimulation
tactile, on prévoit encore une possibilité de plus d'amplifier le pouvoir de différenciation, car l'augmentation d'intensité du courant de stimulation tactile renferme un
plus grand nombre et une majeure profondeur d'éléments tactiles stimulés (recrute-
ment d'éléments sensoriels) ce qui conduit, en définitive, à une nouvelle modification
topographique par rapport à la représentation corticale de l'aire réceptive tactile
primaire; (6) C'est à prévoir pour les processus d'expérimentation qui sont en train
de se faire, que la complexité d'information emmagasinée antérieurement dans le
cerveau des animaux auxquels la prothèse a été employée durant des périodes d'ouïe
normale, que la valeur de discernement puisse augmenter, puisqu'il est possible
qu'ils soient mises en marche, patterns neuronales plus complexes, déchaînés par la
stimulation tactile moyennant la prothèse que fournira simplement des patterns
fragmentaires mais de création simultanée pendant les périodes d'apprentissage.

Le point de vue final de cette étude est d'arriver à la déduction des possibilités
d'application des prothèses pareilles à l'être humain affecté de surdité périphérique,
parce qu'avec cette prothèse on envisage comme possible la connection du sourd avec
un système qui le renseignera, quoique de manière fragmentaire, du niveau auditif ou
d'un signal non habituel dans l'ambiance, permettant de lui donner au moins, la
possibilité d'une réaction d'avis ou d'alerte par rapport au son ou au bruit, malgré sa
surdité, afin de lui faciliter la mise en activité d'autres systèmes sensoriels non altérés.

D'autre part, pour les déficits d'intégration au langage ou bien pour faciliter son
apprentissage bucal, on prévoit aussi l'utilisation de prothèses pareilles à la ci-dessus
décrite, qui permettront de fournir par son moyen un feedback lequel, malgré que
fragmentairement, pourvoira à l'individu totalement sourd, une indication en fonction
avec l'émission de sons que lui-même émette, en lui donnant en conséquent, un
contrôle d'emission et une facilité pour la nuancer.

SUMMARY

Electronic systems have been set up provided with two microphones with outlets
specially installed to facilitate alerting and spacial guidance as well as with independent outlets of weak current to be topographically distributed over the skin, always
in the same areas. These outlets come from amplifiers independently fitted with
frequency filter systems so that each frequency or specific range of frequencies can
act on a concrete topographical distribution, which should always be the same. The
intensity and distribution of the outlets of such amplifiers are elementary transfer
functions as regards the stimulating sounds that have action on the microphones.

This set up is applied on dogs which have been previously deafened through
coagulation of the organs of Corti, likewise on normal dogs after their having had a few
days' adaptation with the prosthesis, suffering an operation to cause deafness in them.

Comparative studies are made on the behaviour of such dogs to significant audio

References p. 178

signals, transformed into electric signals which provoke tact stimulation, by means of the electronic device described which provides a topographical or spacial distribution of the tact signals as a function of the frequency of sounds, in order to facilitate and achieve their discrimination.

After the theoretical neurophysiological checking of the differentials and similarities of the audio and tact senses, and of the procedures of cerebral analysis and integration regarding same, the possibilities of a similar prothesis are pointed at, even if more complex, to provide deaf persons with a possibility of information through tact as a function of sound (its quality and its intensity).

Another deduction is the possibility of this protesis in the procedure of training deaf children or children with a serious disturbance of their audio reception, providing an information that may allow the control of their own emission of sounds, in such a way facilitating the correct phonetic integration of their language.

Through generalisation the possibilities of similar systems are extrapolated for compensating deficits in information in cases of neurology diseases affecting sense or transmission systems and which are liable to be replaced by other sense routes which have not been affected, thus providing new channels for giving the brain new possibilities of action in connection with and in spite of the affected systems.

REFERENCES

ADAMCZYK, A., (1960); Med. Cibernetica. *Proceedings of the Ist. Iinternational Congress on Cybernetic Medicine, Napoli*, pp. 185–195.

CHAUCHARD, P., (1960); *Le cerveau et la conscience*. Du Seuil, Paris.

GRANIT, R., (1955); *Receptors and sensory perception*. Yale University Press.

GALAMBOS, R., (1954); Neural mechanisms of audition. *Physiol. Rev.*, **34**, 497–528.

GALAMBOS, R., AND DAVIS, H., (1943); The responses of single auditory nerve fibers to acoustic stimulation. *J. Neurophysiol.*, **6**, 39–57.

HAGEN, E., KNOCHE, H., SINCLAIR, D. C., AND WEDDELL, G., (1953); The role of specialised nerve terminals in cutaneous sensibility. *Proc. Roy. Soc.*, **141**, 279–287.

HOBER, R., (1941); *Fisiologia Humana*. Labor, Barcelona.

HURST, J. B., (1939); Conduction velocity and diameter of nerve fibers. *Amer. J. Physiol.*, **127**, 132–139.

IVANOV-SMOLENKI, (1955); *Esbozos sobre la patofisiologia de la actividad nerviosa superior*. University of Buenos Aires Press.

LABORIT, H., (1961); *Physiologie Humaine cellulaire et organique*. Masson, Paris.

MORIN, G., (1962); *Physiologie du Système Nerveux central*. Masson, Paris.

PENFIELD, W., AND RASMUSSEN, T., (1950); *The cerebral cortex of man*. Macmillan.

SAMSO DIES, J. M., VILA BADO, AND TORRES CASSO, (1958); Problemas del lenguaje del niño. La audio-EEG. *Med. Clin.*, **30**, 185–195.

SAMSO DIES, J. M., (1962); Aspectos ciberneticos en neurologia. Leccion II. *Curso cibernetica Medica*. Academia Ciencias Medicas Barcelona.

STARK, L., AND HERMANN, H., (1961); The transfer function of a photoreceptor organ. *Kibernetik*, **1**, 124–129.

TENTURI, A. R., (1944); Audio frequency localization in acoustic cortex of dog. *Amer. J. Physiol.*, **141**, 397.

WALSH, G., (1961); *Fisiologia sistema nervioso*. Buenos Aires.

WEDDELL, G., (1941); The pattern of cutaneous innervation in relation to cutaneous sensibility. *J. Anat.*, **75**, 346–367.

WIENER, N., (1961); *Cybernetics or control and communication in the animal and the machine*. The M.I.T. Press, New York.

WIENER, N., (1962); *Posibilidades de protesis ciberneticas*. Conferencia Instituto Estudios Norteamericano. Barcelona.

Überraschungswert und Auffälligkeit

HELMAR G. FRANK

Institut für Kybernetik an der Pädagogischen Hochschule Berlin,
Berlin-West (Deutschland)

INHALT

1. EINORDNUNG DES THEMAS IN DIE KYBERNETISCHE GESAMTPROBLEMATIK

a. Die Kybernetik in Deutschland

Die Kybernetik hat wie in manchen anderen Ländern auch in Deutschland eine Vorgeschichte, die noch vor dem Erscheinen des epochemachenden Werkes von Norbert Wiener (1948) begann. Sie wird zweifellos ein erregendes Kapitel einer noch zu schreibenden Wissenschaftsgeschichte liefern. Die wichtigste Rolle dürfte dabei in Deutschland wohl dem Regelungstechniker Hermann Schmidt zuzuschreiben sein, der schon zu Beginn der vierziger Jahre in enger Fühlungnahme mit Biologen eine 'allgemeine Regelungskunde' (später, 1962, vom ihm 'Regelkreislehre' oder auch 'Theorie der Kreisrelationen' genannt) konzipiert hatte, die 'sich über die Technik hinaus an den Physiologen wendet' und die 'mathematische Darstellung der allgemein gültigen Gesetze des Regelkreises' anstrebte, um zu ermöglichen, Einzelfälle 'durch Unterordnung unter die Grundaufgabe der allgemeinen Regelungskunde nach deren Lösungsregeln zu bearbeiten' (Schmidt, 1941, S. 8 und 12).

Trotz dieser Vorbereitung dauerte es relativ lange, bis sich das Wort 'Kybernetik' in der deutschen Fachwelt einbürgerte, und auch heute noch, 15 Jahre nach dem Erscheinen der 'Cybernetics', sind die Beziehungen zwischen den drei hierzulande an der Kybernetik hauptsächlich interessierten Gruppen nicht sehr eng. Unter den sogenannten 'Geisteswissenschaftlern' waren es zunächst Max Bense (1951), Wolfgang Meyer-Eppler (1959) und deren Schüler, die das Wort 'Kybernetik' im Zusammenhang mit ihrer Arbeit verwendeten. Diese Gruppe begründete 1960 auch die erste deutschsprachige Zeitschrift für Kybernetik, die 'Grundlagenstndien aus Kybernetik und Geisteswissenschaft'. Bei den Biologen dürfte die von Bernhard Hassenstein (1960) und Werner Reichardt gemeinsam begründete 'Forschungsgruppe Kybernetik' diese Bezeichnung verbreitet haben. Erst in jüngster Zeit bürgert sie sich unter dem Einfluss der Forschungsgruppen von Karl Küpfmüller und Karl Steinbuch (Steinbuch, 1963) in stärkerem Masse auch bei den Ingenieuren ein. Da zwischen diesen drei Lagern keine ausreichende Uebereinstimmung über den Begriff 'Kybernetik' besteht, und dieser ausserhalb von Deutschland kaum weniger schillert, bedarf die Einordnung unseres Themas in den Problemkreis der Kybernetik einer Rechtfertigung.

b. Unterscheidung zwischen allgemeiner Kybernetik und regionalen Kybernetiken

Nach der ursprünglichen Konzeption von Norbert Wiener (1948) ist die Kybernetik eine allgemeine Theorie über die Aufnahme, Verarbeitung und Übertragung von Nachrichten durch Systeme, von deren konkreter Beschaffenheit abstrahiert wird: sie könnten ebensowohl physikalisch wie physiologisch wie psychologisch* am angemessensten zu kennzeichnen sein. Hinsichtlich der Anwendbarkeit der Kybernetik auf psychologisch zu kennzeichnende Systeme, insbesondere auf die menschliche Gesellschaft, äussert sich Wiener auf den letzten Seiten der 'Cybernetics' am wenigsten

---

* Dass wir hier aus der Doppeldeutigkeit des kybernetischen Systems bei Wiener (Maschine *oder* Lebewesen) eine Dreideutigkeit machen, hat keine metaphysischen sondern lediglich methodologische Hintergründe. Auch wenn für *praktische Zwecke* die Kenntnis der funktionalen Zuordnungsgesetze von Reaktionen zu Reizen ausreicht und der Behaviourist sie vollständig finden könnte, und obwohl überdies *im Prinzip* alle Information über die zwischen Reiz und Reaktion verlaufenden Prozesse im 'System Mensch' in den Objekten der Neurophysiologie stecken dürfte, *empfiehlt* sich die (direkte oder indirekte) Verwendung der Introspektion als kennzeichnendes Erkenntnismittel der Psychologie. Denn wegen der Verquickung von Beobachtungsprozess und Beobachtungsgegenstand ist diese Informationsübermittlung zwar gestört, aber die Transinformation ist nicht gleich Null! Im übrigen postulieren unsere *drei* Aspekte des kybernetischen Systems ebensowenig eine 'Seele', wie Wieners *zwei* Aspekte eine 'Entelechie'.

optimistisch. An eine *Anwendung*, also an eine *Aufhebung der Abstraktion*, war also von vornherein gedacht, und der heute übliche Sprachgebrauch rechnet demgemäss zur Kybernetik auch die Theorie kybernetischer Geräte, die Biokybernetik (Wiener und Schadé, 1963) und sogar die kybernetische Pädagogik (Frank, 1962a, 1963a) obwohl diese Disziplinen sehr wohl die physikalische bzw. physiologische bzw. psychologische Bestimmbarkeit ihrer Gegenstände berücksichtigen. Daher möge die abstrakte Kybernetik im Sinne Wieners hier als 'allgemeine' (oder 'formale') Kybernetik bezeichnet werden. Nach dem Gesagten kann sich die allgemeine Kybernetik in drei Bereichen konkretisieren: im Bereich der Ingenieurwissenschaften, der Biologie und der sogenannten Geisteswissenschaften. Das führt zu drei 'materialen' (oder 'regionalen') Kybernetiken: der Ingenieurkybernetik, der Biokybernetik und der Informationswissenschaft (Fig. 1).

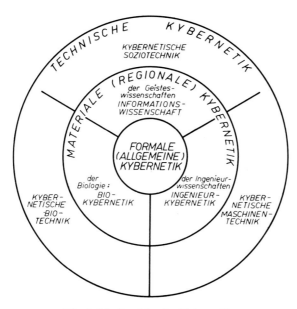

Fig. 1. Die Bereiche der Kybernetik.

Aber auch die Zufügung der drei regionalen Kybernetiken erreicht noch nicht die Grenze des heute üblichen Kybernetik-Begriffs, denn die Kybernetik ist nicht auf die Ebene der Reflexion beschränkt, sondern betrifft auch die Ebene der Tat. Im Begriff der Kybernetik steckt also eine Zweideutigkeit zwischen Theorie und Verwirklichung, d.h. zwischen Wissenschaft und Technik im allgemeinen Wortsinn, demnach Technik der Einsatz verfügbarer Mittel zur Erreichung gesetzter Ziele ist. In Fig. 1 wurde daher jeder regionalen Kybernetik ein entsprechender technischer Bereich angefügt, um so einerseits zu einem, gemessen am üblichen Sprachgebrauch, genügend weiten Kybernetik-Begriff zu kommen, und andererseits eine Unterteilung zu erhalten, die wenigstens für eine erste Orientierung ausreicht.

c. Die vier Stufen der allgemeinen (formalen) Kybernetik

Da sich die allgemeine Kybernetik mit informationsaufnehmenden, -verarbeitenden und -übertragenden (kurz: informationellen) Systemen schlechthin beschäftigt, liegt eine Unterteilung in vier aufeinander aufbauende Disziplinen nahe (Fig. 2):

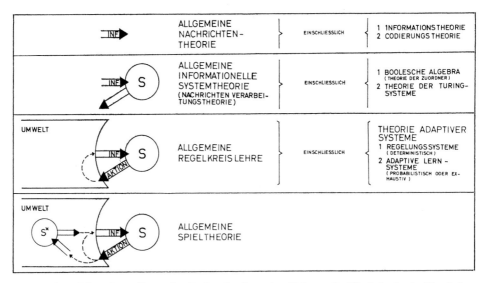

Fig. 2. Die aufeinander aufbauenden Stufen der formalen Kybernetik. Für jede der in Fig. 1 dargestellten materialen Kybernetiken gilt dieselbe Stufeneinteilung*.

(1) Die allgemeine Nachrichtentheorie, einschliesslich Zeichen-, Informations- und Codierungstheorie, beschäftigt sich überhaupt noch nicht mit den informationellen Systemen, sondern zunächst nur mit denNachrichten selbst. Die Informationstheorie beschäftigt sich mit dem Informationsgehalt, die Codierungstheorie mit der Struktur von Nachrichten.

(2) *Die allgemeine Nachrichtenverarbeitungstheorie* (oder informationelle System-theorie) betrachtet im einfachsten Falle die informationellen Systeme als Zuordner (Steinbuch, 1959), die entsprechend dem Funktionsbegriff der Mathematik jedem Eingangselement (z.B. '8 × 3 = ?') aus einem zugelassenen Repertoire (im gegebenen Beispiel: dem kleinen Einmaleins) eindeutig ein Ausgangselement ('24') zuordnen. In diesem Zusammenhang gehört insbesondere die Boolesche Algebra. Im komplizierteren Falle (der in der Realisierung meist ökonomischer ist!) erfolgt die Zuordnung des Ausgangswerts zum Eingangswert (z.B. 8 × 357 = ?') nicht momentan, vielmehr durchläuft das System ein zu untersuchendes Kontinuum oder eine endliche Folge von Zwischenzuständen. (Dazu treten übrigens im *Innern* des Systems in der Regel schon Kreisrelationen auf.)

---

* Eine feinere Einteilung insbesondere der 4. Stufe wurde vorgenommen in H. Frank, Kybernetische Analysen subjektiver Sachverhalte, Schnelle Quickborn, 1964, S. 49.

Die Theorie der Turing-Systeme behandelt solche Prozesse. In jedem Falle sieht die allgemeine, informationelle Systemtheorie (Nachrichten-verarbeitungstheorie) noch von Rückwirkungen der *Umwelt* der informationellen Systeme ab.

(3) *Die allgemeine Regelkreislehre* (die Theorie allgemeiner Kreisrelationen im Sinne von Hermann Schmidt, 1962) interessiert sich dafür, wie sich infolge eines Ausgangswerts eines informationellen Systems dessen Umwelt und damit die künftigen Eingangswerte ändern. Den wichtigsten Gegenstand dieser Theorie bilden die Anpassungssysteme (adaptive Systeme). Diese sind zu Regelungssysteme und adaptive Lernsysteme. Ein Regelungssystem, beispielsweise ein Thermostat bei der Kontrolle der Raumtemperatur, sieht in einem gewissen Sinne voraus, wie oder zumindest mit welchem Vorzeichen sich ein beobachteter Umweltparameter, z.B. die Raumtemperatur, infolge einer infinitesimalen oder zumindest kleinstmöglichen Änderung des Ausgangswertes, im Beispiel also der Einstellung der Heizleistung, ändern wird. Demgemäss strebt ein Regelungssystem in einer im Prinzip deterministischen Weise dem Soll-Wert zu. Demgegenüber sieht ein adaptives Lernsystem, etwa eine Ratte im Labyrinth, nicht voraus, durch welchen Ausgangswert, d.h. durch welches Momentanverhalten es dem Ziel näher kommt und durch welches es sich im Gegenteil von ihm entfernt. Ein solches System erreicht sein Ziel durch Versuch und Irrtum, also im Prinzip probabilistisch oder in Ausnahmefällen exhaustiv (d.h. durch systematisches Durchprobieren sämtlicher Möglichkeiten). In jedem Falle ist für die allgemeine Regelkreislehre die Umwelt des informationellen Systems passiv, d.h. diese enthält nicht selbst wieder adaptive Systeme.

(4) *Die allgemeine Spieltheorie* interessiert sich für die verschiedenen möglichen Entwicklungen, die sich bei einem adaptiven System in einer Umwelt, die mindestens ein weiteres adaptives System enthält, ergeben können, und zwar als Funktion der von den beteiligten adaptiven Systemen gewählten Strategien. Die allgemeine Spieltheorie nimmt also die Stufe höchster Komplexität innerhalb der allgemeinen Kybernetik ein. Die mathematische Theorie der Spiele von Von Neumann (1928), ist nur ein Teilgebiet dieser 'allgemeinen Spieltheorie', da letztere weder auf Spiele noch auf nur zwei Partner noch auf den Fall der Unverträglichkeit der Zielsetzungen der beteiligten Systeme beschränkt sein soll. Statt 'allgemeine Spieltheorie' sollte deshalb besser ein völlig unmissverständlicher neuer Ausdruck geprägt werden, z.B. 'allgemeine Systemkomplextheorie' oder 'Oligologie'.*

d. Einordnung unseres Problemkomplexes

Im folgenden zweiten Teil dieser Arbeit wird auf den Ebenen der allgemeinen Nachrichtentheorie und der allgemeinen informationellen Systemtheorie versucht, neben dem Informationsgehalt noch weitere Aspekte der Nachricht messbar zu machen. Der dritte Teil liefert experimentelle Bestätigungen für die Zweckdienlichkeit dieser

---

* Die Konkretisierung dieser Stufe der Kybernetik enthält insbesondere die kybernetische Pädagogik, die Organisationskybernetik und die cybernétique Ampères, d.h. die 'Lehre von den möglichen Verfahrensweisen beim Regieren'.

Masse im Bereich der Informationswissenschaft, insbesondere der Informationspsychologie. Im Anschluss daran wird versucht, aus diesen empirischen Befunden
einige kreisrelationale und sogar systemkomplextheoretische ('spieltheoretische')
Folgerungen für den informationswissenschaftlichen Bereich zu ziehen. Da wir den
biokybernetischen Hintergrund aller informationswissenschaftlichen Erscheinungen
nicht leugnen, werden im Schlussteil einige sich an Gedankengänge von Wiener (1948)
anlehnende biokybernetische Hypothesen vorgeschlagen, welche die informationspsychologischen Befunde erklären würden. Die gesamte Untersuchung bleibt also im
Rahmen der wissenschaftlichen Kybernetik, wie wir sie anhand von Bild 1 zu um-
reissen suchten.

2. DAS SHANNONSCHE INFORMATIONSMASS UND DIE DARAUF AUFGEBAUTEN MASSE DES ÜBERRASCHUNGSWERTS UND DER AUFFÄLLIGKEIT

a. Feld und Superierung

Eine Situation kann ein sogenanntes 'endliches Möglichkeits-Feld' Z festlegen, wenn
in dieser Situation genau *ein* beliebiges von endlich vielen (nämlich u(Z)) möglichen
Ereignissen (bzw. Zeichen oder Nachrichten) erwartet werden kann, und zwar jedes
mit einer bestimmten Wahrscheinlichkeit $p(z_k) = p_k$, so dass

$$\sum_{k=1}^{u(Z)} p(z_k) = 1. \tag{1}$$

Die Menge $\{z_k\}$ heisst Repertoire von Z, die geordnete Menge der zugehörigen
Wahrscheinlichkeiten heisst Wahrscheinlichkeitsverteilung von Z. Das Feld ist damit
gegeben durch das Schema

$$Z \equiv \begin{pmatrix} z_1\, z_2\, \ldots\, z_u \\ p_1\, p_2\, \ldots\, p_u \end{pmatrix}.$$

Beim Roulettspiel kann interessieren, in welches von u(R) = 37 Fächern die Kugel
nach der nächsten Drehung fällt. In dieser Situation ergibt sich das Feld

$$R \equiv \begin{pmatrix} 0 & 1 & 2 & \ldots & 36 \\ \dfrac{1}{37} & \dfrac{1}{37} & \dfrac{1}{37} & \ldots & \dfrac{1}{37} \end{pmatrix}.$$

In einer anderen Situation möge eine Entscheidung durch den Wurf einer so stark
deformierten Münze herbeigeführt werden, dass nur mit der Wahrscheinlichkeit
1/37 'Kopf' zu erwarten ist. Das so festgelegte Feld lautet:

$$W \equiv \begin{pmatrix} Kopf & Wappen \\ \dfrac{1}{37} & \dfrac{36}{37} \end{pmatrix}, \text{ mit } u(W) = 2.$$

Die sogenannte 'Superierung' (der 'Birkhoffsche Uebergang'; vgl. Frank, 1959, S.40)
führt zu einer veränderten Situation, die sich in einer Aenderung des Repertoires
bestehender Möglichkeiten und damit in einer Feldänderung ausdrückt. Es ist zu

unterscheiden zwischen der Superierung durch Klassenbildung und der Superierung durch Komplexbildung. Eine Superierung durch Klassenbildung vollzieht z.B. ein Spieler, der auf Zéro setzt und sich nur noch für eine von *zwei* Nachrichten interessiert: 'Das Resultat ist Zéro!' oder: 'Das Resultat ist nicht Zéro!' Das superierte Feld ist

$$R^* \equiv \begin{pmatrix} O & \text{nicht } 0 \\ \dfrac{1}{37} & \dfrac{36}{37} \end{pmatrix}.$$

Eine Superierung durch Komplexbildung entspricht z.B. der Situation, in welcher das Roulettergebnis und zugleich das Ergebnis eines Münzenwurfs interessiert. Das superierte Feld ist hier das Produktfeld RW mit Ereignis*paaren* als Elementen des Repertoires. Soweit die Teilereignisse voneinander unabhängig sind, liefert das Produkt ihrer Wahrscheinlichkeiten die Wahrscheinlichkeit der entsprechenden Elemente des superierten Repertoires:

$$RW \equiv \begin{pmatrix} (O; \text{Kopf}) & (0; \text{Wappen}) & \ldots & (36; \text{Wappen}) \\ \dfrac{1}{1369} & \dfrac{36}{1369} & \cdots & \dfrac{36}{1369} \end{pmatrix}.$$

b. Information und Unsicherheit

Die mathematische Informationstheorie schreibt der Nachricht, im Felde Z sei das Ereignis z_k eingetreten, bzw. diesem Ereignis selbst, einen Gehalt an Information zu. Man kann leicht zeigen, dass nur das im Prinzip auf Shannon (1948) zurückgehende Informationsmass

$$i(z_k) = {}^2\!\log \frac{1}{p(z_k)} \equiv \text{ld} \frac{1}{p(z_k)} \tag{2}$$

folgende vier Bedingungen erfüllt (Luce, 1960 S. 23 f.):

(1) Falls die Ereignisse r_m, w_n zweier Felder R und W voneinander unabhängig sind, gilt

$$i(r_m; w_n) = i(r_m) + i(w_n).$$

(2) $i(z_k)$ ist eine Funktion der einzigen Variablen $p(z_k)$.

(3) $i(z_k)$ ist eine stetige Funktion von $p(z_k)$.

(4) $i(z_k) = 1$, falls $p(z_k) = \frac{1}{2}$.

Durch die erste Bedingung wird die Information eine blosse Zahl, wobei von der Struktur der Nachricht abstrahiert wird (so wie für die Masse die Struktur eines Stücks Materie irrelevant ist). Durch die zweite Bedingung erhält die Nachricht 'Das Resultat ist 17!' im Felde R dieselbe Information wie im Felde W die Nachricht: 'Das Resultat ist Kopf!', obgleich diese letztere Nachricht eine ungleich viel grössere Überraschung auslöst; die Information misst also nicht unmittelbar den Überraschungswert einer Nachricht. Die dritte Bedingung lässt gebrochene und sogar irrationale Informationswerte zu; die Information gibt also nicht (unmittelbar) an, durch wieviel binäre Codezeichen eine Nachricht (ein Ereignis) ökonomisch zu verschlüsseln ist. Die vierte Bedingung dagegen ist nicht einschneidend: sie legt nur die Masseinheit (das 'bit') fest.

Der Erwartungswert der Information bei gegebenem Feld Z (auch 'mittlere Information' oder — etwas unglücklich — 'Entropie' genannt), nämlich

$$H(Z) = \sum_{k=1}^{u(Z)} p(z_k) \cdot ld \frac{1}{p(z_k)}, \tag{3}$$

steigt bei konstantem Repertoireumfang u(Z), wenn sich die Wahrscheinlichkeitsverteilung einer Gleichverteilung annähert. Herrscht jeweils Gleichverteilung, dann ist H(Z) desto grösser, je grösser u(Z) ist. H(Z) ist daher ein geeignetes Mass für die *Unsicherheit* in der gegebenen Situation, die das Feld festlegt. Beim Feld W ist die Unsicherheit gering, $H(W) \approx 0.179$ bit. Sie erreicht 1 bit, sobald 'Kopf' und 'Wappen' gleichwahrscheinlich sind. Noch grösser ist sie beim Felde R: $H(R) \approx 5,209$ bit.

c. Überraschungswert

Nun wird verständlich, weshalb trotz gleicher Information (5,209 bit) das Ereignis 'Rouletteergebnis 17' im Felde R weniger überrascht als im Felde W das Ereignis 'Kopf ist gefallen': dort entsprach die Information genau ihrem Erwartungswert, während sie diesen im zweiten Falle um ein Vielfaches übertrifft. Wir definieren daher als Überraschungswert einer Nachricht (eines Ereignisses, Zeichens etc.) das Verhältnis ihrer Information zu der durch diese beseitigten Unsicherheit:

$$ü(z_k) = \frac{i(Z_k)}{H(Z)}. \tag{4}$$

Im Felde R hat also jedes mögliche Ereignis den Überraschungswert ü = 1. Im Felde W hat das Ereignis 'Kopf ist gefallen' den Überraschungswert 29,1, das gegenteilige Ereignis nur den Ueberraschungswert 0,22. Der Ueberraschungswert 1 stellt den neutralen Punkt dar: was darüber liegt, wirkt überraschend, was darunter liegt, wirkt banal. (Durch Logarithmieren von ü erhält man ein Mass, das diesen Unterschied schon im Vorzeichen ausdrückt).

Dieselbe Nachricht 'Zéro!' mit *derselben* Information 5,209 bit hat im Felde R den Überraschungswert 1, im Felde R* den Überraschungswert 29,1, gemäss der durch die Superierung bewirkten kleineren Unsicherheit. Denn die Superierung durch Klassenbildung verringert die Information wenigstens einiger der ursprünglichen Ereignisse ohne andererseits irgendeinen Informationswert zu vergrössern, so dass der Erwartungswert der Information, d.h. die Unsicherheit verringert wird. Die Superierung durch Komplexbildung verringert den Erwartungswert der Gesamtinformation oder lässt ihn im Grenzfall der Unabhängigkeit der Teilfelder unverändert, gemäss der bekannten Formel

$$H (XY) \leqq H (X) + H (Y). \tag{5}$$

In unserem Beispiel ist also H (RW) = H (R) + H (W). Dagegen ist die Unsicherheit über Muttersprache und Staatsangehörigkeit eines Europäers kleiner als die Summe der Unsicherheiten über jedes einzelne dieser beiden Merkmale.

d. Übertragung auf Folgen

Tritt die das Feld Z festlegende Situation zu den Zeitpunkten t = 1, 2, 3, ... , N (Z) ein, wobei aber die Wahrscheinlichkeitsverteilung von Z sich ändern kann, dann sind die Wahrscheinlichkeiten Funktionen von t, symbolisiert durch $p_t(z_k)$. (Dasselbe gilt für $i(z_k)$, $\ddot{u}(z_k)$ und H (Z).) Durch einen Beobachtungsoperator $b_t(z_k)$ registrieren wir, zu welchen Zeitpunkten das Ereignis z_k eintrat: Es soll gelten

$b_t(z_k) = 1$, falls zum Zeitpunkt t das Erreignis z_k eintrat;
$b_t(z_k) = 0$, im anderen Falle.

Nachdem die Situation N (Z) mal eintrat, ist der gesamte Informationsbeitrag von z_k

$$I(z_k) = \sum_{t=1}^{N(Z)} b_t(z_k) \cdot i_t(z_k), \tag{6}$$

wobei $i_t(z_k)$ der Informationsgehalt ist, der z_k nach Gleichung (2) zum Zeitpunkt t zukommt, wenn dort die Wahrscheinlichkeit $p_t(z_k)$ eingesetzt wird.

Ist $p_t(z_k) = p(z_k) = $ const, dann folgt aus Gleichung (6):

$$I(z_k) = i(z_k) \cdot \sum_{t=1}^{N(Z)} b_t(z_k) = i(z_k) \cdot N(z_k) = i(z_k) \cdot h(z_k) \cdot N(Z), \tag{6a}$$

wobei N (z_k) die absolute, h (z_k) die relative Häufigkeit von z_k ist. Der Erwartungswert von h (z_k) ist dann bekanntlich p (z_k).

Den Quotienten aus Informationsbetrag und Gesamtlänge N (Z) der Folge nennen wir die 'informationelle Ausnutzung der Folge zugunsten von z_k':

$$A(z_k) = \frac{I(z_k)}{N(Z)}, \tag{7}$$

also bei konstanter Wahrscheinlichkeitsverteilung gemäss (6a):

$$A(z_k) = h(z_k) \cdot i(z_k). \tag{7a}$$

A (z_k) gibt an, wieviel Informationen pro Zeichen im Mittel durch das spezielle Zeichen z_k übertragen wurde.

Analog zum Informationsbeitrag berechnet sich der *Überraschungsbeitrag*

$$\ddot{U}(z_k) = \sum_{t=1}^{N(Z)} b_t(z_k) \cdot \ddot{u}_t(z_k), \tag{8}$$

also bei konstanter Wahrscheinlichkeitsverteilung:

$$\ddot{U}(z_k) = \ddot{u}(z_k) \cdot N(z_k). \tag{8a}$$

Den Quotienten aus Überraschungsbeitrag und Gesamtlänge N (Z) der Folge nennen wir Überraschungsdichte:

$$v(z_k) = \frac{\ddot{U}(z_k)}{N(Z)}, \tag{9}$$

also bei konstanter Wahrscheinlichkeitsverteilung:

$$v\,(z_k) = \mathrm{h}\,(z_k) \cdot \ddot{\mathrm{u}}\,(z_k). \tag{9a}$$

e. Auffälligkeit (Penetranz)

Wir schreiben nun einem Ereignis hohe *Auffälligkeit* zu, wenn es nicht nur bei häufiger Wiederholung der Situation möglichst oft eingetreten ist, sondern dabei auch jedesmal einen möglichst hohen Überraschungswert bzw. viel Information beinhaltete. Der Ausdruck in (8a) kann daher im Falle konstanter Wahrscheinlichkeitsverteilung als zur Auffälligkeit a (z_k) proportional angesehen werden. Allgemein definieren wir:

$$\mathrm{a}(z_k) = \frac{\mathrm{I}(z_k)}{\Sigma\,\mathrm{I}(z_k)}, \tag{10}$$

d.h. ein Zeichen (Ereignis) ist desto auffälliger, je grösser sein Informationsbeitrag im Verhältnis zur Gesamtheit der Information ist, die bei N(Z)-maliger Wiederholung der Situation diese klärte. Im Falle der konstanten Wahrscheinlichkeitsverteilung folgt mit (6a) aus (10)

$$\mathrm{a}(z_k) = \frac{\mathrm{h}(z_k) \cdot \mathrm{i}(z_k)}{\displaystyle\sum_k \mathrm{h}(z_k) \cdot \mathrm{i}(z_k)}, \tag{10a}$$

d.h. für genügend grosses N (Z) gilt mit beliebig hoher Wahrscheinlichkeit beliebig genau

$$\mathrm{a}(z_k) = \frac{\mathrm{p}(z_k) \cdot \mathrm{ld}\,\dfrac{1}{\mathrm{p}(z_k)}}{\mathrm{H}(Z)}. \tag{10b}$$

In diesem Grenzfall stimmen Überraschungsdichte und Auffälligkeit überein, und könnten wegen Gleichung (7a) als 'relative informationelle Ausnützung' bezeichnet werden. Man könnte den Überraschungswert auch als 'lokale Auffälligkeit' und die Auffälligkeit als 'globalen Überraschungswert' deuten. In Bild 3 ist die Auffälligkeitsfunktion nach Gleichung (10b) für verschiedene Werte der mittleren Information H eingezeichnet. Sie erreicht für konstantes (nicht zu kleines) H (Z) ihr Maximum für p = 1/e $\approx$ 36,7879%.

f. Systemtheoretische Varianten

Bis hierher haben wir uns auf der elementarsten Stufe der allgemeinen Kybernetik, nämlich auf der Ebene der allgemeinen Nachrichtentheorie bewegt, wobei wir uns bei der Aufstellung der Definitionen selbstverständlich von introspektiv gewonnenen, subjektiven Erfahrungen beeinflussen liessen. Wir beziehen nunmehr das informationsaufnehmende (und zumindest in diesem Sinne *lernende*!) System in die Betrachtung ein, gehen also zur komplexeren Stufe der allgemeinen informationellen Systemtheorie über,

Das informationsaufnehmende System S kann die Wahrscheinlichkeiten der möglichen Elemente eines Repertoires in der Regel nicht a priori kennen, sondern allenfalls aufgrund seiner Erfahrung sich in irgend einer Weise 'an sie gewöhnen'. Im Normalfall wird also die subjektive Wahrscheinlichkeit w_k und damit die subjektive Information $ld\ 1/w_k$ von der jeweiligen objektiven Grösse teils nach oben, teils nach unten abweichen. Man beweist aber leicht (Frank, 1962, b), dass für den Erwartungswert der subjektiven Information (nicht notwendig auch für die subjektive Unsicherheit!) gilt

$$H_{sub} \equiv \sum_k p_k \cdot ld\ \frac{1}{w_k} > \sum_k p_k \cdot ld\ \frac{1}{p_k} \equiv H,\ \text{falls}\ p_k \not\equiv w_k. \tag{11}$$

Der Erwartungswert der aufzunehmenden Information wird also durch das Lernen der Wahrscheinlichkeit verringert, einen Prozess, den wir (Frank, 1959, S. 17) 'informationelle Akkomodation' nannten.

Da auch die Festlegung des Repertoires, in welches das aus der Umwelt kommende Informationsangebot aufgelöst wird (also die Festlegung, ob beim Roulettespiel nur die Ereignisklasse 'Nicht Zéro!' interessiert, oder die Farbe oder der Dutzendbereich, oder gar die resultierende Zahl selbst!), vom System S geleistet werden muss, hat dieses durch die Superierung noch eine weitere Möglichkeit zur Informationsreduktion.

Man kann demgemäss auf der Stufe der informationellen Systemtheorie definieren ein System S lerne, wenn S den Gehalt an subjektiver und bisher unbekannter (d.h. noch nicht in S gespeicherter) Information seiner Umwelt verringert. Demnach gibt es drei wesentlich verschiedene Lernprozesse: die Speicherung (das 'Einprägen', 'Auswendiglernen' usf.), die informationelle Akkomodation und die Superierung ('Superzeichenbildung'; Frank, 1959, S. 34 ff).

Betrachtet man S als digital funktionierendes System, dann muss für die subjektive Information die Stetigkeitsforderung aufgegeben werden. Damit wird die subjektive Information gleich der Anzahl der zur internen Codierung verwendeten (z.B. binären) Codeelemente. Shannon (1949) gab ein Verfahren an, wie die Zeichen eines Repertoires binär durch

$$\left[ld\ \frac{1}{p_k} \right]$$

Elemente codiert werden können, also durch eine Zahl, die um weniger als 1 grösser ist als die nach Gleichung (2) definierte Information. Demgemäss gilt für den Erwartungswert der zur Codierung nach Shannon benötigten Elementezahl:

$$H \leq \sum_k p_k \cdot \left[ld\ \frac{1}{p_k} \right] < H + 1. \tag{12}$$

Es gibt Codes, die noch sparsamer sind als der Shannonsche (Fano; Huffman); grundsätzlich kann jedoch der Erwartungswert der zur Codierung erforderlichen Binärelemente den Erwartungswert H der Information nicht unterschreiten.

Man kann *mutatis mutandis* die Beziehungen 3, 4, 6–10 auch dann beibehalten, wenn für die Information stets die subjektive Information $ld\ \frac{1}{w_k}$ einzusetzen, und diese womöglich noch ganzzahlig, nämlich gleich der Zahl der zur Codierung intern verwendeten Binärzeichen ist. (w_k wird dabei zu einer fiktiven Grösse).

3. INFORMATIONSWISSENSCHAFTLICHE ANWENDUNGEN

a. Die Übertragbarkeit der eingeführten Grössen auf die Experimentalpsychologie

Schon seit mehr als einem Jahrzehnt hat sich das Shannonsche Informationsmass (Gleichungen 2 und 3) in zwei experimentalpsychologischen Problemkreisen bewährt: bei der Analyse der im absoluten Urteil steckenden Transinformation und bei der Analyse des Zeitbedarfs von Wahrnehmungsprozessen. Nur diese letztere ist für das folgende relevant.

Es hat sich gezeigt (vgl. die Referate in Frank, 1962a und 1963b):

(1) dass die zur Erkennung eines Einzelzeichens erforderliche Zeit proportional zu dessen Informationsgehalt ist (Howes und Solomon);

(2) dass von einer Zeichenfolge in einer gegebenen Zeitspanne ein desto grösserer *Prozentsatz* apperzipiert werden kann, je geringer ihr gesamter Informationsgehalt (also je grösser ihre Redundanz) ist, dass dabei zweitens in derselben Zeitspanne jeweils gleichviel *Information* apperzipiert wird, (Miller, Bruner und Postman) und diese Information drittens eine lineare Funktion der Grösse der Zeitspanne ist;

(3) dass auch die Reaktionszeit, wenigstens im Mittel, eine lineare Funktion der im Reiz stehenden Information ist (Merkel und Hyman). Hierbei konnten Morin *et al.* (1961) sogar einen klar ausgeprägten Lernprozess einer 'Superierung durch Klassenbildung' beobachten, ohne ihn allerdings selbst schon von dem von uns in Teil 2 eingenommenen Standpunkt aus zu deuten.

Wenn demnach der subjektiv erlebte Zeitbedarf für Apperzeption, Verständnis und Beantwortung von Nachrichten eine lineare Funktion von deren Information, und wahrscheinlich sogar die additive Konstante in dieser Beziehung gleich Null ist (sie taucht vermutlich nur aufgrund von bewusstseinsferneren nervösen Prozessen bei der äusseren Registrierung der Versuchsergebnissen auf), dann gewinnt die durch Gleichung (10) abstrakt definierte Auffälligkeit eine konkrete informationspsychologische Bedeutung. Auffälligkeit eines Zeichens bzw. eines Ereignisses in einer Folge von Zeichen bzw. Ereignissen desselben Repertoires ist demnach das Verhältnis der Zeit, während welcher das Subjekt S seine Aufmerksamkeit im Verlaufe der Folge eben diesem Zeichen bzw. Ereignis samt seinen Wiederholungen zuwandte, zur Gesamtzeit, während welcher diese Folge die Aufmerksamkeit von S beanspruchte.

Wenn zweitens vereinfachend angenommen wird, dass der Erwartungswert der Zeit, während welcher ein soeben apperzipierter einheitlicher Wahrnehmungsinhalt (Zeichen oder Ereignis) dem Bewusstsein gegenwärtig bleibt, von seinem Ueberraschungswert (der nunmehr konkret als relative Apperzeptionszeit deutbar ist) unabhängig ist und daher als konstante 'Gegenwartsdauer' (rund 10 sec) angesprochen werden kann, dann ergibt sich eine zweite, informationspsychologische Deutung der Auffälligkeit. Ordnet man nämlich dem introspektiv gesicherten Phänomen der Gegenwartsdauer eine Speichervorrichtung zu, die wir 'Kurzspeicher' nennen (Wiener,

1958, S. 143, vergleicht sie mit einem Schieberegister bei konstanter Verschiebungsgeschwindigkeit), dann ist die Auffälligkeit eines Zeichens bzw. Ereignisses gleich dem Erwartungswert des prozentualen Anteils, welche die Codierung dieses Wahrnehmungsinhalts einschliesslich seiner Wiederholungen von der Speicherkapazität des Kurzspeichers beansprucht.

Da die am Schluss von Teil 2 für S geforderte Fähigkeit des Wahrscheinlichkeitslernens für den Menschen experimentell vielfach bestätigt ist (vgl. z.B. das Referat darüber in Frank, 1962a), darf bei genügend langen, stationären Zeichen bzw. Ereignisfolgen vorausgesetzt werden, dass die subjektive Information ihrer Elemente für S mit deren objektiver Information übereinstimmt, so dass im Idealfall die Auffälligkeit nach Beziehung (106) bestimmt werden kann.

Die entscheidende Frage lautet nun: existieren empirische Befunde, welche sich am einfachsten durch Verwendung des Auffälligkeitsmasses quantitativ beschreiben lassen? Denn nur dadurch hätten unsere auf dem Informationsmass aufgebauten Definitionen einen Sinn, und zugleich könnte sich, falls die empirischen Befunde psychologischer Art sind, das Informationsmass dadurch indirekt in einem dritten experimentalpsychologischen Problemkreis neben den beiden eingangs genannten bewähren. Es wären dann damit auch ausreichend viele Grundtatsachen aufgewiesen, um von einer 'Informationspsychologie' als Zweig der Informationswissenschaft sprechen zu dürfen.

Tatsächlich kann unsere Frage von drei Seiten her bejaht werden:

(1) Die durch Gleichung (10) definierte Auffälligkeit entspricht der Häufigkeitsempfindung.

(2) Was umgangssprachlich als 'Auffälligkeit' bezeichnet wird, hat mit der durch (10b) definierten Funktion den Ort des Maximums ($p = 1/e$) gemeinsam.

(3) Das Auffälligkeitsmass ist geeignet, die Beeinflussbarkeit scheinbar freier Verhaltensweisen statistisch vorauszusagen.

b. Die Häufigkeitsempfindung

Die Häufigkeitsempfindung kann quantitativ dadurch geprüft werden, dass einer Versuchsperson (kurz: Vp, Plural: Vpn) die Aufgabe gestellt wird, die Häufigkeiten der Zeichen eines Repertoires zu schätzen, die in einer langen Folge von N Wiederholungen einer Situation mit jeweils demselben Feld auftraten. Das Feld kann beispielsweise das Repertoire der Buchstaben unseres Alphabets zusammen mit deren Wahrscheinlichkeiten in deutschen Texten sein. Eine Situation ist in diesem Falle das Noch-Ausstehen des folgenden Buchstabens eines Textes. Bekanntlich bleibt dabei die Wahrscheinlichkeitsverteilung nicht konstant. (Man kann auch den ganzen Text als ein Element des 'Superzeichenrepertoires' eines Produktfeldes auffassen, dessen N Teilfelder den 1., 2., 3. usf. Buchstaben des Textes erzeugen. Diese Teilfelder sind dann voneinander stark abhängig. (Vgl. für deutsche Texte Frank *et al.*, 1963). Sieht man davon in erster Näherung ab, berechnet man also die Auffälligkeit der Buchstaben in deutschen Texten für den deutschen Leser (bei dem die informationelle Akkomodation an die Wahrscheinlichkeitsverteilung als abgeschlossen vorausgesetzt

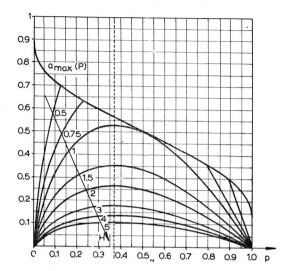

Fig. 3. Die Auffälligkeit a als Funktion der Wahrscheinlichkeit p und der Unsicherheit H im Grenzfall stationärer Wahrscheinlichkeiten und Übereinstimmung derselben mit den relativen Häufigkeiten der Stichprobe (Frank, 1963c).

werden darf!) nach der Gleichung (10b) unter Verwendung von Gleichung (3), dann erhält man den in Fig. 4 dargestellten Verlauf der Auffälligkeit a_i in einer Stichprobe. Die eingezeichneten Kreuze und Kreise stellen die durchschnittlichen Schätzwerte s_i für dieselben Buchstaben durch je eine kleine Gruppe erwachsener deutscher Vpn dar. Wie man sieht streuen die Schätzwerte eher um die (angenäherte) Auffälligkeitskurve als um die Gerade $s_i = h_i$, die bei durchschnittlich richtiger Schätzung hätte resultieren müssen. (Diese Beobachtung hat wohl als erster Attneave (1953) beschrieben, natürlich

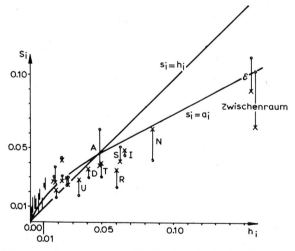

Fig. 4. Mittlere Schätzwerte s_i der Buchstabenhäufigkeiten durch eine Gruppe von 5 Vpn (X) und eine andere Gruppe von 4 Vpn (0). Für kleine relative Häufigkeiten h_i ist nur der Streubereich der s_i durch senkrechte Striche angegeben. $s_i = a_i$ ($a_i =$ Auffälligkeiten) beschreibt den empirischen Befund besser als $s_i = h_i$ (Frank, 1963c).

ohne schon eine quantitative Begründung durch das Auffälligkeitsmass geben zu können.)

Wenn die Schätzungen im Häufigkeitsschätzen nicht geübter Vpn am zutreffendsten durch die Auffälligkeitswerte vorauszusagen sind, dann müsste diese Theorie sich durch zwei Konsequenzen überprüfen lassen, die wir hier noch besprechen wollen.

(1) Vpn, welche nicht an die Häufigkeitsverteilung der dargebotenen Reizelemente gewöhnt sind, müssten die Häufigkeit als *grösser* angeben als der Formel (10b) entspricht, wenn die tatsächliche relative Häufigkeit die subjektive Wahrscheinlichkeit übersteigt, im umgekehrten Falle als *kleiner*. (Zur Berechnung hätte man in Gleichung (10a) die subjektive statt der objektiven Information einzusetzen). Dies konnte mit Vpn ohne Französischkenntnisse beim Schätzen der Buchstabenhäufigkeiten eines zuvor 'buchstabierten' französischen Textes nachgewiesen werden. Wegen der sofort einsetzenden informationellen Akkomodation und wegen des geringen Umfangs der Gruppe (nur 3 Vpn!) wurde natürlich nur eine geringe Genauigkeit erzielt. Beschränkt man die Versuchsauswertung auf die Buchstaben A, F, L, M, N, O, P und U, deren Häufigkeit einerseits im Französischen grösser als 1% ist (so dass der 'buchstabierte Text' nicht zu kurz war!) und andererseits von der Häufigkeit im Deutschen genügend stark abweicht, dann betrug die Korrelation zwischen den Abweichungen der Schätzwerte von den nach (10b) berechneten Auffälligkeitswerten einerseits und den theoretisch vorhergesagten Abweichungen andererseits 70%.

(2) Wenn die Häufigkeit eines Zeichens jenseits der Maximumstelle der Auffälligkeitsfunktion liegt, dann müsste die Häufigkeitsschätzung wieder *kleiner* werden, so dass das häufigste Element des Repertoires wegen seiner geringeren statistischen Auffälligkeit als weniger häufig geschätzt werden könnte als das nächst häufige. Dieser theoretisch vorhergesagte 'Maximumeffekt' konnte tatsächlich auch nachgewiesen werden (Frank, 1962a, 1963b), wobei sich zur verbesserten quantitativen Erklärung der Versuchsergebnisse erstmals die Notwendigkeit ergab, statt des Shannonschen Informationsmasses gemäss den Überlegungen am Schluss von Teil 2 die Zahl der Codeelemente bei einer redundanz-sparenden Codierung (Fano oder Huffman) zugrundezulegen.

Um den Einwand zu entkräften, nicht die statistische sondern eine irgendwie inhaltlich verursachte Auffälligkeit verursache den systematischen Schätzfehler, wurde inzwischen noch folgender Versuch durchgeführt. Es wurden zwei Zeichenfolgen der Länge N = 66 aus den Ziffern 1 bis 6 mit den absoluten Häufigkeiten 1, 2, 3, 9, 27 und 24 zugrundegelegt. Daraus wurden zwei Reizfolgen dadurch erzeugt, dass jeweils 1 durch die laut genannte und gleichzeitig durch eine Farbtafel gezeigte Farbe 'weiss', entsprechend 2 durch 'schwarz', 3 durch 'blau' und 4 durch 'grün' codiert wurde. Bei der Reizfolge A wurde 5 durch gelb, 6 durch rot codiert, bei der Reizfolge B umgekehrt 5 durch rot, 6 durch gelb. Die beiden Reizfolgen waren also zueinander isomorph. Die Folge A wurde insgesamt 57 Gymnasiasten, die Folge B 59 Gymnasiasten verschiedener Schulklassen gezeigt*. Obgleich die Häufikgeit der roten Farbe

---

* Der Autor dankt dem Gymnasium Kornwestheim für die Unterstützung dieser und der weiter unten zu besprechenden Versuche.

in der Reizfolge A geringer war als die Häufigkeit der gelben Farbe (36,4% gegen
40,9%), verhalten sich die mittleren Schätzwerte der Schüler gerade umgekehrt
(34,6% zu 34,0%). Bei der Reizfolge B war die rote Farbe häufiger als die gelbe,
jedoch schätzten die Schüler im Mittel 34,3% 'rot' gegen 35,8% 'gelb'. Eine Beein-
flussung der einen Gruppe von Vpn durch die andere war nicht möglich.

Das Ergebnis zeigt, dass unabhängig von möglicherweise vorhandenen farbpsycho-
logischen Wirkungen allein schon der statistische Informationswert das Verhalten
determinieren kann! (Übrigens war der Versuch mit der Reizfolge A schon früher
— Frank (1960) — mit anderen, wesentlich jüngeren Schülern durchgeführt worden,
wobei der Maximumeffekt sehr viel stärker auftrat. Ansonsten ergaben sich fast
genau wieder die seinerzeit gewonnen Schätzwerte).

c. Der umgangssprachliche Auffälligkeitsbegriff

Um zu prüfen, ob der umgangssprachliche Auffälligkeitsbegriff mit userem infor-
mationstheoretisch definierten wenigstens den Ort des Maximums ($p = 1/e$) gemeinsam hat, kann man sich zunächst auf ästhetische Untersuchungen stützen. Kunst-
werke sind Zeichenkomplexe. Dabei kan es aufgrund übergeordneter (meist seman-
tischer) Erfordernisse wünschenwert sein, ein Zeichen so auffällig wie möglich zu
machen, es 'maximal zu betonen', zum Beispiel in der Lyrik zur Erzielung einer
lautmalenden Wirkung oder in der Malerei aus farbsymbolischen Gründen. In einer
früheren Arbeit (Frank, 1959) wurde bereits durch Beispiele aus verschiedenen
Kunstgattungen belegt, dass dabei eine Verwendungshäufigkeit des möglischst auffällig zu gestaltenden Zeichens in der Grössenordnung von 37–40% gewählt wird.
Wie aus Bild 3 ersichtlich, ist eine erhöhte Auffälligkeit allenfalls bei *geringerer*
Häufigkeit (nich bei grösserer!) möglich, aber nur dann, wenn die mittlere Information der verwendeten Zeichen und damit die Gesamtinformation sehr klein wird.
In diesem Sinne ist z.B. eine kleine Perle auf einem grossen, homogenen, roten Tuch
extrem auffällig. Aber ein solches 'Kunstwerk' hat eben zu wenig Informationsgehalt,
als dass es die Aufmerksamkeit lange fesseln könnte.

Man kann auch umgekehrt Vpn beauftragen, aus einem gegebenen Repertoire von
Zeichen einen Zeichenkomplex aufzubauen und dabei ein bestimmtes Zeichen so
auffällig wie möglich werden zu lassen. Dazu erhielt eine Gruppe von — im Umgang
mit Farben geschulter — Vpn* weisse Blätter mit einem dünnen Raster aus 10 mal 14
Quadratfeldern mit 1,5 cm Kantenlänge und den Auftrag, jedes Quadrat mit genau
einer Farbe auszufüllen, jede von 7 zugelassenen Farben mindestens einmal zu
benützen und eine vorgeschriebene davon möglichst auffällig zu machen. Eine
Korrektur war nicht möglich. Von den 10 Vpn erklärten sich hernach 3 mit ihrer
Komposition unzufrieden (in Bild 5 durch '?' gekennzeichnet). Die übrigen 7 Vpn
(schraffierte Kästchen in Fig. 5) hatten durchschnittlich 34,2% der Felder mit der
maximal auffälig zu verwendenden Farbe ausgefüllt. Um Korrekturen möglich zu

---

* Der Autor dankt der Kunstwerkschule Offenbach für die Ermöglichung dieses Versuchs.

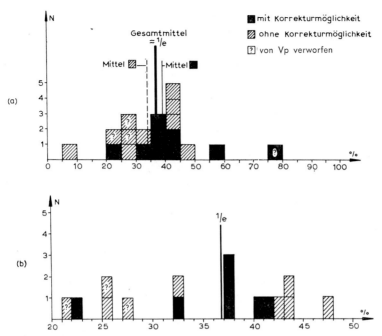

Fig. 5. Bei der Aufgabe, eine Fläche bunt auszulegen und dabei eine bestimmte Farbe möglichst auffällig zu gestalten, wird ein Prozentsatz von etwa $1/e$ für die mit dieser Farbe bedeckte Fläche bevorzugt (a). Das Ergebnis wird noch deutlicher, wenn die Auszählung in Intervallen von 1% statt von 5% Grösse erfolgt (b).

machen und zugleich zu verhindern, dass durch Druckunterschiede bei der Benutzung der Buntstifte zuätzliche, nicht statistische Auffälligkeitseffekte erzielt werden könnten, wurden für eine zweite Versuchsserie quadratische Farbplättchen vorbereitet, mit denen 9 Vpn, die überwiegend im Umgang mit Farben völlig ungeschult waren*, dasselbe Quadratfeldraster belegen sollten. Als Farben wurden verwendet: rot, gelb, blau und grün von starker, etwa gleicher Sättigung, sowie dieselben Farben in geringerer Sättigung. Jede Vp hatte eine der vier stark gesättigten Farben möglichst auffällig zu verwenden, und jede andere Farbe mindestens einmal zu benützen, ausser der schwach gesättigten Variante der hervorzuhebenden Farbe, die nicht zur Verfügung gestellt wurde. Bei den 8 gelieferten Kompositionen, mit denen sich die Vpn zufrieden erklärten, ist die jeweils maximal zu betonende Farbe durchschnittlich zur Belegung von 38,6 % der Felder verwendet worden (schwarze Kästchen in Fig. 5). Eine Vp, die 'rot' auffällig machen sollte, war mit der Häufigkeit schon beim ersten Entwurf so weit über die Maximumstelle hinausgekommen, dass sie nacheinander verschiedene andere Farben als auffälliger empfand und deshalb immer mehr Plättchen der entsprechenden Farbe durch rote Plättchen ersetzte. Sie bemerkte nicht, dass damit ein *positiver feedback-Mechanismus* einsetzte, und erklärte die Aufgabe als unlösbar‚

---

* Angestellte und Mitarbeiter des Instituts für Nachrichtenverarbeitung in Karlsruhe. Den Vpn war — ebenso wie jenen aus Offenbach — der Maximumeffekt zuvor unbekannt.

als sie 107 der 140 Felder mit rot bedeckt hatte (in Bild 5 durch '?' gekennzeichnet), und die anderen Farben intensiv auf diesem 'roten Teppich' herausleuchteten. Im Durchschnitt beider Versuchsreihen wurden in den 15, von ihren Autoren gut geheissenen Arbeiten durchschnittlich 36, 52% der Fläche für die jeweils hervorzuhebende Farbe verwendet, im Durchschnitt aller 19 Arbeiten sogar 36,768%. Das entspricht einer Abweichung von unserem theoretischen Wert $1/e = 36,7879\ldots\%$ von $-0,27\%$ bzw. -0.02%, also einem prozentualen Fehler von nur etwa 0.7% bzw. $0,05\%$ (wobei die Genauigkeitssteigerung im zweiten Falle natürlich Zufall ist!). Um einen Eindruck von der Verteilung zu vermitteln ist in Fig. 5a jedes in ein 5%-Intervall fallende Einzelergebnis durch ein Kästchen eingetragen; der Block von 20 bis 50% ist in Fig. 5b durch Auflösung in 1%-Intervalle verfeinert dargestellt, wobei die Häufung bei $1/e$ noch deutlicher wird. Die drei Resultate im Intervall von 37–38% wurden mit den Farben gelb, rot und grün erzielt.

d. Statistische Beeinflussbarkeit 'freier' digitaler Verhaltensweisen

Um schliesslich zu prüfen, inwiefern unser Auffälligkeitsmass auch geeignet ist, die Beeinflussbarkeit scheinbar freier Verhaltensweisen statistisch vorherzusagen, wurde mit verschiedenen Klassen 10- bis 18-jähriger deutscher Gymnasiasten beiderlei Geschlechts folgende Versuchsreihe durchgeführt. Den Schülern wurden Folgen der binären Zeichen X ('Kreuz') und 0 ('Kreis') bzw. in einer anderen Versuchsreihe Folgen der vier Ziffern 0, 1, 2 und 3 vorgelesen (Geschwindigkeit: etwa 2 Zeichen pro Sekunde). Jeder dieser (künftig 'Reizketten' genannten) Folgen enthielt 16 Zeichen. Nach dem Anhören jeder Reizkette sollten die Schüler eine Folge von 8 Zeichen desselben Repertoires niederschreiben (künftig 'Reaktionsketten' genannt). Im Vorversuch zu der Versuchsreihe mit Binärzeichen, die insgesamt mit fünf Schulklassen (einmal 1959 mit 27 Schülern (Frank, 1960, 1962a) viermal 1962 mit den auch für den erwähnten Häufigkeitsschätztest verwendeten 121 Schülern einer anderen Stadt) durchgeführt wurden, lauteten die beiden Reizketten (Nummern — 1 und 0 in den Fign. 9–12):

> XX OO OO XX OX XO XO OX
> OX· XX XO OO XX OX OO OX

In beiden Reizketten haben also beide Binärzeichen die Häufigkeit $\frac{1}{2}$. Die entsprechenden Reaktionsketten eines 10 jährigen Mädchens lauteten beispielsweise

> O O X O X X X O
> X X O O X O O X

Erwartungsgemäss sind auch hier beide Binärzeichen jeweils gleich häufig, und so war es näherungsweise auch im Gesamtmittel aller Klassen (vgl. Tabelle I).

Von der dritten Reizkette an (n = 1 in Tabelle II) war die Häufigkeitsverteilung plötzlich 75% : 25%. Die zwölf Reizketten sind in Tabelle II wiedergegeben. Die durchschnittliche Reaktion der 27 10–11-jährigen Schülerinnen und Schüler bei der ersten Durchführung dieser Versuchsreihe ist in Bild 6 dargestellt. Offensichtlich besteht nach Änderung der Häufigkeitsverteilung in den Reizketten (dicke Linien) zunächst

TABELLE I

Zeichen	Reize	Relative Häufigkeit in der Folge der Reaktionen		
		1959	1962	theoretisch
X	0,500	0,497	0,517	0,500
O	0,500	0,503	0,483	0,500

TABELLE II

n (Nummer der Folge)	Reizfolge							
1	OX	XX	XO	XX	OX	XX	OX	XX
2	XX	XO	XX	XO	XX	XX	OX	OX
3	XX	XO	XO	XX	XX	OX	XX	OX
4	OX	XX	XO	XX	XO	XX	OX	XX
5	OO	XX	XX	XX	XO	OX	XX	XX
6	XX	OX	XX	OX	XX	XX	OX	OX
7	XX	XX	OO	XX	XX	XO	XO	XX
8	OX	XO	XX	XX	XX	OO	XX	XX
9	OX	OX	XX	XX	XX	XX	OX	OX
10	XX	XX	XO	OX	OO	XX	XX	XX
11	XX	XX	XX	OO	XX	XX	XO	XO
12	XX	XX	OX	OX	XX	OX	OX	XX

eine Tendenz, die Häufigkeitsverteilung in den Reaktionsketten (dünne Linien) daran anzugleichen, jedoch wird dann anscheinend eine davon verschiedene Grenzverteilung von 0,611 : 0,389 angenommen. Die theoretische Begründung, die wir dafür aus den Betrachtungen von Teil 2 ableiten werden, liefert eine theoretische Grenzverteilung (Tabelle III), die vom empirischen Mittelwert (gestrichelte Linien) zu wenig ab-

TABELLE III

Zeichen	Reize	Relative Häufigkeit in der Folge der Reaktionen		
		1959	1962	theoretisch
X	0,750	0,611	0,613	0,616
O	0,250	0,389	0,387	0,384

weicht, um in Bild 6 davon unterscheidbar zu sein. Dasselbe theoretische Modell liefert auch eine gute Begründung für die Resultate der anderen Versuchsreihe mit einem quaternären Zeichenrepertoire. Fig. 7 zeigt, dass die Ziffern 0, 1, 2 und 3 in Vorversuch mit der Verteilung $\frac{1}{4} : \frac{1}{4} : \frac{1}{4} : \frac{1}{4}$, in den 12 anschliessenden Reizketten jedoch im Verhältnis $\frac{1}{4} : \frac{1}{8} : \frac{1}{8} : \frac{1}{2}$ auftraten. Fig. 7 zeigt ferner, dass die Grenzverteilung (dicke Linien) in den Reaktionsketten (wobei für die Zeichen 1 und 2 der Mittelwert eingetragen wurde) besser mit den theoretisch vorhergesagten Werten (gestrichelte Linien) als mit der Verteilung in den Reizketten übereinstimmt.

Der naheliegendste Ansatz zur Deutung der in Fig. 6 und Fig. 7 registrierten empirischen Kurven lautet bei Berücksichtigung der oben besprochenen anderen Resultate: die Häufigkeitsverteilung in den Reaktionsketten ist numerisch gleich der Verteilung der Auffälligkeiten der entsprechenden Zeichen in den Reizketten.

Berechnet man diese Auffälligkeiten nach Gleichung (10b), indem man dort die Wahrscheinlichkeiten durch die relativen Häufigkeiten in den Reizketten ersetzt, dann

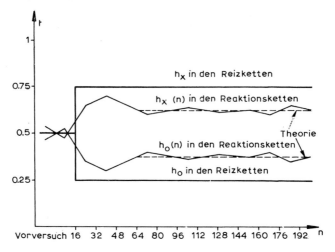

Fig. 6. Ändert sich die Häufigkeitsverteilung der Zeichen X, O in den Reizketten von h(x) : h(o) = $\frac{1}{2} : \frac{1}{2}$ auf h(x) : h(o) = $\frac{3}{4} : \frac{1}{4}$, dann approximiert die Häufigkeitsverteilung in den Reaktionsketten im Mittel einen auffälligkeits- und codierungstheoretisch vorhersagbaren Wert.

erhält man sowohl für die Versuchsreihe mit den binären wie für jene mit den quaternären Zeichen Resultate, die weit von den in Fig. 6 bzw. Fig. 7 dargestellten empirischen Werten abweichen und daher unseren Ansatz eindeutig zu widerlegen scheinen.

Zumindest für die erste Reizkette nach dem Vorversuch ist jedoch die Verwendung von Gleichung (10b) auch theoretisch unzulässig, da die subjektiven Wahrscheinlichkeiten unmöglich sofort schon gleich den neuen relativen Häufigkeiten sein konnten. Diese Ueberlegung allein reicht jedoch noch nicht aus, um den Ansatz in Einklang mit den empirischen Befunden zu bringen. Vielmehr sind zwei zusätzliche Voraussetzungen erforderlich:

(1) In beiden Versuchsreihen waren die Reize als Paare (in Form von Jamben, z.B. 'Kreuz *Kreis*') gesprochen und demnach höchstwahrscheinlich ebenso apperzipiert worden. Demgemäss müssten diese Paare, also Superzeichen, als Elemente eines

superierten Reizrepertoires betrachtet, und *dafür* Informations- bzw. Auffälligkeitswerte berechnet werden.

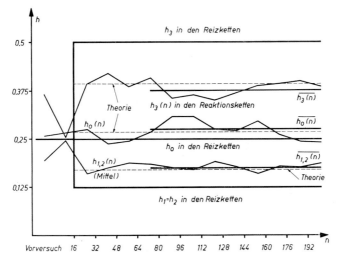

Fig. 7. Der in Fig. 6 beschriebene Effekt ist auch für 4 verschiedene Zeichen (0, 1, 2, 3) nachweisbar.

(2) Wie schon im Zusammenhang mit dem Wahrscheinlichkeitsschätzen erwähnt,
scheint der Mensch ein System zu sein, welches zur digitalen Informationsverarbeitung fähig ist, so dass auch hier eine bessere Uebereinstimmung zwischen
Theorie und Experiment zu erzielen sein könnte, wenn statt des Shannonschen
Informationsmasses in Gleichung (10a) die Zahl der Codeelemente bei einer
redundanzsparenden Binärcodierung (Fano oder Huffman) eingesetzt wird.

Gemäss der Häufigkeitsverteilung der vier Zeichenpaare xx, xo, ox und oo in den
zwölf Reizketten nach dem Vorversuch kommt man zu einem der beiden in Fig. 8

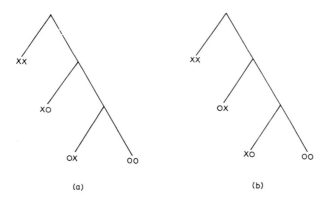

Fig. 8. Redundanzsparende Codebäume für die 4 Superzeichen OO, OX, XO und XX. Dabei ist XX
als häufigstes, OO als seltenstes vorausgesetzt. Der durch (a) dargestellte Code ist sparsamer, wenn
XO häufiger ist als OX, andernfalls ist der durch (b) dargestellte Code sparsamer.

References p. 208

dargestellten Codebäume. Dem Paar xx schreiben wir also regelmässig 1 bit subjektiver Information, dem Paar oo 3 bit subjektiver Information zu. Für die Paare mittlerer Häufigkeit ox und xo entnimmt man den beiden Codebäumen verschiedene Informationswerte. Die einfachste Annahme lautet: ist in einer Reizkette (erstmals in der zweiten des Vorversuchs!) das eine dieser beiden Paare häufiger als das andere, dann erhält es von der *nächsten* Reizkette an nur 2 bit subjektiver Information, das andere Paar 3 bit. Diese Informationswerte werden beibehalten, bis in einer Reizkette (erstmals in der Kette mit Nummer $n = 7$!) sich das Häufigkeitsverhältnis umkehrt; dann sollen auch die beiden. Informationswerte von der darrauffolgenden Kette an vertauscht werden. D.h. wir machen die vereinfachende Annahme, die informationelle Akkomodation erfolge vollständig zwischen zwei aufeinanderfolgen den Reizketten.

Durch diese Voraussetzungen ist ein Algorithmus definiert, der mittels Gleichung (10a) Auffälligkeitswerte zu berechnen gestattet, deren Mittelwerte (gemittelt über die letzten 9 Ketten) die theoretischen Werte der Tabelle III liefern. Diese stimmen

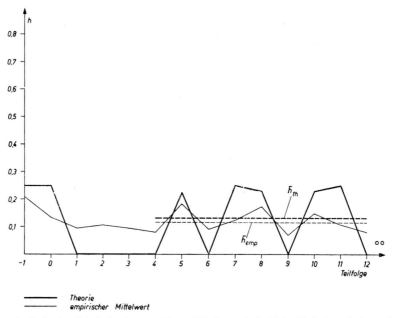

Fig. 9. Durchschnittshäufigkeit des Superzeichens OO theoretisch (dicke Linien) und als empirischer Mittelwert von 121 Vpn (dünne Linien). Die beiden Kurven korrelieren zu 80,2%. Das über die letzten 9 Teilversuche gemittelte theoretische und empirische Ergebnis ist nahezu dasselbe.

mit den empirischen Werten ausgezeichnet überein (weniger als 1% prozentuale Abweichung!). Der analoge Algorithmus führt bei der Versuchsserie mit den vier Ziffern zu den in Fig. 7 eingezeichneten theoretischen Mittelwerten, die ebenfalls in relativ befriedigendem Einklang mit den empirischen Befunden stehen.

Falls jedoch die zugrundegelegte Theorie zutrifft, müssten auch die theoretischen Zwischenwerte über die Paarhäufigkeiten mit den empirischen Paarhäufigkeiten

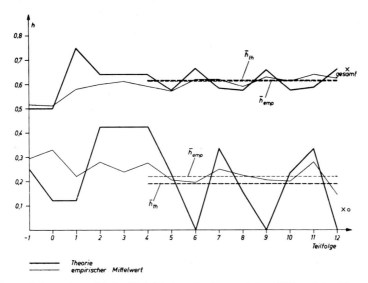

Fig. 10. Theoretische und empirische Häufigkeiten des Superzeichens XO und des Unterzeichens X. Im Mittel der letzten 9 Teilergebnisse ist die theoretische Vorhersage ziemlich gut: h_{th} (X) $\approx h_{emp}$ (X). Für XO ist die entsprechende Annäherung weniger gut. Der Korrelationskoeffizient zwischen theoretischer Vorhersage und Durchschnittsverhalten der Versuchsgruppe ist 81%.

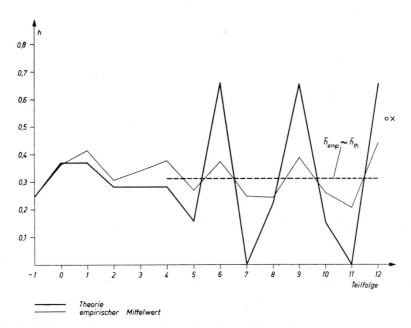

Fig. 11. Die Häufigkeitsschwankungen der von den Vpn gelieferten Superzeichen OX sind wesentlich geringer als theoretisch vorhergesagt, korrelieren aber mit der theoretischen Kurve zu 87,5%. Theoretischer und empirischer Mittelwert der letzten 9 Teilversuche weichen voneinander so wenig ab, dass die Differenz im Bild nicht mehr sichtbar wird!

übereinstimmen. Bisher hatten wir aus den Paarhäufigkeiten die Häufigkeiten der Einzelzeichen berechnet und nur diese Werte mit den empirischen Befunden verglichen.

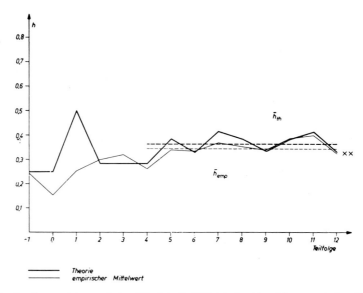

Fig. 12. Für das Superzeichen grösster Häufigkeit, XX, ist die Abweichung zwischen Theorie und experimentellem Ergebnis am geringsten, obwohl der Korrelationskoeffizient (84,2%) etwas niedriger ist als bei OX.

Die Fign. 9–12 zeigen die durchschnittlichen Resultate der 121 Vpn in den 1962 durchgeführten Versuchen. Selbst bei den letzten 9 Ketten stimmen Theorie und Experiment nicht besonders gut überein, jedoch ist die Uebereinstimmung der *Mittelwerte* von Theorie und Experiment auch bei der Analyse der Paarhäufigkeiten sehr befriedigend, ebenso wie die Korrelation der Häufigkeitsschwankungen mit deren theoretischer Voraussage. Am besten wird die theoretische Kurve für das häufigste Superzeichen, xx, von der Beobachtung bestätigt (Fig. 12), jedoch erweist sich die Theorie auch für das seltenste Superzeichen, oo, als nicht schlecht. Für die Paare ox und xo ähnelt die theoretische Voraussage ein wenig der Wettervorhersage: nur die allgemeine Tendenz und die Mittelwerte treffen zu. Viel mehr dürfte aber bei den vereinfachenden Annahmen über die hier ins Spiel kommende informationelle Akkomodation auch nicht erwartet werden! Bei homogeneren Reizketten hätte mit einer besseren Bestätigung der Theorie gerechnet werden können. (Die Reizketten der Tabelle II waren aus Zufallsfolgen gegebener Wahrscheinlichkeitsverteilung nach dem Kriterium ausgewählt worden, dass die relativen Häufigkeiten der Einzelzeichen, aber nicht notwendig auch die der Paare, exakt gleich den entsprechenden Wahrscheinlichkeiten sein sollten). Uebrigens ist die Abweichung zwischen Theorie und Experiment auch im Falle der Superzeichen oo und xx nicht völlig durch zufällige Streuungen zu erklären. Fig. 13 zeigt nämlich die durchschnittlichen Häufigkeiten dieser Superzeichen sowie der einzelnen Kreuze für 12 Schüler mittlerer Schulleistung im Alter von 10–11 Jahren bei dem 1959 angestellten Versuch, und dieselben Grössen für 12 Schüler desselben Alters und derselben Schulleistung bei dem Experiment von 1962. Die Abweichungen der beiden Kurven untereinander sind geringfügiger als ihre Abweichung von unserer Theorie!

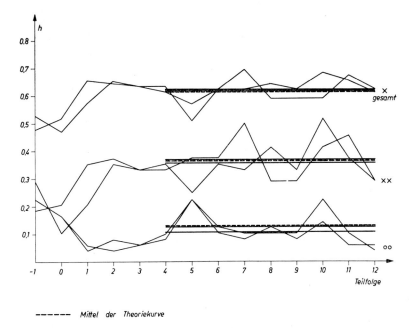

- - - - - Mittel der Theoriekurve

Fig. 13. Die gute Reproduzierbarkeit der durch Fign. 9–12 dargestellten Versuchsergebnisse drückt sich in der guten Übereinstimmung der Durchschnittskurven zweier aus je 12 Vpn bestehender Gruppen aus (Gymnasiasten, die 1959 bzw. 1962 10–11 Jahre alt waren).

e. Konsequenzen

Die drei beschriebenen, sehr verschiedenartigen Gruppen von Versuchen dürften die Zweckmässigkeit der auf dem Informationsmass aufgebauten Definition eines Auffälligkeitsmasses und damit indirekt die damit zusammenhängende Definition eines Masses für den Überraschungswert bestätigt haben. Die informationswissenschaftlichen Konsequenzen der Versuchsergebnisse liegen in den verschiedensten Bereichen.

(1) Vielfach müssen Schlüsse aus Häufigkeitsschätzungen darin nicht geübter Beobachter gezogen werden (z.B. in der Rechtspraxis oder bei ersten Empfehlungen von Verwaltungsorganisatoren). Hierfür ist es von Wichtigkeit, die systematische Überschätzung des Seltenen und Unterschätzung des Häufigen abschätzen zu können.

(2) Da nur ein Bruchteil der pro Sekunde in den Kurzspeicher (das 'Bewusstsein') gelangenden Information in das vorbewusste Gedächtnis dringt (etwa 3–5%; vgl. die Kapazitätsabschätzungen bei Frank, 1962a), ist es für die Zwecke der Pädagogik, der Werbepsychologie usf. von erheblichem Interesse, *welche* Bewusstseinsinhalte ausgewählt werden. Möglicherweise ist die landläufige Antwort, behalten werde was interessiert, eine voreilige Verlagerung des Problems in quantitativen Methoden schwerer zugängliche Bereiche. Wahrscheinlicher als die Annahme einer (unbewusst) *bewertenden Instanz* zwischen Kurzspeicher und vorbewusstem Gedächtnis scheint uns die Annahme zu sein, dass ein introspektiv zu bestätigendes Phänomen allein ausreicht, die leichtere Einprägbarkeit des Interessierenden zu begründen, nämlich das Phänomen, dass wir unsere Aufmerksamkeit bevorzugt auf das Interessierende richten,

d.h. dass dieses häufiger zu Bewusstsein kommt und daher insgesamt länger im Kurzspeicher enthalten ist, als andere mögliche Bewusstseinsinhalte. Die Auswahl der ins vorbewusste Gedächtnis aufzunehmenden Inhalte des Kurzspeichers kann dann in erster Näherung als völlig zufällig angesehen werden! In zweiter Näherung wird man den Ansatz machen, die Wahrscheinlichkeit, mit welcher ein bestimmter Inhalt des Kurzspeichers als nächster vom vorbewussten Gedächtnis übernommen wird sei seinem Platz im Kurzspeicher, folglich seinem Überraschungswert proportional — bzw. seiner Auffälligkeit, da er ja mehrfach innerhalb der Gegenwartsdauer apper-zipiert werden konnte. Vom Standpunkt dieser statistischen Gedächtnishypothese aus gewinnen die Masse der Überraschungsdichte, der Auffälligkeit und der information-ellen Ausnutzung pädagogisches und werbepsychologisches Interesse (Frank, 1962a, 1963c). Hofmann (1963) hält den Maximumeffekt geradezu für eine Entdeckung von grundlegender Bedeutung für die Werbepsychologie. Moles (1963) baut auf dem Maximumeffekt sogar eine Theorie über die Verteilung der Preise eines Warenhauses auf, wenn der Eindruck besonderer Preisgünstigkeit ohne entsprechenden mittleren Preisnachlass erreicht werden soll.

(3) Die berichteten Befunde über die statistische Beeinflussbarkeit und ihre auf-fälligkeitstheoretische Deutung könnten über die Ebene der informationellen System-theorie (die wir bisher auf dem informationswissenschaftlichen Sektor einnahmen) hinaus von Bedeutung für die Erforschung von Kreisrelationen werden. Denn würde man als Reizketten, also als 'Vorbild' jeweils eine vorangegangene Reaktionskette wählen, dann würde aus dem Reiz — Reaktions — Experiment die Untersuchung eines Regelkreises werden (Fig. 14). Das ist insofern von Interesse, als die 'subjektive'

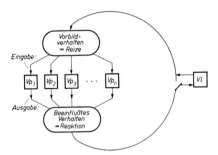

Fig. 14. Wenn der Versuchsleiter Vl statt die Reize selbst zu erzeugen ihnen die im jeweils vorange-gangenen Versuch erhaltenen Reaktionen zugrundelegt, entsteht aus einem klassischen Reiz-Reak-tions-Versuch, also einer systemtheoretischen Untersuchung, ein Experiment auf der nächst-höheren Stufe, der Kreisrelationen, wobei 'Regelschwingungen' möglich sind (Frank, 1964).

Auffälligkeit nach Formel (10a) grösser als die relative Häufigkeit des Reizes werden kann, wenn dessen subjektive Information genügend gross, d.h. seine subjektive Wahrscheinlichkeit genügend klein war, wenn also der Reiz bisher selten auftrat. Nach unserer Theorie könnten dadurch in dem geschlossenen System vorausberechen-bare Regelschwingungen entstehen die möglicherweise das Prinzip der sprichwört-lichen Schwankungen der Mode darstellen (Frank, 1963c, 1964). Mit diesem, zugege-benermassen spekulativen Ausblick sollte lediglich die Möglichkeit der Anwendbarkeit der vorgetragenen Untersuchungen auch auf der höchsten Stufe der Kybernetik, der Stufe der Systemkomplextheorie, aufgewiesen werden.

4. BIOKYBERNETISCHE DEUTUNGEN UND HYPOTHESEN

a. Abgrenzung der bisherigen Untersuchung gegenüber der Biokybernetik

Der erste Teil dieser Arbeit war überwiegend philosophischer, der zweite formal-kybernetischer und der dritte informationswissenschaftlicher Art. Obgleich sich der Autor für den biokybernetischen Sektor (in dem oben definierten Sinne von 'Bio-kybernetik') nicht für zuständig betrachten darf, mögen einige abschliessende bio-kybernetische Anmerkungen gestattet sein.

Die im letzten Teil behandelten Erscheinungen fallen zwar in den Bereich der Lebewesen, nicht in den Bereich der kybernetischen Maschinen, jedoch sind unsere Untersuchungen nicht biokybernetischer sondern informationswissenschaftlicher Art. Denn weder wurden Beobachtungen durch Eingriff in den Organismus gewonnen, noch wurden Verhaltensweisen von Tieren untersucht. Den Vpn wurde umgangs-sprachlich ihre Aufgabe erläutert, d.h. sie wurden vom Versuchsleiter als ihm wesens-gleich betrachtet, er setzte bei ihnen also ähnliche interne Prozesse voraus, wie er sie introspektiv bei sich selbst wahrnahm. Darauf waren die Versuche gegründet; sie sind demnach wesensverschieden von biokybernetischen Versuchen.

Das bedeutet nicht, dass ähnliche Resultate nicht auch durch Versuche mit höheren Tieren gewonnen werden könnten, und noch viel weniger bedeutet es, dass die Ergeb-nisse nicht im Prinzip neurophysiologisch begründbar sind. Beides ist jedoch erheblich viel schwieriger, so dass in beiden Fällen die informationswissenschaftlich gewonnenen Resultate eine nennenswerte Transinformation auch für den Bereich der Biokybernetik enthalten dürften.

b. Die Streitfrage nach Digitalprozessen im Nervensystem

Für die Neurophysiologie werfen insbesondere die Resultate über die bessere Be-gründbarkeit der Beobachtungen durch Verfahren der Binärcodierung erneut eine Frage auf, die von manchem Fachmann schon für negativ entschieden erklärt wurde: die Frage nach der Existenz digitaler Nachrichtenverarbeitungsprozesse im Zentral-nervensystem. Bekanntlich war diese Existenz vor 15 Jahren vorausgesetzt worden, eine Annahme, die sich auch in Wieners 'Cybernetics' findet und viel zur Verbreitung der Kybernetik beitrug. Nun setzt die Digitalität nervöser Prozesse mehr als das Alles-oder-Nichts-Gesetz voraus, das auch bei Frequenzmodulation erfüllt ist, also bei einem Verfahren der analogen Verschlüsselung. Digitalität zentralnervöser Pro-zesse liegt nur dann vor, wenn ein zentraler Zeitgeber existiert, der in regelmässigen oder unregelmässigen Abständen einen Zeitpunkt definiert, zu dem das Auftreten oder Nichtauftreten einer Entladung in einem Neuron eine Information beinhaltet, während eine solche Entladung zu jedem anderen Zeitpunkt entweder unmöglich, oder informationslos ist. Es ist heute unbestritten, dass der sensorische Teil des

Umweltnervensystems so nicht funktioniert, sondern dem Prinzip der Analogverschlüsselung verpflichtet ist. Damit stimmen auch viele Beobachtungen im Zentralnervensystem überein. Der vielfach gezogene Schluss, es existiere demnach überhaupt keine digitale oder gar binäre Nachrichtenverarbeitung im Gehirn, ist (1) logisch gesehen nicht zwingend, wurde (2) durch neurophysiologische Beobachtungen an einem wenn auch sehr kleinen Teil des Zentralnervensystems (aber dort so, dass ein Zweifel an der Existenz einer binären Informationsverarbeitung mit einer konstanten Taktzeit kaum möglich bleibt!) stark erschüttert (Schwartzkopff, 1962), und würde schliesslich (3) einige der referierten informationspsychologischen Beobachtungen schwer verständlich machen wenn nicht gar zu einem Pseudobeweis für die metaphysische Behauptung ausarten, das seinem Wesen nach digitale geistige Geschehen habe keine wesentliche Grundlage in den ihrem Wesen nach analogen physiologischen Prozessen.

Der Autor sieht im Gegensatz dazu in der Digitalität des menschlichen Denkens und in der digitalen Deutbarkeit primitiverer informationspsychologischer Befunde ein Argument dafür, dass Wieners ursprünglichen Gedankengängen über Entsprechungen zwischen Digitalrechnern und menschlichem Gehirn wenigstens in kleinem Umfange — aber eben in einem für die Psychologie ausschlaggebenden Umfange — zutreffen. Die im letzten Teil dargelegten und manche anderen Befunde würden sich am leichtesten deuten lassen, wenn der Biokybernetik der Nachweis folgender, im wesentlichen schon in Wieners 'Cybernetics' enthaltener Hypothesen gelänge:

(1) Im Gehirn werden Wahrnehmungsinhalte und womöglich auch assoziierte Gedächtnisinhalte in einem redundanzsparenden Binärcode verschlüsselt.

(2) Diesem Binärcode liegt für die (subjektiv) mit Bewusstsein verbundenen Prozesse eine Taktzeit von der Grösse des subjektiven Zeitquants, also zwischen 1/18 und 1/15 sec zugrunde. Wir weichen damit geringfügig von der Vermutung Wieners (1948, S. 165) ab, die Periodenlänge des Alpha-Rhythmus bilde die Taktzeit. Die wichtigsten unserer Argumente haben wir anderweitig (Frank, 1963d) schon dargelegt. Ein weiteres Argument kann darin gesehen werden, dass die additive Konstante bei dem oben erwähnten Merkel-Hyman-Versuch ebenso wie die Reaktionszeit beim bedingten Reflex, nämlich etwa 165 msec, gerade um zwei subjektive Zeitquanten grösser ist als die Reaktionszeit beim unbedingten Reflex, die etwa 40 msec beträgt.

(3) Die Speicherung dieser Informationen während einer der Gegenwartsdauer entsprechenden Zeit erfolgt durch Fortleitung dieser Binärelemente in mehreren synchron arbeitenden parallelen Neuronenketten irgendwo im Gehirn, z.B. im Stammhirn, so dass der hypothetisch als 'Ort' der bewusstseinsgegenwärtigen Information eingeführte Kurzspeicher hirnanatomisch lokalisierbar wäre.

c. Die kybernetische Synthese aus Verhaltensforschung und Geisteswissenschaft

Ob auf diese oder ob auf eine andere Weise eine biokybernetische Begründung informationspsychologischer Beobachtungen möglich sein wird, unbestritten dürfte jedenfalls sein, dass in den letzteren eine Transinformation über physiologische Prozesse steckt. Dadurch erweist sich die Kybernetik einmal mehr als 'Brücke zwischen den Wissenschaften'. Diese Rolle beginnt sie im Gegenstandsbereich der Informationswissenschaft in noch viel stärkerem Ausmasse zu spielen, und dies zu zeigen war der eigentliche Zweck der gegenwärtigen Untersuchung: die Kybernetik ist im Begriff, den Gegensatz zwischen den sogenannten Geisteswissenschaften und insbesondere der 'verstehenden Psychologie' einerseits und den radikal behaviouristischen Strömungen andererseits zu überbrücken und — im dreifachen Sinne des Hegel'schen Wortes — aufzuheben. Der radikale Behaviourist stellt sich nach der Zurückweisung der Introspektion auf die Ebene der informationellen Systemtheorie, betrachtet also das 'System Mensch' als mathematisch analysierbaren Zuordner von Reaktionen zu Reizen. Die verstehende Psychologie wie jede Geisteswissenschaft erfährt den Menschen durch Introspektion als zweckhaft handelnd, steht also zumindest schon auf der viel schwierigeren Stufe der Kreisrelationen, meist sogar gleich auf der schwierigsten Stufe der Systemkomplextheorie (Fig. 2). Voreilig wurde aus der Kompliziertheit der Verhältnisse auf dieser Stufe der Schluss gezogen, die Mathematik vermöge hierzu keine adäquaten Forschungs- und Darstellungsmethoden zu liefern. In kybernetischer Sicht erscheinen nicht nur die beiderseitigen *Anliegen* als verschiedene Stufen desselben umfassenden Problems, sondern auch die beiderseitigen *Methoden* als durchaus vereinbar. Unsere Untersuchung über den Überraschungswert und die Auffälligkeit sollte zeigen, wie unter kritischer Verwendung introspektiv gewonnener Einsichten mathematische Ansätze über den behaviouristischen Forschungsbereich hinaus auf höhere Ebenen übertragbar werden.

KURZFASSUNG

Nach zwei Gesichtspunkten lassen sich die Probleme der Kybernetik einteilen. Vom ersten Gesichtspunkt aus lassen sie sich in Probleme der formalen Kybernetik und Probleme der auf Maschinen oder Lebewesen konkretisierten materialen Kybernetiken sowie in Probleme der zugehörigen Bereiche der technischen Kybernetik einteilen. Der zweite Klassifikationsstandpunkt liefert statt dieser Nebeneinanderstellung verschiedener Problemkreise eine hierarchische Ordnung von vier Stufen:

(1) die Behandlung der blossen Nachricht

(2) die Behandlung des informationsverarbeitenden Systems, das eingegebene Nachrichten in ausgegebene umsetzt,

(3) die Behandlung von Kreisrelationen, die Ausgabegrössen mit Eingabegrössen verbinden, also die Behandlung von informationellen Rückwirkungssystemen, und

(4) die Behandlung des Gesamtverhaltens eines Komplexes verschiedener, miteinander kommunizierender informationeller Systeme, wie es insbesondere in der Spieltheorie geschieht.

Das in der vorliegenden Arbeit behandelte konkrete Problem betrifft den Bereich der lebenden Systeme, genauer bestimmte, mit Bewusstsein verknüpfte menschliche Verhaltensweisen. (Aus diesem Grunde wird das Problem eher als informationswissenschaftliches denn als biokybernetisches Problem bezeichnet, sofern 'Biokybernetik' eine zu präzisierende engere Bedeutung annimmt.) Die maschinelle Simulierung der beschriebenen informationspsychologischen Prozesse ist unschwer möglich. Vom bekannten Shannonschen Informationsmass werden diverse weitere Masse abgeleitet, insbesondere Masse für den Überraschungswert und die Auffällikgeit. Verschiedene, auf den ersten Blick kaum zusammenhängende experimentalpsychologische Ergebnisse können durch diese Masse quantitativ gedeutet werden. Das theoretische Vorgehen demonstriert überdies die Nützlichkeit jeder der genannten kybernetischen Problemstufen für die Behandlung von Problemen der jeweils höheren Ebene. Ein Teil der zur Sprache kommenden experimentalpsychologischen Befunde dürfte zugunsten der bekannten Vermutung Wieners sprechen, dass irgendwo im menschlichen Gehirn digitale Nachrichtenverarbeitungsprozesse stattfinden.

SUMMARY

Two different classifications of cybernetic problems are given. The first distinguishes the abstract, general cybernetics from its concretisations to machines or living systems, and from the technical applications of these concretisations. The second classification distinguishes four degrees of cybernetic problems, degrees of growing complexity:

(1) the treatment of the isolated messages

(2) the treatment of information-processing systems as input-output-relators

(3) the treatment of circular relations from the output to the input, *i.e.* of feedback-systems, and

(4) the treatment of the interaction between several information-processing systems, especially in game-theory.

The problem investigated in the article concerns living systems, more precisely the conscious behaviour of human beings. (Therefore the problem treated in the article is rather called a problem of the informational sciences than a biocybernetic one, when the term 'biocybernetics' is used in a narrow sense.) Imitations by machines of the psychological processes described are easely feasible. From the Shannon measure of information a measure for the surprising value is deduced, and in connection with it a measure for something that could be called 'preconscious astonishingness' (Auffälligkeit). Several, not at all closely related psychological experiences can be explained quantitatively in terms of these measures, which hence are justified. Furthermore the theoretical procedure shows the utility of each of the first three degrees of cybernetics for the treatment of problems of the next degree respectively. Some of the experimental psychological results presented in the article give evidence for Wieners well-known suggestion, that there should be some digital information-processing somewhere in the brain.

REFERENCES

ATTNEAVE, F., (1953); Psychological Probability as a function of experienced frequency. *J. exp. Psychol.*, **46**, 81–86.

BENSE, M., (1951); *Die Philosophie*. Frankfurt. Suhrkamp Verlag.

FRANK, H., (1959); Grundlagenprobleme der Informationsästhetik und erste Anwendung auf die mime pure (Diss. T. H. Stuttgart). Waiblingen. Verlagsbuchhandlung Hess.

FRANK, H., (1960); Über das Intelligenzproblem in der Informationspsychologie. *Grundl.st. Kybernetik Geisteswiss.*, **1**, 85–96.

FRANK, H., (1962a); *Kybernetische Grundlagen der Pädagogik — Eine Einführung in die Informationspsychologie.* Baden-Baden. Agis-Verlag. [Russisch: Moskau, Verlag der Akademie der pädagogischen Wissenschaften. Französisch: Paris, Gauthier-Villars].

FRANK, H., (1962b); Quelques résultats théoriques et empiriques concernant l'accomodation informationelle. *IRE-Transactions on information theory*, **IT-8/5**, 150–154.

FRANK, H., (1963a); Kybernetik und Lehrmaschinen. In: *Lehrmaschinen in kybernetischer und pädagogischer Sicht.* H. Frank, Herausgeber. Stuttgart und München. Verlagsgemeinschaft E. Klett und R. Oldenbourg (pp. 13–26).

FRANK, H., (1963b); Informationspsychologie und Nachrichtentechnik. In: *Nerve, Brain and Memory Models.* N. Wiener und J. P. Schadé, Herausgeber. Amsterdam, London, New York. Elsevier (p. 79–98).

FRANK, H., (1963c); Kybernetik und Informationspsychologie. In: *Der Wettlauf um den Kunden von morgen.* W. Lorch, Herausgeber. Frankfurt. Deutscher Fachverlag. (pp. 81–97).

FRANK, H., (1963d); Eine probabilistische Deutung des Zeitauflösungsvermögens. *Grundl.st. Kybernetik Geisteswiss.*, **4**, 27–35.

FRANK, H., (1964); The psychological link of a statistical feedback mechanism explained by means of information theory. *Proceedings of the 18th Symposion of the Society for Experimental Biology.* Cambridge (England). S. 327–342.

FRANK, H., KLUGMANN, D., UND WENDT, S., (1963); Über den Informationsgehalt der Laute in der deutschen Sprache. *Grundl.st. Kybernetik Geisteswiss.*, **4**, 65–72.

HASSENSTEIN, B., (1960); Die bisherige Rolle der Kybernetik in der biologischen Forschung. *Naturwissensch. Rundschau*, **13**, 349–355, 373–382, 419–424.

HOFMANN, H. W., (1963); Informationstheorie und Werbung. In: *Zukunft der Werbung/Werbung der Zukunft*, **1**, 10–13. Nürnberg. Verlag Maul und Co.

LUCE, R. D., (1960); The theory of selective information and some of its behavioral applications. In: *Developments in Mathematical Psychology*, R. D. Luce, Herausgeber. Glencoe (Ill.), The Free Press of Glencoe.

MEYER-EPPLER, W., (1959); *Grundlagen und Anwendungen der Informationstheorie.* Heidelberg. Springer-Verlag.

MOLES, A. A., (1963); Notiz über die Anwendung der Informationstheorie auf die Verteilung der Einzelhandelspreise. *Grundl.st. Kybernetik Geisteswiss.*, **4**, 108–112.

MORIN, R. E., FORRIN, B., UND ARCHER, W., (1961); Information Processing behavior: the role of irrelevant stimulus information. *J. exptl. Psychol.*, **61**, 89–96.

SCHMIDT, H., (1941); Denkschrift zur Gründung eines Institutes für Regelungstechnik. Berlin, VDI-Druck. 2. Auflage in: *Grundl. st. Kybernetik Geisteswiss.*, **2**, Beiheft.

SCHMIDT, H., (1962); Bemerkungen zur Weiterentwicklung der Allgemeinen Regelkreislehre. *Grundl. st. Kybernetik Geisteswiss.*, **3**, 75–84.

SCHWARTZKOPFF, J., (1962); Über Nervenzellen mit problematischen Kodierungsweisen. *Grundl. st. Kybernetik Geisteswiss.*, **3**, 97–109.

SHANNON, C. E., (1948); A mathematical theory of communication. *Bell System Techn. J.*, **27**, 379–423, 623–656.

SHANNON, C. E., (1949); Communication in the Presence of Noise. *Proc. IRE*, **37**, 10–21.

STEINBUCH, K., (1959); Die logische Verknüpfung als Einheit der Nachrichtenverarbeitung. *Nachr. techn. Z.*, **12**, 169–175.

STEINBUCH, K., (1963); *Automat und Mensch — Kybernetische Tatsachen und Hypothesen.* Heidelberg. Springer-Verlag.

VON NEUMANN, J., (1928); 'Zur Theorie der Gesellschaftsspiele', *Mathematische Annalen*, **100**, 295–320.

WIENER, N., (1948); *Cybernetics, or, Control and Communication in the Animal and the Machine.* Paris, Hermann.

WIENER, N., UND SCHADÉ, J. P., Herausgeber: (1963); *Nerve, Brain and Memory Models.* Amsterdam, London, New York. Elsevier.

Taxis, Kinesis and Decussation

V. BRAITENBERG

Centro di Cibernetica del C.N.R., Istituto di Fisica Teorica, Università di Napoli, Naples (Italy)

(1) A basic fact of vertebrate neurology is the crossed representation of the world in the brain: an external stimulus at one side of the animal has its most marked physiological effect in the brain of the opposite side, and electrical stimulation of one side of the brain has its most evident motor effect in the musculature of the opposite side.

The anatomical counterpart of this crossed projection is the evidence that the majority of fiber tracts somewhere cross the midline of the brain or spinal cord. Such crossings are called *commissures* when they connect homologous parts of the two halves of the brain (*e.g.* the anterior commissure and corpus callosum connecting symmetrical regions of the right and left cerebral cortex).

They are called *decussations*, on the other hand, when they cross-connect non-homologous parts (*e.g.* the optic chiasm of lower vertebrates, connecting the retina of each eye with the tectal hemispheres of the opposite sides, or the decussation of the pyramidal tracts between brain stem and spinal cord). Quite obviously we look at the decussations rather than the commissures as the embodiments of crossed projection.

(2) Since it was first discovered, the fact of crossed projection has presented a puzzle and various explanations have been attempted. These have ranged from simple mechanical interpretations to elaborate constructions involving teleological arguments about image processing within the central nervous system. We will mention a few examples without attempting to be exhaustive. At the simplest level, it has been argued that the abundance of crossed fiber bundles makes the brain mechanically more stable, by a lacing or weaving effect. Another very general argument places the origin of decussations in the transition from a primitive (hypothetical) brain with spherical symmetry to the bilaterally symmetrical brain of most animals. It is argued that as, in this transition, a median plane becomes defined, we may rename the connections, initially supposed to be random, as local, commissural, and decussational: the longest and therefore most important fiber bundles will be decussated. Apart from weak points in this argument, it should be as valid for invertebrate as well as vertebrate brains, but while crossed projection may occur in invertebrate brains, it does not seem to be the general rule.

Possibly the best known explanation of decussation is that provided by Ramon y Cajal (1898) to account specifically for the decussation of the optic tracts, which he interpreted as a correction of the image inversion which occurs for reasons of geo-

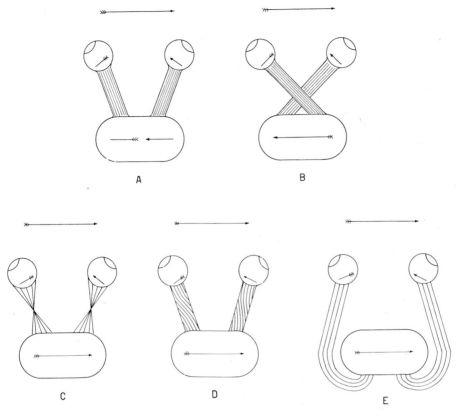

Fig. 1. To illustrate Ramon y Cajal's argument on the optic chiasm, as well as some counter arguments (see text).

metrical optics in camera eyes. His argument is as follows: suppose the right and left halves of the visual field are projected, with optical inversion, onto the right and left retinae. If these two half-images were projected by uncrossed fiber bundles onto the right and left halves of a common receiving surface, there would be a midline discontinuity in the mapping of the visual field on this surface (Fig. 1A). Ramon y Cajal saw the chiasmal crossing as a simple means of avoiding this discontinuity (Fig. 1B).

Several objections to Ramon y Cajal's argument may be raised, both on the basis of the reasoning involved and in the light of experimental results since his time.

(a) Crossing is sufficient, but not necessary, for correction of optical inversion. For example, a 180° rotation of uncrossed fiber bundles or the equivalent internal crossing of fibers within each bundle, would permit correction without decussation (Fig. 1C, D). Similarly, recurved and uncrossed bundles projecting onto the posterior poles of the optic lobes would also correct for discontinuity (Fig. 1E).

(b) The cogency of his argument requires that points in the environment on or near the midline should have their central representation also on the midline of the common receiving surface. If the receiving surface is identified with the optic tectum (as apparently Ramon y Cajal did) then experimental studies of the topography of projection on the tectum are pertinent (Akert, 1949; Gaze, 1958; Apter, 1945). Gaze, for example, found in the frog an orderly projection of left visual field onto right tectum and *vice versa*, but the orientation of the projection is such that the required continuity between right and left is not evident. The line along which the two optic lobes are fused corresponds to points on the periferies of the upper posterior quadrants of the visual fields; while points adjacent to the midline of the visual field are projected to anterior regions of the tectal hemispheres (Fig. 2).

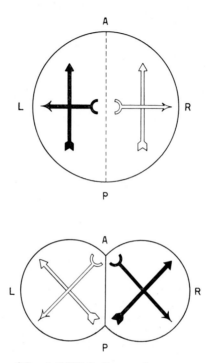

Fig. 2. Diagrammatic version of Gaze's (1958) findings on the representation of the visual field in the tectum of the frog. Only the orientation, not the size and exact position of the arrows should be considered. The upper diagram represents the combined right and left visual fields, as a cupola over the frog, seen from above. The lower diagram represents the optic tectum, seen from above. A: anterior; P: posterior; L: left; R: right.

(c) Ramon y Cajal's argument contains implicitly a subtle cybernetic point. His preoccupation with midline continuity is justified only if the receiver itself is prepared to take advantage of the continuity; the receiver should operate as effectively and uniformly over the midline as it would on either side. The anatomical evidence appears to be against such a functional continuity (Fig. 3).

J. Z. Young (1962) in discussing the question 'Why two brains?', also touched upon the problem of decussation. If we read his argument correctly, he takes the view that the various central maps of sensory experience must correspond spatially one to another, and to motor activity, so that, for example, 'up' must have the same sense for all sensory modalities and for consequent motor activity. He argues that the

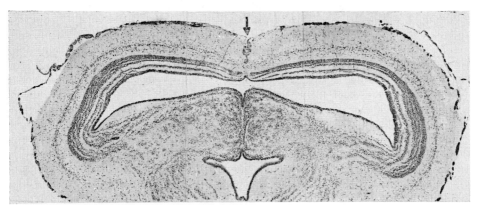

Fig. 3. Frontal section through frog mesencephalon, Nissl stain, enlargement 50 : 1, to show the marked fissure and discontinuity of the cell layers on the midline (marked by an arrow).

orientation of central representations will also conform to that of the world. Decussation can then be seen as a special means to this end of oriented representation. His argument is interesting in that it requires the top-bottom inversion found by Gaze.

The argument most closely related to the approach we will explore is that usually attributed to Coghill (we have been unable to locate the source). The argument assumes the primacy of negative taxis in primitive creatures, of avoidance responses involving action of the motor organs on the side opposite to the stimulation. Thus crossing between sensory organs of one side and motor organs of the other is plausible. Prosse (1934) gives a correlation of a photic avoidance response (in earthworms) with decussating fibers in the brain.

(3) Our own argument is intended to show that decussation of fiber tracts is a simple and effective means of ensuring certain animal behaviours describable as taxes. By a *taxis* we mean an orienting movement of an animal with respect to a source of stimulation. The particular taxes of our interest are those in which there is oriented locomotion toward or away from a source of stimulation, as in pursuit of prey and flight from a predator.

In order to explore the behavior of a number of hypothetical toys with simple 'neurological' structure, we will introduce an environment consisting of a plane on which the toys move. With each point of this plane we will associate a stimulus magnitude. We will assume the magnitudes to vary smoothly, and to form peaks or plateaus that may be identified as sources of stimulation.

All our toys have a body axis with a head end, and movement is always head first. Each toy is equipped with sense organs able to measure the local stimulus strength, and with motors whose speed depends on the amount of stimulation received by the sense organs to which they are connected. The toys are limited to the cases in which there is one-to-one connection of sense organs to motors.

An especially simple case is toy A (Fig. 4) which has only one sense organ and one motor. They are connected positively, so that the greater the local stimulus the greater

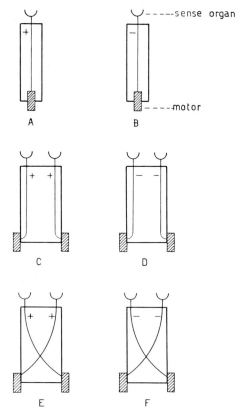

Fig. 4. Six different schemes of sensorimotor connections.

the speed of the motor. In the absence of disturbances of direction, this toy will follow a straight course fully determined by its initial orientation, though with speeds determined by the strength of stimulus at the points it passes. It will reach — and pass — a stimulus peak only if initially aimed toward it.

Toy B differs from A in that the sensorimotor connection is negative, so that the stronger the local stimulus the slower the motor. Again the behaviour is limited to straight runs, but with speed reduced in regions of high stimulation, and increased in regions of low stimulus strength.

Neither toys A nor B shows taxis, since they do not orient toward or away from sources of stimulation. Their only relation to stimulation is increase or decrease of motion, *i.e.*, positive or negative *kinesis*. If anything, toy A, with positive kinesis, will tend to spend less time in regions of high stimulation, since there its speed is greater. Toy B, conversely, will saunter where stimulation is high, and race where it is low.

Our other toys are closer to the vertebrate plan, in that they have paired sensory organs and paired motors. This makes it possible for their behaviour to depend on differences of stimulation between right and left. The behaviour can include turning, as a result of the differential action of the motors (Fig. 5). We shall suppose that the motors will turn the animal to the opposite side. In other words, the motors act like

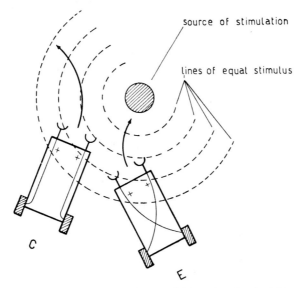

Fig. 5. Behaviour of toys C and E in the vicinity of a stimulus hill.

a pair of oars on a boat, or a pair of jets firing backwards and located to the right and left of the midline, or a pair of pectoral fins, etc. A different arrangement of the motors is however also possible and perhaps occurs in the eel-like motion in fishes, where the stronger contraction on one side will turn the animals toward the same side (Gray, 1933). We shall postpone the discussion of the latter case and shall equip our toys with jet-like motors.

Using positive and negative, crossed and uncrossed symmetrical connections between sense organs and motors we can make four toys. Toy C has uncrossed positive connection. Like toy A, its kinesis will be positive, but it will also show a taxis. If it is put where stimulation is greater on one side, the motor of the same side will show greater activity, swinging the toy to the side of the lower stimulation, i.e., away from the source of stimulation. The turning will continue until the stimuli are the same on the two sides, when the toy is pointed directly away from the source of stimulation. Thus it shows positive kinesis but negative taxis.

The next toy, D, has uncrossed negative connections, and reacts to unequal stimuli by turning to the side of the greater stimulus until the stimuli match, whereupon it is pointed directly to a source of stimulation, toward which it will move more and more slowly. Thus its kinesis is negative and its taxis is positive.

Finally we come to decussations. Toy E has crossed connections but is like toy C in that the connections are positive. Thus its kinesis is positive, but unlike toy C, its taxis is also positive. It not only orients toward a source of stimulation, but proceeds toward it with increasing speed as the stimulation increases.

The last of our toys, F, has crossed negative connections. Like E, its kinesis and taxis are alike in sign, in this case negative. It turns away from any source of stimulation except one directly ahead, and moves more sluggishly the stronger the stimulation.

Each of these gadgets shows an exceptional behaviour when the source of stimulation is directly in front or directly astern, as the case may be, since irrespective of the sign of their taxis they will move ahead when the two motors are symmetrically activated. These exceptional behaviours are however highly unstable, since the least disturbance producing a deviation from the straight course will reinstate the orienting behaviour typical for each case.

Thus the behaviour of these four toys, C, D, E, F, may be described simply by the signs of their taxis and kinesis, of which they represent all the possible combinations:

	C	D	E	F
kinesis	+	—	+	—
taxis	—	+	+	—

(4) We are now in a position to state our case tentatively by showing that a scheme of crossed sensorimotor connections carries certain advantages in terms of the taxic–kinetic behaviour with which it is associated. The two cases with decussations, E and F have *taxis and kinesis of the same sign*, which means that their behaviour may be even more simply described as one of *attraction* toward the source of stimulation (positive taxis and kinesis, case E) or *repulsion* from the source of stimulation (negative taxis and kinesis, case F).

The comparison with familiar situations in physics is tempting, but cannot be carried through too literally, since *e.g.* toy F, though it will be slowed down when it is headed toward the thing from which it is 'repelled', it will not be accelerated if the repelling thing approaches it from the back. Rather, we may see in the type of behaviour characterized by the corresponding signs of taxis and kinesis a fundamental codification of the envronment into *good* and *bad* things, things which the animal tends to approach actively on one hand, and things which it tends to avoid on the other hand.

This is, because of its intrinsic simplicity, essentially an aesthetically appealing feature. It is another and very difficult matter to show that such simple attractive and repulsive behaviour was, in terms of evolution a feature with such evident selective advantage that we may base on it an explanation of the decussated scheme of the vertebrate nervous system. This is all the more difficult, since we know next to nothing about the ancestral protovertebrate in which this scheme was first, once and for ever, established, about its behaviour and about its environment. Up to this point we made only one tacit assumption on the nature of the ancestral protovertebrate: that its propulsion was not eel-like, but jet-like, or more plausibly, was dependent on lateral appendages functioning as oars which, when unilaterally activated, turned the animal to the opposite side.

(5) We will not extend our argument to invertebrates, although decussation clearly

exists there too, and our arguments may apply. Nor will we discuss the *unilateral* chiasms found in many invertebrates (cephalopods, crabs, insects, isopods) associated with the visual system.

Speaking of vertebrates alone, the first objection we have to meet is that in spite of decussations the relation between sensory input and motor action is not crossed, since, for example, visual input on one side projects to the opposite side of the brain, which will in turn control motor action on the side of the original visual input. Thus the double crossing amounts to no crossing at all. This is true for vision, tactile and proprioceptive senses and largely for audition. Such double crossing, by the way, is a serious embarrassment to Coghill's argument given above.

There is, however, a striking exception to crossed representation of sensory information in the brain: *the olfactory system*. Each olfactory tract is directly continuous with the telencephalic hemisphere of the same side, and although fiber anatomy of the olfactory system is wonderously complex, it is safe to say that the main stream of olfactory connections remains on the same side. Since we know the crossed relation between the hemispheres and motor output, we have a single sensorimotor decussation on which to base our argument: the crossing of the neuronal chains leading from the olfactory organs to the effectors.

We can now add a further point to our picture of the ancestral protovertebrate. If we want to base our case on decussations on the relation between taxis and kinesis, we must suppose that *the ancestral protovertebrate was governed chiefly by olfactory taxes and kineses*.

(6) Having given the olfactory sense a priority (contrary to Ramon y Cajal's and Coghill's choice of vision) in the evolution of decussations, we must supply an explanation of the doubly crossed *i.e.* effectively homolateral, relation between the other senses and the motor organs. This we can do by sketching a likely evolutionary transition from our hypothetical creature to the well known vertebrate type. Although it is unrealistic to consider that the ur-ancestor was devoid of other senses, we will suppose that they were of subordinate importance, in the sense that they carried little information about the environment or that the motor effect which they produced remained local (segmental). To such an animal the environment, varied as it may be chemically, would be represented on an extremely rudimentary spatial map consisting essentially in the differenciation of a right and left half, or if we wish, in the localization of events in the right and left nostril respectively. We agree with professor Young in supposing that the further evolution of the vertebrate nervous system was largely dependent on the elaboration of topographical maps of the environment within the brain, and that in this process a principle of economy requires the maps of the various senses to share common spatial coordinates. But which is the first sense to impose a map of the environment on the brain, and to determine its orientation in further evolution for all other senses? Our argument gives olfaction evolutionary priority, but the olfactory map, being merely two valued, clearly lacks complexity. What does have complexity comparable to that of the later tactile and visual maps is the motor map, *i.e.* the central topographical representation of the musculature of

the animal. *This representation in our hypothetical animal is crossed.* We may reconstruct the further story with as high a plausibility as any reconstruction of evolution
will permit. Let us take proprioception first. The right musculature is comanded by
the left brain. Most appropriately for its functional role in the control of motor activity,
proprioception from the right will feed into the left brain, thus establishing the first
doubly crossed connection between sense organ and motor output. The cutaneous
senses, which bear an intimate local relation to the musculature, will also conform
to the muscle map. Hence the animal's body is represented in a crossed fashion in
its own brain. From there it is an easy step to postulate that the representation
of the environment beyond the animal's skin should agree with the topographical
map of the animal's body, with which it is contiguous. It follows that distance
senses also should have crossed pathways, explaining the chiasm of the optic nerves
(which in most vertebrates is a complete crossing). The only sense that would not
agree is that of our starting point: olfaction, but this is not a difficulty if we note
that in further evolution the olfactory map has been virtually reduced to a single
point in most animals.

(7) Perhaps the worst fault of our toys as models of taxic and kinetic behaviour is, to
use an engineering term, their linearity, *i.e.* the proportionality between motor output
and sensory input. This is in contrast with many responses in animal behaviour which,
though graded, either occur or do not occur, depending on the intensity of the stimulus.
An animal will either rest or walk, without any intermediate type of behaviour, a
flight or aggressive pattern will either occur or not etc. Accordingly, we may amend
our toys by equiping them with a rudimentary *brain* (Fig. 6), a decision organ inter-

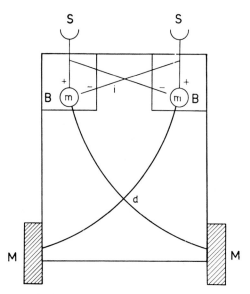

Fig. 6. Toy E with rudimentary brain interposed between input and output. The commissure between
the two halves of the brain is better explained in Fig. 7. S: sense organs; M: motors; B: brain;
i: fibers for mutual inhibition; m: motor cells; d: decussating connections.

posed between sense organs and motors, which will activate the motors (or stop
normally active motors) only when the stimulus intensity surpasses a certain threshold
value. There are drawbacks in such all-or-none action, as becomes evident when we
observe the taxic behaviour of our newly amended toys. Differential action of the
motors, and therefore the turning movements necessary for taxis are possible only
in a narrow range in which one sense organ receives a stimulus above threshold, and
the other one below threshold. Outside of this range both motors are either active
or inactive and no orientation is possible. This difficulty is again overcome by the
application of a wiring scheme, known in biology as 'lateral' or 'mutual inhibition'.
The excitation received by each sense organ, multiplied by a factor slightly less than
1, is subtracted from the excitation received by the other sense organ. There is output
only if the result of this operation is positive (Fig. 7).

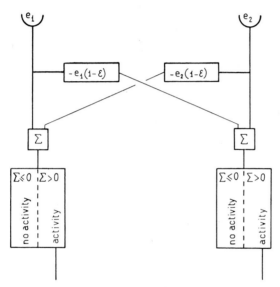

Fig. 7. Scheme of mutual inhibition. e_1, e_2: magnitudes of sensory excitation; ε: a small quantity;
Σ: sum.

The whole arrangement will have the following characteristics: when the stimulus
is absent, there will be no output on either side of the brain; when the stimulus is
equal on both sides, there will be output on both sides. For unequal stimuli, only the
side receiving the stronger stimulus will give output.

We mention this arrangement because, if we invoke it hypothetically for the
function of the olfactory sense, we find the necessary wiring described by Cajal in
olfactory histology. The excitation reaching the olfactory bulb from the sense cells
in the olfactory mucosa, besides being relayed toward further olfactory waystations
in the homolateral telencephalic hemisphere through the axons of the mitral cells
(A in Fig. 8) is projected to the opposite olfactory bulb through the axons of Cajal's
tufted cells (B in Fig. 8) where it is inserted in the same synaptic network from which
it was derived on the original side. We are strongly tempted to suppose that the

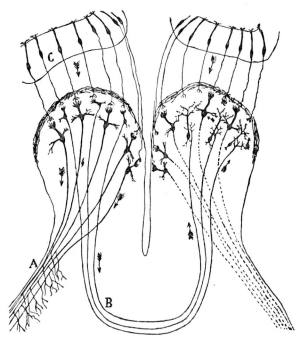

Fig. 8. Course of secondary fibers in the olfactory bulbs, from Cajal (1911). A: mitral cells; B: tufted cells; C: bipolar olfactory cells.

junction is inhibitory, and that the histological arrangement described by Cajal may be understood as a mechanism for mutual inhibition and consequently, for enhancing the differential action of the two olfactory bulbs.

This interpretation of the histology is prompted by some recent physiological experiments, (Mancia et al., 1962) which revealed an inhibitory coupling between the two olfactory bulbs in the rabbit, or, as the authors put it, almost a 'mirror image' response in the two bulbs when either olfactory mucosa was stimulated independently.

We learn from these observations that the olfactory sense is at least in some vertebrates fully equipped for differential action and thus represents a plausible sensory input for taxic behaviour, even if this may appear surprising to us microsmatic humans who are used to think in terms of our own, relatively poor and certainly spatially adimensional olfactory experience.

(8) It is not within our competence to discuss the plausibility of our argument on decussations on the basis of other evidence related to the origin of vertebrates. We may however point out some crucial points which such a discussion would have to consider. There is, first of all the importance of paired olfactory sense organs in our argument, which besides the neurological equipment for differential action, already considered in the preceding paragraph, requires even more fundamentally two spatially separated olfactory mucosae and two independent nostrils. This is a condition which is not fulfilled in animals such as cyclostomes which are often put close

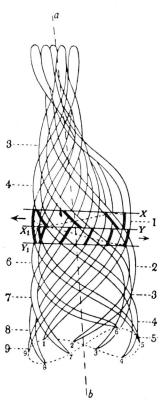

Fig. 9. (from Gray, 1933) Diagram to show waves of flexion traveling along the body of a swimming eel. 1–9: successive positions; ba: direction of motion.

to the root of the vertebrate evolutionary tree. We would state as a consequence of our hypothesis that it was certainly not in cyclostomes that the decussating plan of the nervous system was first established.

Another crucial point is the type of motors, which we had supposed to be oar-like, *i.e.* such that one motor by itself will turn the animal to the opposite side and not eel-like, *i.e.* such that unilateral activation will turn the animal to the same side. Now, though propulsion in fishes is predominantly eel-like (Fig. 9, from Gray, 1933), we are forced to look for an ancestral vertebrate in which at least the movements associated with olfactory taxes are the responsability of oar-like lateral appendages. This may not be too serious a difficulty, since even in many recent fishes which rely on undulating movements for fast propulsion, slow tracking and browsing is a function of lateral fins.

The most serious criticism which we advance toward our own hypothesis lest someone else may use it, is that corresponding signs of taxis and kinesis are not intrinsically advantageous, unless a particular environment is invoked. It may well be argued that rapid action in the presence of 'bad' stimuli and slow action in the presence of 'good' ones, *i.e.* opposite signs of taxis and kinesis under some other conditions would be the better choice. We are inclined to take the correspondence of signs in taxis and kinesis as a more generally valid scheme, since in a competitive environment it is clear at least for positive olfactory taxes that associated positive kinesis would have selective advantages. Food finding is largely a question of who gets there first. For negative olfactory taxes we should perhaps not think in terms of avoidance and flight from predators (which requires positive kinesis), but rather in terms of a mechanism working in push-pull together with positive taxes, a mechanism concerned with those chemical stimuli which provide negative conditions for food finding and which should therefore be the exact opposite of the positive taxic mechanism.

ACKNOWLEDGEMENT

Research reported in this document was sponsored in part by USAF through Grant AF-EOAR 63–89 and by Grant NB 03922–02 from the National Institute of Health.

SUMMARY

One of the most general rules of functional neuroanatomy is the crossed representation of the world in the brain. The origin of this puzzling phenomenon has been explained in the past on the basis of a primary optic decussation which was interpreted as a necessary correction of the image inversion in lens eyes.

The validity of this scheme is doubted here and an alternate hypothesis is presented. The supposition of a vertebrate ancestor governed mainly by olfactory taxes allows one to derive the crossed representation under the assumption that (a) positive kinesis associated with positive taxis (and *vice versa*) is advantageous, and (b) an evolutionary transition has occured from a chiefly taxic chordate to one which is governed by the principle of the representation of objects in 'internal maps' of the environment within the brain.

REFERENCES

AKERT, K., (1949); Experimenteller Beitrag zur zentralen Netzhaut-Representation im Tectum Opticum. *Schweiz. Arch. Neurol. Psychiat.*, **64**, 1–16.

APTER, J. T., (1945); Projection of the retina on the superior colliculus in cats. *J. Neurophysiol.*, **8**, 123.

CAJAL, S. R. Y, (1898); Estructura del kiasma optico y teoria general de los entrecruzamientos de las vias nerviosas. *Rev. trimest. micrograf.* LLL, quoted in Cajal, 1911.

CAJAL, S. R., Y, (1911); *Histologie du Système Nerveux de l'Homme et des Vertébrés*. Paris. Maloine.

GAZE, R. M., (1958); The representation of the retina on the optic lobe of the frog. *Quart. J. exp. Physiol.*, **43**, 209–214.

GRAY, J., (1933); Directional control of fish movement. *Proc. roy. Soc. B.*, **113**, 115–125.

MANCIA, M., (1963); Specific and unspecific influences on the olfactory bulb. The Physiological Basis of Mental Activity. *Electroenceph. clin. Neurophysiol.*, Suppl. **24**, 1–13.

MANCIA, M., VON BAUMGARTEN, R., AND GREEN, J. D., (1962); Response patterns of olfactory bulb neurons. *Arch. ital. Biol.*, **100**, 449–462.

PROSSE, C. L., (1934); Effect of the central nervous system on responses to light in *Einea foetida* Sav. *J. comp. Neurol.*, **59**, 61–91.

YOUNG, J. Z., (1962); Why do we have two brains? Interhemispheric Relations and Cerebral Dominance. V. B. Mountcastle, Editor. Baltimore. Johns Hopkins Press (pp. 7–24).

Universal Embedding Spaces for Automata

JOHN H. HOLLAND

University of Michigan, Ann Arbor, Mich. (U.S.A.)

The tremendous upsurge of interest over the past two decades in mathematical theories of organism, much of it occasioned by Norbert Wiener's signal work *Cybernetics*, has yet to reach its crest. One important part of this activity has been a continued attempt to bring logic and automata theory to bear on complicated problems such as self-reproduction and adaptation. The present paper seeks to look more closely at such attempts by examining the notion of construction in the context of automata theory.

1. INTRODUCTION

In his unfinished manuscript, *The Theory of Automata*, von Neumann introduces an unusual space obtained by iterating a 29-state automaton to form an infinite 2-dimensional array. The 29-state automaton is so chosen that the resulting space is computation-universal ('logical-universal'): given any computation, there is a pattern of initial states which will cause that computation to be carried out in the space. Although particular examples and classes of computation-universal spaces have been considered since (Burks, 1960; Church, 1957; Holland, 1960a; Moore, 1962; Myhill, 1962) our knowledge of the role of these spaces in the study of automata and computation remains meager.

In spite of this lack, there can be little doubt of the possibilities offered by universal spaces. Von Neumann's particular usage shows just how far-reaching and unusual these may be: By using his space as a framework within which to represent the construction of automata from simple elements, he was able to give the first careful treatment of self-reproducing automata. In a different vein, computation theory offers several appealing opportunities for the use of universal spaces. For instance, a universal space can serve as a uniform formal context for comparing computation procedures as to complexity and efficiency. The usual approach via Turing machines fixes 'work square', 'description', and similar conventions at the outset, typically with metalevel statements; thus effects of changes in convention are placed beyond the theory's reach. In contrast, the conventions associated with different computation procedures can be dealt with explicitly in a universal space. This is an important gain since changes in convention drastically affect the procedure employed (the machine required) to carry out a computation.

The present paper seeks to bring the possibilities of universal spaces into sharper focus. It begins (Compositions of Finite Automata) by characterizing the automata which can be built up from an arbitrary finite or countably infinite set of atomata. The general idea of representing (or embedding) the structure of one automaton in another is then examined (Embeddings and Computation Procedures). Finally a general class of universal embedding spaces is defined, some important subclasses are distinguished and several properties of the subclasses apropos to studies of computation and construction are investigated (Universal Compositions).

In treating construction, one cannot escape a preliminary commitment to definition of automata in terms of 'connected' sets of component automata. A straightforward way to accomplish this is to treat an automaton as a device for transforming sequences into sequences: the two finite functions used to define an automaton, the transition and output functions, can easily be extended to functionals mapping sequences into sequences. (This contrasts with the usual treatment based upon acceptance of finite strings.) 'Connection' then amounts to using the output sequence of one automaton as the input sequence of another. A function, called a 'composition function' in Part 2, can be used to specify which input sequences are to be identified with which output sequences. By restricting the class of composition functions appropriately, it can be assured that:

(i) the composition of a finite set of automata is an automaton;

(ii) the composition of a countably infinite set of automata effectively defines a unique output sequence for any component automaton for each choice of free input sequences and assignment of initial states (free input sequence = an input sequence not constrained by the composition function).

Von Neumann's space is an example of a composition on a countably infinite set of copies of a single 29-state automaton. Part 2 gives these ideas a more rigorous formulation. Functionals, of a restricted kind mapping sequences into sequences, become the mathematical objects of study corresponding to the component automata. From the mathematical point of view, then, the composition function induces a set of simultaneous equations on the functionals. These equations correspond to the constraints imposed by the identification of sequences. (In effect, the automaton corresponding to a given composition function is defined by imposing constraining equations on a set of functionals corresponding to a 'free' product-automaton.) A composition function is considered admissible only if it satisfies a requirement of 'local effectiveness'; this requirement assures a unique solution to the (possibly in-finite) set of simultaneous equations. The unique solution defines a new functional. If the set of components is finite, there will exist some finite automaton with transition and output functions extending to this functional. That is, the result of composition in this case is again a finite automaton.

Von Neumann's interest in construction procedures set three important require-ments on the space he defined:

(1) it had to be possible to represent (or embed) an automaton in that space as a connected set of components (that is, the representation had to be 'structural' as well as 'behavioral' so that one could study processes whereby simpler automata are connected (or composed) to produce more complex automata);

(2) the space had to be homogeneous (so that the same component could be represented in the same way at any position in the space — an important consideration if construction procedures were not to be dependent upon their location in the space);

(3) given any computation, it had to be possible to represent in the space some automaton capable of carrying out that computation (to avoid a priori restrictions on the procedures which could be represented and, hence, studied).

By defining similar properties for compositions one can characterize a fairly general class of computation-universal spaces. The generalization of property 1 to compositions depends in an essential way upon the notion of embedding — mapping one composition (the object composition) into another (the image composition) with preservation of structure and behavior. Specifically, for a mapping from one composition to another to be an embedding it must satisfy two conditions: the functionals corresponding to a component of the object composition and its image under the mapping must be the same; the images of sequences identified by the composition function of the object composition must be identified by the composition function of the image composition. With this definition homogeneity, property 2, becomes a requirement that, if a composition can be embedded at all, the same embedding procedure must serve *mutatis mutandis* to embed that composition anywhere in the image composition. Finally, property 3 becomes a requirement that, given any computation, some composition capable of carrying out that computation must be embeddable in the image composition (in what follows this requirement will be restricted to computations which can be carried out by finite automata — a weakening not altering essential points of the discussion). Part 3 of the paper develops these concepts.

The above properties can be combined, as indicated, to define the set, U, of homogeneous, computation-universal compositions. It can easily be shown (Part 4) that each member of this set is a composition over a countably infinite set of copies of a single automaton (a single generator) and that the elements of the composition can be located in a regular fashion in an n-dimensional cartesian coordinate system. A natural subclass, U_d, can be defined by adding as a requirement one further property of the von Neumann space — a requirement that inputs of the generating automaton affect its outputs only after a non-zero 'delay'. In other words, the generating automaton is required to be of the Moore type. The subclass U_d includes the natural n-dimensional generalizations of von Neumann's two-dimensional space (Von Neumann, unpublished) and counterparts of Church's potentially-infinite automata (Church, 1957); it excludes 'most' of the iterative circuit computers (Holland, 1960a) although these fall within the class U. A second sub-class, U_c, of U can be defined by strengthening property 3 to a requirement that all finite compositions be embeddable; *i.e.*, elements of U_c must be composition-universal and homogeneous. Certain of the iterative circuit computers belong to the class U_c.

Part 4 investigates and compares U, U_d, and U_c. It is proved there that 'most' finite compositions can *not* be embedded in a composition of class U_d, even if the notion of embedding is considerably weakened. This is so even though every computation can be realized in the space by some embedded composition. The theorem turns on the failure of Kleene's representation theorem (Kleene, 1956) for the embedded compositions. It is a consequence of the theorem for U_d that two compositions which are embeddable in a space of type U_d may be further composed (interconnected) in such a way that the resulting composition is no longer embeddable (assuming a common 'input rate' for all images). Stated in another way: Various construction procedures will not be realizable in spaces of type U_d unless 'input rates' are permitted to go to zero as the complexity of the embedded compositions increases. A further consequence: Several different computation procedures may employ a common subroutine, realizable by a single composition, and yet in a space of type U_d the embedded compositions corresponding to the different computations will not have a corresponding common part.

Since there do exist compositions which are not only computation-universal but composition-universal as well, the classes U_d and U_c must be non-empty and disjoint. Hence for a composition to be composition-universal it is necessary that its generating element be of the Mealy type — it must have states for which the input-to-output delay (lag-time) is zero. As a consequence compositions of type U_c, though locally effective, may in some states exhibit arbitrarily long (finite) connected sequences of elements with zero lag-time.

Part 5 provides a closing commentary on definitions and results. Two plans for studying computation and construction procedures are contrasted: One may identify the class of 'realistic' universal spaces with the class U_d, restricting the admissible realizations of finite automata (by requiring a less than exponential 'fan out' in compositions) so as to retain universality. Alternatively one may identify the class of universal spaces with the class U_c, permitting channels with zero delay. It can be shown that any space of type U_d can be embedded in a space of type U_c; thus either approach can in fact be implemented via the spaces U_c.

2. COMPOSITIONS OF FINITE AUTOMATA

This study of computation-universal spaces is based upon the possibility of defining an automaton in terms of a 'connected' set of component automata. Hence, the first task is to characterize the automata which can be defined by connecting elements of an arbitrary, finite or countably infinite, set of finite automata. A composition function will specify the connections in each case; thus we must characterize the automaton corresponding to each composition function. Since composition is to be defined over arbitrary sets of automata, the sets may include automata of the Mealy type. That is, the output of some component automaton, in some states, may depend upon its current input. (The logical nets of Burks and Wright (Burks and Wright, 1953), which are defined over a set of primitives including 'non-delay' switches, are examples of such compositions). In order that the behavior of the resulting compositions be effectively defined it is necessary to restrict the class of composition functions by a requirement of 'local effectiveness'. Roughly, a composition is locally effective if the state of each component automaton at any time is uniquely determined by the transition functions of automata in some finite 'neighborhood' of the component. That is, the state of a component at time $t + 1$ can be computed from the internal states and states of free inputs (inputs not constrained by connection), at time t, of a finite, connected subset of elements of the composition — a subset which may in general change with time. In the definitions below most of the complications come from this requirement. However, unless the class of compositions is to be unduly narrowed (excluding thereby 'most' logical nets), the requirement cannot be avoided. It will be shown that the behavior of each component of a locally effective composition is uniquely and effectively defined.

Compositions will be defined for any indexed set of elements $\{a_\alpha \ni \alpha \; \varepsilon \; A\}$ satisfying the following conditions:

A is a finite or countably infinite ordered set

$$a_\alpha = \; < I_a, S_a, O_a, f_a, u_a >$$

$$I_a = \Pi_{i=1}^{m_a} I_{a,i}, \text{ a cartesian product on finite sets } I_{a,i};$$

S_a, a finite set;

$$O_a = \Pi_{j=1}^{n_a} O_{a,j}, \text{ a cartesian product on finite sets } O_{a,j};$$

$$f_a : I_a \times S_a \to S_a;$$
$$u_a : I_a \times S_a \to O_a.$$

X and Y will designate the (lexicographically ordered) sets of all pairs of indices used to specify sets $I_{a,i}$ and $O_{a,j}$ respectively:

$$X = \{(a, i) \ni \alpha \; \varepsilon \; A \text{ and } i \leq m_a\}$$
$$Y = \{(a, j) \ni \alpha \; \varepsilon \; A \text{ and } j \leq n_a\}$$

Each quintuple a_α with attendant conditions constitutes one of the standard definitions of a finite automaton: the elements of $I_{a,i}$ being interpreted as the states of the ith input of a_α, the elements of S_a as the internal states and the elements of $O_{a,j}$ as the states of the jth output. The quintuple is used to define recursively two families of functionals F_a and U_a (parametrised by S_a) from infinite sequences on I_a (input sequences) to infinite sequences on S_a and O_a respectively (internal state sequences and output sequences):

$$F_a : I_a^N \times S_a \to S_a^N$$

$$U_a : I_a^N \times S_a \to O_a^N, \qquad\qquad N = \{0, 1, 2, \ldots\}$$

$$\text{where } I_a^N = \{\underline{I}_a \ni \underline{I}_a : N \to I_a\}$$

$$S_a^N = \{\underline{S}_a \ni \underline{S}_a : N \to S_a\}$$

$$O_a^N = \{\underline{O}_a \ni \underline{O}_a : N \to O_a\}$$

The functions I_a, S_a, O_a are interpreted as infinite sequences. The recursive extension of f_a and u_a to F_a and U_a can be given as follows:

$$F_a\,(\underline{I}_a\,(0),\,s) = s$$
$$F_a\,(\underline{I}_a\,(t+1),\,s) = f_a\,(\underline{I}_a\,(t),\,F_a\,(\underline{I}_a\,(t),\,s))$$
$$U_a\,(\underline{I}_a\,(t),\,s) = u_a\,(\underline{I}_a\,(t),\,F_a\,(\underline{I}_a\,(t),\,s)) \qquad s\,\varepsilon\,S_a,\,t\,\varepsilon\,N.$$

An *unrestricted composition*, $\underline{A}$, on $\{a_a\}$ is a quintuple $<I_A,\,S_{\underline{A}},\,O_A,\,f_{\underline{A}},\,u_{\underline{A}}>$ such that:

$$S_{\underline{A}} = \Pi_{a\varepsilon A}\,S_a = \{s : A \to \,^{U}_{\,a}S_a \ni a\,\varepsilon\,A \text{ and } s\,(a)\,\varepsilon\,S_a\}$$

$$I_{\underline{A}} = \Pi_{a\varepsilon A}\,\Pi_{i=1}^{m_a}\,I_{a,i} = \Pi_{x\varepsilon X}\,I_x = \{i : X \to \,^{U}_{\,x}I_x \ni x\,\varepsilon\,X \text{ and } i\,(x)\,\varepsilon\,I_x\}$$

$$O_{\underline{A}} = \Pi_{a\varepsilon A}\,\Pi_{j=1}^{n_a}\,O_{a,j} = \Pi_{y\varepsilon Y}\,O_y = \{o : Y \to \,^{U}_{\,y}O_y \ni y\,\varepsilon\,Y \text{ and } o(y)\,\varepsilon\,O_y\}$$

Under interpretation, $i : X \to \,^{U}_{\,x}I_x$ is a particular input state assignment to the inputs indexed by X, and $I_{\underline{A}}$ is the set of all possible input state assignments (functions); $S_{\underline{A}}$ and $O_{\underline{A}}$ are interpreted similarly. The transition function $f_{\underline{A}} : I_{\underline{A}} \times S_{\underline{A}} \to S_{\underline{A}}$ is thus a functional, from assignment functions into assignment functions, satisfying the requirement:

$$f_{\underline{A}}\,(i,\,s)\,(a) = s'\,(a) = f_a\,(i\,(a),\,s\,(a))$$

where

$$i\,\varepsilon\,I_{\underline{A}},\quad s,\,s'\,\varepsilon\,S_{\underline{A}}$$

$$i\,(a) = (i\,(a,\,1),\,i\,(a,\,2),\,\ldots,\,i\,(a,\,m_a)).$$

Similarly $u_{\underline{A}} : I_{\underline{A}} \times S_{\underline{A}} \to O_{\underline{A}}$ satisfies

$$u_{\underline{A}}\,(i,\,s)\,(a) = o\,(a) = u_a\,(i\,(a),\,s\,(a)).$$

Each composition over $\{a_a\}$ will be defined in terms of a *composition function* γ satisfying the following conditions:

(i) domain, $Y' \subset Y$
(ii) range, $X' \subset X$
(iii) $\gamma : Y' \to X'$, 1–1 onto
(iv) $O_y \subset I_{\gamma\,(y)}$.

Under interpretation the function γ determines which inputs of automata in set $\{a_a\}$ are connected to outputs of automata in the set. Property (iii) is a requirement that every output be connected to at most one input — 'junctions' or 'fan-outs' must be represented by a component automaton with multiple outputs. [Note that $\{a_a\}$ may include 'fan-out' elements with no delay: $u_y\,(i,\,s) = i$ for $y = (a,\,1),\,\ldots,\,(a,\,n_a)$, where $u_y = \,_{df}\text{proj}_y\,u_a\,(i,\,s)$]. Property (iv) assures the compatability of the symbols of the output of index y with the symbols of the input of index x — all encoding and decoding procedures must be carried out explicitly by component automata. Each x ε X' in the range of γ selects an input of the unrestricted composition $\underline{A}$ which is to be constrained by the requirement

$$(\forall t) \, [\underline{I}_x \, (t) = \underline{O}_{\gamma^{-1}(x)} \, (t)].$$

More formally the composition function induces a set of equations of the form

$$U_y \, (\underline{I}_a, \, s) = \underline{I}_\gamma \, (y).$$

(For y = (a, j), $U_y \, (\underline{I}_a \, (t), \, s) = {}_{df} \text{proj}_y \, U_a \, (\underline{I}_a(t), \, s)$, an infinite sequence over $O_{a,j}$; $\underline{I}_{\gamma(y)}$ is defined similarly).

Not all functions γ satisfying conditions (i)–(iv) will yield a consistent set of equations: it may be impossible for the sequences $O_y \, (t)$, y ε Y', to satisfy both the equations induced by γ and the equations defining the O_y in terms of the functions u_a. That is, γ may specify the equivalent of a cycle of switches without delay, e.g. a negation element with its output connected to its input. Or, if $\{a_a\}$ is countably infinite, γ may specify a two-way infinite line of switches, none of which involves delay. To assure the consistency of the equations (*), γ must satisfy a further requirement which imposes 'local effectiveness' on the equations. This can be accomplished as follows:

A sequence $y_1, \ldots, y_l$ such that $y_h \varepsilon$ Y', $1 \leq h \leq l$, will be called *connected* if, for h < l, $\text{proj}_1 \, \gamma \, (y_h) = \text{proj}_1 \, y_{h+1}$ [where $\text{proj}_1 \, y = a$ if y = (a, j)]. If $\text{proj}_1 \, y_1 = a$, $\text{proj}_1 \, y_l = \omega$ and $l < \infty$, the connected sequence will be called a sequence from a to ω of length l. A connected sequence may also be infinite, either because an infinite number of distinct elements of Y' are involved or because there exists, say, a sequence $y_1, \ldots, y_l$ such that $\text{proj}_1 \, \gamma \, (y_l) = \text{proj}_1 \, y_1$ (such as would be generated from elements connected in a cycle by γ, cf. Holland, 1960). A connected sequence $\varrho = \{y_1, \ldots, y_l\}$ will be called acyclic if $h \neq h'$ implies $\text{proj}_1 \, y_h \neq \text{proj}_1 \, y_{h'}$, $1 \leq h, \, h' \leq l$.

γ will be called *consistent* with respect to $s \, \varepsilon \, S_{\underline{A}}$ if, for each $a \, \varepsilon \, A$, there is an integer $l_{s,a}$ such that every connected sequence to a of length $l_{s,a}$ contains an element $y_h = (\delta, j)$ such that $u_{\delta,j}$ depends only on the state of a_δ, s (δ), and composition inputs of a_δ, $(\delta, i) \, \varepsilon$ X-X'. The requirement that $u_{\delta,j}$ depend only on the state and composition inputs of a_δ can be stated more formally as:

$$(\forall i_1, \, i_2 \, \varepsilon \, \underline{I}_{\underline{A}}) \, [i_1 \, |\text{X-X}' = i_2| \, \text{X-X}' \Rightarrow u_{\delta,j} \, (i_1 \, (\delta), \, s \, (\delta)) = u_{\delta,j} \, (i_2 \, (\delta), \, s \, (\delta))]$$

By *composition input states* (and *composition output states*) we mean possible state assignments for inputs (and outputs) not constrained by γ:

$$I_{\gamma,\underline{A}} = \{i \mid \text{X-X}' \ni i \, \varepsilon \, \underline{I}_{\underline{A}}\}$$
$$O_{\gamma,\underline{A}} = \{o \mid \text{Y-Y}' \ni o \, \varepsilon \, \underline{O}_{\underline{A}}\}.$$

Theorem. If γ is consistent with respect to $s \, \varepsilon \, S_{\underline{A}}$ then each $i' \, \varepsilon \, I_{\gamma,\underline{A}}$ has a unique extension to an $i \, \varepsilon \, I_{\underline{A}}$ satisfying equations (*).

Proof outline: Let $R_{s,a}$ be the set of all finite acyclic sequences to a, $\{y_1, \ldots, y_h, \ldots, y_l\}$, such that $u_{y_1}, y_1 = (\delta, j)$, depends only on s (δ) and composition inputs to a_δ, $(\delta, i) \, \varepsilon$ X-X', while each u_{y_h}, $1 > h \geq l$, depends upon at least one input indexed by x ε X'. (Under interpretation, the first element of each sequence involves a 'delay' while the remaining elements are 'non-delay' switches, when $\underline{A}$ is a state s).

If γ is consistent with respect to s then no sequence in $R_{s,a}$ is of length greater than $l_{s,a}$ and every connected sequence to a contains some sequence in $R_{s,a}$ as a final sub-sequence. Note that $R_{s,a}$ is finite and can be effectively determined in this case.

Let $B_{s,a} = \{\beta \ni \beta = \text{proj}_1 \, y \text{ for y an element of some sequence of } R_{s,a}\}$. $B_{s,a}$ indexes the set of automata having outputs belonging to sequences in $R_{s,a}$.

For any $i' \varepsilon I_{\gamma,\underline{A}}$ and for each x such that $\text{proj}_1 \, x \, \varepsilon \, B_{s,a}$, the equations induced by γ determine i (x) uniquely, using just $i' \mid B_{s,a}$ and $s \mid B_{s,a}$. Moreover, if $\text{proj}_1 \, x \, \varepsilon \, B_{s,\beta}$, $\beta \neq a$, the value for i (x) determined from $B_{s,\beta}$ is the same as that determined from $B_{s,a}$. All of this follows readily upon modifying the algorithm of Theorem X, (Burks and Wright, 1953), so that it applies to the sets $R_{s,a}$.

Since for every $x \, \varepsilon \, X'$ there exists at least one set $B_{s,a}$ such that $\text{proj}_1 \, x \, \varepsilon \, B_{s,a}$, i' can be extended to $i \, \varepsilon \, I_{\underline{A}}$ as follows:

$$
i(x) =
\begin{cases}
i'(x) \text{ if } x \, \varepsilon \, X\text{-}X' \\
\text{the unique value, } u_{\gamma-1 \, (x)} \, (i \, (\text{proj}_1 \, x), \, s \, (\text{proj}_1 \, x)), \text{ determined by the Burks-Wright algorithm if } x \, \varepsilon \, X'.
\end{cases}
$$

For γ consistent with respect to s, let $\mu_s \, (i') \, \varepsilon \, I_{\underline{A}}$ denote the extension of i' guaranteed by the above theorem.

γ will be called a *locally effective composition function* (LECF) if the following conditions are satisfied:

(i) there exists a computable function $s \, \varepsilon \, S_{\underline{A}}$ for which γ is consistent,

(ii) if γ is consistent for $s \, \varepsilon \, S_{\underline{A}}$ then, for every $i' \, \varepsilon \, I_{\gamma,\underline{A}}$, γ is consistent with respect to $f_{\underline{A}} \, (\mu_s \, (i'), \, s)$.

For γ a LECF define:

$$S_{\gamma,\underline{A}} = \{s \, \varepsilon \, S_{\underline{A}} \ni \gamma \text{ is consistent w.r.t. s and s is computable}\}$$
$$f_{\gamma,\underline{A}} \, (i', s) = f_{\underline{A}} \, (\mu_s \, (i'), s)$$
$$u_{\gamma,\underline{A}} \, (i', s) = u_{\underline{A}} \, (\mu_s \, (i'), s) \quad \text{for } i' \, \varepsilon \, I_{\gamma,\underline{A}}, \, s \, \varepsilon \, S_{\gamma,\underline{A}}.$$

For each LECF γ and unrestricted composition $\underline{A}$ the corresponding *composition* A_γ, on $\{a_a\}$ is the quintuple $<I_{\gamma,\underline{A}}, \, S_{\gamma,\underline{A}}, \, O_{\gamma,\underline{A}}, \, f_{\gamma,\underline{A}}, \, u_{\gamma,\underline{A}}>$. (Where no confusion can arise the subscript $\underline{A}$ will be dropped, i.e., I_γ will denote $I_{\gamma,\underline{A}}$, etc.). Thus the set $\{\underline{A}_\gamma \ni \underline{A} \text{ is an unrestricted composition and } \gamma \text{ is LECF over } \underline{A}\}$ will be the set of all (finite and countably infinite) compositions (see $\underline{A}_\gamma$ and $\underline{B}_{\gamma_1}$ of Fig. 1 as examples). The definitions given earlier for finite automata will be used for all compositions; thus $S_\gamma^N = \{\underline{S}_\gamma \ni \underline{S}_\gamma : N \to S_\gamma\}$ etc.

Under interpretation, a composition is so defined that there is at least a unit delay in every cycle of elements and in every infinite non-repeating sequence of elements; note that the delays need not appear at the same position each time and that they may, for instance, become less and less 'dense' in the space with time.

Theorem. If $\underline{A}$ is over a finite set $\{a_a\}$ then, for any LECF γ over $\underline{A}$, $\underline{A}\gamma$ is a finite automaton.

Theorem. If $\underline{A}$ is over a countably infinite set $\{a_\alpha\}$ then, given any $t \; \varepsilon \; N$ and any $\alpha \; \varepsilon \; A$, $\gamma \, (St) \mid \alpha$ can be calculated from $\underline{S}_\gamma \, (0) \mid B \, (\alpha, \, t)$ and $\underline{I}_\gamma \, (0) \mid B \, (\alpha, \, t), \ldots$, $\underline{I}_\gamma \, (t) \mid B \, (\alpha, t)$ where B is a computable function and $B \, (\alpha, \, t)$ is a finite subset of A containing α.

(Under interpretation, this theorem says that the state of any element a_α of the composition at any time t can be determined from the initial state and composition input sequence up to time t of a finite portion of the composition, indexed by $B \, (\alpha, \, t)$ — $B \, (\alpha, \, t)$ will in general be an unbounded function of time. Repeated use of the Burks-Wright algorithm enables determination of $B \, (\alpha, \, t)$ for any α and t.)

Theorem. The property LECF is decidable for all γ over finite $\underline{A}$. (The proof of this theorem follows from a variant of the algorithm for determining admissible states of a finite automaton, *cf.* [Burks and Wright, 1953]).

Theorem. The property LECF is not decidable for all γ over all $\underline{A}$. (The proof of the theorem depends upon the representability of all Turing machines in particular $\underline{A}$ constrained by γ: There exist γ and $\underline{A}$ such that, if a_δ goes into state s^*, γ is not consistent for any s_γ for which $s_\gamma \, (\delta) = s^*$. Moreover, γ can be so selected that deciding whether a_δ takes on state s^* depends upon a solution of the halting problem. Thus, decidability of LECF for γ would yield a decision procedure for the halting problem). For some extensive sub-classes over countably infinite sets $\{a_\alpha\}$, such as the class of iterative circuit computers, it can be proved that all associated γ are LECF.

The following definitions will be useful:

$\{a_1, \ldots, a_k\}$ will be called a set of *generators* for $\underline{A}_\gamma$ if $\{a_\alpha \ni \alpha \; \varepsilon \; A\}$ consists only of copies of elements of $\{a_1, \ldots, a_k\}$.

$B_{\gamma'}$, over $\{b_\beta \ni \beta \; \varepsilon \; B\}$ will be called a *subcomposition* of $\underline{A}_\gamma$ over $\{a_\alpha \ni \alpha \; \varepsilon \; A\}$ if: (i) $\{b_\beta\} \subset \{a_\alpha\}$, (ii) $\gamma' = \gamma \mid Y_{\underline{B}}$ where $Y_{\underline{B}} = \{y \; \varepsilon \; Y' \ni \text{proj}_1 \, y \; \varepsilon \; B \text{ and } \text{proj}_1 \, \gamma \, (y) \; \varepsilon \; B\}$.

3. EMBEDDINGS AND COMPUTATION PROCEDURES

The central objective of an embedding is to mark out, in some (image) composition, a sub-composition which will exhibit the same local behavior as a given (object) composition. For every element in the object composition there must be distinct part (a sub-sub-composition) of the image which defines the same functionals (over images of the free input sequences). Among other things, this amounts to complete preservation of local properties of the information flow. Thus one can study such properties in the embedding. If many compositions can be embedded in a single image composition, various comparisons and interactions can be implemented and studied. Note that only part of the inputs (or outputs) of the image sub-composition may be required for the embedding; also it may be that several inputs (outputs) of the sub-composition will be required to 'encode' a single input (or output) of the object composition. This 'encoding' causes problems when one tries to reflect the connection scheme of the object composition in the image sub-composition. The definitions are cumbrous largely on this account.

We will consider first a strict notion of embedding which preserves all local behavior on the original time-scale. Afterward this notion will be weakened so that the object composition can be partitioned and only behavior of and connections between elements of the partition need be preserved and this only on a dilated time-scale.

Let $\underline{A}_\gamma$ be a composition with associated index sets A, X, Y. Let $\underline{B}_{\gamma 1}$ with associated index sets A_1, X_1, Y_1 be a sub-composition of $\underline{C}_{\gamma 2}$. Let φ be a mapping from A, X, Y and $S\gamma$, $I\gamma$, $O\gamma$ to *subsets* of A_1, X_1, Y_1, $S_{\gamma 1}$, $I_{\gamma 1}$, $O_{\gamma 1}$ respectively (*i.e.* $\varphi(a) \subset A_1$, $\varphi(x) \subset X_1$, etc.). φ will be called a *strict embedding* of $\underline{A}_\gamma$ in $\underline{C}_{\gamma 2}$ (on $\underline{B}_{\gamma 1}$) if the following conditions are satisfied:

(i) Distinct {elements, inputs, outputs} map onto distinct sets of {elements, inputs, outputs}:
$a \neq a_1 \Rightarrow \varphi(a) \cap \varphi(a_1) = \Lambda$, $x \neq x_1 \Rightarrow \varphi(x) \cap \varphi(x_1) = \Lambda$, and $y \neq y \Rightarrow \varphi(y) \cap \varphi(y_1) = \Lambda$, where Λ is the null set.

(ii) Each {input, output, composition ($\underline{A}_\gamma$) input, composition ($\underline{A}_\gamma$) output} of an element of index a maps onto a set of {inputs, outputs, composition ($\underline{B}_{\gamma 1}$) inputs, composition ($\underline{B}_{\gamma 1}$) outputs} of the subset of elements in $\underline{B}_{\gamma 1}$ indexed by $\varphi(a)$:
$proj_1 \, \varphi(x) \Rightarrow \varphi(proj_1 \, x)$, $proj_1 \, \varphi(y) \Rightarrow \varphi(proj_1 \, y)$
$x \; \varepsilon \; X\text{-}X' \rightarrow \varphi(x) \Rightarrow X_1\text{-}X_1'$, $y \; \varepsilon \; Y\text{-}Y' \rightarrow \varphi(y) \Rightarrow Y_1\text{-}Y_1'$.

(iii) If y is connected to x by γ then all outputs in $\varphi(y)$ must be connected by γ_1 to all inputs in $\varphi(x)$:
$\varphi(\gamma(y)) = \gamma_1(\varphi(y))$.

(iv) If two {internal, input, output} states of $\underline{A}_\gamma$ assign the same state to {element a, input x, output y} then the images of these states must assign the same state to {$\varphi(a)$, $\varphi(x)$, $\varphi(y)$}:

$$s(a) = s_1(a) \Rightarrow \varphi(s) \mid \varphi(a) = \varphi(s_1) \mid \varphi(a)$$
$$i(x) = i_1(x) \Rightarrow \varphi(i) \mid \varphi(x) = \varphi(i_1) \mid \varphi(x)$$
$$o(y) = o_1(y) \Rightarrow \varphi(o) \mid \varphi(y) = \varphi(o_1) \mid \varphi(y).$$

(Note that not all states of $\underline{B}_{\gamma 1}$ need be images of states of $\underline{A}_\gamma$).

(v) When $\underline{B}_{\gamma 1}$ is in state $\varphi(s)$ the state transition function, $f_{\gamma 1}$, depends only on $\varphi(s)$ and states assigned to images of composition inputs of $\underline{A}_\gamma$:
$i' \mid \varphi(X\text{-}X') = i_1' \mid \varphi(X\text{-}X') \Rightarrow f_{\gamma 1}(i', \varphi(s)) = f_{\gamma 1}(i_1', \varphi(s))$
  where i', $i_1' \; \varepsilon \; I_{\gamma 1}$.

(vi) The state transition function of the image of a acting upon images of input and internal states of a must yield the image of the successor state produced by the transition function of a, f_a; similarly for u_a:

$$f_{\varphi(a)}(\varphi(i) \mid \varphi(a), \varphi(s) \mid \varphi(a)) = \varphi f_a(i \mid a, s \mid a)$$
$$u_{\varphi(a)}(\varphi(i) \mid \varphi(a), \varphi(s) \mid \varphi(a)) = \varphi u_a(i \mid a, s \mid a)$$

where $f_{\varphi(a)}$ is the transition function of the sub-composition indexed by $\varphi(a)$ and similarly for $u_{\varphi(a)}$.

Conditions (v) and (vi) assure that, for every pair of local transformations (F_a, U_a) in the object composition, there is a sub-composition of the image with transformations $(F_{\varphi(a)}, U_{\varphi(a)})$ which can be restricted so as to be the same as (F_a, U_a). Conditions

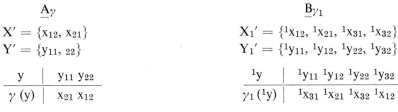

$\underline{A}_\gamma$

$X' = \{x_{12}, x_{21}\}$

$Y' = \{y_{11}, 22\}$

y	y_{11} y_{22}
$\gamma(y)$	x_{21} x_{12}

$\underline{B}_{\gamma_1}$

$X_1' = \{{}^1x_{12}, {}^1x_{21}, {}^1x_{31}, {}^1x_{32}\}$

$Y_1' = \{{}^1y_{11}, {}^1y_{12}, {}^1y_{22}, {}^1y_{32}\}$

${}^1y$	${}^1y_{11}$ ${}^1y_{12}$ ${}^1y_{22}$ ${}^1y_{32}$
$\gamma_1({}^1y)$	${}^1x_{31}$ ${}^1x_{21}$ ${}^1x_{32}$ ${}^1x_{12}$

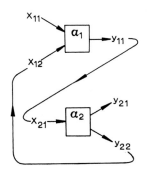

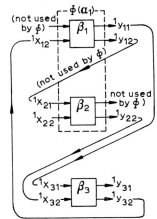

$\varphi(a_1) = \{\beta_1, \beta_2\}$ $\varphi(y_{11}) = \{{}^1y_{11}, {}^1y_{22}\}$ $\varphi(x_{11}) = \{{}^1x_{22}\}$

$\varphi(a_2) = \{\beta_3\}$ $\varphi(y_{21}) = \{{}^1y_{31}\}$ $\varphi(x_{12}) = \{{}^1x_{12}\}$

                   $\varphi(y_{22}) = \{{}^1y_{32}\}$ $\varphi(x_{21}) = \{{}^1x_{31}, {}^1x_{32}\}$

$\varphi(S_{a_1}) \subset S_{\beta_1} \times S_{\beta_2}$, etc.

Note: $\text{proj}_1 \varphi(y_{11}) = \text{proj}_1 \{{}^1y_{11}, {}^1y_{12}\} = \{\beta_1, \beta_2\} \subset \{\beta_1, \beta_2\} = \varphi(a_1) = \varphi(\text{proj}_1 y_{11})$ and $\varphi(\gamma(y_{11})) = \varphi(x_{21}) = \{{}^1x_{31}, {}^1x_{32}\} = \{\gamma_1({}^1y_{11}), \gamma_1({}^1y_{22})\} = \gamma_1(\varphi(y_{11}))$ etc., as required.

Fig. 1. Example of strict embedding.

(i)-(iv) assure the proper composition of these transformations in the image. Fig. 1 presents an example of a strict embedding.

    If φ satisfies the following weakened requirements it will be called a weak and b-slow embedding or, briefly, an *embedding*:

    (i)-(vi) All requirements for strict embedding stand except as altered by (vii) and (viii).

[weak] (vii) Let $\underline{A}_\gamma$ be partitioned into a set of disjoint sub-compositions. Each such sub-composition may be treated as a single element and be embedded accordingly. Thus γ need only be preserved over connections between sub-compositions. More formally: Let $\underline{A}_\gamma$ be partitioned by a partitioning, $\mathit{\Pi}$, of its index set, A. Let $\{\underline{A}_\gamma \mid Y_P\}$ represent the set of induced sub-compositions. Then condition (iii) is to apply only to $y \,\varepsilon\, Y_P\text{-}Y_P'$, $P \,\varepsilon\, \mathit{\Pi}$. All other conditions are modified similarly. (Under interpretation, a weak embedding permits one to ignore all structure and information flow within the sub-compositions $\{\underline{A}_\gamma \mid Y_P\}$; only preservation of the associated functionals, $F_\gamma \mid Y_P$ and $U_\gamma \mid Y_P$ is required).

[slow] (viii) A b-slow embedding yields an image with a time scale $t' = bt$, where t is the time index of $\underline{A}_\gamma$. That is, if o_γ is the output state of $\underline{A}_\gamma$ at time t, the output state of the embedded composition will be $\varphi\,(o_\gamma)$ at time bt. To accomplish this, input sequences are 'slowed' by the 'insertion' of b-1 'no-signal' states between signals, *cf.* McNaughton, 1962. Formally, the definition depends upon an extension of $f_{\gamma 1}$ and $u_{\gamma 1}$ to strings on $I_{\gamma 1}$ in the usual way (*cf.* Rabin and Scott, 1959). $I_{\gamma 1}^b$ will denote strings of length b over $I_{\gamma 1}$ and, if $i^* \; \varepsilon \; I_{\gamma 1}^{b-1}$, $\varphi\,(i) \cdot i^*$ will denote a string of length b with first (earliest) element $\varphi\,(i)$. The following formal condition for a b-slow embedding weakens requirement (vi):

For all $i \; \varepsilon \; I_\gamma$ there exists a string $i^* \; \varepsilon \; I_{\gamma 1}^{b-1}$ such that for all $s \; \varepsilon \; S_\gamma$ and $y \; \varepsilon \; Y\text{-}Y'$ (with $f_{\gamma 1}$ and $u_{\gamma 1}$ extended to $I_{\gamma 1}^b$)

$$f_{\gamma 1}\,(\varphi\,(i) \cdot i^*, \; \varphi\,(s)) \mid \varphi\,(a) = \varphi\,(f_\gamma\,(i, s)\,(a))$$
$$u_{\gamma 1}\,(\varphi\,(i) \cdot i^*, \; \varphi\,(s)) \mid \varphi\,(y) = \varphi\,(u_\gamma\,(i, s)\,(y))$$

Thus the strings $\varphi\,(i) \cdot i^*$ of length b become the images of the input states i. The conditions assure that, if $I_{\gamma 1} = \varphi\,(I_\gamma)$, then, for all t, $\underline{S}_{\gamma 1}\,(bt) = \varphi\,(\underline{S}_\gamma\,(t))$ and $\underline{O}_{\gamma 1}\,(bt) = \varphi\,(\underline{O}_\gamma\,(t))$. (Under interpretation the signal-processing rate of the image is 'slowed' by a factor b).

The reader can develop a considerable understanding of slow embeddings by a close reading of McNaughton's discussion of 'slow automata' (McNaughton, 1962 and draft).

The following additional definitions will be useful:

An *isomorphic embedding* φ of $\underline{A}_\gamma$ on $\underline{B}_{\gamma 1}$ is a strict embedding such that:

$$a \simeq \varphi\,(a) \quad x \simeq \varphi\,(x) \quad y \simeq \varphi\,(y)$$
$$S_a \simeq S_{\varphi\,(a)} \quad I_x \simeq I_{\varphi\,(x)} \quad O_y \simeq O_{\varphi\,(y)}$$

Two embeddings, φ_1 and φ_2, of $\underline{A}_\gamma$ in $C_{\gamma 2}$ will be called *identically oriented* if: (i) there is an isomorphic embedding, θ, of the sub-composition indexed by $\varphi_1\,(A)$ on the sub-composition indexed by $\varphi_2\,(A)$ such that $\theta \varphi_1 = \varphi_2$; (ii) for all a, $a' \; \varepsilon \; A$ and for any connected sequence ϱ {from $\varphi_1\,(a)$ to $\varphi_1\,(a')$, from $\varphi_1\,(a)$ to $\varphi_2\,(a)$} there exists a connected sequence ϱ' {from $\varphi_2\,(a)$ to $\varphi_2\,(a')$, from $\varphi_1\,(a')$ to $\varphi_2\,(a')$} such that $\mathrm{proj}_2\,\varrho = \mathrm{proj}_2\,\varrho'$ (where $\mathrm{proj}_2\,\varrho = (i_1, \ldots, i_h, \ldots, i_l)$ just in case $y_h = (\beta_h, i_h)$, $1 \leq h \leq l$).

The characterization of homogeneous compositions (in the next section) will be based upon this definition of identical orientation.

Prior to defining computation-universality for compositions we also need a relevant definition of computation. The definition which follows is related to that of Burks (Burks, 1960):

Let $\Sigma_j = \{\sigma : N \to N_j \ni N_j = \{0, 1, \ldots, j \}\}$. Let $\Gamma : \Sigma_i \to \Sigma_j$ be a functional from sequences into sequences. We wish to define a finite computation procedure for Γ (of course, only some Γ will admit of such procedures). Augment a composition $\underline{A}_\gamma$ by two mappings:

$$\lambda_1 : N_i \cup \{\Omega\} \to I_{\gamma}' \quad \text{1-1 onto,} \quad I_{\gamma}' \subset I_{\gamma}$$
$$\lambda_2 : O_{\gamma}' \to N_j \cup \{\Omega\} \quad \text{1-1 onto,} \quad O_{\gamma}' \subset O_{\gamma}$$

The symbol 'Ω' under interpretation determines the 'non-signal' states. The mappings λ_1 and λ_2 are extended to infinite sequences $\sigma \ \varepsilon \ \Sigma_i$ and $O_{\gamma} \ \varepsilon \ O_{\gamma}^N$ (treating sequences as strings and allowing 'signals' to be separated by 'no signal' sequences) as follows:

$$\lambda_1^1 (n) = \lambda_1 (n), \ \lambda_1^b \ (n) = \lambda_1^{b-1} (n) \cdot \lambda_1 (\Omega), \quad n \ \varepsilon \ N_i \cup \{\Omega\}$$
$$\lambda_1 (\sigma, b, \tau, s) = ([\lambda_1^{\tau} (\Omega) \cdot \lambda_1^b (\sigma (1)) \cdot \lambda_1^b (\sigma (2)) \cdot \ldots], s), \quad s \ \varepsilon \ S_{\gamma}$$
$$\lambda_2 (O_{\gamma}) = \lambda_2 (O_{\gamma} (t_1)) \cdot \lambda_2 (O_{\gamma} (t_2)) \cdot \ldots$$
where $\lambda_2 (O_{\gamma} (t)) \neq \Omega$ just in case $t = t_j$.

$<A_{\gamma}, \lambda_1, \lambda_2, s>$ will be called a *b-uniform computation* procedure for Γ and Γ will be called (b-) *uniformly computable* if

$$(\forall \sigma \ \varepsilon \ \Sigma_i, \tau \ \varepsilon \ N) \ (\exists \tau' \ \varepsilon \ N) \ [\lambda_2 \ U_{\gamma} \lambda_1 (\sigma, b, \tau, s) = \Gamma (\sigma)]$$
and $[U_{\gamma} \lambda_1 (\sigma, b, \tau, s) (t) \neq \Omega$ just in case $t = \tau' + jb]$.

That is, at the rate of one input (output) 'signal' every b time-steps, and independent of elapsed time τ before the first signal, A_{γ} must transform signals corresponding to successive elements of σ into signals corresponding to successive elements of $\Gamma (\sigma)$.

The set of finitely computable Γ could be broadened considerably (and naturally) by using $\lambda_1^*: N_i^d \to I_{\gamma}^b$ and $\lambda_2^*: O_{\gamma}^b \to N_j^d$ in place of λ_1 and λ_2. If, under quite general conventions, some finite A_{γ} can compute Γ then one can show that A_{γ} can be composed with an acyclic (encoding) composition $E_{\gamma 1}$ so that the resultant composition computes Γ via λ_1^* and λ_2^*. Thus the extended definition would serve well for the study of finitely computable Γ. However, this line will be avoided here because it is more complicated and because the theorems and corollaries of part 4 hold for any class of finitely computable Γ containing the uniformly computable Γ as a subclass.

Theorem: If Γ is finitely computable in the sense of (Burks, 1960) then Γ is uniformly computable.

Theorem. Corresponding to each regular event over a given alphabet there is a distinct uniformly computable Γ.

Note that the elements of Σ_j can be interpreted as representations of fractional real numbers. With appropriate restrictions various non-trivial uniformly computable Γ can be interpreted as continuous real functions.

Lemma. Let $\Gamma : \Sigma_i \to \Sigma_j$ and $\Gamma' : \Sigma_j \to \Sigma_k$ be arbitrary b-uniformly computable functionals except that the range of Γ is the domain of Γ'. Let $<A_{\gamma}, \lambda_1, \lambda_2, s>$ and $<A'_{\gamma'}, \lambda_1', \lambda_2', s'>$ be arbitrary b-uniform computations for Γ and Γ' respectively. Then there exists an acyclic composition $E_{\gamma 1}$ such that:

(i) the composition outputs of A_{γ} can be identified in 1-1 fashion with the composition inputs of $E_{\gamma 1}$ and the composition outputs of $E_{\gamma 1}$ can be identified in 1-1 fashion with the composition inputs of $A'_{\gamma'}$, to form a new composition $C_{\gamma 2}$ involving only A_{γ}, $A'_{\gamma'}$, and $E_{\gamma 1}$,

(ii) the output functional of $\underline{C}_{\gamma 2}$ satisfies the equation

$$U_{\gamma 2} = U_{\gamma'} \; U_{\gamma 1} \; U_{\gamma},$$

(iii) $<\underline{C}_{\gamma 2}, \lambda_1, \lambda_2', s''>$, for an appropriate $s'' \; \varepsilon \; S_{\gamma 2}$, is a b-uniform computation procedure for $\Gamma'\Gamma$ since

$$(\forall \sigma \; \varepsilon \; \Sigma_i, \tau \; \varepsilon \; N) \; [\lambda_2' \; U_{\gamma'} \; U_{\gamma 1} \; U_\gamma \lambda_1 \; (\sigma, \, b, \, \tau, \, s'') = \Gamma'\Gamma \, (\sigma)].$$

(Under interpretation the output of A_γ can be connected to the input of $\underline{A}'_{\gamma'}$, via the combinatorial recoding $\underline{E}_{\gamma 1}$ so that the resulting composition computes the composition of the functionals Γ and Γ'').

Theorem. Let b $(\underline{A}_\gamma, \Gamma) = \min_b \{ b \ni \underline{A}_\gamma$ can b-uniformly compute $\Gamma \}$, undefined if $\underline{A}_\gamma$ cannot b-uniformly compute Γ. Given Γ, Γ', and $\underline{C}_{\gamma 2}$ as in the previous lemma, $\underline{C}_{\gamma 2}$ can at best b_0-uniformly compute $\Gamma''\Gamma$ where $b_0 = \max \{ b \, (\underline{A}_\gamma, \Gamma), b \, (\underline{A}'_{\gamma'}, \Gamma') \}$. (The 'speed' of the faster computation procedure is wasted).

Theorem. If $\underline{A}_\gamma$ can b-uniformly compute Γ and if $\varphi \, (\underline{A}_\gamma)$ is a b'-slow embedding of $\underline{A}_\gamma$ then $\varphi \, (\underline{A}_\gamma)$ can $b'b$-uniformly compute Γ.

4. UNIVERSAL COMPOSITIONS

Using the definitions thus far set down we can at last attain a definition, fairly general and fairly concise, of the principal objects of study.

A composition $\underline{V}_\nu$ of index V will be called universal and homogeneous for (uniformly) computable Γ or *computation-universal* if:

(i) for each (uniformly) computable Γ there is an embedding φ, into $\underline{V}_\nu$, of a composition $\underline{A}_\gamma$ capable of (uniformly) computing Γ (It is assumed that the class of computable Γ, however defined, includes the class of uniformly computable Γ.);

(ii) if φ_1 embeds $\underline{A}_\gamma$ of index A in $\underline{V}_\nu$ then, given arbitrary $a \; \varepsilon \; A, \xi \; \varepsilon \; \varphi \, (a)$ and $\xi' \; \varepsilon \; V$, there exists φ_2 embedding $\underline{A}_\gamma$ in $\underline{V}_\nu$ with identical orientation so that

$$\theta \, (\xi) = \xi'$$

(where θ is the isomorphic embedding specified by the definition of identical orientation).

Condition (ii) assures that, if a composition can be embedded at all, it can be embedded anywhere in the space with identical orientation. Thus, in a sense made precise in the next theorem, all 'translations' of the original image are also images. As a result, properties of the image such as its connection scheme can be made independent of the 'location' of the image. If the universal space is to be used to study growing automata and construction procedures this requirement is critical.

A composition $\underline{W}_\xi$ of index W will be called universal and homogeneous for finite compositions or, briefly, *composition-universal* if:

(i) given any finite composition $\underline{A}_\gamma$ there exists an embedding φ of $\underline{A}_\gamma$ in $\underline{W}_\xi$;
(ii) as for computation-universal.

The work of von Neumann [von Neumann, unpublished] establishes the existence of computation-universal compositions. It can also be shown that there exist composition-universal compositions (the class of iterative circuit computers [Holland, 1960] is an effectively defined class of compositions containing a subset of composition-universal compositions). Note that the class of composition-universal compositions, U_c, is a subclass of the class of computation-universal compositions, U.

Theorem. The following conditions are necessary for a composition $\underline{V}_\nu$ to be computation-universal:

(i) the composition must be generated by a single element,
(ii) it must be over a countably infinite set of elements,
(iii) strings of output indices are commutative, *i.e.* if $\sigma = \mathrm{proj}_2\,\varrho$ where ϱ is a connected sequence from α to β, then for each permutation σ' of σ there exists a connected sequence ϱ' from α to β such that $\sigma' = \mathrm{proj}_2\,\varrho'$.

Proof outline: For (i), let a_α and a_β be any two elements of $\underline{V}_\nu$ and consider the one-element composition $\underline{A}_\gamma$ which is simply a copy of a_α. Obviously there exists φ_1 embedding $\underline{A}_\gamma$ at α in $\underline{V}_\nu$. Hence, by the second condition in the definition of computation-universal, there must be an embedding φ_2 of $\underline{A}_\gamma$ at β and an isomorphic embedding θ of $\varphi_1\,(\underline{A}_\gamma) = a_\alpha$ at β such that $\theta\varphi_1 = \varphi_2$. It follows immediately that the quintuples $<I_\beta, S_\beta, O_\beta, f_\beta, u_\beta>$ and $<I_a, S_a, O_a, f_a, u_a>$ must be identical.

(ii) follows at once from (i) and the existence, for arbitrary k, of Γ computable only by compositions $\underline{A}_\gamma$ wherein the cardinality of S_γ exceeds k.

(iii) follows from the common cardinality of all input (output) index sets (since $\underline{V}_\nu$ is generated by a single element) and the following argument: Let $\varrho = (y_1, y_2)$ be any two-element connected sequence in $\underline{V}_\nu$ with, say, $y_1 = (\alpha, i)$, $y_2 = (\beta, j)$, and $\mathrm{proj}_1\,\nu\,(y_2) = \delta$. Let θ be an identically oriented isomorphic embedding of the sub-composition on elements α, β with $\theta\,(\beta) = \delta$. But then y_2 constitutes a one-element connected sequence from β to δ whence by identical orientation there must be a connected sequence ϱ_1 from α to $\theta\,(\alpha)$ such that $\mathrm{proj}_2\,\varrho_1 = \mathrm{proj}_2\,y_2 = j$. Moreover, since y_1 constitutes a connected sequence from α to β, there must be a connected sequence ϱ_2 from $\theta\,(\alpha)$ to $\theta\,(\beta)$ such that $\mathrm{proj}_2\,\varrho_2 = \mathrm{proj}_2\,y_1 = i$. The sequence $\varrho' = (\varrho_2, \varrho_1)$ is connected, from α to $\theta\,(\beta) = \delta$, and $\mathrm{proj}_2\,\varrho' = (j, i)$. Since $\mathrm{proj}_2\,\varrho = (i, j)$, with i, j arbitrarily chosen, this proves commutativity of indices for arbitrary pairs. From this, commutativity for arbitrary strings of indices can be established in the usual way.

It is a consequence of this theorem that we can 'co-ordinatise' the computation-universal spaces in terms of a subset $\{n_1, \ldots, n_k\}$, $n_k \leq n_a$, of the output indices of the generator: Define a non-oriented connected sequence from α to β to be the same as a connected sequence except that, for each y_h, *either* $\mathrm{proj}_1\,(y_{h+1}) = \mathrm{proj}_1\,\nu\,(y_h)$ *or* $\mathrm{proj}_1\,(y_h) = \mathrm{proj}_1\,\nu\,(y_{h+1})$ is permitted. Count an index occurrence as −1 in the latter case. Choosing some α as origin, the position of any α' is given by a k-tuple having its jth component equal to the sum of the (signed) occurences of index n_j in any nonoriented connected sequence from α to α'. The above theorem assures the uniqueness of this number; the resulting co-ordinatization is the usual k-dimensional (integral) cartesian grid.

The theorem also enables us to define simply one further class of compositions: $U_d = \{\underline{V}_\nu \ni \underline{V}_\nu$ is computation-universal with a Moore automaton as generating element$\}$.

Elements of U_d are the most natural generalizations of von Neumann's 'logical-universal' space because each exhibits the 'propagation-delay' or non-zero lag time which plays an important part in von Neumann's development. Referring to the definition of slow embedding, lag time can be more formally defined: a composition $\underline{A}_\gamma$ has *lag-time b* if (extending u_γ to strings of length $b + 1$):

$$(\exists i, i' \; \varepsilon \; I_\gamma) \; (\forall s \; \varepsilon \; S_\gamma) \; (\forall i^*, i^{**} \; \varepsilon \; I_\gamma{}^b) \; [u_\gamma \; (i^*, s) = u_\gamma \; (i^{**}, s)$$
$$\text{and} \; u_\gamma \; (i \cdot i^*, s) \neq u_\gamma \; (i' \cdot i^*, s)].$$

If $\underline{V}_\nu \; \varepsilon \; U_d$ has a generator with lag-time b and if the shortest connected sequence from α to β in $\underline{V}_\nu$ has length l, it will take at least bl units of time for the output of element a_β to be affected by an input to a_α.

The central result of this section establishes the set U_d as disjoint from the set U_c of composition-universal compositions; *i.e.* elements of U_d are not composition-universal. It follows at once that the generating element of any composition of type U_c must be a Mealy type automaton. The result actually shows that, given any finitely computable Γ, 'almost none' of the compositions capable of computing Γ can be embedded in a composition of type U_d. This has several consequences, stated as corollaries and discussed thereafter, for the study of computation (and construction) procedures in computation-universal spaces.

In the following discussion: $\underline{V}_\nu$ will be a composition of type U_d on a generator g with n outputs and lag-time $\tau_g \geq 1$; G will be a finite set of automata, arbitrary except that it contains at least one element with two or more input-dependent outputs (every set of generators complete for all finitely computable Γ must contain at least one such element); τ_G will be the minimum lag-time for elements of G having two or more outputs; $[\underline{A}_\gamma]_{\beta,l}$ will be the (unique) sub-composition of $\underline{A}_\gamma$ consisting of all elements a_α of $\underline{A}_\gamma$ such that, for some connected sequence ϱ from β of length l, α occurs in $\text{proj}_1 \, \varrho$ (*i.e.* $[\underline{A}_\gamma]_{\beta,l}$ is the sub-composition consisting of all elements belonging to connected sequences of length l from β).

Theorem. Given any $\underline{V}_\nu$, G, and $b \; \varepsilon \; N$ there exists a composition $\underline{A}_\gamma$ generated by G which cannot be embedded in $\underline{V}_\nu$. (In fact for each $\underline{V}_\nu$, G, and b there exists a constant c and a function $e \, (l)$ such that the theorem holds for any $\underline{A}_\gamma$ containing a sub-composition $[\underline{A}_\gamma]_{\beta,l}$, $l \geq c$, with at least $e \, (l)$ elements; the proof shows that $e \, (l)$ and c are such that 'almost all' $\underline{A}_\gamma$ over G satisfy the condition).

Proof outline: Given $\underline{V}_\nu$ and G there will be a positive integer k such that no composition $\underline{B}_{\gamma 1}$ over G consisting of more than k elements can be weakly embedded in the generator g of $\underline{V}_\nu$.

Because of commutativity of strings of output indices in $\underline{V}_\nu$, fewer than $(2l)^n$ distinct elements can belong to any sub-composition $[\underline{V}_\nu]_{\beta,l}$ of $\underline{V}_\nu$ (where n is the number of outputs of g).

But then any composition $\underline{A}_\gamma$ over G containing more than $k(2l)^n$ elements will have an image in $\underline{V}_\nu$ under weak embedding with at least one acyclic connected sequence of length $>l$.

There are compositions $\underline{A}_\gamma$ over G consisting of $2^{l+1}-1$ elements and having no acyclic sequence of length $>l$.

Since there exists c_0 such that $k(2l)^n < 2^{l+1}-1$ for $l \geq c_0$, there are compositions over G which can only be embedded in $\underline{V}_\nu$ if some acyclic sequence in the image has length $l + l_1 > l$.

By simply increasing c_0 we can show, in fact, that there exists c for which, when $l \geq c$

$$(l + l_1)\,\tau_g \geq \max\,(l\tau_G,\ b);$$

thus for any $\underline{A}_\gamma$ over G consisting of more than $k(2l)^n$ elements, with $l \geq c$, the lag-time $\tau_{\varphi(A_\gamma)}$ of the image under an embedding φ must exceed both b and the lag-time τ_{A_γ} of $\underline{A}_\gamma$:

$$\tau_{\varphi(A_\gamma)} > \max\,(\tau_{A_\gamma},\ b).$$

Therefore, if A_γ as specified is to be embedded, the embedding φ must be slow since other types of embedding (weak but not slow) preserve lag-time.

Let $\underline{C}_{\gamma 2}$ contain A_γ as a sub-composition in such a way that some composition outputs of $\underline{C}_{\gamma 2}$ depend upon composition outputs of $\underline{A}_\gamma$. Since the lag-time of $\varphi(A_\gamma)$ will be $\varphi(A_\gamma) > \tau A_\gamma$, the overall lag-time of composition outputs of $\varphi(C_{\gamma 2})$ must exceed that of $\underline{C}_{\gamma 2}$. Otherwise the slow embedding requirement that composition output values occur synchronously will not be satisfied. (Under interpretation: since signals through $\varphi(A_\gamma)$ are unduly delayed, the proper phasing of signals at the output can only be restored by delaying the other signals accordingly.) The result will be an overall increase in the lag-time τ of $\varphi(C_{\gamma 2})$ to at least $\tau_{\varphi(A_\gamma)} > b$.

Consider the image $\varphi(C_{\gamma 2})$ of $\underline{C}_{\gamma 2}$ in $\underline{V}_\nu$ under a b-slow embedding φ. For the moment assume $2b \geq \tau$. Because $\tau > b$, $\varphi(S_{\gamma 2}(t))$ can at best be determined in $\varphi(C_{\gamma 2})$ at time $(b-1)t + \tau > bt$, even if $(S_{\gamma 2}(t-1))$ is available at time $(b-1)t$. In fact, in order that $\varphi(S_{\gamma 2}(t-1))$ *always* be determined by time bt, for arbitrary t, it is necessary that $\varphi(S_{\gamma 2}(t + 1))$ be determined directly from $\varphi(S_{\gamma 2}(t-1))$ rather than from $\varphi(S_{\gamma 2}(t))$. This is only possible if the transition function of the image, in effect, has images of $S_{\gamma 2}(t-1)$, $\underline{I}_{\gamma 2}(t-1)$ and $I_{\gamma 2}(t)$ as arguments at time bt — a sufficient (and for particular $\underline{C}_{\gamma 2}$, necessary) condition for determination of $\varphi(S_{\gamma 2}(t + 1))$. $\varphi(I_{\gamma 2}(t))$ will be available at time bt, but $I_{\gamma 2}(t-1)$ will be available only if the set of states of the image is the image of the set $I_{\gamma 2} \times S_{\gamma 2}$. (Under interpretation: new storage elements would have to be added to the embedded network to 'hold' the image of $\underline{I}_{\gamma 2}(t-1)$). This violates requirements (iv) and (vi) of the definition of embedding. Yet all of this is necessary to preserve the function $U_{\gamma 2}$ under φ (by meeting the requirement that the image of $O_{\gamma2}$ (t) always occur at time bt in $\underline{V}_\nu$ under a b-slow embedding). Hence the assumption that $\underline{C}_{\gamma2}$, as specified, can be b-slow embedded in $\underline{V}_\nu$ leads to a contradiction.

A similar argument requiring $S_{\gamma2}$ (t—k_1), $\underline{I}_{\gamma2}$ (t—k_1), $\underline{I}_{\gamma2}$ (t—k_1 +1), ..., $\underline{I}_{\gamma2}$ (t) applies when $(k_1 + 1)$ b $\geqq \tau > k_1$b.

Note that 'almost all' compositions on G as specified will include a sub-composition $[A_\gamma]_{\beta,l}, l \geqq c$, containing more than $k (2l)^n$ elements.

Corollary. Given any finite composition $\underline{A}_\gamma$ and any b-slow embedding φ of $\underline{A}_\gamma$ in space $\underline{V}_\nu$ of type U_d, there exists a composition $\underline{A}'_{\gamma'}$ which contains $\underline{A}_\gamma$ as a sub-composition and which cannot be b-slow embedded in $\underline{V}_\nu$.

In fact, given any b ε N, 'almost all' compositions containing $\underline{A}_\gamma$ cannot be b-slow embedded in $\underline{V}_\nu$. Thus most schemes for composing $\underline{A}_\nu$ with other compositions cannot be represented in $\underline{V}_\nu$ using b-slow embeddings, even when $\underline{A}_\nu$ itself is embeddable.

Corollary. Given $\underline{V}_\nu \varepsilon U_d$, any b ε N, and any set of generators G as specified above, there exists an infinite sequence of functionals $\Gamma_1, \Gamma_2, ..., \Gamma_j, ...$ such that:

(i) each Γ_j is b-uniformly computable by a composition $[\underline{A}_j]_{\gamma_j}$ over G,

(ii) $[\underline{A}_j]_{\gamma_j}$ can at best be b_j-slow embedded in $\underline{V}_\nu$ where $b_j > b_{j-1}$, $b_j \varepsilon$ N.

Note that $\lim_j b_j = \infty$ so that the computation rates of the images of the $[\underline{A}_j]_{\gamma_j}$ in $\underline{V}_\nu$ must approach zero. If $\underline{A}_\gamma$ can b-uniformly compute Γ then a composition $[\underline{C}_j]_{\gamma_j}$, containing $\underline{A}_\gamma$ and $[\underline{A}_j]_{\gamma_j}$ as subcompositions, can b-uniformly compute $\Gamma_j' = \Gamma_j\Gamma$. However there is no b' ε N such that all $[\underline{C}_j]_{\gamma_j}$ can be b'-slow embedded in $\underline{V}_\nu$. Hence, although $\underline{A}_\gamma$ can serve as a common 'sub-routine' for computing all Γ_j', there need be no corresponding common sub-routine for computations of the Γ_j' in $\underline{V}_\nu$ (assuming a minimal signal rate 1/b' specified).

The restrictions just noted do not hold for the composition-universal spaces U_c. In fact there exist composition-universal spaces such that any finite composition can be *strictly* embedded in the space. The spaces U_c are compositions and hence satisfy local effectiveness conditions; however, each such space is generated by a Mealy-type automaton, and may exhibit arbitrarily long (finite) connected sequences of elements with zero lag-time (*cf.* the similar situation for logical nets).

Theorem. Given any composition $\underline{V}_\nu \varepsilon U_d$ there exists a composition $\underline{C}_\gamma\varepsilon U_c$ in which $\underline{V}_\nu$ can be strictly embedded.

Proof outline: As indicated earlier all compositions in U can be given Cartesian coordinates; one can then determine a unique dimension for each. $\underline{V}_\nu$ has a single finite automaton as generator and that generator can be strictly embedded in a finite n-cube of some space $\underline{C}_\gamma \varepsilon U_c$ of dimension n. If the dimension of $\underline{V}_\nu$ is less than or equal to n, a set of image n-cubes can be arrayed in $\underline{C}_\gamma$ with the same geometry as the elements of $\underline{V}_\nu$.

5. COMMENTARY

The central definitions of this paper are structural — involving no statements quantified over time. Thus, the compositions are defined via a composition function which specifies the graph of connections between component automata, the behavior of the resulting structure being defined by a set of simultaneous equations induced by the composition function. An embedding selects a sub-composition of an image composition and constrains certain of its state components. These constraints are invariant (hereditary) under a natural restriction of the transition function of the image composition: a restriction wherein input states to the sub-composition are restricted to images of the input states of the object composition. Only when the inputs to the image depart from this condition will the embedding cease to reflect the behavior of the object composition.

The full set of finite compositions may for some purposes be too broad, containing 'unrealistic' elements. A natural way to achieve a 'realistic' subset is to admit only compositions over a selected set of 'realistic' generators. For example, a generator may be designated 'realistic' only if it has non-zero lag-time (the Moore type automata). The results of Part 4 are intrinsic in this respect: No matter how one limits the set of 'realistic' elements by selection of generators, almost none of the compositions over the selected generators will b'-slow embeddable, for any $b' \, \varepsilon \, N$, in any $V_\nu \, \varepsilon \, U_d$. Thus, given any $b' \, \varepsilon \, N$, almost none of the b-uniform computation procedures over the generators can be embedded in V_ν as $b'b$-uniform computation procedures. Instead of a computation rate $1/b$, almost all images will have a rate less than ε, for any $\varepsilon > 0$ — an undesirable consequence if the space is to be used to study computation procedures. Two alternatives for avoiding this consequence present themselves:

(i) One can accept the spaces U_d as the only 'realistic' universal spaces and avoid the above consequence by further narrowing the set of admissible representations of finite automata. This can *not* be achieved by selecting a set of 'realistic' primitives; it can only be done by restricting the connection procedures. (The heart of the difficulty lies in the unrestricted cascading of fanout elements.) Such a restriction would considerably modify current notions of representation and several theorems, such as the Kleene representation theorem for regular events (Theorem 3 — Kleene, 1956), would be lost.

(ii) One can use the spaces U_c with their concomitant of connected sequences of elements exhibiting negligible delay. This introduces no mathematical difficulty because the spaces U_c are compositions and hence satisfy strong local effectiveness conditions; nevertheless one may question how 'realistic' such spaces are in allowing propagation of signals with negligible delay over arbitrarily long channels.

The second alternative seems preferable to me: Criteria which argue for alternative (i) can be applied, via the last theorem of Part 4, to restrict the transition function of spaces of type U_c. Thus such criteria can both be implemented and studied under the second alternative. At the same time, there are useful restrictions of U_c not readily translatable to U_d.

In this context the study of construction procedures, or growing automata (leading to studies of self-reproduction, adaptation, etc.) becomes the study of sequences of compositions. Such sequences become state sequences in a universal composition — an embedding must transform structural features of the object composition into properties of the state pattern of the universal composition. The fixed connection scheme of the universal composition can only supply an invariant framework. Note that the state sequence corresponding to a sequence of compositions must involve departures from the constraints imposed by embedding. That is, the image of one composition can be altered to that of another only by departing from the conditions set by the embedding. A restriction of the transition function of the universal space will still be involved; it will be similar to, but weaker than, that required for embeddings. The restriction must be such that any state trajectory under this restricted function corresponds to a sequence of compositions. Note that a construction procedure involving structures that cannot be embedded will not be representable. More than this, given a universal space, there will be construction procedures, involving only embeddable structures, which still fail of representation. That is, some recursive enumerations of embeddable structures will not be representable through a restriction of the transition function. This is not necessarily undesirable: If it is assumed that the 'size' of given composition in a construction sequence is a function of the 'size' of its predecessor, then most recursive enumerations of compositions will not be construction sequences. Questions related to characterization of the construction procedures representable in various universal spaces remain open.

ACKNOWLEDGEMENTS

I would like to thank Robert McNaughton for sending me an early draft of his extensive work on badly timed elements — a portion of which appeared in 1962 (McNaughton, 1962); the work he has done and the work reported here are complementary in several parts. I would like to thank James Thatcher for many helpful comments and suggestions based on a careful reading of an early draft of the manuscript; in several places the notation derives directly from his comments. The research reported here was in part supported by U.S. Air Force contract AF 33 (615)-1162.

SUMMARY

This paper defines the class of homogeneous, computation-universal spaces and investigates properties of these spaces apropos to studies of computation, construction, self-reproduction and adaptation in the context of automata theory. Three prerequisite concepts are first developed:

    (i) composition ('connection') of countable sets of automata;

    (ii) embedding ('simulating') one composition in another;

    (iii) computation by finite automata.

The universal spaces are defined in terms of these concepts and necessary conditions for a composition to be universal are derived. The subset, U_c, of composition-universal spaces (all finite compositions can be embedded therein) is distinguished, as is the subset, U_d, which includes the natural generalizations of Von Neumann's 'logical-universal' space. It is shown that U_c and U_d are disjoint and that this fact bears importantly upon the use of universal spaces for the study of computation and construction.

REFERENCES

BURKS, A. W., (1960); Computation, behavior and structure in fixed and growing automata. *Self-Organizing Systems*. Marshall Yovits and Scott Cameron, Editors. New York. Pergamon Press (pp. 282–311).

BURKS, A. W., AND WRIGHT, J. B., (1953); Theory of logical nets. *Proc. Inst. Radio Engineers*, **41**, 1357–1365.

CHURCH, A., (1957); Application of recursive arithmetic to the problem of circuit synthesis. *Summaries, Summer Institute for Symbolic Logic*. Cornell University, Institute for Defense Analysis (pp. 3–50).

HARTMANIS, J., (1961); On the state assignment problem for sequential machines. *Institute for Radio Engineers, Transactions on Electronic Computers EC-10*, **3**, 157–165.

HOLLAND, J. H., (1960); Cycles in logical nets. *J. Franklin Inst.*, **270**, 3, 202–226.

HOLLAND, J. H., (1960a); Iterative circuit computers. *Proc. Western Joint Computer Conf.*, San Francisco (pp. 259–265).

KLEENE, S. C., (1956); Representation of events in nerve nets and finite automata. *Automata Studies*. C. E. Shannon and J. McCarthy, Editors. Princeton, New Jersey. Princeton University Press (pp. 3–41).

McNAUGHTON, R., (1962); On nets made up of badly timed elements, I. *Summer Conference Notes on Parallel Computers, Automata and Adaptive Systems*. Ann Arbor. The University of Michigan.

McNAUGHTON, R., (draft); On nets made up of badly timed elements. Continuation of On nets made up of badly timed elements, I.

MOORE, E. F., (1962); Machine models of self-reproduction. *Mathematical problems in the biological sciences*. Providence. American Mathematical Society (pp. 17–33).

MYHILL, J., (1962); Self-reproducing automata. *Summer Conference Notes on Parallel Computers, Automata and Adaptive Systems*. Ann Arbor. The University of Michigan.

RABIN, M. O., AND SCOTT, D., (1959); Finite automata and their decision problems. *IBM J. Res. Developm.*, **3**, 114–125.

VON NEUMANN, J., (unpublished); The theory of automata: construction, reproduction, homogeneity.

Fields and Waves in Excitable Cellular Structures

R. M. STEWART

Space General Corporation, El Monte, Calif. (U.S.A.)

> "Study of living processes by the physiological method only proceeded laboriously behind the study of non-living systems. Knowledge about respiration, for instance, began to become well organized as the study of combustion proceeded, since this is an analogous operation . . . ."
>
> J. Z. YOUNG (1951(

I. INTRODUCTION

Our study of electrical fields in densely-packed cellular media is prompted primarily by a desire to understand more fully their possible importance to brain mechanism and to behavior and has more specifically been directed toward an attempt to model such structures and mechanisms, using relatively simple inorganic materials.

The prototype for such experiments is the 'Lillie iron-wire nerve model' (for review articles see: Lillie, 1936; Franck, 1956). Over a hundred years ago, it had been observed that visible waves were produced on the surface of a piece of iron submerged in nitric acid when and where the iron is touched by a piece of zinc. After a short period of apparent fatigue, the wire recovers and can again support a wave when stimulated. Major support for the idea that such impulses are in fact directly related to peripheral nerve impulses came from Lillie around 1920. Along an entirely different line, various persons have noted the morphological and dynamic similarity of dendrites in brain and those which sometimes grow by electrodeposition of metals from solution. Gordon Pask (1958), especially, has pointed to this similarity and has discussed in a general way the concomitant possibility of a physical model for the persistent memory trace.

By combining and extending such concepts and techniques, we hope to produce a macrosopic model of 'gray matter', the structural matrix of which will consist of a dense, homogeneously-mixed, conglomerate of small pellets, capable of supporting internal waves of excitation, of changing electrical behavior through internal fine-structure growth, and of forming temporal associations in response to peripheral shocks.

A few experimenters have subsequently pursued the iron-wire nerve-impulse analogy further, hoping thereby to illuminate the mechanisms of nerve excitation, impulse-transmission and recovery, but interest has generally been quite low. It has remained fairly undisturbed in the text books and lecture demonstrations of medical students, as a picturesque aid to their formal education. On the outer fringes of biology, still less interest has been displayed; the philosophical vitalists would surely be revolted by the idea of such models of mind and memory and, at the other end of the scale, contemporary computer engineers generally assume that a nerve cell operates much too slowly to be of any value. This lack of interest is certainly due, in part, to success in developing techniques of monitoring individual nerve fibers directly, to the point that it is just about as easy to work with large nerve fibers (and even peripheral and spinal junctions) as it is to work with iron wires. Under such circumstances, the model has only limited value, perhaps just to the extent that it emphasizes the role of factors other than specific molecular structure and local chemical reactions in the dynamics of nerve action.

When we leave the questions of impulse transmission on long fibers and peripheral junctions, however, and attempt to discuss the brain, there can be hardly any doubt that the development of a meaningful physical model technique would be of great value. Brain tissue is soft and sensitive, the cellular structures are small, tangled, and incredibly numerous, and so (Young, 1951), '... physiologists hope that after having learned a lot about nerve-impulses in the nerves they will be able to go on to study how these impulses interact when they reach the brain. [But], we must not assume that we shall understand the brain only in the terms we have learned to use for the nerves. The function of nerves is to carry impulses — like telegraph wires. The function of brains is something else'. But, confronted with such awesome experimental difficulties, with no comprehensive mathematical theory in sight, we are largely limited otherwise to verbal discourses, rationales and theorizing, a hopelessly clumsy tool for the development of an adequate understanding of brain function. A little over ten years ago Sperry (1952) said, 'Present day science is quite at a loss even to begin to describe the neural events involved in the simplest form of mental activity'. That situation has not changed much today. The development, study, and understanding of complex high-density cellular structures which incorporate characteristics of both the Lillie and Pask models may, we hope, provide some useful clues. There would also be fairly obvious technological applications for such techniques if highly developed and which, more than any other consideration, has prompted support for this work (Stewart, 1964).

Experiments to date will be described which demonstrate the following basic physical and functional characteristics:

(1) Control of bulk resistivity of electrolytes containing closely-packed, poorly-conducting pellets.

(2) Circulation of regenerative waves on closed loops.

(3) Strong coupling between isolated excitable sites.

(4) Logically-complete wave interactions, including facilitation and annihilation.

(5) Dendrite growth by electrodeposition in 'closed' excitable systems.

(6) Subthreshold distributed field effects, especially in locally-refractory regions.

In addition, our attention has necessarily been directed to various problems of general experimental technique and choice of materials, especially as related to stability, fast recovery and long life. However, in order to understand the possible significance of and motivation for such experiments, some basic current concepts of neurophysiology, histology and psychology will be reviewed just briefly. These concepts are, respectively:

(1) The 'fine-structure' of gray matter.   (4) Inhibition.

(2) Short-term memory.   (5) Long-term memory.

(3) Synaptic transmission.   (6) Field effects and learning.

II. SOME CONTEMPORARY CONCEPTS

Since we are attempting to duplicate processes other than chemical, *per se*, we will forego any reference to the extensive literature of neurochemistry. It should not be surprising through if, at the neglect of the fundamental hereditary processes of growth, reproduction and metabolism, it proves possible to imitate some learning mechanisms with grossly less complex molecular structures. There is also much talk of chemical versus electrical theories and mechanisms in neurophysiology. The distinction, when it can be made, seems to hinge on the question of the scale of size of significant inter-actions. Thus, 'chemical' interactions presumably take place at molecular distances, possibly as a result of or subsequent to a certain amount of thermal diffusion. 'Elec-trical' interactions, on the other hand, are generally understood to imply longer range or larger scale macroscopic fields.

(1) The 'Fine-Structure' of Gray Matter

The human brain contains approximately 10^{10} neurons to which the neuron theory assigns the primary role in central nervous activity. These cells occupy, however, a relatively small fraction of the total volume. There are, for example, approximately 10 times that number of neuroglia, cells of relatively indeterminate function. Each neuron (consisting of cell body, dendrites and, sometimes, an axon) comes into close contact with the dendrites of other neurones at some thousands of places, these synapses and 'ephapses' being spaced approximately $5\,\mu$ apart (Bok, 1959). The total number of such apparent junctions is therefore of the order of 10^{13}. In spite of in-finite fine-structure variations, when viewed with slightly blurred vision the cellular structure of the brain is remarkably homogeneous. In the cortex, at least, the exten-sions of most cells are relatively short, and when the cortex is at rest, it appears from the large EEG alpha-rhythms that large numbers of cells beat together in unison. Quoting again from Sperry, 'In short, current brain theory encourages us to try to correlate our subjective psychic experience with the activity of relatively homogeneous nerve cell units conducting essentially homogeneous impulses, through roughly homogeneous cerebral tissue'.

(2) Short-Term Memory

A train of impulses simply travelling on a long fiber may, for example, be regarded as a short-term memory much in the same way as a delay line acts as a transient memory in a computer. A similar but slightly longer term memory may also be thought of to exist in the form of waves circulating in closed loops (Young, 1938). In fact, it is almost universally held today that most significant memory occurs in two basic interrelated ways: first of all, an ephemeral, circulating, reverberatory or regenerative pattern which, however, could not conceivably persist through such things as coma, anesthesia, concussion, extreme cold, deep sleep and convulsive seizures and thus, secondly, a long-term memory trace which must somehow reside in a semipermanent fine-structural change. As Hebb (1949) stated, 'A reverberatory trace might cooperate with a structural change and carry the memory until the growth change is made'.

(3) Synaptic Transmission

The current most highly regarded specific conception of the synapse is largely due to and has been best described by Eccles (1961): '. . . the synaptic connections between nerve cells are the only functional connections of any significance. These synapses are of two types, excitatory and inhibitory, the former type tending to make nerve cells discharge impulses, the other to suppress the discharge. There is now convincing evidence that in vertebrate synapses each type operates through specific chemical transmitter substances . . .'. In response to a presentation by Hebb (1961), Eccles was quoted as saying, 'One final point, and that is if there is electrical interaction, and we have seen from Dr. Estable's work the complexity of connections, and we now know from the electronmicroscopists that there is no free space, only 200 Å clefts, everywhere in the central nervous system, then everything should be electrically interacted with everything else. I think this is only electrical background noise and, that when we lift with specific chemical connections above that noise we get a significant operational system. I would say that there is electrical interaction but it is just a noise, nuisance.' Eccles' conclusions are primarily based on data obtained in the peripheral nervous system and the spinal cord. But there is overwhelming reason to expect that cellular interactions in the brain are an entirely different affair. For example (Boycott and Young, 1950), 'The highest centres in the octopus, as in vertebrates and arthropods, contain many small neurons. This finding is such a commonplace, that we have perhaps failed in the past to make the fullest inquiry into its implications. Many of these small cells possess numerous processes, but no axon. It is difficult to see, therefore, that their function can be conductive in the ordinary sense. Most of our ideas about nervous functioning are based on the assumption that each neuron acts essentially as a link in some chain of conduction, but there is really no warrant for this in the case of cells with many short branches. Until we know more of the relations of these processes to each other in the neuropile it would be unwise to say more. It is possible that the effective part of the discharge of such cells is not as it is in conduction in long pathways, the internal circuit that returns through the same fibre, *but the external circuit that enters other processes . . . .*'

(4) Inhibition

The inhibitory chemical transmitter substance postulated by Eccles has never been detected in spite of numerous efforts to do so. The mechanism(s) of inhibition is perhaps the key to the question of cellular interaction and, in one form or another, must be accounted for in any adequate theory.

Other rather specific forms of excitation and inhibition interaction have been proposed at one time or another. Perhaps the best example is the polar neuron of Gesell (1940) and, more recently, Retzlaff (1954). In such a concept, excitatory and inhibitory couplings differ basically because of a macroscopic structural difference at the cellular level; that is, various arrangements or orientation of intimate cellular structures give rise to either excitation or inhibition.

(5) Long-Term Memory

Most modern theories of semipermanent structural change (or *engrams*, as they are sometimes called) look either to the molecular level or to the cellular level. Various specific locales for the engram have been suggested, including (1) modifications of RNA molecular structure, (2) changes of cell size, synapse area or dendrite extensions, (3) neuropile modification, and (4) local changes in the cell membrane. There is, in fact, rather direct evidence of the growth of neurons or their dendrites with use and the diminution or atrophy of dendrites with disuse. The apical dendrite of pyramidal neurones becomes thicker and more twisted with continuing activity, nerve fibers swell when active, sprout additional branches (at least in the spinal cord) and presumably increase the size and number of their terminal knobs. As pointed out by Konorski (1948), the morphological conception of plasticity according to which plastic changes would be related to the formation and multiplication of new synaptic junctions goes back at least as far as Ramon y Cajal in 1904. Whatever the substrate of the memory trace, it is, at least in adults, remarkably immune to extensive brain damage and as Young (1951) has said: '. . . this question of the nature of the memory trace is one of the most obscure and disputed in the whole of biology'.

(6) Field Effects and Learning

First, from Boycott and Young (1950), 'the current conception, on which most discussions of learning still concentrate, is that the nervous system consists essentially of an aggregate of chains of conductors, linked at key points by synapses. This reflex conception, springing probably from Cartesian theory and method, has no doubt proved of outstanding value in helping us to analyse the actions of the spinal cord, but it can be argued that it has actually obstructed the development of understanding of cerebral function'.

Most observable evidence of learning and memory is extremely complex and its interpretation full of traps. Learning in its broadest sense might be detected by a semipermanent change of behavior pattern brought about as a result of experience. Within that kind of definition, we can surely identify several distinctly different types of learning, presumably with distinctly different kinds of mechanisms associated with each one. But, if we adhere to our criterion of detection of a semipermanent change of behavior as a definition for learning, then we may also be misled into considering the development of a neurosis, for example, as learning, or even a deep coma as learning.

When we come to consider field effects, current theories tend to get fairly obscure;

but there seems to be an almost universal recognition of the fact that such fields are significant. For example, Morrell (1961) says in his review of electrophysiological contributions to the neural basis of learning, 'a growing body of knowledge (see reviews by Purpura, Grundfest, and Bishop) suggests that the most significant integrative work of the central nervous system is carried on in graded response elements — elements in which the degree of reaction depends upon stimulus intensity and is not all-or-none, which have no refractory period and in which continuously varying potential changes of either sign occur and mix and algebraically sum.' Gerard (1955) also makes a number of general comments along these lines. 'These attributes of a given cell are, in turn, normally controlled by impulses arising from other regions, by fields surrounding them — both electric and chemical — electric and chemical fields can strongly influence the interaction of neurones. This has been amply expounded in the case of the electric fields'.

Learning situations involving 'punishment' and 'reward' or, subjectively, 'pain' and 'pleasure' may very likely be associated with transient but structurally widespread field effects. States of distress and of success seem to exert a lasting influence on behavior only in relation to *simultaneous* sensory events or, better yet, sensory events just immediately *preceding* in time. For example, the 'anticipatory' nature of a conditioned reflex has been widely noted (Thorpe, 1950). From a structural point of view, it is as if recently active sites regardless of location or function were especially sensitive to extensive fields. There is a known inherent electrical property of both nerve membrane and passive iron surface that could hold the answer to the mechanism of spatially-diffuse temporal association; namely, the surface resistance drops to less than 1 per cent of its resting value during the refractory period which immediately follows activation.

III. EXPERIMENTAL TECHNIQUE

In almost all experiments, the basic signal-energy mechanism employed has been essentially that one studied most extensively by Lillie (1925), Bonhoeffer (1948), Yamagiwa (1950), Matumoto and Goto (1955) and others, *i.e.*, activation, impulse propagation and recovery on the normally passive surface of a piece of iron immersed in nitric acid or of cobalt in chromic acid (Tasaki and Bak, 1959). The iron we have used most frequently is of about 99.99% purity, which gives performance more consistent than but similar to that obtained using cleaned 'coat-hanger' wires. The acid used most frequently by us is about 53–55% aqueous solution by weight, substantially more dilute than that predominantly used by previous investigators. The most frequently reported concentration has been 68–70%, a solution which is quite stable and, hence, much easier to work with in open containers than the weaker solutions, results in very fast waves but gives, at room temperatures, a very long refractory period (typically, 15 min). A noble metal (such as silver, gold or platinum) placed in contact with the surface of the iron has a stabilizing effect (Matumoto and Goto, 1955) presumably through the action of local currents and provides a simple and useful technique whereby, with dilution, both stability and fast recovery (1 sec) can be achieved in simple demonstrations and experiments.

Experiments involving the growth by electrodeposition and study of metallic dendrites are done with an eye toward electrical, physical and chemical compatibility with the energy-producing system outlined above. Best results to date (from the standpoints of stability, nonreactivity, and morphological similarity to neurological structures) have been obtained by dissolving gold chloride crystals in nitric acid.

An apparatus has been devised and assembled for the purpose of containing and controlling our primary experiments (Fig. 1). Its two major components are a test chamber (on the left in Fig. 1) and a fluid exchanger (on the right). In normal operation the test chamber, which is very rigid and well sealed after placing the experimental assembly inside, is completely filled with electrolyte (or, initially, an inert fluid) to

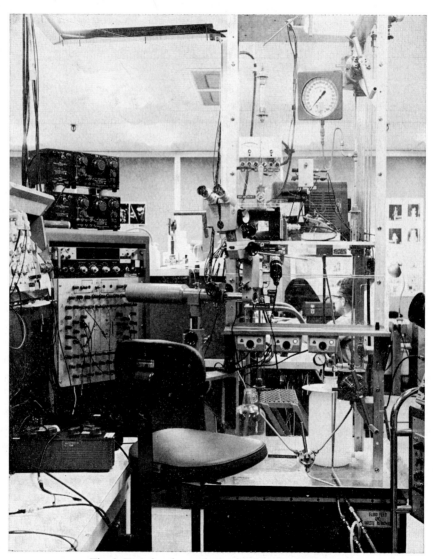

Fig. 1. Test chamber and associated instrumentation.

the exclusion of all air pockets and bubbles. Thus encapsulated it is possible to perform experiments which would otherwise be impossible due to instability. The instability which plagues such experiments is manifested in copious generation of bubbles on and subsequent rapid disintegration of all 'excitable' material (*i.e.*, iron). Preliminary experiments indicated that such 'bubble instability' could be suppressed by constraining the volume available to expansion. In particular, response and recovery times can now be decreased substantially and work can proceed with complex systems of interest such as aggregates containing many small iron pellets.

The test chamber is provided with a heater (and thermostatic control) which makes possible electrochemical impulse response and recovery times comparable to those of the nervous system (1–10 msec). The fluid-exchanger is so arranged that fluid in the test chamber can be arbitrarily changed or renewed by exchange within a rigid, sealed, completely liquid-filled ('isochoric') loop. Thus, stability can be maintained for long periods of time and over a wide variety of investigative or operating conditions.

Most of the parts of this apparatus are made of stainless steel and are sealed with polyethylene and teflon. There is a small quartz observation window on the test chamber, two small lighting ports, a pressure transducer, thermocouple, screw-and-piston pressure actuator and umbilical connector for experimental electrical inputs and outputs.

IV. BASIC EXPERIMENTS

The several experiments described in the following sections are numbered for comparison to correspond roughly to the fundamental biological concepts summarized in Part II.

(1) Structural Matrix

The primary object of our research is the control and determination of dynaicm behavior in response to electrical stimulation in close-packed aggregates of small pellets submerged in electrolyte. Typically, the aggregate contains (among other things) iron and the electrolyte contains nitric acid, this combination making possible the propagation of electrochemical surface waves of excitation through the body of the aggregate similar to those of the Lillie iron-wire nerve model. The iron pellets are imbedded in and supported by a matrix of small dielectric (such as glass) pellets. Furthermore, with the addition of soluble salts of various noble metals to the electrolyte, long interstitial dendritic or fibrous structures of the second metal can be formed whose length and distribution change by electrodeposition in response to either internal or externally generated fields.

Coupling between isolated excitable (iron) sites is greatly affected by this fine structure and by the bulk resistivity of the glass and fluid medium which supports and fills the space between such sites. In general (see Section 3, following) it is necessary, to promote strong coupling between small structures, to impede the 'short-circuit' return flow of current from an active or excited surface, through the electrolyte and back through the dendritic structure attached to the same excitable site. This calls for control (increase) of the bulk resistivity, preferably by means specifically

Fig. 2. Two-phase aggregate — maximum resistivity mix.

independent of electrolyte composition, which relates to and affects surface phenomena such as recovery (*i.e.*, the 'refractory' period). Figure 2 illustrates the way in which this is being done, *i.e.*, by appropriate choice of particle size distributions. The case illustrated shows the approximate proper volume ratios for maximum resistivity in a two-size-phase random mixture of spheres.

(2) Regenerative Impulse Patterns

Figure 3 shows an iron loop (about 10 cm diameter) wrapped with a silver wire helix which is quite stable in 53–55% acid and which will easily support a circulating pattern of three impulses. For demonstration, unilateral waves can be generated by first touching the iron with a piece of zinc (which produces two oppositely travelling waves)

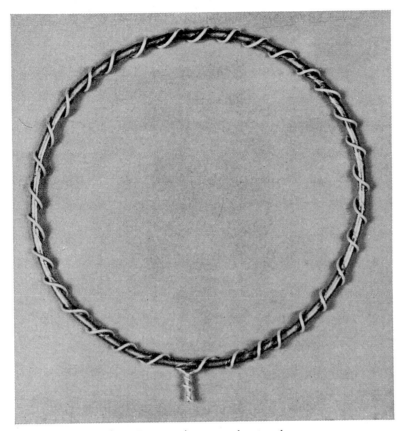

Fig. 3. Regenerative or reverberatory loop.

and then blocking one of them with a piece of platinum or a small platinum screen attached to the end of a stick or wand. Carbon blocks may also be used for this purpose.

The smallest regenerative or reverberatory loop which we are at present able to devise is about 1 mm in diameter. Multiple waves, as expected, produce stable patterns in which all impulses are equally spaced. This phenomenon can be related to the slightly slower speed characteristic of the relative refractory period as compared with a more fully recovered zone.

(3) Intercellular Impulse Transmission by Electrical Induction

If two touching pieces of iron are placed in a bath of nitric acid, a wave generated on one will ordinarily spread to the other. As is to be expected, a similar result is obtained if the two pieces are connected through an external conducting wire. However, if they are isolated, strong coupling does not ordinarily occur, especially if the elements are small in comparison with a 'critical size', σ/ϱ where σ is the surface resistivity of passive iron surface (in $\Omega \cdot \mathrm{cm}^2$) and ϱ is the volume resistivity of the acid (in $\Omega \cdot \mathrm{cm}$). A simple and informative structure which demonstrates the essential

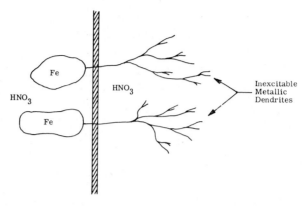

DIELECTRIC BARRIER

Figure 4

conditions for strong electrical coupling between isolated elements of very small size may be constructed as shown in Fig. 4. The dielectric barrier insures that charge transfer through one dipole must be accompanied by an equal and opposite transfer through the surfaces of the other dipole. If the 'inexcitable' silver tails have sufficiently high conductance (*i.e.*, sufficiently large surface area, hence preferably, dendrites), strong coupling will occur, just as though the cores of the two pieces of iron were connected with a solid conducting wire. Similar behavior can be demonstrated in the isolated dipoles or 'bipolar cells' are simply imbedded in a dense dielectric aggregate.

(4) 'Logically complete' Impulse Interactions

If a third 'dipole' is inserted through the dielectric membrane in the opposite direction, then excitation of this isolated element tends to inhibit the response which would otherwise be elicited by excitation of one of the parallel dipoles. Fig. 5 shows the first such 'logically-complete' interaction cell successfully constructed and demonstrated. It may be said to behave as an elementary McCulloch–Pitts (1943) neuron. Further analysis shows that similar structures incorporating many dipoles (both excitatory and inhibitory) can be made to behave as general 'linear decision functions' in which all input weights are approximately proportional to the total size or length of their corresponding attached dendritic structures.

(5) Field-induced Dendrite Growth and Morphology

Figure 6 shows a sample gold dendrite grown by electrodeposition (actual size, about 1 mm) from a 54% nitric acid solution to which gold chloride was added. When such a dendrite is attached to a piece of iron (both submerged), activation of the excitable element produces a field in such a direction as to promote further growth of the dendritic structure. Thus, if gold chloride is added to the solution used in the elementary interaction cells described above, all input influence 'weights' should tend to increase with use and, hence, produce a familiar form of functional plasticity.

Fig. 5. Electrochemical excitatory-inhibitory interaction cell.

(6) Field Effects in Locally-Refractory Regions

Our measurements indicate that, during the refractory period following excitation, the surface resistance of iron in nitric acid drops to substantially less than 1 % of its resting value in a manner reminiscent of nerve membranes (Cole and Curtis, 1939). Thus. if a distributed or gross field exists at any time throughout a complex cellular aggregate concomitant current densities in locally-refractive regions will be substantially higher than elsewhere and, if conditions appropriate to dendrite growth exist (as described above), growth rates in such regions will also be substantially higher than elsewhere. It would appear that, as a result, recently active functional couplings (in contrast to those not associated with recently active cells) should be significantly altered by widely distributed fields or massive peripheral shocks. This mechanism might thus underlie the apparent ability of the brain to form specific temporal associations in response to spatially diffuse effects such as are generated, for example, by the pain receptors.

References p. 257

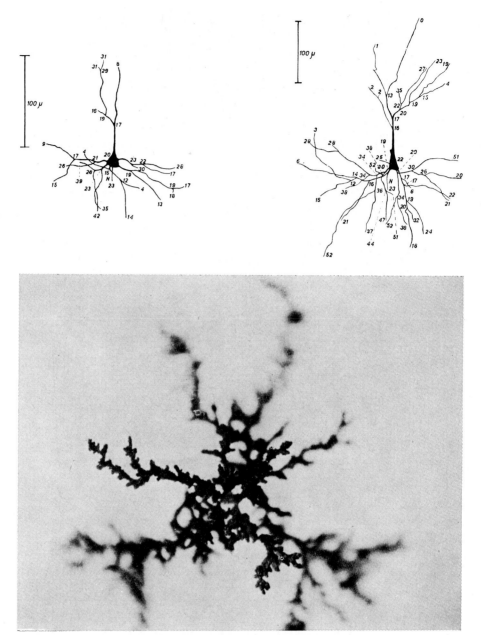

Fig. 6. Dendritic structures, living and non-living. (*A*) Cat dendrite trees (From Bok, 1959).
(*B*) Electrodeposited gold dendrite tree.

SUMMARY

An attempt is being made to develop meaningful electrochemical model techniques
which may contribute toward a clearer understanding of cortical function. Variants
of two physical processes are being joined: (1) the Lillie iron-wire nerve model, and

(2) growth of metallic dendrites by electrodeposition. Particular attention is being directed to systems of filamentary bipolar cells imbedded in a fine closely-packed glass aggregate which is flooded with electrolyte. Stable, fast response has been obtained by operating at elevated temperatures and pressures.

REFERENCES

Bok, S. T., (1959); *Histonomy of the Cerebral Cortex*. Amsterdam. Elsevier.

Bonhoeffer, K. F., (1948); Activation of passive iron as a model for the excitation of nerve. *J. gen. Physiol.*, **32**, 69–91.

Boycott, B. B., and Young, J. Z., (1950); The comparative study of learning. S. E. B. Symposia, IV. *Physiological Mechanisms in Animal Behavior*. Cambridge. Academic Press.

Cole, K. S., and Curtis, H. J., (1939); Electric impedance of the squid giant axon during activity. *J. gen. Physiol.*, **22**, 649–670.

Eccles, J. C., (1961); The effects of use and disuse on synaptic function. *Brain Mechanisms and Learning*. Oxford, Blackwell Scientific Publications.

Franck, U. F., (1956); Model for biological excitation processes. *Progress in Biophysics and Biophysical Chemistry*. J. A. V. Butler, Editor. London and New York. Pergamon Press (pp. 171–206).

Gerard, R. W., (1955); Biological roots of psychiatry. *Science*, **122**.

Gesell, R., (1940); A neurophysiological interpretation of the respiratory act. *Ergebn. Physiol.*, **43**, 477–639.

Hebb, D. O., (1949); *The Organization of Behavior, A Neuropsychological Theory*. New York. John Wiley and Sons.

Hebb, D. O., (1961); Distinctive features of learning in the higher animal. *Brain Mechanisms and Learning*. Oxford. Blackwell Scientific Publications.

Konorski, J., (1948); *Conditioned Reflexes and Neuron Organization*. Cambridge. Cambridge University Press.

Lillie, R. S., (1925); Factors affecting the transmission and recovery in the passive iron nerve model. *J. gen. Physiol.*, **4**, 473.

Lillie, R. S., (1936); Passive iron-wire model of protoplasmic and nervous transmission and its physiological analogues. *Biol. Rev.*, **11**, (2), 181–209.

Matumoto, M., and Goto, K., (1955); A new type of nerve conduction model. *Gunma J. med. Sci.*, **4**.

McCulloch, W. S., and Pitts, W., (1943); A logical calculus of the ideas immanent in nervous activity. *Bull. mathemat. Biophys.*, **5**, 115–133.

Morrell, F., (1961); Electrophysiological contributions to the neural basis of learning. *Physiol. Rev.*, **41**.

Pask, G., (1958); The growth process inside the cybernetic machine. *Proceedings of the 2nd Congress International Association Cybernetics*. Paris, Gauthier-Villars.

Retzlaff, E., (1954); Neurohistological basis for the functioning of paired half-centers. *J. comp. Neurol.*, **101**, 407–443.

Sperry, R. W., (1952); Neurology and the mind-brain problem. *Amer. Scientist*.

Stewart, R. M., (1964); Research on electrochemical adaptive systems, Techn. Rept. ALTDR 64-254, Air Force Avionics Laboratory, available from Office of Technical Services, U.S. Dept. of Commerce.

Tasaki, I., and Bak, A. F., (1959); *J. gen. Physiol.*, **42**, 899.

Thorpe, W. H., (1950); The concepts of learning and their relation to those of instinct. S.E.B. Symposia, Number IV. *Physiological Mechanisms in Animal Behavior*. Cambridge. Academic Press. (pp. 387–405).

Yamagiwa, K., (1950); The interaction in various manifestations (Observations of Lillie's nerve model). *Jap. J. Physiol.*, **1**, 40–54.

Young, J. Z., (1938); The evolution of the nervous system and of the relationship of organism and environment. *Evolution* (Essays on Aspects of evolutionary biology presented to Professor E. S. Goodrich). G. R. De Beer, Editor. Oxford. Clarendon Press. (pp. 179–204).

Young, J. Z., (1951); *Doubt and Certainty in Science, A Biologist's Reflections on the Brain*. Oxford. Oxford Press.

Pattern Recognition and Self-Organization using Wiener's Canonical Forms

DONALD B. BRICK

Sylvania Electronic Systems, A Division of
Sylvania Electric Products Inc., Waltham, Mass. (U.S.A.)

INTRODUCTION

Wiener (1958, 1961) initiated a new approach to non-linear problems with his polynomial expansion procedure, a procedure which relies upon the use of a random noise (Brownian motion) input. He applied it to the analysis of electrical circuits and other non-linear processes and for their synthesis as well. At several points in *Cybernetics* (Wiener, 1961), he emphasized the importance of this approach in cybernetics. He indicated how, not only are non-linear processes that can be analyzed and synthesized using Brownian processes as test excitations, important in both engineering and biology, but that the Brownian process itself is closely related to important excitation processes in biology, reproduction, and self-organization, in addition to the better-known ones in engineering. Further, he discussed the relationship of his expansion procedure to predictors, learning machines, and their physiological counterparts.

A step in the realization of the above relationship was taken by Brick and Zames (1962), who showed how Wiener's expansion procedure could be used to synthesize decision functions for stochastic inputs. Moreover, they found it possible to extend the class of input processes to a broader class of stochastic inputs than the Brownian-type process to which Wiener limited himself. Furthermore, self-adaptive or learning properties were noted. In the present paper, this approach is extended to the multiple-alternative, sequential decision problem which is characteristic of pattern recognition. When considered in the light of its self-adaptive properties, we arrive at a fairly powerful class of automata applicable to a broad class of stochastic inputs.

Minsky (1961) has identified five main areas of artificial intelligence: search, pattern recognition, learning, planning and induction. He further states that search is enormously inefficient but with the use of certain pattern recognition techniques the efficiency can be greatly improved. Learning efficiency is further improved by directing search in accord with earlier experiences and planning. Induction is identified with some rather more global concepts of how one might obtain intelligent machine behavior as discussed below. Pattern recognition in its broadest sense, combined with learning, form a major element of intelligence.

Ashby (1961) provides one point of view on this subject when he states 'Not a single clear counter example has been given in the last ten years to show that an intelligent system is anything other than one which achieves appropriate selection'. He then goes on to relate appropriate selection and intelligence to regulation (*i.e.*, survival as a goal) in the living organism. In particular, Ashby (1956, 1957) points out that getting an answer to a problem is essentially a matter of selection; such selection can be amplified; and the first estimate of the time to solve a difficult problem suggests an excessively long time (random selection); closer examination shows that this estimate is biased to an upper bound; the lower bound, achievable in some cases, is the time necessary to write down the answer in binary notation. A measure of intelligence is the time required (as a measure of efficiency of appropriate selection) to solve the problem correctly. The process of intelligent selection indicates a process of optimum classification or pattern recognition.

A few other points made by Ashby (1961) are worth noting here: (i) 'There is no 'real' intelligence' '. . . if by 'real' one means the intelligence that can perform great feats of appropriate selection without prior reception and processing of the equivalent quantity of information'; (ii) 'With the remaining definition of intelligence, the computing engineer should stop asking 'How can I make an intelligent machine?' because he is, in fact . . . . and has been doing it for the last twenty years;' (iii)' . . . the rule about appropriate selection applies not merely to the final goal, but to all subgoals that have to be found on the way to it, and to all qualifying goals that may be set up;' (iv) Two other problems are brought up — how to dichotomize, repeatedly, becomes an object of search and *where* to bring corrective feedbacks', ... this again can be done only where information exists. If it does not exist either a simple random decision must be made or further information must be obtained, either systematically or unsystematically by trial and error; and so on . . .'

Cherry (1957) presents a counter-opinion when he discusses the difference between *recognition*, the knowing again of something real or abstract, which has already fallen within our experience — and the *perception* of some radically new concept. Recognition implies a classification of the recognized object into an existing class; but the setting up of a new class is a creative act.

MacKay (1956) presented two conceptual models for automata. His second model has the capability to expand its conceptual framework 'to match the stationary statistical features of the world, and new hypotheses — in the form of tentative organizing routines — are always being framed'. This capability of a machine to develop and symbolize for itself new (unpreconceived) concepts as the occasion might arise is in theory laudable, if we are to model human intelligence. However, in practice, it has been an elusive goal, the major difficulty being the definition, or even appreciation, of adequate criteria for the generalization of existing hypotheses and for the generation of new ones. We find ourselves speculating on the length, drift, bias, convergence and stability of unsupervised and postsupervised learning phases. We are led to the question of the role of a trainer, if he is at all present, during these phases, or how we can specify, ascertain, or determine when post-conditioning transitions or environmental changes are taking place.

References p. 278

The major problem alluded to above is, however, normally skirted, in practice. In this paper it is accomplished by adopting Ashby's approach to intelligence. Thus creativity, planning, induction, and hypothesis generation are features which will not specifically concern us for the present model of our automaton. However, generalization of existing hypotheses and selection, recognition and learning with respect to these are major factors in the present study.

The model of the recognition system derived here is, in fact, a form of conditional probability computer (Uttley, 1956) which operates on stochastic processes. Of major interest is the fact that this procedure appears to avoid the tendency towards exponential growth normally considered to be characteristic of conditional probability computers (Minsky, 1961, and Minsky and Selfridge, 1961).

The narrowing-down of the artificial intelligence problem to the recognition, learning, and prediction phases, however one proceeds to justify it (*e.g.*, as above), is not without precedence. Selfridge (1959), Greene (1960), Newell *et al.* (1960), Minsky and Selfridge (1961), Rosenblatt (1962), Block (1961), Tou and Fu (1961), Fu (1962), Maron (1962) Ullman (1963), Brick and Owen (1964), and even Wiener (1961), to name but a few, have preceded us here. We therefore feel justified in proceeding without further ado in this direction.

REVIEW OF PREVIOUS RESULTS

In an earlier paper (Brick and Zames, 1962), it was shown how Wiener-like functionals (Wiener, 1958)* could be applied to risk theory (Wald, 1950) to obtain canonical mathematical forms which could, in turn, be synthesized in terms of electronic circuit structures for the desired Bayes' optimum systems (Middleton, 1960), when the underlying phenomena were members of a broad class of stochastic processes**. Particular application was made to the problems of estimation, prediction, and binary detection. However, multiple-alternative or M-ary discrete decisions, characteristic of pattern recognition problems, and sequential decisions were not treated in detail in the earlier work.

Some of the advantages of these decision forms over earlier ones (*cf.* Middleton, 1960) are that they are not limited to a particular class of statistical behavior (*e.g.*,

---

* Wiener's original functions were applicable for a Wiener (Brownian motion) process; the present ones are called Wiener-like because they are identical functionals of a broader class of processes. In both, the input and its history are characterized by the coefficients of a series expansion of the process with respect to time and non-linear operations are synthesized by polynomial series expansions of the coefficients of the time expansion. The appropriate series expansions for the Wiener process are Hermite polynomials of Laguerre coefficients and we have standardized on that choice except in unusual circumstances. In the course of the earlier derivation of these forms for decision structures, a structure in which the time-base expansion was a sample-time series and the non-linearities were provided by Hermite functions was arrived at. In some cases this formulation is useful, however its primary virtue has been in leading to an explanation of the Wiener functionals since one of the major virtues of the latter is its departure from the normal constraints of time sampling.
** Although a broad class of processes is encompassed, the size of the class is as yet unspecified (Brick and Zames, 1962). It is determined by conditions of separability, conditions on the continuity of the probability density distribution of the process and of the process itself, and on proper behavior in the remote past.

Gaussian, Rayleigh, Poisson, etc.) or range of signal-to-noise ratios and always result in physically realizable and time-invariant operations. However, perhaps the most important advantage which is fully realized in cases when no feedback is required is the self-adaptive property inherent in the fact that, as a circuit structure adaptation to different processes is accomplished simply by adjusting amplifier gains or, mathematically, only constant coefficients need be adjusted, the functional dependence remaining invariant. For ergodic or quasi-ergodic processes these adjustments can be made automatically from a set of learning samples.

The fundamental results of the previous work required in the present application are summarized below:

Using the results of the earlier paper, it can be shown* that the ratio, W_R, of the probability density distribution describing the statistical behavior of each member of a stochastic process, $V(t)$, to the probability density distribution characteristic of the identical member, path, or time history of a Wiener (or Brownian) process, $x(t)$, can be expanded canonically as:

$$W_R(\beta) \sim \lim_{p \to \infty} \sum_{k_1=0}^{\infty} \ldots \sum_{k_p=0}^{\infty} b_{k_1 \ldots k_p} \prod_{r \to 1}^{p} H_{k_r} [V_r(\beta)] \tag{1a}$$

Likewise the ratio of the density distribution of $V(t)$ conditional on a parameter S to that of $x(t)$ can be expanded as

$$W_R(\beta|S) \sim \lim_{p \to \infty} \sum_{k_1=0}^{\infty} \ldots \sum_{k_p=0}^{\infty} \overset{(S)}{b_{k_1 \ldots k_p}} \prod_{r=1}^{p} H_{k_r} [V_r(\beta)] \tag{1b}$$

where β is an indexing variable, $0 \le \beta \le 1$, which labels each member or path of the process, $V(t)$, except for a set of probability measure zero. (Since β defines a path, the identical path of $x(t)$ is also identified by β.). Both $V(t)$ and $x(t)$ are assumed to have started in the remote past ($t = -\infty$) and run to time $t = 0$. H_{k_r} is a Hermite polynomial of order k_r and $V_r(\beta)$ is the coefficient of the rth term in a Laguerre function expansion of the β path of $V(t)$.

The $\{H_{k_r} [V_r(\beta)]\}$ can be interpreted circuitwise as Hermite polynomial non-linear operations performed on the outputs of Laguerre filters (Wiener, 1958, Brick and Zames, 1962). The coefficients $b_{k1 \ldots k_p}$ which are determined from

$$\left. \begin{matrix} b_{k_1 \ldots k_p} \\ \text{or} \\ \overset{(S)}{b_{k_1 \ldots k_p}} \end{matrix} \right\} = \int_0^1 \left\{ \begin{matrix} W_R(\beta) \\ \text{or} \\ W_R(\beta|S) \end{matrix} \right\} \prod_{r=1}^{p} H_{k_r} [V_r(\beta)] \, \mathrm{d}\beta, \tag{2a} \tag{2b}$$

can be instrumented as amplifier gains on the respective non-linear circuit outputs,

For an ergodic process, Equations (2), which are in the form of ensemble averages, can be converted to appropriate time averages of $H_{k_r} [V_r(\beta)]$. In this case a sufficiently long sample of the process either characterized by parameter S for (2b) or averaged over all values of S for (2a) obtained at an earlier time can be used for

---

* The pertinent definitions, conditions, steps, and details leading to these results are summarized in the Appendix to this paper.

References p. 278

preadjusting the b's. If the process is not ergodic, the statistics of the process, $V(t)$, must be known or estimated and used in Equations (2) to compute the b's (see Brick and Zames, 1962).

RELEVANT ASPECTS OF DECISION THEORY (HYPOTHESES TESTING)

We shall now summarize the required relationships for the decision problem:

The average or expected sequential risk, $R(P, \delta, d_j)$, (Wald, 1947, 1950) may be written, for non-randomized decision rules*, as (Blackwell and Gershick, 1954)

$$R(P, \delta, d_j) = \sum_{q=0}^{N} \sum_{m=1}^{M} \int_{\{V\}\varepsilon\delta_q} d\,\{v\}\,[C_q(\{v\}) + L(S_m, d_j(q, \{v\}))]\,W(\{v\}|S_m)\,P(S_m)$$

$$= \sum_{m=1}^{M} P(S_m)\,r(S_m, \delta, d_j) \tag{3}$$

where r is the conditional risk.

$\{v\}$ is the set of observables assumed to be continuous and multi-dimensional.

$\{V\}$ is the space of $\{v\}$ for $q + 1$ stages.

M is the number of parameters, S_m.

$q + 1$ is the number of discrete stages or steps in any sampling plan.

$N + 1$ is the total number of stages.

δ_q is the sampling plan consisting of q non-terminal decisions (functions of the observables up to that stage and previous decisions) followed by a terminal decision rule.

d_j is the terminal decision or hypothesis choice (at the $q + 1^{\text{th}}$ stage) to choose alternative j following q stages of non-terminal decisions according to sampling plan δ_q.

C is the cost for performing q experiments prior to making a terminal decision on the $q + 1^{\text{th}}$ experiment, $C = 0$ for $q = 0$.

L is the loss function corresponding to decision d_j when S_m is the actual parameter.

$W(\{v\}|S_m)$ is the probability density of $\{v\}$ given that S_m has occurred. It is often called the conditional likelihood function of $\{v\}$.

$P(S_m)$ is the *a priori* probability of S_m.

$W(\{v\}, S_m) = P(S_m)\,W(\{v\}|S_m)$, the joint distribution of its arguments and is often called the likelihood function of $\{v\}$ and S.

When the number of stages is fixed, a non-sequential decision rule results. The corresponding risk function may be written in the usual non-sequential form:

$$R_1(P, \delta, d_j) = \sum_{m=1}^{M} \int_{\{V\}} d\{v\}\,L(S_m, d_j(\{v\}))\,W)(\{v\}|S_m)\,P(S_m)$$

$$= \sum_{m=1}^{N} P(S_m)\,r_1(S_m, \delta, d_j). \tag{4}$$

---

* The class of non-randomized decision rule has been shown to contain an optimum decision rule for many decision problems of importance (*cf.* Dvoretzky *et al.*, 1951).

The optimum decision rule is defined generally as one which minimizes the average risk, R, if the *a priori* probability distributions $\{P(S_m)\}$ are known or the conditional risk, r, if the $\{P(S_m)\}$ are not known; the so-called Bayes solutions (Wald, 1950); or as an alternative, which in some cases makes much more sense, a minimax rule is applied to r (minimize the maximum conditional risk).

Minimizing the non-sequential risks, R_1 and r_1, leads to generalized likelihood decision rules of the type shown in Equations (5) and (6) (Wald, 1950, Blackwell and Gershick, 1954, Chow, 1957, Middleton, 1960). Choose d_j based upon

$$\text{Inf}_j \sum_{m=1}^{M} L(S_m, d_j) \, P(S_m) \, W(\{v\}|S_m), \text{ all } j, \tag{5}$$

the generalized unconditional likelihood rule which minimizes R_1, and

$$\text{Inf}_j \sum_{m=1}^{M} L(S_m, d_j) \, W(\{v\}|S_m), \text{ all } j, \tag{6}$$

the generalized conditional likelihood rule which minimizes r_1, assuming equal $P(S_m)$.

For special assignments of loss function, Equations (5) and (6) reduce to comparisons between, and/or threshold operations on, the probability terms in the summation, (*cf.* Wald (1950), Fu (1962), Marril and Green (1960), Middleton (1960), and Cooper (1963)). In particular for the loss function, $L(S_m, d_j) =$

$$\begin{cases} O, j = m \\ C, \text{ all } j \neq m \end{cases}, \text{ Equations (5) and (6) reduce respectively to:}$$

Decide d_j if $P(S_j) \, W(\{v\}|S_j) > P(S_m) \, W(\{v\}|S_m)$ for some j and all $m \neq j$. (7)

Decide d_j if $W(\{v\}|S_j) > W(\{v\}|S_m)$ for some j and all $m \neq j$, (8)

the so-called maximum likelihood decision rules.

For the sequential Bayes solution, the decision procedure is also of the likelihood type at each stage. However, it is more complicated than the simple computation of an extremum or comparison over the range of M possible hypotheses; the decision to continue experimenting presents an $M + 1^{\text{th}}$ choice. The weighting given this $M + 1^{\text{th}}$ choice in the comparison procedure varies from stage-to-stage and is a function of the past history of the observable $\{v\}^*$.

Blackwell and Gershick (1954) have shown the Bayes sequential procedure for R to be the following:

At each stage of observation q, compute

$$U_q(\{v\}) = C_q + \text{Inf}_j \frac{\sum_{m=1}^{M} L(S_m, d_j) \, P(S_m) \, W(\{v\}|S_m)}{\sum_{m=1}^{M} P(S_m) \, W(\{v\}|S_m)} \tag{9}$$

Compute also $a_q(\{v\}) \equiv \begin{cases} \min[U_q, E_q(a_{q+1}(\{v\}))], o \leqslant q \leqslant N \\ U_N \qquad\qquad , q = N \end{cases}$ (10)

---

* Fu (1961, 1962), Bellman (1961), and Brick and Owen (1964), among others have pointed out the analogy between this procedure and one phase of learning in machines and organisms.

References p. 278

Where E_q indicates an expectation with q observables given, $\{v\}_1, \ldots, \{v\}_q$, and $N - q$ observables distributed according to $W(\{v\}|S_m, \{v\}_1, \ldots, \{v\}_q)$.

The decision procedure is then:

If $U_q = a_q$ choose d_j corresponding to the j which minimized U_q. If $U_q > a_q$ proceed to the next stage, $0 \leqslant q < N$, until we reach the Nth stage where $U_N \equiv a_N$ (11)

The procedure when all $P(S_m)$ are assumed to be equal to $\dfrac{1}{M}$ is identical, and the $P(S_m)$ terms therefore may be removed and need not appear in the results:

Of course the computations involved here in practice in proceeding from the generalized statements of Equations (10) and (11) to simple operations are far from simple except in special cases. A dynamic programming attack on the problem is normally called for (Bellman, 1961).

A notable simplification results for the binary or single alternative situation. When the samples are identically distributed and independent from stage-to-stage, the Bayes procedure is a simple likelihood ratio test (Wald and Wolfowitz, 1948):

$$\lambda_q = \frac{W(\{v\}|S_2)}{W(\{v\}|S_1)} \tag{12}$$

where if, $A \leq \lambda_q \leq B$, continue to experiment; if $\lambda_q > B$, make decision d_2; or if $\lambda_q < A$, make decision d_1.

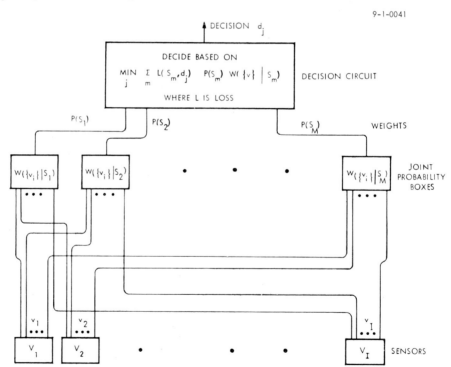

Fig. 1. Nonsequential classical Bayes net or conditional probability model. If the lower case v's are statistically independent, the capital W's are products of $W(\{v_i\} | S_m)$. The links connecting the sensor boxes and the joint probability boxes may then be weighted by the appropriate $P(S_m)$ and the joint probability box is then simply a product computer.

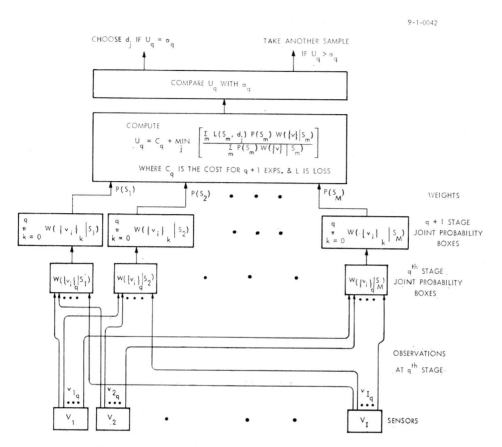

Fig. 2. Sequential classical Bayes net or conditional probability model. If the lower case v_q's are statistically independent, the capital W's are products of $W(\{v_i\}_q \, S_m)$. The links connecting the sensor boxes and the joint probability box is then simply a product computer.

For our present purposes no further delving into the detailed characteristic of the decision rules is desirable since our major concern is with the operations involved in calculating the relevant likelihood functions and not with the succeeding operations.

Functional diagrams for the non-sequential and sequential cases are given in Figs. 1 and 2, respectively. In Fig. 2, it is assumed for simplicity that the observations from stage-to-stage are independently distributed so that $W(\{v\}|S) = \prod\limits_{k=0}^{q} W(\{v\}_k|S)$. The notation used in these figures is that associated with the pattern recognition problem to be discussed in the following sections, where the parameter S_m identifies the pattern to be recognized. When the pattern is a time-varying function, the sensing operation in the figures may include a time-sampling operation. In fact, if the pattern is a wave-form identification problem, the usual approach is to use time samples for observational parameters. In that case the sensors $V_1, V_2, \ldots, V_I$ indicate time-sampling operations and the $\{v_i\}$ are the time samples. The Wiener approach adopts an alternative sampling operation, although as mentioned earlier, the author has shown

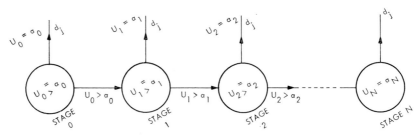

Fig. 3. Tree-type structure characteristic of sequential decision rule.

how a similar canonical synthesis may be obtained using time samples (Brick and Zames, 1962).

In Fig. 3, the tree-type structure which characterizes the sequential decision is illustrated.

APPLICATION TO STOCHASTIC PROCESSES

The application of the decision procedure to stochastic processes when the process is characterized by its time samples has been discussed above. If these samples are taken at fixed time points, then the indexing parameter, q, is identified with time since an additional stage of observation is equivalent to an observation at a later time, usually one fixed time sampling interval later.

However, for purposes of the present work, the process is considered as a function of continuous time starting in the remote past and running to time $t = 0$. We adapt Equations (3)–(11) to this process by substituting $V(t)$, $-\infty \le t \le 0$, for $\{v\}$. q also becomes a function of time; its functional dependence will be discussed later. The parameter, S_m, labels a particular deterministic waveform, or even a particular class of stochastic waveforms, which is a parameter of $V(t)$.

The Bayes decision procedures are described by Equations (5) and (6) and (9), (10), and (11) for non-sequential and sequential decision procedures, respectively. Dividing all terms, $W(V(t)|S_m)$ and $(W(V(t)) = \sum\limits_{m=1}^{M} P(S_m)\, W\,(V(t)|S_m)$, by the probability density distribution characteristic of an identical time path or history of a Wiener or Brownian process and recalling the definition of $W_R(\beta)$ and $W_R(\beta|S)$, in Equations (1), we get Equations (13) and (16) replacing the aforementioned ones, respectively.

Thus, for non-sequential decisions, the Bayes rules become:
Choose d_j which satisfies

$$\underset{j}{\text{Inf. lim}}\; \underset{p\to\infty}{}\; \sum_{m=1}^{M}\; \sum_{k1=0}^{\infty}\; \ldots\; \sum_{k_p=0}^{\infty}\; b_{k_1}^{(S_m)} \ldots {}_{k_p}\; \prod_{r=1}^{P} H_{k_r}\, [V_r(\beta)]\, L(S_m, d_j)\, P(S_m) \qquad (13)$$

minimizing R_1, and with all $P(S_m)$'s equal to $\dfrac{1}{M}$,

$$\underset{j}{\text{Inf. lim}}\; \underset{p\to\infty}{}\; \sum_{m=1}^{M}\; \sum_{k_1=0}^{\infty}\; \ldots\; \sum_{k_p=0}^{\infty}\; b_{k_1}^{(S_m)} \ldots {}_{k_p}\; \prod_{r=1}^{p} H_k\, [V_r(\beta)]\, L(S_m, d_j) \qquad (14)$$

minimizing r_1. The decision is made at time $t = 0$.

For sequential decisions, the Bayes procedure becomes for R:

Compute, for each stage q, (without worrying at present about the definition of a stage)

$$U_q(\beta) = C_q + \underset{j}{\text{Inf.}} \frac{\lim\limits_{p \to \infty} \sum\limits_{m=1}^{M} \sum\limits_{k_1=0}^{\infty} \ldots \sum\limits_{k_p=0}^{\infty} b_{k_1}^{(S_m)} \ldots k_p \prod\limits_{r=1}^{p} H_{k_r}[V_r(\beta)] L(S_m, d_j) P(S_m)}{\lim\limits_{p \to \infty} \sum\limits_{k_1=0}^{\infty} \ldots \sum\limits_{k_p=0}^{\infty} b_{k_1} \ldots k_p \prod\limits_{r=1}^{p} H_{k_r}[V_r(\beta)]}$$

(15)

$$= C_q + \underset{j}{\text{Inf.}} \frac{\lim\limits_{p \to \infty} \sum\limits_{m=1}^{M} \sum\limits_{k_1=0}^{\infty} \ldots \sum\limits_{k_p=0}^{\infty} b_{k_1}^{(S_m)} \ldots k_p \prod\limits_{r=1}^{p} H_{k_r}[V_r(\beta)] L(S_m, d_j) P(S_m)}{\lim\limits_{p \to \infty} \sum\limits_{m=1}^{M} \sum\limits_{k_1=0}^{\infty} \ldots \sum\limits_{k_p=0}^{\infty} b_{k_1}^{(S_m)} \ldots k_p \prod\limits_{r=1}^{p} H_{k_r}[V_r(\beta)] P(S_m)}$$

and compute

$$a_q(\beta) \equiv \begin{cases} \min\left[U_q(\beta), E_q\, a_{q+1}(\beta)\right), & 0 \leqslant q < N \\ U_N(\beta) & , \quad q = N \end{cases}$$

(16)

and make a decision in an identical manner to Equation (11). Note that the two expressions for the right side of Equation (15) provide equivalent alternate approaches to the computational problem.

For assumed equal $P(S_m)$, the Bayes procedure is the same as Equations (15) and (16) except that the $P(S_m)$ terms are omitted.

If we were to limit ourselves to a rigorous application of the Wiener-type expansions for ergodic inputs, there would be no need for the sequential approach, (whereby the possibility of taking additional samples at a cost for the purpose of improving the accuracy of the decisions exists) because we already have an infinite sample of the process (from time $t = -\infty$ to time $t = 0$). However, in practice, we do not have ergodic processes; at most we have quasi-ergodic, quasi-stationary, or locally-stationary processes. Neither did they begin at time, $t = -\infty$, even though they may have begun in the relatively remote past. As a matter of fact, such processes are the more interesting ones, from an adaptive point of view.

Furthermore, we would like to truncate the Laguerre and Hermite function series in the interests of computational or circuit component economy. The accuracy with which the past is described by the Laguerre series is roughly proportional to the number of terms in the series; the more remote the past, the more terms required. Hence truncating the number of Laguerre coefficients is equivalent to limiting the extent of the past of the process.

Thus, although not obvious at first, upon further examination, we conclude that a sequential processor is of potential value for processes of present interest.

Having developed our fundamental tools, we now turn to the recognition and self-organization problem, proper.

PATTERN RECOGNITION AND ITS RELATIONSHIP TO DECISION THEORY

In general, pattern recognition implies the assignment of a name* or representation to a class (or group of classes) of stimuli whose members have something in common in the way of origins, values, goals, or problem-solving abilities. They are 'similar' in a useful sense. If they arise from a class of identical stimuli or parameters (with any variation, distortion, or noise being that added by the environment or representation) they form an important sub-class of patterns — the so-called 'prototype-derived' patterns (Minsky, 1961). Pattern recognition can then be thought of as grouping certain sets into common categories which are given common descriptions. It is logical to expect (or hope) that these descriptions will be simpler than the original sets.

To put these intuitive concepts into more concrete terms, consider a multisensor system (or multi-property filter system) with sensors (or property filters), V_1, V_2, ..., V_i ..., V_I, each of which provides a measure of a characteristic or property of a stimulus or pattern. In a geometrical pattern-measuring system the sensors may be retinal elements while for the waveform patterns of present interest, they could be time samples of the waveforms, spectral-sample measurements, or, as in our present case, filter responses or combinations thereof. The goal is to utilize the joint responses, $\{v_i\}$, of these sensors to classify the stimulus into one of M pattern (or parameter) classes. Thus the problem is immediately recognizable as one of classification, into a multiplicity of categories, of a multi-dimensional sample or, in other words, multiple hypothesis testing in decision theory. However, the statistical nature of the pattern recognition problem has yet to be explicitly introduced here.

In most cases, a stimulus class or parameter, S_m, does not provide a unique set of sensor (or property-filter) response values, $\{v_i\}$. More often members of each class, $\{v_i\}$, for a particular S_m form aggregates of response values. These M aggregates of arrays may be viewed as defining M sets of points in I-dimensional space. In practically all real situations, if the sensors are sufficiently sensitive, these pattern classes are found to have a degree of randomness associated with them. Furthermore, thermodynamic considerations indicate that the sensors (or property filters) themselves will add additional randomness. Finally a probabilistic relationship between the individual members of the sets composing the pattern classes to the classes themselves has been implied throughout the paper**. Certainly this is true for noisy or stochastic waveforms. In other words, given the occurrence of the class, there is a probability of occurrence of each member of the class, or a probability density on the Borel set of measurements of members of the class. Most real situations of interest fall into this category. However, unless we have had sufficient prior experience with the pattern classes, or, can accurately describe the physical model into which these patterns fall

---

* The name need not be given explicitly; the class may be an unnamed association, concept, or the selection of a course for possible action.

** Statistical methods may, in some pattern recognition cases, serve only as a convenient or simplifying tool or algorithm for describing the behavior of large numbers of members of the individual pattern sets. Consequently true or complete randomness may not exist; statistical tools being introduced in these cases from the point of view of convenience or unification in large number theory.

so that we can describe their behavior, the relevant probability distributions are not initially known to us. The estimation or learning of these distributions is another type of learning. Fortunately in the Wiener-canonical approach the probability distributions are not required when the process is ergodic (or, in approximation, quasi-ergodic or locally stationary).

Thus, the pattern recognizer can be cast as a problem in statistical hypothesis testing whose functional implementation is represented by Figs. 1 and 2. Uttley (1956) has introduced the concept of a conditional probability machine in animal behavior and automata theory. Such a machine is, in effect, equivalent to Fig. 1, as shown by Minsky (1961) for the binary case. The analogy between this machine and a neural net has been discussed by the above authors.

STRUCTURE OF WIENER CANONICAL PATTERN RECOGNIZERS

Equations (13) and (14) for the non-sequential processor and Equations (11), (15), and (16) for the sequential processor are the formulas describing the Wiener canonical form of the Bayes or conditional probability pattern recognizer, where S_m is the pattern to be recognized. These can either be used as the basis for computation or for

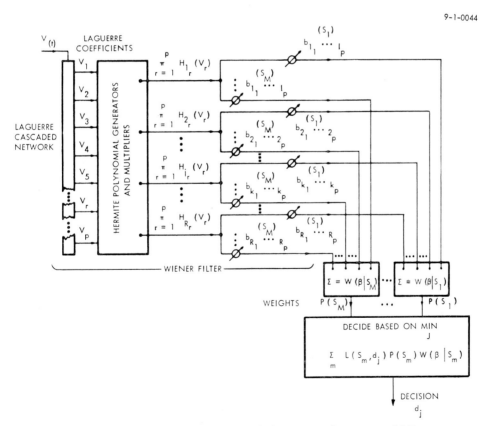

Fig. 4. R-term approximation of Wiener canonical structure of non-sequential Bayes net.

a circuit synthesis procedure. The corresponding circuit structures, derived as in the earlier work (Brick and Zames, 1962), are shown for R_1 and R, respectively, in Figs. 4 and 5. For the conditional Bayes processors, r_1 and r, they differ only in that the weight functions, $\{P(S_m)\}$, are omitted.

Note that the summations over each of the R_i have been truncated to R Hermite polynomial terms since an infinite number is, of course, impossible in any physical situation. The number of terms required in these summations for a given degree of approximation to the $W_R(\beta|S_m)$ function is a function of how non-linear W_R is in its argument. For any particular class of $V(t)$'s this will have to be determined. Of course the number of terms required here is one of the determining factors defining the usefulness, in practice, of this synthesis procedure or its meaningfulness as a model. For a large class of input processes $V(t)$, the convergence of the series has been proven. How large this class is remains to be determined. Conditions for and rates of convergence of both the Hermite and Laguerre series, described below, are the subject of additional investigations.

The number of Laguerre filter terms, p, as mentioned earlier, depends roughly on the length of time over which the process is significantly correlated and its high-frequency content. Here, again, the number of terms required for a particular degree of approximation will depend upon the process $V(t)$.

9-1-0045

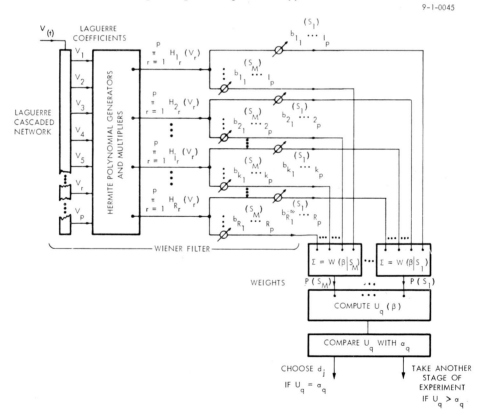

Fig. 5. R-term approximation of Wiener canonical structure of sequential Bayes net.

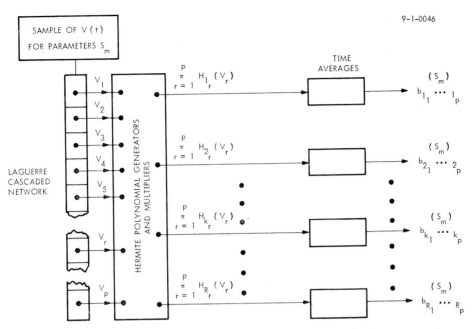

Fig. 6. Structure of R-term approximation to coefficient computer (stationary process).

If the process is not ergodic, the b's must be computed from expectations; normally this requires an *a priori* knowledge or estimate of the relevant statistical behaviors. If the process is ergodic, the statistical averages can be replaced by time averages and a coefficient computer of the type shown in Fig. 6 results. In this case, adjustment of the b's is accomplished by feeding the computer samples of $V(t)$ for each S_m. (The possibility of time varying and random $S(t)$ is introduced later.)

Figs. 4 and 5 are constructed under as general conditions as possible. For many particular situations, the structures are greatly simplified. As an example, in the binary situation, only two sets of channels in Figs. 4 and 5 are required followed by a divider to compute λ_q, Equation (12). The decision circuit then consists simply of one or two threshold comparisons for λ_q.

As discussed at other points in the paper, rigorous application of the procedure for time average computations of the b's specifies the use of semi-infinite averaging times. However, approximations using finite time averages for quasi-ergodic or locally-stationary processes are satisfactory and, in fact, necessary for meaningful adaptive operation. Here again, the accuracy of the approximation using finite averaging times and the specification of the required lengths of these times are functions of the class of $V(t)$'s and will be the subject for additional research in conjunction with the previously-mentioned truncation approximations.

Since the processing is continuous with time in this approach, it is not necessary to define a discrete stage of experimentation for the sequential processor. Thus, various criteria for sequential operation can be chosen; again depending upon the system function and requirements and the explicit characteristics of the class of $V(t)$'s.

References p. 278

Minsky (1961) and Minsky and Selfridge (1961) have mentioned the tendency of the conditional probability computer to grow exponentially as the number of dimensions required in the joint probabilities increases. In the present structures, we are concerned instead with the number of Hermite and Laguerre terms required. Hopefully, these numbers can be reasonably bounded as discussed earlier.

TIME VARYINGS

Up to this point, S_m has been treated as a constant parameter of $V(t)$. In fact, however, there is nothing restrictive in the formulation to preclude S_m from being a time-varying function, $S_m(t)$, $-\infty \leq t \leq 0$. If it is a deterministic function, the earlier formulation is unchanged (except to replace S_m directly by $S_m(t)$ in the formulae) and $V(t)$ may be thought of as consisting of a deterministic signal in noise (e.g., additive noise, multiplicative noise, the convolution of signal and noise, or more generally, a noisy transformation of the signal).

If $S_m(t)$ is non-deterministic, it must be a member of the mth subset of the $S(t)$ space in the multiple alternative or multiple discrete pattern class context of this paper. Its membership and behavior are defined by the probability density distribution, $W(S(t)|S_m) P(S_m)$, where the W term is the density distribution of the $S(t)$ which are members of parameter class m denoted as S_m and $P(S_m)$ is now the *a priori* probability of class m, and d_j is a decision that a member of the jth, subset of the $S(t)$ space, S_j, is the parameter. The behavior of $V(t)$ is defined by

$$W(V(t), S(t)|S_m)P(S_m).$$

However, we are concerned only with

$$W(V(t)|S_m) = \int_{S \text{ space}} W(V(t), S(t)|S_m)dS(t) \text{ or}$$

$$W_R(\beta|S_m) = \int_{S \text{ space}} W_R(\beta, S(t)|S_m)dS(t)$$

in this problem; defined now as the probability of $V(t)$ or β, conditional on class S_m, rather than parameter S_m. In so far as the mechanics of the decision maker or pattern recognizer are concerned, once the substitution is made the problem is unchanged.

However, in the determination of these probability density distributions, additional computation is introduced; for here the distribution must be known or estimated conditional on a whole class $\{S_m\}$ rather than for a single parameter. In the estimation of $W(V \text{ or } \beta|S_m)$, this implies that learning samples be included for each value of $S(t)$ or for a representative set of values, each $S(t)$ having occurred with the proper frequency of occurrence. This procedure is complicated but not impossible to apply.

COMMENTS ON LEARNING AND SELF-ORGANIZATION

In an earlier paper the author has identified four types of learning associated with a Bayesian model of an 'intelligent' pattern recognizer and has discussed the relationship of this model to other cybernetical models, notably neural nets, hill climbing procedures, and Pandemonium (Selfridge, 1959), (Brick and Owen, 1964). The four types of learning are:

(a) the learning implied in the use of the probability measures which are characteristic of the observed statistical behavior of each class whether these probability measures are precisely known *a priori* or are estimated from sample data during a conditioning phase* prior to the operational phase of the machine or organism;

(b) that involved with the experience factor of a sequential decision procedure, as discussed earlier;

(c) if the probability measures used are estimated initially or if the statistical behavior of the process drifts as a function of time**, the learning involved in reestimating or updating the probabilities while the machine is operating (unsupervised learning), and

(d) learning involved in the employment of 'intuitive' techniques based on seeking unique, orthogonal, or invariant pattern characteristics, features, or universals, *e.g.*, searching for methods of simplifying or reducing the dimensionality of the observation space as an aid towards computability and reduction of the tendency towards exponential growth of the system. (Suggested procedures were reinforcement, reward and extinction, and coordinate transformations aimed at simplifying, directly, the estimated probability distributions.)

Learning of types (a) and (b) has already been discussed in the light of the present model. Fortunately, the Wiener expansion alleviates the requirement for explicit knowledge of the probability measures, since only expectations with respect to them are required. Thus, if these expectations can be computed without explicit reference to the probabilities, simplification can be achieved in those cases where the statistics are unknown. This is just the case for the ergodic (or quasi-ergodic) processes where the expectations are equivalent to time averages. The initial computation of the coefficients as discussed earlier is a supervised learning procedure.

Learning of type (c) can be readily built into the present model. It involves simply allowing the coefficient computer, Fig. 6, to operate continuously. The outputs of the coefficient computer are used to update the respective coefficients in Fig. 4 or 5. The respective coefficients are determined by the value of the parameter or class S_m that persists during the most recent observation period. The value of this parameter could be fed to the system or determined by a trainer as in the original supervised learning phase. Both of these occurrences are either unrealistic or of limited utility. As an alternative, the most recent estimate of S_m made by the system could be used. This is a true continuously self-organizing or unsupervised learning procedure.

---

* During a conditioning or supervised learning phase, the system is fed samples of each particular stimulus class and asked to respond to (or learn) this class and/or is fed samples from all classes at random with the proper *a priori* probabilities but is corrected or graded on its response to each by a trainer. In an unsupervised phase no external grading is exercised.
** The word 'drift' is used vadvisedly here since unpredictable rapid statistical changes are virtually impossible to adapt to in a conditional probability type of machine. This becomes obvious from the discussion of this type of learning for the present system model. However it might be possible to detect and reject (not accept) such processes when their presence is detected.

However, there is considerable danger to be wary of here, for instead of converging on the correct behavior, such a procedure may lead to drifts towards larger and larger errors or even to unstable situations. Consequently, before applying a technique such as this, further investigation or simulation studies of the behavior of the system to determine the advisability of such an approach and, if useful, optimum criteria for its application in any particular situation are required.

No work has been done to date on the application of learning of type (d) to the present model.

As a final note, it should be observed that the introduction of a non-deterministic set of parameters $S(t)$ is tantamount to the generalization of existing hypotheses. The creation of new hypotheses in the form of mutations could be accomplished by combining or imposing (deterministic or random) transformations on members of the existing set of hypotheses.

APPENDIX

*Wiener Canonical Formulation**

Wiener (1958) introduced as independent variables, functionals of the form**

$$F_i(a) = \int_A \varphi_i(\tau)dx(-\tau,a); \varphi_i(\tau)\varepsilon L_2^{***}, \text{ all } i, \tau\varepsilon A \qquad (17)$$

which, if they could be interpreted as ordinary Stieltjes integrals, would correspond to the responses of filters, with impulse responses $\varphi(t)$, to a signal $dx(t,a)/dt$ at time $t = 0$. The Wiener analysis is aimed at analyzing non-linear processes and utilizes, as a probing function, a one-dimensional simple Brownian process (which we will choose to start at $t = -\infty$) for $x(t,a)$. ($dx(t,a)/dt$ thereby represents white noise and consequently cannot be interpreted in the ordinary manner).

So far we have not mentioned the meaning and significance of a. To each continuous member of the Brownian process, a value a, [0,1], is assigned. This representation turns out be unique. Furthermore, the mapping of members of the process into the unit interval, $0 \le a \le 1$, is carried out in such a manner that the metric or Lebesque measure on any subinterval of the unit a interval is the probability that a member of the process $x(t,a)$ coincides with any of the paths mapped into that interval. In other words a is a mapping of the distribution function of $x(t,a)$ such that the Lebesque measure on a is the corresponding Lebesque-Stieltjes measure of the process $x(t,a)$.

The limits of integration, ([A]), on the functional have been omitted previously. It is convenient to choose our limits of integration and time scale on the basis of the latest available data point (*e.g.*, the present) calling this $t = 0$ and all previous points, $t < 0$, corresponds to choosing limits 0 to ∞ in Equation (17). Not only can each $F_i(a)$ be identified with a filter response at time, $t = 0$, but, if the $\{\varphi_i(\tau)\}$ are ortho-

---

* This Appendix consists, in the main, of material presented in more detail in the earlier work (Brick and Zames, 1962). For further details the reader is referred to that work.
** Suitable modifications on signs to suit the purposes of this work have been made.
*** Likewise, Wiener (1958) has shown $F_i(a)$ to be L_2 in a, where the notation L_2 indicates that the Lesbesque integral of the absolute value of the square of the function exists.

normal and complete in the τ interval $[0,\infty]$, identification of each term with the coefficient of a Fourier Series describing the past of the white noise process is possible. A convenient orthonormal set of functions suggested by Wiener (1958) is the set of normalized Laguerre functions,

$$\varphi_n(\tau) = \frac{e^{+\frac{\tau}{2}}}{n_g} \frac{d^n}{d\tau^n}(\tau^n e^{-\tau}),$$

and hence the aforementioned series is a Laguerre series, although other choices are possible. In this case, the $F_i(a)$ are Laguerre coefficients. Furthermore, Wiener has shown that if the $\{\varphi_i(\tau)\}$ are complete over $[A] = [0 \leqslant t \leqslant \infty]$, *any* non-linear operation or network response to a white-noise signal, which can be represented by

its a mapping* $F(a) = \int\limits_{0}^{\infty} f(\tau)dx(-\tau,a)$ can be synthesized by series of polynomials of

the $\{F_i(a)\}$ which are orthonormal over the space of $F(a)$. The appropriate polynomials are products of the Hermite polynomials, $H_n(x)$**, since $F(a)$ is derived from a normal process, $x(t,a)$, and $H_n(x)$ is orthonormal with respect to the normal distribution. Hence, we deal with Hermite polynomials of the Laguerre coefficients. Consequently it has been concluded, so far, that any $F(a)$, $F(a)\varepsilon L_2$, can be synthesized by a series of Hermite polynomials of the Laguerre coefficients, $F_i(a)$, of a white noise process, (Wiener's canonical form), where the polynomials provide the non-linearity (non-linear, no-memory operations) and the functional coefficients (linear filtering) provide the memory, delay, and/or dependence on the past history, replacing the time samples in other expansions.

To proceed from here we note that we desire to specify a canonical structure to synthesize the density distributions of $V(t)$. In order to accomplish this in the Wiener form, they must be converted to L_2 functions of a. We proceed to do this in the following by identifying the probability measures of V as functions of a which must be L_2.

The advantage of utilizing the Laguerre functions is that filters synthesizing them have been designed and the whole hierarchy of functions can be synthesized by taps on one cascaded filter structure. Therefore we shall define the Laguerre coefficients due to our observable waveform, $V(t)$, $-\infty \leqslant t \leqslant 0$, $\lim\limits_{t \to -\infty} V(t) = 0$, in a manner

analogous to those due to white-noise excitation $F_i(a)$, as

$$V_i(\beta) = \int\limits_{0}^{\infty} \varphi_i(\tau) \, V(-\tau)d\tau = \int\limits_{0}^{\infty} \varphi_i(\tau) \, dV\tau(-\tau, \beta). \qquad (18)$$

---

* $f(t)$ is the response of the network to an impulse at $t = 0$. $F(a)$ must be L_2. $F(a)$ is L_2 if $f(t)$ is L_2, $[0,\infty]$ (Wiener, 1958).

** $H_n(x) = (-1)^n e^{\frac{x^2}{2}} \dfrac{d^n e^{\frac{x^2}{2}}}{dx^n}$ $n = 0,1,\ldots$

References p. 278

β has been introduced to indicate the history and measure of the process giving rise to the functional. β is defined, as a mapping in probability, analogously to α, except that it maps members of process

$$\mathbf{V}(t,\beta) = \int_{-\infty}^{t} V(\tau)\mathrm{d}\tau,$$ a function of the past, $-\infty \leq t \leq 0$, rather than $x(t,\alpha)$ into

the line, $0 \leq \beta \leq 1$.

Now it is convenient to introduce one more parameter, call it ξ, which is defined as a mapping in probability for process $V(t)$ in a manner analogous to α for $x(t,\alpha)$ and β for $\mathbf{V}(t,\beta)$, i.e., ξ is defined for $V(t,\xi)$ to indicate a path of V and its Lebesque measure is the Lebesque-Stieltjes measure for the corresponding members of $V(t,\xi)$.

Since points in the 0 to 1 α-domain bear a one-to-one relationship to all possible paths of a Brownian motion initiated at $t = -\infty$ (except for a set of zero measure) they, in turn, bear a one-to-one relationship (again except for a set of measure zero) to all possible paths of a large class of functions that vanish at $-\infty$. This class is the acceptable class for V. Consequently, *to each point in the 0-to-1 β and ξ domains representing a possible path of the functions $\mathbf{V}$ and V, respectively, there corresponds a point of α representing the same path as a member of x. This one-to-one relationship is the defining relationship for the functions $\beta(\alpha)$ and $\xi(\alpha)$ of Fig. 7.*

9-1-0047

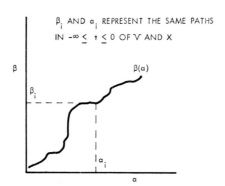

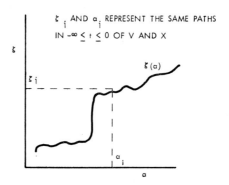

Fig. 7. Definition of β and ξ.

We now desire to identify and expand the density distributions of V, $W[V(t)]$ and $W(V(t)|S)$ as functions of α. Following the earlier procedure we expand instead, the ratio of these distributions to that of x. The procedure is as follows:

Assume that the probability measures are general non-linear operations on the observed $V(t)$, $t \leq 0$. Describe the non-linear operators by the associated Wiener canonical development in terms of a white noise input, which in turn synthesizes a structure and response which are functions of α. The response of this same structure to $V(t)$, a function of β, is the desired estimator.

Define (without worrying here about the behavior of the functions or existence)

$$\frac{W[V(t, \zeta)] \, dV(t, \zeta)}{W[x(t, \alpha)] \, dx = da} = W_R(\alpha) = \frac{d\,\zeta(\alpha)}{d\alpha} \tag{19}$$

and

$$\frac{W[V(t, \zeta)|S] \, dV(t, \zeta)}{W[x(t, \alpha)] \, dx = da} = W_R(\alpha/S) = \frac{d\,\zeta(\alpha/S)}{d\alpha} \tag{20}$$

The W_R are then expanded canonically

$$\begin{Bmatrix} W_R(\alpha) \\ \text{or} \\ W_R(\alpha|S) \end{Bmatrix} \sim \lim_{m \to \infty} \sum_{k_1=0}^{\infty} \sum_{k_m=0}^{\infty} \begin{Bmatrix} b_{k_1 \cdots k_m} \\ \text{or} \\ b_{k_1 \cdots k_m}^{(S)} \end{Bmatrix} \prod_{q=1}^{M} H_{k_q} \left[\begin{Bmatrix} F_q(\alpha) \\ \text{or} \\ V_q(\beta) \end{Bmatrix} \right] \tag{21}$$

where the alternate arguments of the Hermite polynomials in each equation arise from the identity (except for a set of measure zero) of each path in β and ξ with one in α and consequently the identity of Equation (20) with α substituted for β, i.e., $V_q(\beta) = F_q(\alpha)$. The second form is used for the right side of Equation (1). (Infinite m indicates dependence on the infinite past and this need only be approached a-symptotically for physical processes.) The coefficients are given by

$$\begin{Bmatrix} b_{k_1 \cdots k_m} \\ \text{or} \\ b_{k_1 \cdots k_m}^{(S)} \end{Bmatrix} = \int_0^1 da \prod_{q=1}^{m} H_{k_g}[F_q(\alpha)] \begin{Bmatrix} W_R(\alpha) \\ \text{or} \\ W_R(\alpha|S) \end{Bmatrix} \tag{22}$$

Again referencing the fact that $V_q(\beta) = F_q(\alpha)$ and realizing that $W_R(\alpha)da$ and $W_R(\alpha|S)da$ are actually the marginal and conditional probability measures for the path $V_q(\beta)$, respectively, we can avoid confusion by actually substituting the values $V_q(\beta)$ for $F_q(\alpha)$ in Equation (22) and β for α since it then becomes only an indexing variable. We then arrive at Equation (2) and also substitute β for α in the W's for Equation (1).

SUMMARY

The author's earlier work, in which Wiener's canonical expansion procedure was used to synthesize decision functions for stochastic inputs, is extended and specialized to the multiple-alternative discrete decision problem characteristic of waveform pattern recognition. Both sequential and non-sequential processing are covered. The resulting model is analogous to a conditional probability computer model of an automaton. However, it is distinguished by rather unique initial conditioning and updating capabilities, its computational or circuit realization, and the fact that its size is determined by rather different considerations from those governing the number of elements in a classical Bayes net. Relevant aspects and procedures of artificial intelligence and learning are discussed and related to the present model. Problem areas requiring further investigation are delineated.

REFERENCES

ASHBY, W. R., (1956); Design for an intelligence amplifier. *Automata Studies*. C. E. Shannon and J. McCarthy, Editors. Princeton, N. J. Princeton University Press (pp. 215–233).

ASHBY, W. R., (1957); *Introduction to Cybernetics*. New York. John Wiley and Sons.

ASHBY, W. R., (1961); What is an intelligent machine. *Proceedings of the Western Joint Computer Conference*. Vol. 19. Paper presented at Joint I.R.E.-A.I.E.E.-A.C.M. Computer Conference, Los Angeles, California, May 9–11, 1961. (p. 275).

BELLMAN, R., (1961); *Adaptive Control Processes: A Guided Tour*. Princeton, N. J. Princeton University Press.

BLACKWELL, D., AND GERSCHICK, M. A., (1954); *Theory of Games and Statistical Decisions*. New York. John Wiley and Sons.

BLOCK, H. D., (1961); Analysis of perceptrons. *Proceedings of the Western Joint Computer Conference*. Vol. 19. Paper presented at Joint I.R.E.-A.I.E.E.-A.C.M. Computer Conference, Los Angeles, California, May 9–11, 1961. (pp. 281–289).

BRICK, D. B., AND OWEN, J., (1964); A Mathematical Approach to Pattern Recognition and Self-Organization. *Computer and Information Sciences*. J. T. Tou and R. Wicox, Editors. Proceedings of COINS Symposium, Washington, D. C. Spartan Press. (pp. 139–168).

BRICK, D. B., AND ZAMES, G., (1962); Bayes' Optimum Filters Derived Using Wiener Canonical Forms. *IRE Trans. Information Theory*, IT-8, S35–S46.

CHERRY, C., (1957); *On Human Communication*. New York and Cambridge, Mass. John Wiley and Sons and M.I.T. Press.

CHOW, C. K., (1957); An optimum character recognition system using decision functions. *IRE Trans. Electronic Computers*, EC-6, 247–254.

COOPER, P. W., (1963); A note on the multiple-category Bayes decision procedure. *IRE Trans. Electronic Computers*, EC-12, 18.

DVORETZKY, A., A., AND WOFOWITZ, J., (1951); Elimination of randomization in certain statistical decision procedures and zero-sum two-person games. *Ann. Mathemat. Stat.*, 22, 1–21.

DVORETZKY, A., WALD, A., AND WOFOWITZ, J., (1951); Elimination of randomization in certain statistical decision procedures and zero-sum two-person games. *Ann. Mathemat. Stat.*, 22, 1–21.

FU, K. S., (1962); A learning system using statistical decision functions, *Winter Meeting American Institute of Electrical Engineers*. New York, N. Y. Conference Proceedings. (pp. 62–82).

FU, K. S., (1962); A sequential decision model for optimum recognition. *Biological Prototypes and Synthetic Systems*. E. E. Bernard, and M. R. Kare, Editors. Proceedings of the Second Annual Bionics Symposium, New York. Plenum Press (p. 270).

GREENE, P. H., (1960); A suggested model for information representation in a computer that perceives, learns and reasons. *Proceedings of the Western Joint Computer Conference*. Vol. 17. Paper presented at Joint I.R.E.-A.I.E.E.-A.C.M. Computer Conference, San Francisco, California, May, 1960.

MACKAY, D. M., (1956); The epistemological problem for automata. *Automata Studies*. C. E. Shannon and J. McCarthy, Editors. Princeton, N. J. Princeton University Press. (pp. 235–250).

MARRIL, T., AND GREEN, D. M., (1960); Statistical recognition functions and the design of pattern recognizers. *IRE Trans. Electronic Computers*, EC-9, 472–477.

MARON, M. E., (1962); Design principles for an intelligent machine. *IRE Trans. Information Theory*, IT-8, S179–S185.

MIDDLETON, D., (1960); *An Introduction to Statistical Communication Theory*. New York. McGrawHill.

MINSKY, M. L., (1961); Steps towards artificial intelligence. *Proc. Inst. Radio Engineers*, Vol. 49, 8–30.

MINSKY, M. L., AND SELFRIDGE, O. G., (1961); Learning in random nets. *Proceedings of Fourth London Symposium on Information Theory*. C. Cherry, Editor. Washington, D. C. Butterworths (p. 335).

NEWELL, A., SHAW, J. C., AND SIMON, H. A., (1960); A variety of intelligence learning in a general problem solver. *Self-Organizing Systems.* M. T. Yovits, and S. Cameron, Editors. New York. Pergamon Press.

ROSENBLATT, F., (1962); *Principles of Neurodynamics: Perceptrons and the Theory of Brain Mechanisms.* New York. Spartan Press.

SELFRIDGE, O. G., (1959); Pandemonium: a paradigm for learning. *Mechanisation of Thought Processes.* National Physical Laboratory, Symposium No. 10. London, England. Her Majesty's Stationery Office.

TOU, J. T., AND FU, K. J., (1961); Digital control concepts for nervous system synthesis and simulation. *Third International Congress on Cybernetics.* Namur, Belgium.

ULLMAN, J. R., (1963); Cybernetic models which learn sensory motor connections. *Medical Electronics and Biological Engineering*, 1. Great Britain. Pergamon Press. (pp. 91–100).

UTTLEY, A. M., (1956); Conditional probability machines and conditioned reflexes. *Automata Studies.* C. E. Shannon and J. McCarthy, Editors. Princeton, N. J. Princeton University Press. (pp. 253–275).

UTTLEY, A. M., (1956); Temporal and spatial patterns in a conditioned probability. *ibid.* (pp. 277–285)

WALD, A., (1947); *Sequential Analysis.* New York. John Wiley and Sons.

WALD, A., (1950); *Statistical Decision Functions.* New York. John Wiley and Sons.

WALD, A., AND WOLFOWITZ, J., (1948); Optimum character of the sequential probability ratio test. *Annals of Mathematical Statistics*, 19, 326–339.

WIENER, N., (1958); *Nonlinear Problems in Random Theory.* New York and Cambridge, Mass. John Wiley and Sons and M.I.T. Press.

WIENER, N., (1961); *Cybernetics.* New York and Cambridge, Mass. John Wiley and Sons and M.I.T. Press.

Solution of Elementary Logical Problems by Animals on the Basis of Extrapolation

L. V. KRUSHINSKY

Laboratory of Pathophysiology at the Chair of Physiology of Higher Nervous Activity, Moscow State University, Moscow (Russia)

All physiological investigations, which are of importance for cybernetics, are characterized by their tendency to elaborate schemes representing the circulation of information in the process of work of the nervous system. A possibly complete and exact description of the functioning of the nervous system on all of its levels is an indispensable pre-condition for disclosing the algorhythms on the basis of which information is retained and processed by the nervous system.

The purpose of this work is to investigate the hitherto insufficiently elaborated question concerning the ability of animals to apprehend, on the basis of express-information* (without any special preliminary training), the elementary relationships between the elements of the environment and to determine the elementary laws of their changes.

The present investigation is important for better knowledge of the systems that control the behaviour of animals.

In order to perform the behavioral acts, on the basis of express-information, the animal must process the latter in the following ways:

(1) It must single out from the entire diversity of the surrounding medium those of its elements which at the given moment are of definite significance for the performance of the adaptive act of behaviour.

(2) It must apprehend the elementary dependences which exist between the aforementioned elements entering the structure of the diversity perceived.

(3) It must determine the most elementary laws which govern the changes taking place in the relationships of the elements of the environment.

Such information processing enables the animal not only to react adequately to static relationships of the stimuli, but also to accomplish some elementary 'prognostic' reactions in accordance with the multiform changes which take place in the environmental phenomena.

---

* We deem it necessary to introduce this new term in order to stress the non-statistic aspect of the information obtained by the animal; in the case of training, it is the statistic aspect of the information which comes to the fore, namely, the combinations of the unconditioned reflex stimulus with the environmental elements which are indifferent to the animal.

These behavioral reactions may, apparently, be regarded as solution of elementary logical problems by the animals, which is done according to certain programmes based on express-information.

One of the manifestations of this physiological, reflex process*, which underlies a given category of behaviour, is the animal's ability to extrapolate, *i.e.* its ability on the basis of the information obtained (in our experiments — express-information) indicating the law-governed pattern of change of a certain dimension in the past, to determine the pattern of its change in the future.

Our researches showed (Krushinsky, 1958–1960) that different animals, studied with the help of various methods, possess different degrees of this ability to extrapolate**.

The general principle lying in the bases of the experiments consists in the following. The experimental animal must find a food stimulus (*A*) which moves in a straight line with constant velocity. At first the food stimulus is moved in full view of the animal; then it disappears behind cover *B*.

In conditions of this form of experimentation the animal is, apparently, able to accomplish an adequate act of behaviour (to find the food) only if it can determine the change in the position of point *A* (the direction of its movement) by its relationship to certain fixed points in space, and then to ascertain by the change of this relationship, the unknown parameter (the direction of movement of *A* when it is no longer perceived).

Experiments showed that the animals not only searched for the stimulus in the direction of its movement, but after apprehending this direction, rapidly approached the place where the moving stimulus had to appear from behind the cover. Thus they accomplished obvious extrapolation of the movement of the stimulus.

The concrete purpose of the present research was to determine:

(1) The ability of certain species of birds and mammals to extrapolate on the basis of express-information;

(2) The role of the ability to extrapolate on the basis of express-information in certain forms of learning;

(3) The consequences of the overstrain of nervous activity in the process of solving elementary logical problems by animals;

(4) The correlations between the forms of behaviour studied and certain morphological structures of the brain.

MATERIAL AND METHODS

The experiments were carried out on grown-up animals and birds: pigeons (27), hens

---

* When speaking of the reflex nature of the behavioral acts studied, we want to emphasize their determination; however, the latter undoubtedly includes to a considerable degree the probability principle of action.
** When simulating acts of thinking in machines, Glushkov (1963) introduced the process of 'extrapolational intelligence' which, as we have already stated earlier (1958–1960), differs from learning.

(129), birds of the crow family — crows, magpies and rooks (42), rabbits (33), cats (42) and dogs (18).

As to the method of experimentation, we used one of the previously applied variants namely, the screen variant (Krushinsky, 1958–1960).

The animal, which could freely move about the room, fed itself through a vertical gap in the centre of a non-transparent screen (2 m long and 75 cm high) (Fig. 1 A).

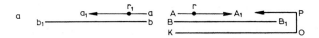

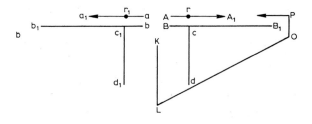

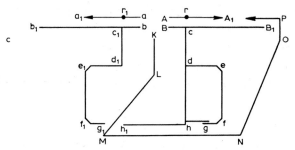

Fig. 1. (a) Scheme of the screen. $b_1 b$ and BB_1: sides of the screen; bB: gap in the screen through which the animal originally gets the food. The feeding bowl containing food is at first situated in position A and is moved to A_I; the empty feeding bowl is simultaneously moved from a to a_I. With insections Ar and ar_1 the animal was able to watch the movement of the bowls through the gap in the screen. In order to solve the problem, the animal had to run from K through O and P to A_I.

(b) First complication of the experiment: corridor cd $c_1 d_1$ is attached. From point K to point L the animal must run in the direction which is perpendicular to the direction of movement of the bowl with food AA_I.

(c) Second complication of the experiment: a labyrinth-like corridor c_1, d_1 e_1 f_1 fedc is attached; $g_1 h_1$ denote the open exit, hg and dh the closed exits; KLMNOP: the animal's route to A_I.

The food was placed in one of two feeding bowls which stood side by side at the gap behind the screen. When the animal began to eat the food, both bowls were moved in straight lines in opposite directions. After covering a distance of 20 cm, they disappeared behind non-transparent flaps. Now to obtain the food, the animal had to run around the screen, on the side behind which the feeding bowl containing food had disappeared. If the animal proved to solve this problem, a short corridor (40 cm long) was joined to the gap (Fig. 1B). As a result of this, when following the initial section of its path, the animal had to run perpendicularly to the vector of movement of the food. If the animal could solve this problem too, a special attachment was joined to the corridor; it directed the animal's initial path not only perpendicularly to the vector of movement of the food but also in the opposite direction (Fig. 1 C). This experiment was carried out twice a week with each animal, and during each experiment the feeding bowls were moved 4 to 8 times alternately in both directions. If the animal rounded the screen in accordance with the direction in which the food was moved, the order of movement of the feeding bowls was changed. Each animal was allowed one minute to solve the given problem.

Objective recording of the behaviour of the animals was done with the help of a cinematographic camera (a 'Moscow-32' camera; frequency 24 stills per sec)*.

The experimental part of the research was carried out by the author jointly with a group of his co-workers (D. A. Fless, L. N. Molodkina, N. P. Popova and E. I. Ochinskaya).

EXPERIMENTATION

1. *Comparative evaluation of the ability of the species of animals studied to solve elementary logical problems*

The evaluation of the ability of the animals to solve elementary logical problems on the basis of extrapolation is presented in Table I. This evaluation is based on the very fact of the animal's walks around the screen, as well as on an analysis of the animal's path of movement.

Table I shows the results of tests with the initial displacement of the food behind

TABLE I

RESULTS OF TESTS WITH THE INITIAL DISPLACEMENT OF THE FOOD

Animals	n	Walks around the screen on the side of the feeding bowl					
		With food		Empty		Total	
		abs.	%	abs.	%	abs.	%
Pigeons	27	2	7.4	—	—	2	7.4
Hens	129	35	27.1	32	24.8	67	51.9
Crow birds	42	30	71.4	6	14.3	36	85.7
Rabbits	33	8	24.2	1	3.0	9	27.2
Cats	42	21	50.0	15	35.7	36	85.7
Dogs	18	14	77.8	2	11.1	16	88.9

* This method was elaborated by the Chair of Cinematography of the Moscow State University (headed by Prof. K. Chibisov) and carried out by Drs. I. Fradkin and E. Pokrovskaya.

References p. 307

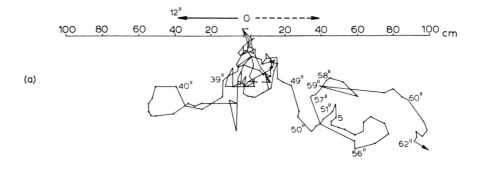

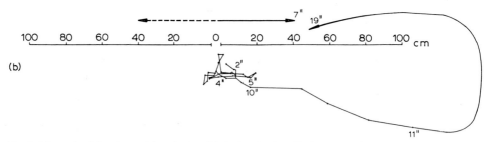

Fig. 2. The path of the pigeon (a) and crow (b) during the first displacement of the food. Solid arrow: direction of movement of the feeding bowl containing food; dotted arrow: direction of movement of the empty bowl; thin line: curve of the animal's movement. Figures on the curves of movement of the bowl with food and on the curve of the animal's movement denote time in sec from the beginning of the experiment.

the screen, when no conditioned reflex connections, which might influence the way of solving the problem offered, could as yet be formed in the animal.

The data presented in the above table and an analysis of the corresponding curves (Fig. 2) allow us to draw the conclusion that in the first experiment it is the pigeons which solved the problem worst of all. When the food disappeared behind the cover, they moved away from the gap in most cases and began to walk in front of the screen in a disorderly way; their behaviour predominantly resembled the Brownian movement. In some cases, however, they exhibited orderly movements in the direction of the moving food, and in two cases they even walked around the screen on the proper side.

The searching movements of the hens after the food had disappeared behind the screen but they proved to be much more orderly; in most cases they manifested obvious searching movements near the screen; sometimes they made peculiar movements as if trying to squeeze through the gap in the screen. In about 50% of all cases they walked round the screen; however, such walks around the screen on the side toward which the bowl with food was moved were as frequent as those on the side of the empty bowl.

The rabbits walked around the screen more often on the side of movement of the bowl containing food than on the side of movement of the empty bowl. However, in comparison with the hens their walking around the screen was of a less purposeful character, as it may be seen from Fig. 3. After apprehending the initial direction in which the food was moved, the rabbits usually turned in that direction and walked along the screen. But reaching the end of it, they ceased their search.

Birds of the crow family and dogs exhibited quite distinct movements in the direction of the bowl containing food; in the overwhelming majority of cases this ended in walking around the screen and finding the food (Figs. 2 and 4). As to cats, they

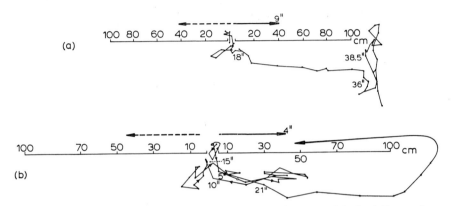

Fig. 3. The path of the rabbit (a) and hen (b) during the first displacement of the food. Denotations — same as in Fig. 2.

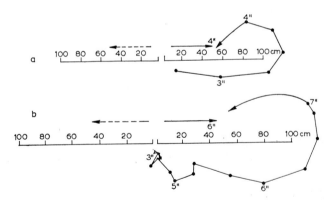

Fig. 4. The path of the cat (a) and dog (b) during the first displacement of the food.

used to walk around the screen almost in 90% of all cases, but in doing so they did not follow the direction of the moving food as frequently as the birds of the crow family and dogs; in comparison with the latter they manifested a relatively greater number of walks around the screen on the side of the empty bowl.

The afore-mentioned facts show that some species of animals are able on the basis of express-information, without any preliminary training, to determine the most elementary laws governing changes in the relationships of the environmental elements, on the basis of which it is possible to work out a programme of adequate behaviour.

The ability to extrapolate on the basis of express-information, which in our experiments is the principal link of the process of forming a programme for the accomplishment of an adaptive behavioral act, is not equally developed in different animal species.

2. *The role of repeated presentations of a problem*

A summary analysis of the results obtained from repeated presentations of a problem does not reveal the qualitatively different methods which are used by various animals in their search for the food.

The analysis showed that two principal types of the animals' behaviour in the course of our experiments may be established.

The I type of behaviour consists in stereotype walking around the screen on one side, irrespective of the direction in which the food moves. As a result, the animal usually reaches the bowl with food in about 50% of all cases of its displacement. This may be regarded as formation of a conditioned reflex to that place behind the screen where the animal finds the food; here it is the movement of the feeding bowl away from the gap, and not the direction of its movement, which serves as a signal making the animal walk around the screen.

The conditioned reflex stereotype character of this way of detecting the bowl with food becomes particularly distinct when we begin to extinguish the animal's walks around the screen on one side, irrespective of the direction in which the food stimulus moves. For this purpose, the bowl with food is invariably moved to the side which is opposite to that where the animal walks round the screen. Observations showed that in the case of some animals (especially, hens and pigeons) dozens of tests must be carried out before the stereotype walking around the screen on one side becomes extinguished, and the animals begin to walk around it on the opposite side. In spite of the fact that after each walk around the screen the animal finds no food, it continues such stereotypical walks on the side which is opposite to the movement of the food.

The II type of behaviour consists in walking around the screen on the side which corresponds to the direction of the moving food. In this case, it is the information concerning the movement of the food, obtained by the animal through the gap in the screen, that serves as a signal and makes the animal walk around the screen. Such behaviour may be regarded as an adequate method of solving the given problem, since every time, on the basis of express-information, the animal works out a programme which leads to the obtainment of the food.

One group of animals (pigeons, hens and rabbits) in the main display the I type of behaviour, while another group (dogs, cats and birds of the crow family) are characterized by the adequate method of solving the given problem.

Essentially important are the principal ways in which both types of behaviour are formed.

The I type of behaviour results either from a gradual formation of a contitioned reflex to the place where the animal meets the food behind the screen, or emerges immediately after the first discovery of the food behind the screen.

The II type of behaviour is formed either as a result of a sharp transition from the I type of behaviour, or immediately after several (and sometimes even one) displacements of the food behind the screen. Some animals gradually improve their programme of finding an adequate solution of the problem. This is expressed in a gradual increase of the number of their walks around the screen conforming to the direction of the moving food.

Let us now designate the animals' walks around the screen on the right side by the letter 'R' and those on the left side by the letter 'L'. 'O' denotes the absence of any such walks.

The arrows show the direction in which the food moves. 'R_1' and 'L_1' denote walks around the screen in conditions of a first-degree complication of the problem (Fig. 1 b); 'R_2' and 'L_2' denote walks around the screen in conditions of a second-degree complication of the problem (Fig. 1 c). The experimental days are separated from one another by points, the figures denote their ordinal numbers. The periods in which the animals accomplish their walks around the screen according to the I type of behaviour are underlined by a broken line, and according to the II type of behaviour by a solid line.

Here are the ways in which the I type of behaviour was formed in various animals. Experiments with the pigeon 'Spoty'.

$$\begin{array}{ccc} 1 & 2 & 3 \\ \text{O O L R R R} & \text{O L O R L R} & \text{O R L R L L} \end{array}$$

$$\begin{array}{ccc} 4 & 5 & 6 \\ \text{O R L R R L} & \text{O R R R R R} & \text{R R R R R O} \end{array}$$

$$\begin{array}{ccc} 7 & 8 & 9 \\ \text{R R R O R} & \text{R R R R R R} & \text{R R R R R R} \end{array}$$

In this case we see that the formation of walks around the screen on one side began after 4 experimental days, *i.e.* in the course of the fifth experiment; it proved to be fully stabilized on the eighth experimental day.

The I type of behaviour may be formed suddenly, after a short period of full absence of any walks around the screen or after a number of disorderly walks now on one side, now on the other. This may be seen from our experiments with pigeon No. A-218.

$$\begin{array}{ccc} 1 & 2 & 3 \\ \text{O R O L O O} & \text{O L L L L L} & \text{L L L L L L} \end{array}$$

$$\begin{array}{c} 4 \\ \text{L L L L L L} \end{array}$$

Stable unilateral walks around the screen are often formed after the animal's first correct experience in this respect on the very first day of experimentation. This is illustrated by our experiments with cock No. A-0696.

$$
\begin{array}{c}
1 \\
\leftarrow \rightarrow \leftarrow \rightarrow \leftarrow \rightarrow \\
\text{L L L L L L} \cdot
\end{array}
\quad
\begin{array}{c}
2 \\
\rightarrow \leftarrow \rightarrow \leftarrow \rightarrow \leftarrow \\
\text{L L L L L L} \cdot
\end{array}
\quad
\begin{array}{c}
3 \\
\leftarrow \rightarrow \leftarrow \rightarrow \leftarrow \rightarrow \\
\text{L L L L L L} \cdot
\end{array}
$$

$$
\begin{array}{c}
4 \\
\rightarrow \leftarrow \rightarrow \leftarrow \rightarrow \leftarrow \\
\text{L L L L L L} \cdot
\end{array}
$$

The above-cited examples show that the I type of behaviour may be formed in two ways: (1) after a certain period of accidental walks around the screen; (2) suddenly, after the first displacement of the food behind the screen.

Experiments with the tom-cat 'Tolstik' provide an example of a faultless solution of a problem which has all degrees of difficulty (the animal only once failed to walk around the screen).

$$
\begin{array}{c}
1 \\
\leftarrow \rightarrow \leftarrow \rightarrow \leftarrow \\
\text{L O R L R L} \cdot
\end{array}
\quad
\begin{array}{c}
2 \\
\rightarrow \leftarrow \rightarrow \leftarrow \leftarrow \\
\text{R L R R L L} \cdot
\end{array}
\quad
\begin{array}{c}
3 \\
\rightarrow \leftarrow \\
R_1 L_1 \cdot
\end{array}
\quad
\begin{array}{c}
4 \\
\rightarrow \leftarrow \\
R_2 L_2 \cdot
\end{array}
$$

$$
\begin{array}{c}
5 \\
\rightarrow \leftarrow \leftarrow \leftarrow \rightarrow \rightarrow \leftarrow \rightarrow \\
R \; L \; L_1 L_2 R_2 R_2 L_2 R_2 \cdot
\end{array}
$$

The adequate solution of the given problem is often followed by a temporary transition to the I type of behaviour when the problem offered is complicated.

This may be illustrated by our experiments with the cat 'Serka'.

$$
\begin{array}{c}
1 \\
\rightarrow \leftarrow \rightarrow \leftarrow \rightarrow \leftarrow \rightarrow \leftarrow \\
R \; L \; R \; L \; R_1 R_1 R_1 R_1 \cdot
\end{array}
\quad
\begin{array}{c}
2 \\
\leftarrow \rightarrow \leftarrow \rightarrow \leftarrow \rightarrow \\
L_1 R_1 L_1 R_1 L_1 R_1 \cdot
\end{array}
\quad
\begin{array}{c}
3 \\
\rightarrow \leftarrow \rightarrow \leftarrow \leftarrow \rightarrow \\
R_1 L_1 R_1 L_1 L_1 R_1 \cdot
\end{array}
$$

$$
\begin{array}{c}
4 \\
\rightarrow \leftarrow \rightarrow \leftarrow \leftarrow \rightarrow \rightarrow \leftarrow \\
R_1 L_1 R_1 L_2 L_2 R_2 R_2 L_2 \cdot
\end{array}
\quad
\begin{array}{c}
5 \\
\leftarrow \rightarrow \\
L_2 R_2
\end{array}
$$

In this case the temporary transition from the II type of behaviour to the I type took place only when the first degree of complication had been applied; the cat could, however, successfully solve a more complex variant of the problem.

In a number of cases the I type of behaviour persists in animals much longer after the introduction of a more complicated variant of the task. This may be seen from the experiments with the dog 'Belka'.

$$
\begin{array}{c}
1 \\
\leftarrow \rightarrow \leftarrow \rightarrow \leftarrow \rightarrow \\
L \; R \; L_1 R_1 L_1 R_1 \cdot
\end{array}
\quad
\begin{array}{c}
2 \\
\leftarrow \rightarrow \leftarrow \rightarrow \leftarrow \rightarrow \\
L \; R \; L \; R \; L_1 R_1 \cdot
\end{array}
\quad
\begin{array}{c}
3 \\
\rightarrow \leftarrow \rightarrow \leftarrow \rightarrow \leftarrow \\
R_1 L_1 R_1 L_1 R_1 L_1 \cdot
\end{array}
$$

$$
\begin{array}{c}
4 \\
\leftarrow \rightarrow \leftarrow \rightarrow \leftarrow \rightarrow \\
L_1 L_1 L_1 R_1 L_1 L_1 \cdot
\end{array}
\quad
\begin{array}{c}
5 \\
\rightarrow \leftarrow \leftarrow \leftarrow \rightarrow \\
R_1 L_1 R_1 L_1 L_1 R_1 \cdot
\end{array}
\quad
\begin{array}{c}
6 \\
\leftarrow \leftarrow \rightarrow \leftarrow \rightarrow \leftarrow \\
L_1 L_1 L_2 L_2 L_2 L_2 \cdot
\end{array}
$$

$$
\begin{array}{c}
7 \\
\rightarrow \leftarrow \rightarrow \leftarrow \rightarrow \leftarrow \rightarrow \leftarrow \\
L_2 L_2 L_2 L_2 R_2 L_2 L_2 L_2 \cdot
\end{array}
\quad
\begin{array}{c}
8 \\
\leftarrow \rightarrow \leftarrow \rightarrow \leftarrow \rightarrow \leftarrow \rightarrow \\
L_2 L_2 L_2 L_2 L_2 R_2 L_2 L_2 \cdot
\end{array}
\quad
\begin{array}{c}
9 \\
\rightarrow \leftarrow \rightarrow \leftarrow \rightarrow \leftarrow \\
L_2 L_2 L_2 L_2 L_2 L_2 \cdot
\end{array}
$$

$$\underset{\text{10}}{\overset{\leftarrow\ \rightarrow\ \leftarrow\ \rightarrow}{L_2\ L_2\ L_2\ L_2\cdot}}\quad \underset{\text{11}}{\overset{\rightarrow\ \leftarrow\ \rightarrow\ \leftarrow\ \rightarrow\ \leftarrow}{L_2\ L_2\ R_2\ L_2\ R_2\ L_2\cdot}}\quad \underset{\text{12}}{\overset{\leftarrow\ \rightarrow\ \leftarrow\ \rightarrow}{L_2\ R_2\ L_2\ R_2\cdot}}\quad \underset{\text{13}}{\overset{\rightarrow\ \leftarrow\ \rightarrow\ \rightarrow\ \leftarrow\ \leftarrow}{R_2\ L_2\ R_2\ R_2\ L_2\ L_2\cdot}}\quad \underset{\text{14}}{\overset{\leftarrow\ \rightarrow}{L_2\ R_2\cdot}}$$

In this case an almost faultless solution of the problem, which began with the first displacement of the food, was immediately succeeded by the I type of behaviour when on the sixth experimental day the most complicated variant of the problem was offered. This behaviour persisted up to the eleventh experimental day when the animal suddenly changed over to the adequate method of solving even this variant.

The above examples show that there are cases of a sudden adequate solution of the problem after the first displacement of the food behind the screen, as well as cases of temporary transitions to the I type of behaviour when complicated variants of the given problem are offered.

One of the ways in which a problem may be adequately solved (II type of behaviour) is a stepped transition from the I type of behaviour.

This may be illustrated by experiments performed on the dog 'Pirat'. This dog displayed a stepped transition from the I type of behaviour to the II type and then solved all the complicated variants offered (having committed only one error).

$$\underset{\text{1}}{\overset{\rightarrow\ \leftarrow\ \rightarrow\ \leftarrow\ \rightarrow\ \leftarrow}{R\ R\ R\ R\ R\ R\cdot}}\quad \underset{\text{2}}{\overset{\leftarrow\ \rightarrow\ \leftarrow\ \rightarrow}{R\ R\ R\ R\ R\cdot}}\quad \underset{\text{3}}{\overset{\rightarrow\ \leftarrow\ \rightarrow\ \leftarrow\ \rightarrow\ \leftarrow}{R\ R\ R\ R\ R\cdot}}$$

$$\underset{\text{4}}{\overset{\leftarrow\ \rightarrow\ \leftarrow\ \rightarrow\ \leftarrow}{L\ R\ L\ R\ L\ R\cdot}}\quad \underset{\text{5}}{\overset{\rightarrow\ \leftarrow\ \rightarrow\ \leftarrow\ \rightarrow\ \leftarrow}{R\ L\ R\ L\ R\ L\cdot}}\quad \underset{\text{6}}{\overset{\leftarrow\ \rightarrow\ \leftarrow\ \rightarrow\ \leftarrow\ \rightarrow\ \rightarrow}{L\ R\ L\ R\ R_1\ R_1\ L_1\ R_1\cdot}}$$

$$\underset{\text{7}}{\overset{\leftarrow\ \rightarrow\ \leftarrow\ \rightarrow\ \leftarrow\ \rightarrow\ \leftarrow\ \rightarrow}{L_1\ R_1\ L_1\ R_1\ L_2\ R_2\ L_2\ O_2}}\cdot\quad \underset{\text{8}}{\overset{\rightarrow\ \leftarrow\ \rightarrow\ \leftarrow\ \rightarrow\ \rightarrow}{R_2\ L_2\ L_2\ R_2\ O_2\ R_2\cdot}}$$

Formation of the II type of behaviour sometimes takes place after a period of a peculiar 'search' by the animal for the most adequate solution of the problem.

Experiments with hen No. 1724 show that certain periods of walking around the screen on one side (either right, or left) are followed by periods when the animal accomplishes a number of disorderly walks around the screen, as well as of adequate walks in the direction of the moving food. Only on the seventh experimental day the II type of behaviour becomes stabilized.

$$\underset{\text{1}}{\overset{\rightarrow\ \leftarrow\ \rightarrow\ \leftarrow\ \rightarrow\ \leftarrow}{L\ L\ L\ R\ R\ R\ R\cdot}}\quad \underset{\text{2}}{\overset{\leftarrow\ \rightarrow\ \leftarrow\ \rightarrow\ \leftarrow\ \rightarrow}{L\ L\ R\ L\ R\ L\ L\ L\cdot}}\quad \underset{\text{3}}{\overset{\rightarrow\ \leftarrow\ \rightarrow\ \leftarrow\ \rightarrow\ \leftarrow}{L\ L\ L\ R\ O\ R\ R\ L\cdot}}$$

$$\underset{\text{4}}{\overset{\rightarrow\ \leftarrow\ \rightarrow\ \leftarrow\ \rightarrow\ \leftarrow}{L\ R\ L\ L\ R\ L\ R\ L\cdot}}\quad \underset{\text{5}}{\overset{\rightarrow\ \leftarrow\ \rightarrow\ \leftarrow\ \rightarrow\ \leftarrow}{R\ L\ R\ R\ R\ R\ L\ L\cdot}}\quad \underset{\text{6}}{\overset{\rightarrow\ \leftarrow\ \rightarrow\ \leftarrow\ \rightarrow\ \leftarrow}{L\ L\ L\ R\ R\ R\ R\cdot}}$$

$$\underset{\text{7}}{\overset{\leftarrow\ \rightarrow\ \leftarrow\ \rightarrow\ \leftarrow\ \rightarrow\ \leftarrow\ \rightarrow}{L\ R\ L\ R\ L\ R\ L\ R\cdot}}\quad \underset{\text{8}}{\overset{\rightarrow\ \leftarrow\ \rightarrow\ \leftarrow\ \rightarrow\ \leftarrow\ \leftarrow}{R\ L\ R\ L\ R\ R\ L\ L\cdot}}$$

This example produces the impression that in some cases the animals search for an adequate method of solving a given problem, and choose it from among various possible variants. This method was described by Krechevsky (1938) and called the 'hypoteses' method. In such cases the animal made different attempts to solve the problem until it 'finally came to respond to the 'important' differentiation and quickly proceed with the solution of the problem set for him by the experimenter'.

In animals, which possess a relatively limited ability to extrapolate, the formation of the adequate method of solving problems may develop gradually (*i.e.* with every subsequent experimental day the number of correct solutions may increase).

Some factors complicate the analysis of such formation of the adequate method of solving problems.

Firstly, even short periods of adequate solutions may be followed by periods of unilateral or disorderly walks around the screen.

Secondly, since in most of the investigated species of animals the ability to extrapolate begins to manifest itself already during the first displacement of the food, repeated presentations of the problem lead only to the *perfection* of this property (but do not train the animal to solve the problem by the adequate method).

In those species of animals whose ability to extrapolate is strongly pronounced, the programme for solving the given problem, already formed during its first presentation, becomes perfected. In animals with a relatively less pronounced ability to extrapolate this perfection is not so distinct. But it may be assumed that even in this case we have only a certain perfection of the programme for solving the problem on the basis of extrapolation.

This hypothesis was verified on hens which in our experiments constituted the most numerous group of animals of the same species.

We performed a sufficient number of experiments on 74 hens with the aim to establish the type of behaviour which would be displayed by each of them.

The I type of behaviour was formed in 55 individuals, and the II type of behaviour was formed in 19 individuals.

A comparison of the backgrounds, which preceded the stabilization of the second type of behaviour (Figs. 5 and 6), disclosed:

(1) a predominance of correct solutions during the first presentation of the problem;

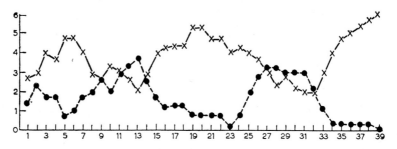

Fig. 5. Averaged curves showing perfection in the solution of a problem by a hen with the II type of behaviour during repeated presentations of the same problem. Along ordinates: number of displacements of the food in one experimental day; along abscissae: number of experimental days. Solid line: walks around the screen on the side of movement of the food; broken line: walks around the screen on the side of the empty bowl.

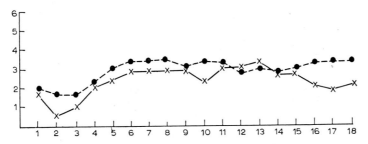

Fig. 6. Averaged curves showing the formation of the I type of behaviour in a hen. Denotations same as in Fig. 5.

(2) a predominance of correct solutions during the first walk around the screen (the first presentation of food does not necessarily lead to the walk around the screen);

(3) a predominance of correct solutions over incorrect ones up to the moment when either the I or the II type of behaviour is formed*.

The probability that the differences in each case were of an occasional character was estimated at 0.12, 0.29, 0.18 respectively (this estimation was done with the help of criterion.χ^2 Assuming that the above estimates are independent** we can obtain a summary estimate for the probability of our hypothesis***. The probability of its being occasional equals to 0.05, which should be regarded as significant.

Thus, even within the limits of one species of animals the solution of a given problem is to a considerable degree determined by the programme for accomplishing the behavioral act under our investigation which begins to take shape already from the moment when the animal obtains express-information during the first displacement of the food behind the screen. This programme becomes only perfected in the process of the subsequent presentation of the problem.

CONSEQUENCES OF THE OVERSTRAIN OF NERVOUS ACTIVITY DURING THE SOLUTION OF LOGICAL PROBLEMS BY ANIMALS

After the introduction of more complex variants of a given problem or after repeated adequate solutions of one and the same problem, the animal begins to show difficulties in its solution.

These difficulties manifest themselves in the following two forms:

(1) The animal begins to walk around the screen not in accordance with the direction of the moving food, and usually only on one side of the screen. These stereotypical walks around the screen on one side may be of a temporary character, as already

---

* The criterion for the first method of solving the problem is 6 successive walks around the screen on the side of the moving food: The criterion for the second method is not less than 12 successive walks around the screen on one of its sides.

** Strictly speaking, they are not absolutely independent.

*** In the summary estimation we proceeded from the fact that when the accepted hypothesis is correct, separate probabilities are equally distributed on the segment [0,1.]

References p. 307

stated above; after that the animal successfully solves the complicated variant of the problem. However, for some animals there exists a certain limit of complexity of the problems which they are able to solve: when the problem offered is too complicated for them, they begin to walk around the screen only on one side; when the problem is simplified again, they demonstrate again the adequate method of its solution. Experiments with the tom-cat 'Markiz' illustrate this phenomenon:

$$
\begin{array}{c}
1 \qquad\qquad\qquad\qquad\qquad 2 \\
\leftarrow \rightarrow \leftarrow \rightarrow \leftarrow \rightarrow \leftarrow \rightarrow \quad \rightarrow \leftarrow \rightarrow \leftarrow \rightarrow \leftarrow \rightarrow \\
\text{L L L L L L R L} \cdot \text{L O R L L L R} \cdot
\end{array}
$$

$$
\begin{array}{c}
3 \qquad\qquad\qquad\qquad\qquad\qquad 4 \\
\leftarrow \rightarrow \leftarrow \rightarrow \rightarrow \leftarrow \rightarrow \leftarrow \rightarrow \leftarrow \rightarrow \leftarrow \rightarrow \leftarrow \quad \rightarrow \leftarrow \rightarrow \leftarrow \rightarrow \rightarrow \leftarrow \leftarrow \\
\text{L L L R R L } R_1 R_1 L_1 L_2 L_2 L_2 L_2 R_1 L_1 \cdot \text{ } L_1 L_1 R_1 L_1 R_1 R_1 L_1 L_1 \cdot
\end{array}
$$

$$
\begin{array}{c}
5 \qquad\qquad\qquad 6 \qquad\qquad\qquad 7 \qquad\qquad\qquad 8 \\
\leftarrow \rightarrow \rightarrow \leftarrow \leftarrow \rightarrow \leftarrow \rightarrow \quad \rightarrow \leftarrow \rightarrow \leftarrow \rightarrow \quad \leftarrow \rightarrow \leftarrow \rightarrow \quad \leftarrow \rightarrow \leftarrow \rightarrow \\
L_1 R_1 R_1 L_1 L_2 R_2 L_2 L_2 \cdot \text{ } L_2 L_2 L_2 L_2 L_2 \cdot \text{ } L_2 L_2 L_1 R_1 \cdot \text{ } L_2 L_2 L_2 L_2 \cdot
\end{array}
$$

This example shows that the tom-cat was unable to solve the most difficult variant of the problem offered; but when the latter was simplified in eight experimental day, the animal proved able to solve the problem again by two presentations.

In a number of cases, however, the transition to unilateral walks around the screen persisted even when the problem was simplified, in spite of the fact that previously the animal had adequately solved simpler variants of the given problem.

This may be illustrated by the experiments which were carried out with the cat 'Alisa'.

$$
\begin{array}{c}
1 \qquad\qquad\qquad 2 \qquad\qquad\qquad 3 \\
\rightarrow \leftarrow \rightarrow \leftarrow \rightarrow \leftarrow \quad \leftarrow \rightarrow \leftarrow \rightarrow \leftarrow \rightarrow \quad \leftarrow \rightarrow \rightarrow \leftarrow \leftarrow \rightarrow \leftarrow \\
\text{R R L O L O} \cdot \text{L R L R L R} \cdot \text{L R R L L R L} \cdot
\end{array}
$$

$$
\begin{array}{c}
4 \qquad\qquad\qquad 5 \qquad\qquad\qquad 6 \\
\rightarrow \leftarrow \leftarrow \rightarrow \rightarrow \leftarrow \quad \leftarrow \rightarrow \rightarrow \leftarrow \rightarrow \leftarrow \rightarrow \quad \rightarrow \leftarrow \rightarrow \leftarrow \rightarrow \leftarrow \\
\text{R L } L_1 R_1 R_1 L_1 \cdot \text{ } L_1 R_1 R_2 R_2 R_2 R_2 R_1 R_1 \cdot \text{ R R R R R} \cdot
\end{array}
$$

(2) The second manifestation of the difficulties experienced by animals during the solution of problems consists in the failure of the animals to walk around the screen on any of its sides, or in the emergence of a morbid fear (phobia) of the experimental situation*.

The rabbit 'Khomyak' provides an example of such failures to walk around the screen. This rabbit first walked around the screen on the side of the movement of the food; but on the eighth experimental day it changed over to unilateral walks around the screen, and subsequently ceased to walk around it altogether.

A phobia of the experimental situation emerges most frequently and is most pronounced in birds of the crow family. Usually it begins to manifest itself after several (4 to 6) walks around the screen in the direction of the moving food. It does not

---

* Emergence of phobias (fear of depth, fire and other stimuli outside the experimental chamber) was described by Petrova (1953) and was regarded as the result of an overstrain of the nervous system during experimental work with conditioned reflexes.

emerge on the day when the animal successfully solves the given problem; but on the next experimental day it becomes already strongly pronounced.

The phobia manifests itself in a quite peculiar way. Usually the animal is most of all afraid of the gap in the screen through which it obtains information concerning the direction of the movement of the food. The phobia gradually diminishes as the animal moves away from the gap. This gradient of emergence of the phobia can be easily measured by means of placing the feeding bowl with food at different distances

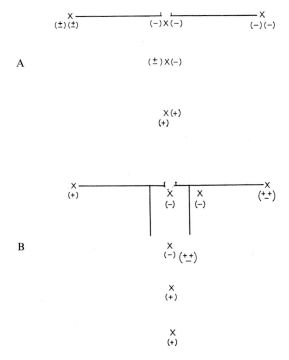

Fig. 7. Spatial gradient of manifestation of a phobia in relation to the gap in the screen. X: places of disposition of the bowls containing food.
(+) approach of the bird to the feeding bowl without any symptoms of a phobia;
(—) failure to approach the feeding bowl containing food;
(±) approach to the feeding bowl with food accompanied by symptoms of a phobia.

from the screen. Fig. 7 shows the gradients of emergence of the phobia in two crows. In both cases the phobia subsided when the crows moved away from the gap in the screen.

Sometimes the phobia extends only to one side of the screen, as it may be seen from Fig. 7 A; in such cases the animals usually do not cross the line of the screen on this particular side.

It should be noted that the phobia emerges specifically, in relation to the screen, since when the latter is removed, the birds fearlessy approach the feeding bowls containing food in those very places which they avoid to approach in the presence of the screen.

As an example illustrating the emergence of this phobia after the solution of a problem on the first experimental day, we may cite the experiments with the crow 'Kralya'.

$$\overset{\underset{\rightarrow\ \leftarrow\ \rightarrow\ \leftarrow}{1}}{R\ L\ R\ L}\cdot \overset{\underset{\leftarrow\ \rightarrow\ \rightarrow}{2}}{O\ O\ O}\cdot \overset{\underset{\rightarrow\ \leftarrow\ \rightarrow\ \leftarrow\ \rightarrow\ \leftarrow}{3}}{O\ O\ R\ L\ O\ O}\cdot \overset{\underset{\leftarrow\ \rightarrow\ \leftarrow\ \rightarrow\ \leftarrow\ \rightarrow}{4}}{O\ R\ O\ R\ L\ O}\cdot \overset{\underset{\rightarrow\ \leftarrow\ \rightarrow\ \leftarrow}{5}}{R\ L\ R\ L}\cdot$$

Phobia of the screen · Phobia of the screen: afraid to walk around, and to approach the food · Phobia of the screen · Insignificant phobia of the screen

$$\overset{\underset{\rightarrow\ \leftarrow\ \rightarrow\ \leftarrow\ \rightarrow\ \leftarrow}{6}}{R\ L\ R_1\ L_1\ R_1\ L_2}\cdot \overset{\underset{\leftarrow\ \rightarrow\ \leftarrow\ \rightarrow\ \leftarrow\ \rightarrow}{7}}{R_1\ R_1\ L_1\ R_2\ L_2\ O_2}\cdot \overset{\underset{\rightarrow\ \leftarrow\ \rightarrow\ \leftarrow\ \rightarrow\ \leftarrow}{8}}{R_2\ R_2\ R_2\ R_2\ R_2\ R_2}\cdot \overset{\underset{\leftarrow\ \rightarrow\ \leftarrow\ \rightarrow\ \leftarrow\ \rightarrow}{9}}{R_2\ R_2\ L_2\ R_2\ R_2\ R_2}\cdot$$

No phobia · No phobia · No phobia · No phobia

The above-described course of experimentation shows that after the first experimental day (during which the bird was solving the problem*) a phobia developed, but it gradually disappeared. The bird proved unable to solve the most complicated variant of the problem: it manifested unilateral walks around the screen, *i.e.* the I type of behaviour. These stereotype walks around the screen did not lead to the development of a phobia.

Experiments carried out with the crow 'Variusha' give a striking example of the emergence in the same bird of sharp transitions from one type of behaviour to another; they also illustrate the emergence of a phobia after the solution of a difficult variant of the problem.

$$\overset{\underset{\rightarrow\ \leftarrow\ \rightarrow\ \leftarrow\ \rightarrow\ \leftarrow}{1}}{R\ L\ R\ R\ R\ R}\cdot \overset{\underset{\leftarrow\ \rightarrow\ \leftarrow\ \rightarrow\ \leftarrow\ \rightarrow\ \leftarrow\ \rightarrow}{2}}{R\ R\ R\ R\ R\ R\ R\ R}\cdot \overset{\underset{\rightarrow\ \leftarrow\ \rightarrow\ \leftarrow\ \rightarrow\ \leftarrow}{3}}{R\ L\ R\ L\ R\ L}\cdot$$

$$\overset{\underset{\leftarrow\ \rightarrow\ \leftarrow\ \rightarrow\ \leftarrow\ \rightarrow}{4}}{L\ R\ L\ R\ L_1\ L_1}\cdot \overset{\underset{\rightarrow\ \leftarrow\ \rightarrow\ \leftarrow\ \rightarrow\ \leftarrow\ \rightarrow\ \leftarrow\ \rightarrow\ \leftarrow\ \rightarrow\ \leftarrow}{5}}{L_1\ L_1\ L_1\ R_1\ L_1\ L_1\ R_1\ L_1\ L_1\ L_1\ R_1\ L_1}\cdot$$

$$\overset{\underset{\rightarrow\ \leftarrow\ \rightarrow\ \leftarrow}{6}}{R_1\ L_1\ R_2\ L_2}\cdot \overset{\underset{\rightarrow\ \leftarrow\ \rightarrow\ \leftarrow\ \rightarrow}{7}}{R\ L\ L_1\ L_1\ R_1}\cdot \overset{\underset{\leftarrow\ \rightarrow\ \leftarrow\ \rightarrow\ \leftarrow\ \rightarrow}{8}}{L_2\ L_2\ L_2\ L_2\ L_2\ L_2}\cdot$$

Phobia (mainly of the gap) · Phobia (mainly of the gap)

The emergence of a phobia may also be observed when the walks around the screen on one side are extinguished as a result of constant movement of the food in the direction which is opposite to the stereotype walks around the screen.

Experiments with the rook 'Bob' may be cited as an example.

$$\overset{\underset{\rightarrow\ \leftarrow\ \rightarrow\ \leftarrow\ \rightarrow\ \leftarrow}{1}}{L\ L\ O\ L\ L\ L}\cdot \overset{\underset{\leftarrow\ \rightarrow\ \leftarrow\ \rightarrow\ \leftarrow\ \rightarrow}{2}}{L\ L\ L\ L\ L\ L}\cdot \overset{\underset{\rightarrow\ \leftarrow\ \rightarrow\ \leftarrow\ \rightarrow\ \leftarrow}{3}}{L\ L\ L\ L\ L\ L}\cdot \overset{\underset{\leftarrow\ \rightarrow\ \rightarrow\ \rightarrow\ \rightarrow\ \rightarrow}{4}}{L\ L\ O\ O\ L\ L}\cdot$$

---

* The emergence of disturbances in the behaviour of the animals after 2 to 4 walks around the screen on the side of the movement of the food is often observed in our experiments; although the statistically reliable probability that they are not of a fortuitous character is insignificant, still we must admit that even such a small number of successful solutions of the problem leads to stable disturbances in the behaviour of the animals.

$\overset{5}{\rightarrow} \rightarrow \rightarrow \rightarrow$ In subsequent experiments: a strongly pronounced phobia.

O O O O ·

Phobia of
the ex-
perimental
situation
appeared

The emergence of phobias as a result of the extinction of the walks around the screen on one side shows that only the necessity to readjust the programme for finding an adequate method of solving the problem may, apparently, lead to the emergence of pathological behaviour.

Transitions from the I type of behaviour to the adequate method of solving the given problem prove to be unstable in species of animals with a feebly developed ability to extrapolate: such animals usually revert to the I type of behaviour.

An example of this phenomenon is provided by our experiments with the cock 'Yurki' which started walking around the screen on the right side on the second experimental day.

$$\overset{1}{\underset{\text{R L L R R L}}{\leftarrow \rightarrow \leftarrow \rightarrow}} \cdot \overset{2}{\underset{\text{L L R R R}}{\rightarrow \leftarrow \rightarrow \leftarrow \rightarrow \leftarrow}} \cdot \overset{3}{\underset{\text{R R R R R R R}}{\leftarrow \rightarrow \leftarrow \rightarrow \leftarrow \rightarrow \leftarrow \rightarrow}} \cdot \overset{4}{\underset{\text{R R R R R}}{\leftarrow \rightarrow \leftarrow \rightarrow \leftarrow}} \cdot$$

$$\overset{5}{\underset{\text{R R R R R R}}{\leftarrow \rightarrow \leftarrow \rightarrow \leftarrow \rightarrow}} \cdot \overset{6}{\underset{\text{R R R R R R}}{\leftarrow \rightarrow \leftarrow \rightarrow \leftarrow \rightarrow}} \cdot \ldots \text{The food is moved only to the left}\ldots$$

$$\overset{38}{\underset{\text{L L L R R R}}{\leftarrow \leftarrow \leftarrow \rightarrow \leftarrow \rightarrow}} \cdot \overset{39}{\underset{\text{L R L R L R}}{\leftarrow \rightarrow \leftarrow \rightarrow \leftarrow \rightarrow}} \cdot \overset{40}{\underset{\text{R R R R R R}}{\rightarrow \leftarrow \rightarrow \leftarrow \rightarrow \leftarrow}} \cdot \overset{41}{\underset{\text{R R R R R R}}{\leftarrow \rightarrow \leftarrow \rightarrow \leftarrow \rightarrow}} \cdot$$

In this case the extinction which contributed to the transition from unilateral walks around the screen to the adequate method of solving the problem, apparently, proved difficult for the bird's nervous system, as a result of which it reverted to the I type of behaviour.

In our experiments we observed 23 cases of strongly pronounced pathological disturbances in the behaviour of the animals. In 17 of these cases the pathological disturbances emerged during the solution of the problem; in 4 cases they occurred in the period of extinction of the unilateral walks around the screen; and in 2 cases during the unilateral walks around the screen.

Although in the last mentioned cases phobias did emerge in the birds (a cock and a crow), which walked around the screen mainly on one side, both of these birds, after obtaining through the gap in the screen the necessary information concerning the direction in which the food stimulus was moving, manifested distinct movements in the same direction.

Fig. 8 shows the directions in which the crow 'Fomka' moved during the first experimental day, after which it began to exhibit obvious symptoms of a phobia. The figure shows that in spite of the fact that the bird walked around the screen on the left side, it accomplished distinct movements in the direction of the moving food during its each displacement to the right side.

References p. 307

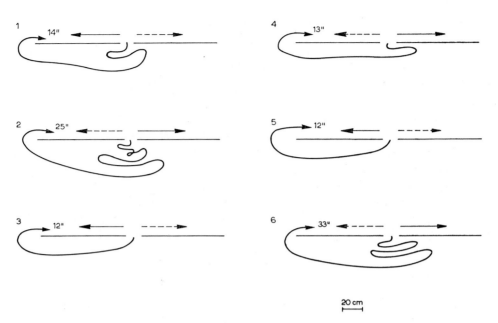

Fig. 8. Scheme illustrating the movement of the crow 'Fomka' during the first experiment. 1–6: ordinal numbers denoting the presentations of the problem. Denotations as in Fig.2.

Our investigations showed that the principal cause of emergence of pathological disturbances in the nervous activity of animals was the solution of the problem itself. But such disturbances may also appear as a result of an extinction of the walks around the screen (when the course of the experiment contributes to a transition from the I to the II type of behaviour), as well as a result of uncompleted attempts to walk around the screen in the direction of the moving food. This shows that even the mere elaboration of a certain programme for such a solution, based on express-information, leads to the development of pathological neurotic behaviour.

ADMINISTRATION OF PSYCHOPHARMACOLOGICAL REMEDIES

Our investigations (Fless et al., 1963) showed that the administration of psychotropic substances proves to be an effective method of analysing the problem studied.

The most essential result of these investigations was the establishment of the fact that if the experimental animal is unable to solve a given problem, it can accomplish this successfully after the administration of certain pharmacological drugs.

Centrophenoxin (Lucidril, ANP-235) appears to be a particularly effective pharma-cological remedy. This drug is described as a 'psycho-cortical tonic agent and central neuroregulator' (Thuiller et al., 1959, 1960; Coirault, 1959, 1960).

Below we cite an example of administration of this remedy in the course of our experiments with the dog 'Shvyrok'.

From this example it may be seen that already on the very first experimental day

1 (19.XII)   2 (22.XII)   3 (26.XII)

→ ← → ← → ← → ←   ← → ← → ← →   ← ← ← → ← →
R R R R R R R ·   R R R R R R ·   R R R R R ·

4 (5.I)   5 (9.I)

← → ← → ← →   → ← → ← → ←
R R R R R R ·   R R R R R R ·

From January 12 to January 30 received 250 mg of Lucidril daily.

6 (16.I)   7 (19.I)   8 (23.I)

← → ← → ← ← → ←   → ← → ← → ←   ← → ← → → ←
R R R R L L R L ·   R L R L R L ·   L R L R R L ·

9 (26.I)   10 (30.I)   11 (2.II)

→ ← → ← → ← → ←   → ← → ← → ←   ← → ← → ← →
R L R_1 L_1 R_1 L_1 L_2 L_2 · R_2 L_2 R_2 L_2 R_2 L_2 · L_2 R_2 L_2 R_2 L_2 R_2 ·

after we started to administer centrophenoxin, the dog manifested a sharp transition from the I to the II type of behaviour and solved the problem in all degrees of its complication (having committed only one error).

The above facts based on experiments with 8 animals show that administration of a psychotropic substance which, according to some data published in the literature, regulates the work of the higher divisions of the brain, apparently, facilitates the solution by animals of difficult logical problems based on express-information about changes taking place in the relationships between the elements of the external environment.

Reverse transitions from adequate solutions of the given problem to unilateral walks around the screen were observed after the administration of large doses of psychotropic drugs (such tranquilizers as benactizine and carbamate of methylpentinol).

The effect produced by the administration of benactizine may be seen from the experiments with the dog 'Mushka'.

This dog walked around the screen with a complicated attachment to it in accordance with the direction in which the food was moved; on the day when benactizine was administered, the dog began to walk around the screen only on one side; but on the next experimental day the problem was again adequately solved.

33 (18.VI)   Benactizine administered (20 mg.) one hour and a half before the beginning of the experiment   34 (22.VI)

→ ← → → ← ← →   → ← → ← → ←
R_2 L_2 R_2 R_2 L_2 L_2 R_2 · R_2 R_2 R_2 R_2 R_2 R

35 (25.VI)

← → ← ←
L_2 R_2 L_2 L_2 ·

Experiments carried out with the dog 'Malyshka' present an example of the effect produced by carbamate of methylpentinol (CMP) on the transition from an adequate solution of the problem to unilateral walks around the screen.

References p. 307

30.III

$\rightarrow \leftarrow \rightarrow \rightarrow \leftarrow$
$R_2\,L_2\,R_2\,R_2\,L_2\cdot$

CMP was administered (700 mg) 2 h before the beginning of the experiment

10.IV

$\leftarrow \rightarrow \leftarrow \rightarrow \leftarrow \rightarrow \leftarrow \rightarrow$
$R_2\,R_2\,R_2\,R_2\,R_1\,R_1\,R_1\,R$

13.IV

$\leftarrow \rightarrow \leftarrow \rightarrow \leftarrow$
$L\ \ R\ \ L\ \ R_1 R_1\cdot$

$\rightarrow \leftarrow \leftarrow \rightarrow \rightarrow \leftarrow \rightarrow$
$R_2\,L_2\,L_2\,R_2\,R_2\,L_2\,R_2\cdot$

This example clearly shows that the administration of a large dose of a given tranquilizer caused a transition to unilateral walks around the screen after the presentation of two complicated variants of the problem.

All the above-cited facts lead to the conclusion that tranquilizers administered in large doses exert definite influence on the type of the animal's behaviour when elementary logical problems are presented to it: temporarily the animal changes over from the adequate method of solving the problem to walks around the screen on one side. This influence is mainly felt during the solution of the most difficult variants of the problem.

Administration of some psychotropic drugs (neuroleptics and tranquilizers) led to the elimination or subsidience of the phobia relating to the experimental situation which develops as a result of the solution by the animal of a difficult problem.

It also proved that chlorpromazine (a single administration) and partly reserpine (chronic administration) led to a temporary subsidience or elimination of the symptoms of the phobia. This may be illustrated by our experiments with the dog 'Trezor'. In this dog a phobia gradually developed after a long period of experiments with the presentation of various elementary logical problems. In the course of experiments with a screen the dog was afraid to approach the gap and to walk around the attachment, although it successfully solved the problem. In 6 experiments chlorpromazine (3 to 8 mg/kg body-weight) was administered to the dog 1 or 2 h before the beginning of each experiment. In all cases we observed a decline or full disappearance of the phobia, which, however, reappeared on the next experimental day.

Administration of reserpine to three birds of the crow family and to one dog suffering from a strongly pronounced phobia led in most cases to the disappearance or subsidience of the phobia during several days.

Meprotan (meprobamate) proved to be the most effective substance; a chronic administration of this substance to crows at doses of 100 to 200 mg eliminated the phobia in all eight cases. As distinct from reserpine and chlorpromazine, its therapeutic effect persisted during several weeks.

It is noteworthy that although meprotan eliminates the phobia, it does not exert any influence on the solution of the problem. If the experimental animal used to walk around the screen only on one side when it suffered from a phobia, this behaviour, as a rule, persisted even after the elimination of the phobia.

This gives ground to assume that pathological disturbances leading to the emergence of a phobia, do not develop in those structures of the brain which are responsible for the solution of elementary logical problems on the basis of express-information. Since according to the data published by some authors (Hess, 1954; Von Holst und

Von Saint Paul, 1960) defensive emotional reactions in birds and mammals are closely associated with the hypothalamus, it may be supposed that the effect of meprotan on the phobias which emerged in the course of our experiments is explained by its blocking action on the internuncial neurons of the diencephalon.

Thus, the difficulties which arise in animals when they solve difficult problems and which manifest themselves in phobias or in a transition to inadequate stereotype walking around the screen, may be eliminated with the help of drugs producing effects of different types: substances regulating the activity of the cortex (of the lucidril type) contribute to the adequate solution of elementary logical problems, while drugs blocking the activity of the stem and diencephalic divisions of the brain (meprotan, chlorpromazine, reserpine) eliminate the phobias.

COMPARATIVE CHARACTERISTICS OF SOME STRUCTURAL FORMATIONS OF THE BRAIN IN THE SPECIES OF BIRDS STUDIED

The last decades have markedly changed the previously widespread idea that the behaviour of birds is less plastic than the behaviour of mammals.

In the well-known experiments of Koehler (1955, 1960), who investigated the ability of animals to learn to operate with numbers, certain species of birds proved to be able to estimate the number of 7 objects, the highest limit for squirrels being also 7.

Numerous investigations carried out by Voronin and his co-workers (1957, 1962) showed that birds (pigeons and members of the crow family) are on the same level with rodents (rabbits) as regards the formation of complex chain conditioned reflexes.

Our own investigations, as it may be seen from the afore-mentioned data, show that birds of the crow family prove to be on a much higher level than rabbits as regards the ability to solve elementary logical problems, and in this respect are equal to dogs.

Thorpe (1958) justly pointed out that one of the arguments usually adduced in favour of the allegedly primitive behaviour of birds in comparison with that of mammals was the insufficient development of those brain structures in birds which correspond to the neocortex of mammals.

In phylogenesis the development of the telencephalon of birds proceeded mainly at the expense of the striatum. According to the generally accepted nomenclature (Rose, 1914; Huber and Crosby, 1929; Ariëns Kappers *et al.*, 1936; Stingelin, 1958; Haefelfinger, 1958), the telencephalon of birds consists of the following basic cellular regions: palaeostriatum, archistriatum, ectostriatum, neostriatum, nucleus basalis, hyperstriatum dorsale and ventrale, nucleus intercalatus hyperstriati, and hyperstriatum accessorium.

The brain cortex of birds is relatively little developed. According to the nomenclature suggested by Svetukhina (1961), it is differentiated into the following structures:

(1) Palaeocortex (tuberculum olfactorium, area periamygdalaris, septum pellucidum).

(2) Archicortex (occupies the dorso-medial and medial surface of the hemispheres, separated from the striatum by the cavity of the ventricle and is differentiated into the fascia dentata and Ammon formation).

(3) Neocortex, is not developed.

Many researches pay much attention to the formation of the telencephalon which was described by earlier authors under the name 'Sagitalwulst', or 'Wulst'. This structural formation consists of the hyperstriatum accessorium and the hyperstriatum dorsale and in some species of birds is covered by a layer of cortical cells, forming a marked eminence on the frontal part of the dorsal wall. In some species of birds a new nuclear zone –Nucleus intercalatus (neopallium)–is differentiated in the region of the 'Wulst' (Stingelink, 1958). According to the investigations carried out by Haefelfinger (1958), the hyperstriatum accessorium, hyperstriatum dorsale and nucleus intercalatus cannot be differentiated one from another in ontogenesis. This gives ground to regard the 'Wulst' as a peculiar single morphological structure. As a result of comparative anatomical investigations, Stingelin came to the conclusion that a progressive growth of the 'Wulst' is one of the most characteristic features of the structural and cytoarchitectonic complication of the telencephalon of birds. A scheme illustrating the evolution of the brain of birds (given by the author on p. 74 of his book) shows that a progressive growth of this formation is the most characteristic structural change taking place in the evolution of the brain of birds from reptiles (varan).

In the literature there exists an opinion (a discussion on this question was cited by Haefelfinger, 1958) that the 'Wulst' may be regarded as a homologue of the neo-cortex. Haefelfinger, basing himself on his ontogenetic investigation of the forebrain of birds, holds the same opinion: 'Der neopalliale Teil bildet das Wulstgebiet und wird mit dem Cortex der Säuger homologisiert'.

Of great significance for our investigation is the fact that this formation, which is progressively developing in the course of evolution and which is regarded as a homologue of the cortex of mammals, is characterized in birds by a very considerable interspecies variability. We may find in this variability a definite parallelism with the ability to solve elementary logical problems which has been established by us within the class of birds.

In his investigations devoted to the study of the relative development of the 'Wulst' Stingelin (1958) considered that pigeons provide an example of a least developed brain with a feebly pronounced 'Wulst' where the nucleus intercalatus is fully absent.

Rose (1914) discovered in fowls a clearly pronounced nucleus intercalatus, which indicates a more differentiated development of their 'Wulst' than that of pigeons.

Of 51 birds (11 orders), studied by Stingelin it is the birds of the crow family which proved to possess the most differentiated brain having a highly developed 'Wulst'.

Fowls were not subjected to any investigation by this author. However, ducks, which according to our investigations (Krushinsky and Parfenov, 1959) are able to solve elementary problems better than pigeons, but worse than birds of the crow family, occupy an intermediate position between these birds also as regards the degree of development of their telencephalon (the 'Wulst' in ducks has three nuclear zones).

Of definite interest is a comparison of the results obtained by Koehler (1955 and 1960) with the ability of different species of birds to detect a box containing food with the help of a numerical code, and to make use of this habit under quite different conditions.

The highest limit of the ability to perceive numbers of objects is: in pigeons 5; in African grey parrots and jackdaws 6; in ravens, rooks, jays, Amazonian parrots and grey parrots 7.

As already stated above, Stingelin's investigations (1958) showed that pigeons possess a feebly developed 'Wulst'; in African grey parrots the 'Wulst' is less developed than in Amazonian parrots, which is directly stated by the afore-mentioned author. Although Stingelin did not investigate jays, ravens and jackdaws, it may be assumed that in these birds of the crow family the 'Wulst' is as well developed as in crows and rooks which were investigated by the author.

It seems to us that on the basis of all the afore-mentioned facts we have good reasons to assume that the degree of development of the 'Wulst' in birds may play an essential role in their solution of elementary problems.

Of considerable interest within the 'Wulst' itself is the hyperstriatum accessorium. This formation consists of small cells mixed up with bigger deeper straining neurons resembling in their character the cortical cellular layer (Ariëns Kappers et al., 1936). According to Stingelin's investigations, very big cells (18 to 25μ) of a compact form with a light nucleus and a considerable amount of tigroid, are very densely distributed in birds of the crow family (and herons), as distinct from other species.

We carried out (Krushinsky, et al., 1963) a confrontation of the relative volumes (compared to the volume of the hemispheres) of some brain structures in the birds studied with their ability to solve elementary logical problems on the basis of extrapolation; as a result, the following was revealed:

(1) There is a direct dependence between the relative volume of the hyperstriatum (pigeons 6.3; hens 7.5; crows 9.6) and the ability to solve logical problems offered.

(2) There is an inverse dependence between the relative volume of the Palaeo- and Archicortex (pigeons 9.4; hens 6.4; crows 3.3) and the ability to solve logical problems.

(3) There is an inverse dependence between the relative volume of the tectum opticum (pigeons 24.6; hens 17.7; birds of the crow family 7.6) and the ability to solve problems offered.

(4) No essential differences between the relative volumes of the whole striatum (pigeons 87.7; hens 90.8; crows 94.0) and striatum without the hyperstriatum accessorium (pigeons 81.4; hens 83.3; crows 84.4) could be established in the birds studied.

We believe that the above data provide sufficient grounds to regard the 'Wulst' with its nucleus hyperstriatum accessorium as the structure of the telencephalon of birds which may play an essential role in the solution of elenentary logical problems. These data indirectly corroborate the correctness of the opinion expressed by some authors that this formation is homologous (functionally, if not morphologically) with the cortex of the cerebral hemispheres of mammals.

As to the cortex of birds (palaeo- and archicortex), its relative dimensions can hardly play a substantial role in the solution of elementary logical problems on the basis of extrapolation.

Similarly, the relative dimensions of the tectum opticum of the mesencephalic end in the visual analyser do not play any appreciable role in the ability to extrapolate on the basis of express-information. Pigeons, whose mesencephalic 'station', receiving the visual information, possesses the relatively biggest tectum opticum, practically proved unable to use it for finding an adequate solution of the problems offered. This shows that in the higher divisions of the analysers — in the structures of the telencephalon — are probably situated those morphophysiological mechanisms which accomplish the processing of the information received, as well as the elaboration of programmes for carrying out behavioural acts on the basis of express-information.

Along with the different degree of development of certain telencephalic formations, in various species of birds, there are also observed some peculiarities in the structure of the nuclear neurons of the striatum.

According to preliminary data (Polyakov, in press) the neurons of the striatum in birds of the crow family (rooks) are characterized by a more complex structural organization in comparison with similar neurons in pigeons. This is expressed in the fact that in rooks efferent neurons with long axons possess considerably more dendrite branchings which are covered by more densely spaced lateral appendages (spines). This structural peculiarity shows that the afore-mentioned neurons may form in birds of the crow family considerably more diverse axo-dendrite connections with other neurons and afferent fibres than in pigeons. It is noteworthy that in birds of the crow family, as distinct from pigeons, the neurons with short axons (Golgi's cells of the second type) are more numerous and prove to be more diverse as regards the form of the cellular bodies and the dendrite and axons branching. At present it is known (Lorento de Nó, 1951) that neurons with short axons are of great importance for retaining the traces of excitation, for coupling the circulation of impulses as well as for the functional unification of groups of efferent neurons (Polyakov, 1961). A particularly appreciable increase of the number and diversity of forms of neurons with short axons both in the cortical and subcortical formations of the hemispheres takes place with the progressive differentiation of the efferent neurons in the evolution of vertebrates. (Polyakov, 1958a, b).

The fact that the neurons of the intracentral connections reach greater degree of complexity of dendro-axon network in crows than in pigeons, may provide the structural basis for longer retention of traces of previous stimulations in the crow birds. Probably, it is this structural and functional mechanism which lies at the basis of the ability of the afore-said species of birds to program the trajectory of movement of a certain object and to accomplish an extrapolation of its further movement in space.

Thus, in species of birds, which display the most pronounced ability to solve elementary logical problems, we observe both an increase in the volumetric correlations of the phylogenetically youngest formations of the striatum ('Wulst') and a complication of the neuronal organization itself which, apparently, allows more effectively to process the express-information for accomplishing adequate behavioral acts.

CONCLUSION

The results of our investigations, as well as the data published previously, give us rise to assert that animals are able to extrapolate on the basis of express-information the changes which take place in the elementary relationships of the environmental elements (in our experiments) — to apprehend the law-governed changes of their disposition in space — for accomplishing certain adaptive acts of behaviour.

Our findings showed that the accomplishment of behavioral acts, which were subjected by us to investigation, greatly varied both in different species of animals, and in individuals of the same species.

Repeated presentations of one and the same problem to the animals demonstrated that the latter manifested two qualitatively different types of behaviour aimed at procuring the food:

I type, or stereotype conditioned-reflex behaviour;

II type, or behaviour based on a certain programme in conformity with the changing experimental conditions.

Both types of behaviour result from two different ways of apprehending, retaining and processing the information obtained.

If a conditioned reflex is formed in the animal, the latter apprehends the law-governed combinations in time and space of indifferent and unconditioned reflex stimuli, between which no direct causal relationships exist (the dog, for example, cannot know the programme of the given experiment which specifies the combinations of the sound of a bell with the presentation of food). It is quite obvious that in this case each subsequent combination makes more reliable the law of combination of the bell with the presentation of food in time, and thus increases the probability of correct responses. This makes it possible to plot a 'typical curve of learning'.

Quite different is the behaviour of the animal when already with the first presentation of the problem (as it occurs in our experiments) it obtains sufficient information concerning the laws of the changing interdependences which exist between the environmental elements. Here it is the ability of the animal's brain to process the information obtained which comes to the fore.

It seems to us that the question of whether learning is a 'sudden' or 'gradual' process, which arouses so many arguments, may be resolved if in each case we clearly distinguish two different phenomena: the type of the information obtained and the possibility of its being processed by the brain.

Of essential significance is the fact that sharp transitions take place from one type of behaviour to another, which was established by our investigations.

Such transitions are observed in the process of presentation of one and the same variant of a problem, and particularly often when the problem is complicated; it is likewise observed by administering of various psychotropic drugs.

The fact of discrete transitions from one type of behaviour to another allows us to assume that different physiological mechanisms (connected with the processing and retaining of information), which lie at the basis of both types of behaviour, may become switched over in a relay-like manner.

References p. 307

At present it is difficult to determine those structural neuronal formations which may be responsible for the effectuation of one type of behaviour or another. In this respect only different hypotheses may be advanced.

One such alluring hypothesis is the idea that both types of behaviour are connected with different ways of retaining and processing the information obtained.

Wiener (1948) advanced the hypothesis that information is retained in the neurons of the brain in two forms: one type of information is retained in the form of lasting memories, while another is in the form of recent ones.

According to Wiener's supposition (very cautiously formulated by him), the first type of information is retained in the form of a certain physical basis; it is probably connected with a change in the synaptic transmission.

The second type of information is partially retained in the form of circulating impulses of excitation in the neurons.

The subsequent development of physiology to some degree substantiates this hypothesis.

On the one hand, some authors have described different forms of retention of lasting memories which are connected with a synaptic delay and summation or morphological change in the synapse itself and in the presynaptic fibre (swelling) (Eccles, 1953, 1957), as well as with a change in the amount of ribonucleic acid (Morrell, 1960, Hydén, 1961, 1961a).

On the other hand, Lorente de Nó (1951) described chains of closed rings of neuronal connections in the cerebral cortex, where recent memories may be retained in an active state*.

At present we have some grounds to establish a definite connection between the ability of the animals to apprehend on the basis of express-information the elementary laws governing the relationships of the environmental elements and the retention of information in the closed chains of neuronal connections (Krushinsky, 1959).

Firstlyk, the researches carried out by Polyakov (1956, 1958a, 1958b) showed that the phylogenetically youngest upper layers of the cerebral cortex, whose development is most advanced in the primates and in man, are characterized, along with a greater complexity and perfection of their neurons, by a relatively larger number of neurons having short branching axons (stellate neurons). These neurons form a system of closed rings of feedback connections and may act as the morphological basis for retaining the 'operative memory' which, apparently, plays an essential role in the progressive evolution of higher nervous activity. Beritov (1961), basing himself on rich factual material, proves that stellate cells with the pericellular axon network situated in the III and IV cortical layers of the central zone of each analyser play a considerable role in reflecting the spatial relationships between the elements of the environment. Beritov associates the system of stellate neurons with the ability of the animals to effect complex adaptive forms of behaviour.

---

* In spite of the insufficient reliability of this hypothesis, it is difficult to explain the physiological processes which are connected with learning without admitting the existence of active closed chains of feedback connections, as rightfully stated by George (1961).

Secondly, as already stated above, Polyakov (Jurnal für Hirnforschung, in press) disclosed certain distinctions between the structure of neurons in pigeons and that in birds of the crow family. Pigeons, which possess a considerably lower ability to solve elementary logical problems than birds of the crow family, also possess a more primitive neuronal organization. The neurons of birds of the crow family with their much more developed dendrite branchings, are, apparently, able to retain the 'operative memory' for a longer time.

From this point of view the considerable volumes of the progressively developed cerebral divisions ('Wulst') of birds of the crow family may be regarded as a greater number of chains of feedback connections which increase the capacity for more adequate processing of the express-information.

Thirdly, according to Wiener's assumption (1948), the involvement of impulses of a great number of neurons into the active process of circulation during the functioning of the 'operative memory' must lead to the emergence of a persistent neurotic fear. Precisely this was observed by us in animals with the II type of behaviour under which the elaboration of a programme for solving a given task requires the presence of an 'operative memory' capable of processing the incoming express-information*.

In the case of the I type of behaviour, which is effected on the basis of a lasting memory, such pathological disturbances were not practically observed in our experiments.

We believe that the afore-mentioned arguments give us the right to connect Wiener's hypothesis concerning two forms of retention and processing of information with the types of behaviour of our animals which manifested themselves during the presentation of elementary logical problems.

Although it is very alluring to explain the distinctions disclosed in the behaviour of the animals by this hypothesis, one cannot deny that there may exist special** structurally determined neuronal constellations formed in the course of the millenia natural selection for the purpose of retaining lasting memories and solving definite types of logical problems with which the animals meet in the conditions of their natural existence.

Billions of neurons with their great diversity of possible combinations may provide a large number*** of possibilities for such a selection, while it is the individual experience that finally determines these forms of behaviour which are effected on the basis of hereditarily fixed codes.****

---

* In animals with the II type of behaviour the elaboration of a programme requires concentrated attention every time when a problem is solved by them. Attention connected with the activating reticular system seems 'most likely to be a further differentiation of gross generalized arousal mechanism' (Jasper, 1958). No wonder, therefore, that there takes place a stationary excitation of the nuclei of the hypothalamus which play a leading part in the effectuation of defensive behaviour.
** Penfield (1952) discovered in the temporal region of the human brain special sections where the retention of lasting memories is effected.
*** We use this term without resorting to the concept of infinite, basing ourselves on the viewpoint expressed by Kolmogorov (1963) on this question.
**** The role of the hereditary pattern in learning has been considered in details in recent years by Lorenz (1961), Shneirla (1956) and Krushinsky (1960).

References p. 307

In this case the observed discrete transitions from one type of behaviour to another may be explained by a relay switch-over from certain neuronal constellations to others.

It seems to us that all the above data give certain grounds to state that the discrete character* of the complex forms of behaviour is based not only on the activity of discrete units (neurons), but also on the activity of functional groups of neurons which are connected with definite distinctions in the retention and processing of the incoming information.

ACKNOWLEDGEMENTS

I wish to express my profound gratitude to Drs. G. I. Polyakov, L. D. Meshalkin and O. S. Vinogradova and I. I. Poletaeva, as well as to all my laboratory co-workers who rendered me valuable help in my present work.

SUMMARY

(1) Animals are able to extrapolate changes in the most elementary laws which underlie the relationships between the environmental elements, for accomplishing adaptive behavioral acts.

(2) In the accomplishment of the behavioral acts studied there have been observed both interspecies and intraspecies distinctions.

(3) Repeated presentations of one and the same problem led to the formation of two different types of behaviour in the experimental animals, namely,

I type, or stereotype conditioned-reflex behaviour, and

II type, or behaviour accomplished on the basis of a programme in conformity with the changing experimental conditions.

(4) In the case of the II type of behaviour there has been observed a frequent emergence of different pathological disturbances of the higher nervous activity which can be eliminated with the help of psychotropic drugs.

(5) Different ways of transition from one type of behaviour studied to the other have been found. Most characteristic among them are discrete transitions which are observed when the same problem is presented to the animal repeatedly during a long period, when the problem is complicated or when psychotropic substances are administered.

(6) Some morphological structures of the brain (of birds), which may be of importance in the accomplishment of behavioral acts, have been investigated.

(7) An analysis has been made of the possible morpho-physiological mechanisms associated with different forms of retention and processing of information which may determine the animal's type of behaviour during the accomplishment of definite behavioral acts.

---

* A diametrically opposite point of view concerning the continuity of transitions from the 'trial and errors' method of solving problems to insight was expressed by Kellog (1938).

REFERENCES

ARIENS KAPPERS, C. U., HUBER, C.C., AND. CROSBY, E. C., (1936); *The Comparative Anatomy of the Nervous System of Vertebrates including Man.* Vol. 2. New York. Macmillan.

BERITOV, I. S., (1961); *Nervous Mechanisms Governing the Behaviour of Higher Vertebrates.* Moscow. Izdatel'stvo Akademii Nauk SSSR.

COIRAULT, R., (1959); Une orientation thérapeutique nouvelle en neuropsychiatrie et en pathologie générale: l'ester diméthylaminoéthylique de l'acide p. chlorophenoxyacétique (ANP 235). *Ann. méd.-psychol.*, 118–1; 119 and 144.

COIRAULT, R., (1960); Un psycho-cortique et neuro-régulateur central l'ester diméthylaminoéthylique de l'acide p. chlorophenoxyacétique (ANP-235). *Rev. lyon. Méd.*, N-special; 179.

ECCLES, J. C., (1953); *The Neurophysiological Basis of Mind: The Principles of Neurophysiology.* Oxford. Clarendon Press.

ECCLES, J. C., (1957); *The Physiology of Nerve Cells.* Baltimore–London. The Johns Hopkins Press–Oxford University Press.

FLESS, D. A., KRUSHINSKY, L. V., MOLODKINA, L. N., AND OCHINSKAYA, E. I., (1963); Regulation of Complex Forms of Behaviour of Animals (Extrapolation Reflexes) with the Help of Psychotropic Substances. Physiological Foundations of Complex Forms of Behaviour, 34–36. Leningrad–Moscow. Izdatel'stvo Akademii Nauk SSSR.

GEORGE, F. H., (1961); *The Brain as a Computer.* Oxford–London–New York–Paris. Pergamon Press.

GLUSHKOV, V. M., (1963); Simulation of Thinking Processes. *Priroda*, **2**, 3–13.

HAEFELFINGER, H. R., (1958); *Beiträge zur vergleichenden Ontogenese des Vorderhirns bei Vögeln.* Basel. Helbing u. Lichtenhahn.

HESS, W. R., (1954); *Das Zwischenchirn.* Basel. Schwabe.

VAN HOLST, E., UND VON SAINT PAUL, U., (1960); Vom Wirkungsgefüge der Triebe. *Naturwissenschaften*, **47**, **18**, 409–422.

HUBER, G., AND CROSBY, E. C., (1929); The Nuclei and Fiber Paths of the Avian Diencephalon, with Consideration of Telencephalic and certain Mesencephalic Centers and Connections. *J. comp. Neurol.*, **48**, 1–186.

HYDÉN, H., (1961); Satellite Cells in the Nervous System. *Sci. American*, December, pp. 62–70.

HYDÉN, H., (1961a); The Neuron. *The Cell*, Vol. IV, pp. 302–308.

JASPER, H., (1958); Reticular-Cortical Systems and Theories of the Integrative Action of the Brain. *Biol. Biochem. Bases Behaviour.* Madison. The University of Wisconsin Press. (p. 37–61).

KELLOG, W. N., (1938); An Eclectic View of some Theories of Learning. *Psychol. Rev.*, **45**, 165–184.

KOEHLER, O., (1955); *Tierische Vorstufen menschlicher Sprache.* Arbeitstagung über zentrale Regulationen der Funktionen des Organismus. Leipzig, 1–3 Dezember.

KOEHLER, O., (1960); Die Beziehung Mensch–Tier. *Verhandl. Schweiz. Naturf. Ges. (Aargau)*, 44–57.

KOLMOGOROV, A. N., (1963); Automatic Machines and Life. Collection of articles: 'The Possible and Impossible in Cybernetics'. Moscow. Izdatel'stvo Akademii Nauk SSSR (p. 10–29).

KRECHEVSKY, I., (1938); A Study of the Continuity of the Problem-Solving Process. *Psychol. Rev.*, **45**, 107–133.

KRUSHINSKY, L. V., (1958); The Bilogical Importance of Extrapolation Reflexes in Animals. *Zh. Obshch. Biol.*, **19**, 457–466.

KRUSHINSKY, L. V., (1959); The Study of Extrapolation Reflexes in Animals. *Probl. Cybernet.*, **2**, 229–282. Moscow. Gosudarstvennoye Izdatel'stvo Fizikomatematicheskoi literaturi.

KRUSHINSKY, L. V., AND PARFENOV, G. P., (1959); Extrapolation Reflexes in Ducks. *Ornitologia*, **2**, 59–62.

KRUSHINSKY, L. V., (1960); *Animal Behaviour, Its Normal and Abnormal Development.* New York. Consultant Bureau.

KRUSCHINSKI, L. W., SWETUCHINA, W. M., MOLODKINA, L. N., POPOWA, N. P., UND MAZ, W. N., (1963); Vergleichende physiologisch-morphologische Erforschung Komplizierter Verhaltensformen von Vögeln. *Z. Tierpsychol.*, **20**, 474–486.

LORENTO DE NÓ, R., (1951); Cerebral Cortex. *Physiology of the Nervous System.* J. F. Fulton, Ed. Oxford, 3rd ed., Oxford University Press.

LORENZ, K., (1961); Phylogenetische Anpassung und adaptive Modifikation des Verhaltens. *Z. Tierpsychol.*, Bd. 18, Heft **2**, 139–187.

MORRELL, F., (1960); *Lasting Changes in Synaptic Organization Produced by Continuous Neuronal Bombardment.* In Background Material for Pavlov Conference, New York, 1960.

PENFIELD, W., (1952); Memory Mechanism. *Arch. Neurol., Psychiat.* **67**, 178–191.

PETROVA, M. K., (1953); Experimental Phobias. Sobranie trudov, tom II, 181–223. Izdatel'stvo Akademii Meditsinskikh Nauk SSSR.

POLYAKOV, G. I., (1956); Relationships between the Principal Types of Neurons in the Human Cerebral Cortex. *Zh. Vysshei Nervnoi Deyatel'nosti*, **5**, 470–478.

POLYAKOV, G. I., (1958a); The Increasing Complexity of the Structure of the Neurons of the Central Nervous System in Man, the Primates and other Mammals. *Sovetsk. Antropol.*, **3**, 35–55.

POLYAKOV, G. I., (1958b); The Increasing Complexity of the Neuronal Structure of the Brain in Man, Monkeys and other Mammals. *Sovjetsk. Antropol.*, **4**, 69–85.

POLYAKOV, G. I., (1961); Some Results of Research into the Development of the Neuronal Structure of the Cortical Ends of the Analyzers in Man. *J. comp. Neurol.*, **117**, 197–212.

ROSE, M., (1914); Über die cytoarchitektonische Gliederung des Vorderhirns der Vögel. *J. Psychol. Neurol.*, **21**, 1, 6–80.

SCHNEIRLA, T. C., (1956); Interrelationships of the 'Innate' and the 'Acquired' in Instinctive Behaviour. 387–452. In: '*L'instinct dans le comportement des animaux et de l'homme*'. Paris. Masson.

STINGELIN, W., (1958); *Vergleichend morphologische Untersuchungen am Vorderhirn der Vögel auf cytologischer und cytoarchitektonischer Grundlage*. Basel. Helbing und Lichtenhahn.

SVETUKHINA, V. M., (1961); Cytoarchitectonic Differentiation of the Telencephalon and Progressive Evolution in the Class of Birds. 3rd Scientific Conference on Evolutionary Physiology dedicated to the memory of Academician L. A. Orbeli. Leningrad (p. 168).

THORPE, W. H., (1958); *Learning and Instinct in Animals*. London. Methuen and Co., Ltd.

THUILLIER, J., RUMPF, P., ET THUILLIER, G., (1959); Dérives des acides régulateurs de croissance de végétaux. Propriétes pharmacologiques de l'ester diméthylaminoéthylique de l'acide p. chlorophenoxyacétique (235 ANP). *Comp. Rend. Soc. Biol.*, **153**, 1914.

THUILLIER, J., (1960); Propriétés pharmacologiques de l'ester diméthylaminoéthylique de l'acide p. chlorophenoxyacétique. *Agressologie*, 1960, **1**, 78.

VORONIN, L. G., (1957); *Lectures on the Comparative Physiology of the Higher Nervous Activity*. Moscow. Izdatel'stvo Moskovskogo Universiteta.

VORONIN, L. G., (1962); Some Results of Comparative Physiological Investigations of Higher Nervous Activity. *Psychol. Bull.*, **59**, 161–195.

WIENER, N., (1948); *Cybernetics or, Control and Communication in the Animal and the Machine*. New York. The Technology Press of MIT and John Wiley and Sons, Inc.

Applications of Information Theory and Decision Theory to Human Perception and Reaction

D. E. BROADBENT

Applied Psychology Research Unit, Medical Research Council, Cambridge (Great Britain)

Since the publication of Wiener's *Cybernetics*, the application to psychology of conceptual techniques derived from the physical sciences has proceeded apace. One of the most stimulating developments of this sort has been the use of information theory in the study of human perception and choice reaction, and the present paper is intended to outline some of the ways in which this has happened. As will be familiar to my readers, information theory originated from considerations of the behaviour of physical communication systems. It deals with a set or ensemble of possible messages which are to be transmitted through a given channel, and the ways in which the signals in that channel may be encoded so as to convey the messages as fast as possible with a given amount of noise (unwanted disturbance) in the channel, and a specified degree of error. It can be shown, for example, that the average time taken per message in such a situation is proportional to $\sum_{i=1}^{i=n} - p_i \log p_i$ where p_i is the probability of the ith message in an ensemble of size n. This expression is known as the average amount of information per message.

From one point of view we can regard a human being, who is perceiving or reacting, as a channel in the foregoing sense. When one of a set of alternative stimuli strikes his senses, he perceives one of a set of possible percepts or makes one of a set of reactions. The novelty of such an approach lay in the treatment of the whole set as relevant even although only one occurs on any particular occasion. Looking back, it seems likely that psychologists of earlier days were too inclined to concentrate upon the relationship between the present stimulus and its representation in experience: and thus to be taken by surprise by phenomena of the sort which are to be considered here.

THE RELATIONSHIP OF INFORMATION THEORY TO PERCEPTION

(a) The Probability of Words

If we present a listener with speech over a noisy telephone channel, he may or may not hear correctly. Naturally the probability of perceiving a particular word varies with the signal-noise ratio, but it is greater for a given word as part of a sentence than it is for the same word in isolation (Miller *et al.*, 1951; Stowe *et al.*, 1963). This is surprising if the stimulus itself is regarded as determining perception; but to the information theorist the presence of the earlier words in the sentence can be regarded as changing the size of the ensemble from which the particular word is chosen, or at least the relative probabilities of the members. Some words do not occur in some contexts, and thus the same physical events at the senses may serve to select the correct word from the small set consistent with the context, when they are insufficient to do so from the large set of the whole dictionary.

Although the effect of context is important in everyday life, it is difficult to assign a number to the increase in objective probability of a word provided by a context, unless extra assumptions are made. Thus it is hard to apply quantitative predictions from information theory. A more tractable type of experiment is to use a fixed and known vocabulary of words and study intelligibility as a function of size of vocabulary. Another is to relate intelligibility of isolated words to the probability of those words as determined by counting their frequency of occurrence in natural samples of the language. In either case intelligibility does appear to be related to the negative logarithm of the probability of the word, at least approximately (Howes, 1957; Miller *et al.*, 1951). To this extent therefore the application of informational analysis seems valid.

(b) Absolute Judgement of Simple Stimuli

An even more simplified approach is to abandon noisy telephone systems, and to construct a fixed vocabulary of simple artificial signals such as pure tones differing only in loudness. The listener is then asked to identify each tone as it is presented. Such an experiment may be carried out for varying sizes of vocabulary, so that the information input to the man is varied: and the amount of information transmitted through him in his responses is then measured. (See Garner (1962) for the calculation of transmitted information.) It is found that the amount transmitted increases with the input up to a certain level, and then remains roughly constant as the input increases. That is, the listener can tell correctly which intensity of tone has been presented until the number of tones in the vocabulary becomes too great, and then he makes the right number of errors to keep the calculated information transmission constant. The critical level, when only one dimension such as loudness, pitch, or length is involved, usually corresponds to an information input of roughly 2.5 bits per signal, that is, correct identification of about five or six signals. The limit does not depend very much upon the physical spacing of the stimuli along the dimension, however, so that we may have the paradox that stimuli which are widely different in, say, pitch may be confused if they form part of a large widely spaced vocabulary, while reasonably discriminable when at the extremes of a small closely-packed vocabulary. (Legge and Summerfield, 1964). If more than one stimulus dimension is involved, the number of discriminable alternatives is larger but not as large as would be expected if each dimension was completely independent.

These findings certainly suggest a mechanism which is limited not by sensory factors but by informational ones, which has in fact an upper bound to its capacity for holding information. There is probably room for more research in this area, since information input seems usually to have been varied by changing the size of vocabulary rather than the relative probabilities of items or the conditional probability of one item following another. Such experiments would be relevant to the exact nature of the limited capacity mechanism. Nevertheless, there is here a clear indication of the value of the informational approach.

(c) Simultaneous Perception of Two Signals

The notion of a limited capacity in human perception leads on to the application of this concept to division of attention. Highly complex signals, chosen from a large ensemble, such as spoken sentences are not easily perceived when more than one is presented at the same time. Two probable or familiar stimuli, however, can be perceived even though they arrive simultaneously. Evidence on this point has been reviewed by Broadbent (1958), and it seems that, in some situations at least, the ability of a man to perceive and react to two simultaneous stimuli can be shown to depend upon the size of the ensemble from which each is drawn.

Thus the difficulty found by most people in 'attending to two things at once' can plausibly be described as due to the information input exceeding the capacity in an informational sense. A particularly striking recent experiment by Baddeley (1962) for example required the subject to call out items such as letters of the alphabet in a random sequence. At the same time he had to sort a pack of cards into various categories such as red/black, the four suits, etc. The informational content of the sequence of letters, that is, its degree of randomness, became less as the number of categories in the card-sorting was increased.

In this latter experiment it appeared again to be the logarithm of the number of categories which gave the simplest relationship: but in general this area of application has not lent itself to quantitative use of information theory, and rather serves as an example of the use of the general conceptual framework.

(d) Pattern Perception and Contours

If we consider every possible combination of states of all the sense organs feeding the brain, the ensemble is clearly exceedingly large and it is a priori likely that further stages in the system will suffer from difficulties due to limited capacity. The experimental results already quoted make this likely too. In fact however the world is so constructed that knowledge of the state of one sense-organ restricts the probabilities as regards other sense-organs. In general, each point in our visual field is adjacent to other points receiving similar stimulation, and it is only at contours, between one mass of colour or shade and another, that the state of the adjacent sense-organs becomes unpredictable. Thus the scenes which pass before a man's eyes in real life are partially redundant, that is, they are drawn from a smaller ensemble than the structure of the senses would permit. The point is similar to the effect of context in speech.

A line of experiment tending to support this approach stems from Attneave (1954). He asked people to guess whether each square in turn in a grid drawn over a black and white picture, was black or white. Subjects were informed of their results, so that they knew the picture up to the point they were now guessing. In general they made most of their errors at the contours. Thus they do appear to be aware of the probability structure of such pictures. Their ability to show this depends upon the sequence of guesses being arranged so that the results of earlier trials do provide evidence concerning later ones. (Courtis and Green, 1963). This does not seem unreasonable from our own point of view.

Another form of redundancy in visual patterns is symmetry or repetition, in which one part of a contour may be predicted from knowledge of another part. Experiments showing that patterns with these characteristics are readily perceived go far back in psychology (Vernon, 1952) and have been developed in more quantitative form within the informational framework (Fitts *et al.*, 1956).

In general terms therefore this approach also has been fruitful, but there have been limits to its quantitative application. In most cases it is not easy to assign any numbers to the ensemble from which a given pattern is chosen, any more than one can do so in the case of context. When this difficulty is overcome by constructing artificial sets of patterns as in the work of Fitts *et al.* (1956), fresh complications emerge. When they displayed a sample pattern and asked men to find the same pattern in a number of others, the task actually became more difficult if the patterns presented for choice were sampled from a smaller rather than a larger ensemble. This is probably because the incorrect patterns then had more features in common with the correct one, so that more observations were necessary in order to reject them. A rather different type of task gave results supporting this interpretation (Anderson and Leonard, 1958).

(e) General Conclusions on Perception

From what has been said it will be clear that considerable and widespread effects on perception have been shown from variations in the ensemble of stimuli which might have been present, and from which the actual one must be distinguished. More detailed quantitative application has not as yet however been sufficient to provide very rigorous uses of the theorems of information theory, rather than its descriptive measures and concepts. A hopeful line for the future is the study of different types of redundancy or dependence of one variable upon another. An analysis which will render such studies easier is that of Garner (1962), who, in addition to a far more detailed review of experiments than has been possible here, presents a conceptual framework for distinguishing different degrees and kinds of structure or interdependence between variables.

INFORMATION THEORY AND REACTION TIME

(a) Lag and Working Rate

We should first distinguish two concepts which are rather different and which do not always seem to have been kept separate in work on reaction time. By '*working rate*' we will indicate the information conveyed by the average number of messages which can be received at one end of a channel in a fixed time. The maximum value of working rate is of course essentially the concept of capacity as usually applied to physical systems. We give it a different name here however to distinguish it from the time taken on average between the beginning of the insertion of each message into the channel, and the end of its emergence at the far end. This latter concept we will call '*lag*'. It is in fact the lag which has usually been measured in most psychological experiments on reaction time, although these are sometimes described as measuring the channel capacity of the human being.

To clarify the distinction, think of a highway which is known to be carrying 3,600 cars per hour. It does not therefore follow that each car takes one second to travel the length of the highway. Confusion between the two measures may however arise because both can be expressed in seconds per car. It is only the former measure, which we are calling working rate, that corresponds to capacity in the usual informational sense. A typical psychological experiment however, as in the classic work of Hick (1952) or Hyman (1955), is to present a stimulus chosen from a prescribed set of alternatives and to measure the time elapsing before an appropriate response occurs. This is, in our present terms, a measure of lag. Even if we measure, as did Crossman (1955), the overall speed with which a man can sort a pack of cards by looking at each and placing it in an appropriate pile, the time taken is an index of the average lag between observing each card and placing it, so long as the subject is unable to see one card until he has dealt with the previous one.

Such measurements do show that the lag is linearly related to the information per response, whether that information is varied by changing the size of the ensemble of responses, changing the relative probability of demanding one response rather than another, changing the probability of sequences of responses, or changing the proportion of errors made by the subject. Where the time of arrival of the stimulus is certain, as in Crossman's experiment, the reaction time $= K \log n$, where n is the number of equiprobable alternative reactions and K is a constant. Where the time of arrival of the stimulus is uncertain, this relationship is not quite adequate: Hick (1952) suggested $K \log (n + 1)$, on the grounds that inaction is an extra alternative, and Welford (1960), in a substantial review, argues for this relationship. Possibly more investigators have preferred the alternative $k + K \log n$, where k is another constant representing those components of reaction time which are unaffected by response information. Such perhaps might be conduction times in nerves.

Whatever the best exact formulation, the uniformity of the relationship over a number of ways of varying information is striking, and tempts one to suggest that we are measuring an inherent limit to human performance due to the capacity of the nervous system. On this view, K would be an inverse measure of this capacity, and Welford (1960) follows Crossman in assigning a value of 5–8 bits/sec to this value on the basis of a number of experiments. Such a view might be justified even although the measurements are of lag rather than working rate, because the lag might be supposed to increase with the duration of the coded signal sent down the channel, even though the lag also continued a fixed component. The duration of the coded signal would be related to capacity. In terms of our highway analogy, the time taken for a certain number of cars to pass completely through the highway (from the first entering to the last leaving) is made up of a fixed time taken by one car plus a time which varies directly with the number of cars in the group and inversely with the working rate of the highway.

References p. 319

If lag is an indirect measure of capacity, we should nevertheless expect working rate to be a direct measure. The type of experiment needed to show this is one in which stimuli are presented at varying speeds and the information per sec in the responses measured and compared with that in the stimuli. Since a stimulus may arrive before the response to the preceding stimulus has been made, any fixed time lag between stimulus and response should be unimportant and we might expect the information output to rise as the input is increased, until the maximum output is reached at the capacity of the system. This however does not appear to be the case. In the experiments of Alluisi *et al.* (1957), using stimuli drawn from ensembles of various sizes, the main limit on performance appeared to be simply the number of stimuli delivered per sec rather than the amount of information conveyed by them. For a constant rate of presentation of information in bits per sec, there was a higher rate of transmission through the man if the stimuli were drawn from a large ensemble and presented slowly rather than from a small ensemble and presented rapidly. Broadly similar results were found by Klemmer and Muller and by Riesz and Deininger (quoted by Garner, 1962, p. 92). More such studies of working rate, rather than lag, are probably needed: especially using changes in the information per stimulus produced by means other than changes in ensemble size. Nevertheless it seems clear that a simple interpretation of changes in lag with stimulus information, as measuring the capacity of the system, cannot be adequate. Human beings must be limited in some other fashion independent of information, which restricts the number of separate actions per sec to two or three. The literature on the psychological refractory period, reviewed by Broadbent (1958, pp. 268–281) is relevant here.

(b) Compatibility and Discriminability

One cannot of course predict the reaction time to a stimulus purely from the probability of that stimulus. Two very important variables are the physical difference between the stimulus and each of the other stimuli which may appear in the situation; and the ease or naturalness of the response which is appropriate to that stimulus. The former problem is that of 'discriminability', and the latter of 'compatibility'.

Discriminability has been studied by a number of investigators from Crossman (1955) to Shallice and Vickers (1964). A particularly comprehensive review is by Welford (1960). It is universally agreed that reaction time, or lag, increases as the various stimuli in a set are made more similar to one another and that the changes are greater when the stimuli become more nearly equal. For a pair of stimuli, the most linear relationship is probably found by plotting response time against the inverse of the logarithm of the ratio of the stimuli. This may be regarded as a modern version of the Weber-Fechner Law, according to which the magnitude of a sensation is a logarithmic function of its physical magnitude. It is interesting that, as yet, there appears to have been little exploration of the implications for reaction time of the Power Law advocated by Stevens (1957). On this view, sensation is an exponential function of physical magnitude. The two laws can be inter-related in various ways (Luce, 1959; Treisman, 1964), but it might nevertheless be possible to improve the prediction of reaction time by taking account of this development. It is clear, however, that attempts to relate reaction time to the difference between two stimuli expressed in informational terms have not, as yet, been as successful as the approach through magnitude of sensation.

The problem of compatibility is even less easy to handle in informational terms. Fitts and his co-workers (Fitts and Seeger, 1953; Fitts and Deininger, 1954) showed that faster reactions were obtained with natural combinations of stimuli and responses; if the left of two buttons is appropriate to the left of two lights, this is an easier task than the right button being appropriate to the left light. Later work has shown however that this advantage is not a constant: it increases for stimuli conveying more information. Thus prolonged practice or an exceptionally natural relationship between stimulus and response may make the usual dependence of reaction time on stimulus information disappear (Mowbray and Rhoades, 1959; Leonard, 1959). Certainly the value of K in the function $k + K \log n$ is reduced by increases in compatibility (Fitts et al., 1963; Broadbent and Gregory, 1965). Thus low compatibility may be compared to noise in the channel, requiring a more lengthy code and reducing the capacity. If K can indeed be reduced to zero, as some experiments show, this would mean that the capacity was now infinite; but as has previously been indicated, there are difficulties in accepting inferences from lag to capacity in any case, and we must therefore regard these experiments as additional evidence against the applicability of straight-forward theorems from information theory to data derived from lags.

(c) General Conclusions on Reaction Time

As in the case of perception, it is quite clear that marked effects on behaviour have been shown in reaction time experiments when the ensemble of possible stimuli has been varied. Furthermore, in this case quantitative relationships have been applied to a greater extent than in perception, and have been quite successful. When pressed to details, however, certain problems arise: performance seems to be limited by a rate of making successive responses independent of the information they convey, by difficulties of discriminating stimuli which are not so far reducible to informational terms, and by the particular mapping of stimuli onto responses which is employed in each experiment.

THE RISE OF DECISION THEORY

(a) The Detection of Signal as opposed to Non-Signal

Since 1954 there has gradually developed another approach to the problems of perception and reaction, which is based primarily upon the analysis of rational decisions in statistical situations rather than upon information theory as originally interpreted. The usual point of origin is taken as the paper of Tanner and Swets (1954) on the detection of simple signals. They contended that a man who was watching or listening for a signal might be regarded as having within him a randomly varying process whose average value was changed by the occurrence of a signal, but which would still vary over a range which might overlap the range of its variation in the absence of a signal. Detection would occur whenever the process exceeded some critical level, whose value was dependent upon the probability of a signal and the rewards or punishments to be expected for the various possible correct and incorrect decisions.

Such a theory places great emphasis on the occurrence of false detections, which are regarded as reflecting essential features of the process rather than the result of superimposed guessing or random events unconnected with detection. The relationship between correct and incorrect detections should, on the Tanner and Swets theory, be quite different from that expected on traditional approaches. In particular, at low rates of false detection, changes in that rate should result in very large changes in the frequency of correct detection. Results supporting this prediction were reported by Tanner and Swets (1954) and in general later work has supported the prediction (Green, 1960). It is particularly well-supported for the observation of signals under conditions resembling real-life tasks of monitoring or inspection work (Broadbent and Gregory, 1963). Possibly experiments under very sensitively controlled conditions may reveal effects of quantal discontinuities in the sensitivity of the senses (Norman, 1963), but even in such cases it is clear that the rate of reporting signals for a given sensory event does depend upon the probabilities and values of the situation.

In general, the more probable a signal is, the more likely are detections both true and false. Equally, the greater the gain from correct detections compared with the loss from false ones, the more detections occur. It is not quite clear however, that the actual performance of such human beings conforms to any suggested decision rule. Approximately, it seems to follow the performance that would arise from a strategy of maximising the average expected gain over a long series of trials (Green, 1960). There are however sizeable remaining deviations from that prediction: people do not detect as many signals as they should when signals are probable, and they detect more than they should when signals are rare.

(b) Choice Between Numerous Alternative Detections

An extension of Tanner and Swets' analysis covers the situation in which there are several alternative signals of which the correct one has to be identified. In this case it may be supposed that each of the alternatives has its own randomly varying process within the man, but only for the correct alternative is the average value of the process shifted. If a sample is taken from each of the processes, the largest value found will probably be from the correct alternative. The larger the number of alternatives, the lower the probability of a correct answer from such a test (Swets, 1959).

This kind of analysis has usually been applied to experiments in which simple signals such as pure tones have been used. In such researches, the alternatives have been, for example, two closely successive time intervals, one of which contains a signal while the other does not. The subject is asked to identify which interval contains the signal. Such a technique is known to give more stable and reproducible results than the 'Yes or No' type of situation considered in the last section. Analysis of both situations by the model so far discussed gives much the same value in both cases for the shift, in the internal process, produced by a signal. It is the changes in the critical value required for a report of 'Yes' which produce the differences between different experiments using the 'Yes–No' method (Swets, 1959).

If changes in the number of alternatives are predicted to give changes in the number of correct reports, it is clear that this kind of model has some possible connection with the effects of vocabulary size on perception, with which we began this paper. An analysis of a number of experiments in vocabulary size shows that the effect of changes in vocabulary is indeed of approximately the form to be expected from the statistical decision model (Green and Birdsall, 1958). It is more difficult to perform an analysis in which one varies the probabilities of some items in a fixed vocabulary. A technique for doing this has however been developed by Luce (1959), using axioms which are rather different from those of Tanner and Swets but which normally lead to closely similar mathematical prediction. It will be interesting to see experimental data analysed in this way.

In general one would expect the number of detections of highly probable signals to be large compared with those of improbable signals, just as one would on the older informational analysis and as we have seen to be empirically the case. An interesting feature of the analysis based on decision or choice is that we would expect the errors to be predominantly choices of probable rather than improbable events: thus in listening to words over a noisy channel the incorrect perceptions should predominantly take the form of frequent rather than infrequent words. The proportion of common words amongst the errors is in fact related in a systematic way to the signal-noise ratio (Pollack, 1962).

(c) Reaction Time in Choice Situations

If a single sample of evidence in a multiple-choice situation, such as those considered in the last section, gives an undesirably high probability of error, a further series of samples will reduce that error. Since as already indicated, a larger ensemble gives a higher error probability, more samples will be needed for a fixed level of accuracy when the ensemble is large. By regarding the reaction time as spent in taking a series of samples, it is possible to produce hypothetical predictions about the change in reaction time with stimulus probability. Stone (1960) showed that the predicted relationship was in fact that reaction time will increase roughly with the logarithm of the size of the response ensemble. At the same time the rate of increase of reaction time depends upon the unreliability of the evidence available in each sample of evidence; if the probability of error is low even with few samples, the reaction time will not increase much as the response ensemble increases. Provided therefore that we regard conditions such as low compatibility as decreasing the reliability of the evidence in favour of any one response, this theory provides a way of explaining the changes in K with compatibility which are found in practice and have already been described.

Stone developed the relationship of reaction time to ensemble size only for the case of a fixed series of samples, the number being decided in advance to give a desired level of error. Such a model is unlikely to be true in this form, because of the fact already mentioned that improbable signals, when they do occur, give responses that are slower than those to probable signals. If the number of samples were fixed in advance, this would not be so. An alternative model was suggested by Stone and developed by Laming (1962), in which each sample is followed by a decision either to react or to take a further sample. Thus the process of sampling continues until the evidence points, with a prescribed degree of confidence, to one reaction as correct. This will take longer for less probable reactions.

An interesting feature of such a model is that the time taken by a response should depend upon the nature of the response and not upon the stimulus which is objectively present. Thus if a man makes a very common reaction correctly to stimulus A and incorrectly to B, the reaction time should be the same. If on the other hand he makes two different reactions to the probable stimulus A, one correct and one both incorrect and improbable the two reaction times will be different. Broadly speaking, though not exactly, this prediction is verified. It is also predicted from the model, and found to be the case, that errors are predominantly of the form that probable responses occur to improbable stimuli rather than the reverse: so that the average reaction time for errors may well be faster than that for correct responses when one ignores the nature of the errors.

CONCLUSIONS

It will be clear from the last section that the introduction of statistical decision theory has allowed us to overcome certain difficulties in the application of information theory to perception and reaction. In particular, it has allowed a more quantitative approach to perceptual problems, and has provided a way round the difficulty of incorporating the effects of compatibility and similar variables into the analysis of reaction times. The two major advances of technique which it has entailed are the study of errors as an inherent part of the process under investigation, and the provision of a place for values and pay-offs. Both of these innovations are clearly justified by results, and the older-style analyses of information which paid little attention to them are thereby superseded.

At the same time this development should be regarded as a sophistication of the approach to human performance through information theory, and not as a discarding of that approach. The emphasis is still upon the man's task as a discrimination between different possible states of his environment, and upon probability as a major variable in deciding the outcome of that discrimination. Indeed, the battle for these causes has been won and no future approach to human performance can neglect them. In the general sense therefore the use of information theory has produced a revolution in psychological thought whose full consequences have not yet been digested; although experiment has disproved naive ideas of a simple representation of the nervous system as a single channel needing no further analysis.

SUMMARY

Experimental work is reviewed on the efficiency of perception of stimuli conveying various amounts of information. Broadly speaking, the nature of the ensemble from which the particular stimulus is drawn has been proved beyond doubt to be an important variable; but quantitative applications of information theory have been less successful. Similarly, experiments on reaction time have established that time often varies with the amount of information being transmitted; in this area numerical predictions have been more successful but there are nevertheless some discrepancies and difficulties. A more recent development has been the application of decision theory as a model for human performance; and this, by emphasising the importance of errors in response, and by providing a place for rewards and losses, seems to be a hopeful line for further advance.

REFERENCES

ALLUISI, E. A., MULLER, P. F., AND FITTS, P. M., (1957); An information analysis of verbal and motor responses in a forced-paced serial task. *J. exp. Psychol.*, **53**, 153–158.

ANDERSON, N. S., AND LEONARD, J. A., (1958); The recognition naming and reconstruction of visual figures as a function of contour redundancy. *J. exp. Psychol.*, **56**, 262–270.

ATTNEAVE, F., (1954); Some informational aspects of visual perception. *Psychol. Rev.*, **61**, 183–193.

BADDELEY, A. D., (1962); *The Coding of Information.* Ph. D. Thesis, University of Cambridge.

BROADBENT, D. E., (1958); *Perception and Communication.* London. Pergamon Press.

BROADBENT, D. E., AND GREGORY, M., (1963); Vigilance considered as a statistical decision. *Brit. J. Psychol.*, **54**, 309–323.

BROADBENT, D. E., AND GREGORY, M., (1965); On the interaction of S-R compatibility with other variables affecting reaction time. *Brit. J. Psychol.*, in press.

COURTIS, M., AND GREEN, R. T., (1963); Information theory and figure perception: the metaphor that failed. *Bull. Brit. Psychol. Soc.*, **16**, 4A (Abstract).

CROSSMAN, E. R. F. W., (1953); Entropy and choice time: the effect of frequency unbalance on choice response. *Quart. J. exp. Psychol.*, **5**, 41–51.

CROSSMAN, E. R. F. W., (1955); The measurement of discriminability. *Quart. J. exp. Psychol.*, **7**, 176–195.

FITTS, P. M., AND DEININGER, R. L., (1954); S-R compatibility: correspondences among paired elements within stimulus and response codes. *J. exp. Psychol.*, **48**, 438–492.

FITTS, P. M., PETERSON, J. R., AND WOLPE, G., (1963); Cognitive aspects of information processing: II. Adjustments to stimulus redundancy. *J. exp. Psychol*, **65**, 507–514.

FITTS, P. M., AND SEEGER, C. M., (1953); S-R compatibility: spatial characteristics of stimulus and response codes. *J. exp. Psychol.*, **46**, 199–210.

FITTS, P. M., WEINSTEIN, M., RAPPAPORT, M., ANDERSON, N., AND LEONARD, J. A., (1956); Stimulus correlates of visual pattern recognition. *J. exp. Psychol.*, **51**, 1–11.

GARNER, W. R., (1962); *Uncertainty and Structure as Psychological Concepts.* London, Wiley.

GREEN, D. M., (1960); Psychoacoustics and detection theory. *J. acoust. Soc. Amer.*, **32**, 1189–1202.

GREEN, D. M., AND BIRDSALL, T. H., (1958); The effect of vocabulary size on articulation score. University of Michigan Electronics Defense Group. Technical Report No. 81.

HICK, W. E., (1952); On the rate of gain of information. *Quart. J. exp. Psychol.*, **4**, 11–26.

HOWES, D., (1957); On the relation between the intelligibility and frequency of occurrence of English words. *J. acoust. Soc. Amer.*, **29**, 296–305.

HYMAN, R., (1955); Stimulus information as a determinant of reaction time. *J. exp. Psychol.*, **45**, 188–196.

LAMING, D. R. J., (1962); A statistical test of a prediction from information theory in a card-sorting situation. *Quart. J. exp. Psychol.*, **14**, 38–48.

LEGGE, C. D., AND SUMMERFIELD, A., (1964); in *Readings in Psychology.* J. M. Cohen, Editor. London. Allen and Unwin.

LEONARD, J. A., (1959); Tactual choice reactions. *Quart. J. exp. Psychol.*, **11**, 76–83.

LUCE, R. D., (1959); *Individual Choice Behavior.* New York. John Wiley and Sons.

MILLER, G. A., HEISE, G. A., AND LICHTEN, W., (1951); The intelligibility of speech as a function of the context of the test materials. *J. exp. Psychol.*, **41**, 329–335.

MOWBRAY, G. H., AND RHOADES, M. V., (1959); On the reduction of choice reaction time with practice. *Quart. J. exp. Psychol.*, **12**, 193–202.

NORMAN, D. A., (1963); Sensory thresholds and response bias. *J. acoust. Soc. Amer.*, **35**, 1432–1441.

POLLACK, I., (1962); Incorrect responses to unknown messages restricted in word frequency. *Lang. and Speech*, **5**, 125–127.

SHALLICE, T., AND VICKERS, D., (1964); Theories and experiments on discrimination times. *Ergonomics*, **7**, 37–50.

STEVENS, S. S., (1957); On the psycho-physical law. *Psychol. Rev.*, **64**, 153–181.

STONE, M., (1960); Models for choice reaction time. *Psychometrika*, **25**, 251–260.

STOWE, A. N., HARRIS, W. P., AND HAMPTON, D. B., (1963); Signal and context components of word-recognition behaviour. *J. acoust. Soc. Amer.*, **35**, 639–644.

SWETS, J., (1959); Indices of signal detectability obtained with various psycho-physical procedures. *J. acoust. Soc. Amer.*, **31**, 511–513.

TANNER, W. P., AND SWETS, J., (1954); A decision-making theory of visual detection. *Psychol. Rev.*, **61**, 401–409.

TREISMAN, M., (1964); Sensory scaling and the psycho-physical law. *Quart. J. exp. Psychol.*, **16**, 11–22.

VERNON, M. D., (1952); *A Further Study of Visual Perception*. Cambridge University Press.

WELFORD, A. T., (1960); The measurement of sensory-motor performance: Survey and reappraisal of twelve years progress. *Ergonomics*, **3**, 189–229.

A Mind's Eye View of the Brain

DONALD M. MACKAY

University of Keele, Department of Communication, Keele, Staffordshire (Great Britain)

INTRODUCTION

Few scientists can have been more successful than Norbert Wiener in arousing the interest of philosophers in the implications of his work. For this reason I have felt it appropriate to offer the following essay as my tribute to his memory. Originally presented at the kind of interdisciplinary seminar* in which Wiener himself so much delighted, it owes much to the stimulus of the ongoing debate that he, Rosenblueth and Bigelow initiated in the early days of 'artificial intelligence' (Rosenblueth *et al.*, 1943).

1. MIND-TALK, BRAIN-TALK, COMPUTER-TALK

The time-honoured problem of relating mind and brain has recently received a new twist with the evolution of artefacts capable of mind-like behaviour. In the old days the philosopher had to juggle with two kinds of discourse, which might be called for short 'mind-talk' and 'brain-talk'. Now, in the last twenty-odd years, these have been joined by a third species — let us call it 'computer-talk' — which mingles untidily with each and gives rise in its turn to a fresh crop of philosophical problems and pseudo-problems.

How are these three related? How can we discipline our talk in the three domains so as at least to avoid nonsense, if not to produce sense?

This is the topic of the present paper. If it has a thesis, it is that although there is scope and need for semantic discipline to clarify our thinking, there remains in this area a real issue — a genuine mystery, if you like — and not only a pseudo-problem to be covered over by what amounts to a linguistic bluff.

Let us begin at grass roots, by asking ourselves: If we had no traditional sophisticated assumptions, and were starting from scratch, what are the *prime* facts in this area, on which we would have to base our ideas? How do we move out from these prime facts into extrapolative beliefs, into speculations, and so forth? I am aware, of course, that we cannot divest ourselves of all presuppositions, so that ultimately we cannot answer our question with any assurance. But the effort itself will be useful, I think, towards a realistic perspective.

---

* I am greatly indebted to the RAND Corporation for assistance in transcribing the talk, given in their Santa Monica Laboratories, on which this chapter is based.

References p. 332

The basic fact for each of us, of course, is *ourselves*. A trite remark, perhaps: yet to agree on taking ourselves, rather than our brains, as our ontological starting point, makes a considerable difference to the way the argument goes, as we shall see. As 'selves' we find our experience compounded of two main, broad categories in varying proportions. On the one hand, things happen *to* us: we undergo, or suffer. On the other, we *do* things: we act, and react. We find our efforts to act limited and constrained; and out of our experiences of 'undergoing' and 'constraint' we form and develop our idea of an external world; we *perceive* and *learn*.

These basic experiences (though not necessarily our inferences from them) are typical of the notions which for each of us are, in a radical sense, indubitable. They are as it were the rock foundations upon which even the business of doubting has to be erected. To paraphrase Descartes, if anyone says 'I doubt whether I exist', you don't answer with an argument, but with a question: 'Well then, who is doubting?'. 'Mind-talk' has a peculiar priority over any other kind of talk, for it is the language in which doubts themselves have ultimately to be expressed.

From this simple-minded starting-point, we meet our problem in the fact that when *we* suffer, act, learn and so forth, there are those among us — the physiologists, information theorists and so on — who tell us, perhaps with a bit of guesswork, but plausibly, a story about correlated brain events. Physically stimulating parts of the brain, for example, can as we say 'give rise to' experience; conversely, certain types of experience (including thinking as well as doing) 'give rise to' or shall we say 'are accompanied by' physical brain-events of the sort that physiologists can register. This then is our problem — to make the right kind of connection between this story in 'brain-talk' and the story in 'mind-talk' which we take as our ontological starting point.

2. PERCEPTION

Let us first consider the perceptual side. I open my eyes, my occipital cortex is stimulated, I see a world of objects. How can we connect these facts? Is it proper to say, for example, that I am 'really' witnessing my brain activity? Is perceiving some kind of internal *observation* of incoming signals from our sense organs? Until recently this was taken for granted by most physiologists, and it is still a respectable view today. It may therefore be worth while to give one or two examples of the difficulties to which it can lead in psychophysiology.

Consider first the problem of the perception of the intensity of a stimulus. If one asks a subject to estimate, say, the brightness of a light by putting a number to it, most subjects choose numbers related to the physical intensity according to a power law. This is 'Stevens' Law', (Stevens, 1957, 1961).

Now it has been known for a long time that, in general, the physiological response of a sense organ is not power-law related, but roughly logarithmically related, to the intensity of the stimulus, I, so that the firing frequency $f = k \log I$ over a certain range. What is more, if one derives a scale of 'subjective intensity' as Fechner (1862) did, by assuming that just noticeable differences (jnd's) are subjectively equal, then since most jnd's are proportional to physical intensity the resulting scale is logarithmic.

On the presupposition that perception is the observation of incoming impulses, it was perhaps natural to take Fechner's law as a corroboration of the physiological law. Accordingly when Stevens produced his power law, both he and his opponents tended to interpret it as throwing doubt on the logarithmic law of receptor response.

I am not now concerned with the facts of the dispute, but only to point out the part played in it by philosophical presuppositions. Once one drops the idea that perception is the witnessing of incoming signals, the problem loosens up, and there is no difficulty in finding a model (MacKay, 1963a) which can find room for Stevens' power-law on the assumption of logarithmic receptor characteristics.

Another illustration is offered by the problem of the stability of the perceived world. During voluntary eye-movement the image of the world moves on the retina, but one gets little or no impression that the world is moving. If however one produces rotation by pressing very lightly on the open eyelid, then the same rotation gives a strong impression of motion. This has led to elaborate theories of 'cancellation' of the shifts in the retinal image, implying that in the voluntary case there must be some neural discharge which in effect moves the optical image backwards by the amount by which it was voluntarily displaced. A cancellation mechanism of this sort is often used in a radar display, where, of course, there *is* an operator witnessing, on an internal screen, an image of the external world. In ship-borne radar, for instance, if the ship turns, the radar map will rotate visibly unless one cancels out the effect of ship rotation by rotating the input to the tube backwards by the same amount. That maintains the stability of the map.

There are physiological difficulties in applying this sort of idea to the visual system. One of them is the accuracy that one would need in order to account for the subjectively observed stability. But the point I want to make is that if we drop this idea that perception is the witnessing of incoming signals, and instead think of perception as an internal *adaptive reaction* to the demands made by the world by way of the receptive organs (MacKay, 1956), then this internal adaptive reaction can remain invariant under voluntary movement precisely *because* the optical image swings. The swinging of the optical image in a voluntary movement is part of the *goal* of the movement. When we look from one point to another, the optical motion that takes place is not a *disturbance* of our organization-to-react; on the contrary, the *absence* of it would be a disturbance — the occurrence of it is part of what we sought to achieve, by moving our eye. On this view, therefore, the stability of the perceived world does not require cancellation in the sense of a backward shift of the image (MacKay, 1962a). Here again, once one drops the idea that in perception an internal ghost witnesses a display screen somewhere in the brain, this loosens up some physiological knots.

A third illustration of the practical importance of such presuppositions may be taken from the phenomena of illusory perception. Consider for example the familiar 'waterfall effect'. After gazing for some seconds at a steadily moving surface such as that of a waterfall, one finds that a stationary surface appears to be in motion in the opposite direction. The odd thing, however, is that what one sees is *motion without displacement*. Although every point in the field previously stimulated by the moving surface seems to be moving, one is simultaneously aware that its position is unchanged.

References p. 332

In terms of an 'internal image' of the world, of course, this makes no sense. No unitary physical *display* could exhibit this dissociation between velocity and change of position, familiar though it is as a formal device in physics. Once we drop the idea of a 'screen of consciousness', however, and think of perception as the internal 'updating' of the organizing system to match incoming stimuli, the problem assumes a more tractable form. Relieved of the need to re-integrate all optical information in a unitary display, we can readily envisage how different features of an optical image (such as motion, or position) might be filtered off to evoke or modify adaptive responses in quite different circuits of the integrated organizing system. It then becomes easy to see how abnormal adaptation of the sub-system handling one such feature (such as motion) might give rise to mutually conflicting perceptions (incompatible adjustments of different circuits of the organizing system).

What I have tried to show by these examples is that the examination of our philosophical presuppositions in this area *makes sense* for anyone who wants to understand perception. This is not just 'table talk'; it can make a difference to the kinds of scientific theory one puts forward and the kinds of folly one is likely to commit or avoid.

I could perhaps summarise the approach that I have found helpful under four heads:

(1) Be *operational* — formulate problems, wherever possible, in terms of events and activities rather than abstract entities. This is a lesson that physicists had to learn in the field of atomic physics, and it seems profitable here too. There is of course no question in this of *debunking* such entities as the mind (an unutterable folly of self-defeat). It is simply that the prime data to which we can point — the phenomena that are least dubitable — are on the whole denoted by hyphenated expressions for activities or events such as 'perceiving-motion' or 'seeing-a-table' or 'making-up-one's-mind'; so that if we want to take the firmest grasp of our problem without begging questions we will be wise to treat these as semantic *units* (*i.e.* without breaking up the hyphens) for as long as possible.

(2) Occam's principle — Be *economical*. Specifically, in thinking of perception, let us not *begin* by presupposing two sets of events, one 'physical', the other 'mental', in some kind of interaction. We should rather explore first the possibility that the physical or 'outside' story and the mental or 'inside' story give two aspects of one and the same set of events, unitary in nature even though logically richer than either 'outside' or 'inside' language alone can encompass. It would seem wise to make no more ontological 'splits', in our thought-model of what goes on in perception, than are necessitated by the data.

(3) Look for correlations between 'outside' and 'inside' stories in terms of *information-processing*. The language and ideas of the theory of information and control have the right kind of hybrid status to serve as a conceptual bridge, enabling data gleaned in physiological terms to bear upon hypotheses in psychological terms, and *vice versa*. One of the reasons for the popularity (if not over-popularity) of information jargon is this real advantage which it offers, by enabling us to journey between the two domains of discourse and, in principle, to make statements in the one which

are vulnerable to test in the other. Perhaps Norbert Wiener's greatest contribution to science was his vision of the timeliness and fruitfulness of such interdisciplinary traffic.

(4) Finally, in relation to perception in particular, I have been suggesting that we look for the physical correlate of perceiving not in the receptive area of the brain, but rather in the organizing system which prepares and maintains the 'conditional readiness' of the organism for the state of affairs giving rise to the received signals. On this basis to perceive something (say an object in one's path) is to respond by internal adaptation to it (setting up *conditional* readinesses to avoid it, grasp it, describe it, etc. in case of need); and the unity or 'wholeness' of an object as perceived reflects the integration of the 'state of conditional readiness' to match the stimuli from it.

Although this principle embodies a hypothesis, it can be supported on grounds of informational economy. Since the function of perception is to keep up to date the total organizing system, there would be 100% redundancy between this updating activity and the contents of any internal display. It thus seems natural to ask whether the updating system itself could not serve to represent, implicitly, the world to which it adapts, so eliminating the redundancy. On this basis, the world would be internally represented in terms of the pattern of demand (actual or conditional) which it imposes on the perceiver (MacKay, 1956). In analysing the brain we would then expect to find something in the nature of a *closed* flow-map; not a mere transmitting system with 'terminals' at which the mind might be imagined as witnessing neural events, but rather a *behaving whole* whose uptodate readiness to act in the current situation *betokens* (or gives evidence of) perceiving.

3. ACTION

Let me now turn more briefly to the correlative problem. As well as 'undergoing', we act, we do things, we decide things. In terms of the 'two-entity' view of the brain as a kind of chariot for the mind, this might be supposed to raise the question, how do I control my brain? If I am the charioteer, what are the reins, what are the control links between me and the chariot which is my brain? It is easy enough, perhaps, to laugh at this as out of date, though I don't think it was as absurd as we might be tempted to think, since I am not sure that any alternative we can propose has anything yet in the nature of *empirical* evidence to make it more attractive. The attraction of a 'two aspect' view, I think, is conceptual rather than empirical. What I do want to suggest, however, that a big question is begged — in other words, we are going beyond the evidence unnecessarily — if we pose the problem in this form.

There is in fact a prior question to be asked: Is it proper to think of our deciding as an *intervention* in our brain's control system? Here, indeed, there is (negative) empirical evidence in the sense that, little though we understand of the details of the brain as yet, there are no signs of any gaps of the right sort, in any of the control mechanisms of the brain, for intervention of this kind. The working hypothesis of physiology, of course, is that there are no such gaps; that if we could trace the information-flow-paths of control in the brain, then we should not find any open loops; but that on the contrary, a closed-loop system would account for all we now know of the way in which the brain behaves, even in processes such as deciding and doing. No gaps here for the action of the mind as an extra force.

As before, the alternative would seem to be to treat deciding, like perceiving, or suffering, as a complex *unity*. We have no grounds for postulating two sets of events, one mental, one physical, with tenuous links between. All our evidence so far justifies only treating human agency as a unity, which however does have two undeniably distinct *aspects* — again, the inside aspect, which is what I feel and know when I am making a decision, and the outside aspect, which is what the physiologist might see if he had the means of looking inside my head. Here would seem to be a tolerable middle way between two extreme positions, both of which can land us in philosophical trouble. One, as we have seen, is dualism, in the sense of belief in a duality of 'stuffs' — mind stuff, brain stuff, and causal interaction between them — for which I am suggesting there is no justification in such evidence as we have. The other, however, which can be equally pestiferous, is reductionism — the kind of reductionism which claims that if we can get a complete story at the brain level, then we don't *need* mental categories at all. Once we have the complete brain story, we can discard mind-talk as an out-of-date relic of the development of thought, or what have you.

In its extreme form, of course, such an argument is open to rather short and effective answers; but my point here is that we do not have to choose between these extremes. Each side, I believe, is seeking to conserve a real truth about man. The reductionist recognizes the autonomy of explanatory behavioural principles at the physical level. The dualist recognizes that the reality of what it is to be an agent is richer — has more to it — than can be described either in mind talk or in brain talk alone. Our suggestion is that it is a mistake to regard these emphases as contradictory. It is not extra-physical *forces* that we must admit in justice to the facts that dualism wants to express, but additional *logical dimensions*, further aspects of the situation, requiring personal categories which are still necessary when we have exhaustively said all we can at the physical level.

4. IS MIND-TALK AN OPTIONAL EXTRA?

But, it may be asked, are these extras really necessary, or are they merely optional? Clearly, there are difficulties about my denying my own mental activity; and it is to the testimony of other people — recognized *as such* — that I have to appeal for corroboration of any scientific story about my brain. But is this recognition of my mental activity optional for other people? Could other people say of us that it is purely optional, whether they recognize us as persons, as distinct from physical systems open to physical explanation?

In so far as the people concerned can keep themselves safely isolated from us, there would seem to be no logical compulsion on them to recognize more than our physical aspect. In principle (we may assume) they could acquire a complete explanatory specification of our physical state, in sufficient detail to account for all our behaviour external or internal. The odd thing, however, is that if they are prepared to contemplate talking to us in anything like a genuine dialogue, then in that situation they would no longer have the option to regard us as fully specifiable physical systems. The reason is that, in dialogue, 'interaction terms' appear in the physical state-description of two individuals as a result of their informational coupling, so that neither can acquire a *complete* and uptodate specification of the other (Popper, 1950; MacKay, 1954, 1957). Indeed, in the common language-system of their dialogue, *no complete physical specification of either exists* upon which they could rightly agree. Any attempt at such agreement would be necessarily self-frustrating in detail, even if their respective brains were as mechanical as clockwork (MacKay, 1964).

To put the same point in another way, any *complete* description of us in brain talk would inevitably have its validity depend on whether or not we believed it. Any change in what we believe presumably necessitates a correlated change in the state of our brain as viewed from the outside. A complete description of our brain, therefore, would either be valid on condition that we did not believe it, or, alternatively, would not become valid unless we believed it. In neither case, therefore, can we say that there exists a complete specification in the common language, which is equally binding on us whether we know it or not, and whether we believe it or not (as, for example, the statement, '13 is a prime number', is equally binding on us whether we believe it or not). There are no 'take-it-or-leave-it' complete descriptions of our brain in the present or the future tense, in the common language (MacKay, 1963).

It is for this reason that it is hopelessly fallacious to suppose that we can use physical descriptive language to supersede the mind-talk dimension, as it were, of our descriptions of one another in the common language. This is not a live option. There is no complete mechanical alternative account of our brain, in the sense of a current story that we would be correct to agree upon, and that is binding on us as a matter of fact whether we believe it or not*.

Here I think we come to the real mystery of this situation, the real problem, which talk about 'mind acting on brain' and the like has only tended to obscure. It would seem that here we have to revise our very notion of what constitutes an explanation. In any other domain we are accustomed to assume the existence in principle of an exhaustive, external physical-type causal description, which, given the axioms of physics and so on, constitutes an explanation. No such explanation can be given, however, no such explanation exists in full detail, *for* us now *about* us now. This is why, basically, there is an irreducible mystery about each of us as describable in the common language. It is not possible, even in principle, to find an exhaustive explanation of actions that we are now taking or a prediction of actions that we have not yet chosen which would be equally binding on us whether we believed it or not.

Granted then that mental categories cannot be ousted by the most sanguine of wishful thinking in physical terms, we have still to ask which categories are appropriate in any given situation. If we want to avoid nonsense, it is not a matter of asking, which

---

* *In retrospect*, of course, we may agree upon such a story; but our agreement does not mean that we would have been correct to believe that story *at the time*: quite the contrary.

categories do I prefer? The *kind* of question we ask determines the kind of category that is relevant. If you ask me 'why did you choose to do such and such', then the categories in terms of which I can offer you a meaningful answer are the categories of option, preference, motive, responsibility, and so on. It is no good my saying, 'I chose to do that because my brain went through such and such motions'. That would amount to a logical howler, like saying '2x + 3 = 5 because the chalk on the blackboard makes it so'. If we write down an equation on the blackboard in chalk, we can certainly say that *were it not for the chalk*, with that particular form, we would not have before us the equation 2x + 3 = 5; but we cannot say that the justification of the statement '2x + 3 = 5' has anything to do with the chalk. The two levels of description are related; they are necessary correlates of one another; but questions asked in the language of the one cannot be meaningfully answered in the language of the other. In cases of physical damage to the brain, we may have to recognize an explanation of an action at a physical level as more meaningful and relevant than any attempt to discuss it in mental terms; but even then we must recognize that what we are so doing is to *reject* the personal question rather than to answer it; and the burden of proof is on us to show that the malfunction is in fact such as to make personal categories inapplicable.

In all other cases, we have to stick to the conceptual level at which a question is framed in order to find a meaningful answer, let alone the true one. Specifically, this means that if we want to use language consistently, we cannot say that *brains* think or decide or do any such things. It is *people* who think or decide. Brains do those physical things appropriate in their own logical dimensions as correlates of what people do when deciding, thinking, feeling, hoping, fearing, believing, and so forth.

5. COMPUTER-TALK AND MIND-TALK

Finally, what light does this sort of analysis throw on the relation between computer talk and mind talk? Can we say, for example, that computing machines think? We can, of course, define 'machine' as we like; but if 'machine' is defined as it usually is, as something logically at the same level as the word 'brain' — in other words, an apparatus of cells and things, — then clearly the answer is 'No'. This is not because of the limitations of what machines can do, but because this use of language does not make sense, any more than it makes sense to say that *brains* think.

Note however that this does not — or at least should not – eliminate the intellectual 'itch' behind our question; it only drives us to frame it more carefully. The proper question, a perfectly good one, is, 'Can a machine do anything that a brain can do?' —quite a different question. All kinds of stupid arguments can be avoided if we discipline ourselves to ask it in that way. Can a machine do what a brain does? The answer given by most of us, I suppose, would be that if we ever achieved the physiologist's model of the (complete) brain, we would expect it to be able to do all that a brain does; so why should not an artificially contrived equivalent of the model do the same? If we accept the goal of neurophysiology, I can see no reason to doubt that in principle some artificially contrived mechanism could do what a brain does. This leaves open the question whether in the end we might have to contrive it in protoplasm, and whether in the end it would not be cheapest to contrive it by growing it *in utero*. Philosophically this seems of minor interest; it would be rather feeble to rest a philosophical case on mere technical inability to contrive an artificially organized information-system with the same information-flow structure as a human brain.

Two difficulties, however, we must not paper over. First, it is all very well to say that a machine can do what the brain does; but this immediately invites the question, what are we trying to claim that the brain does? Once we face that one realistically, we discover a much more profound problem. Is there any guarantee in fact that we *can* ever *exhaust* a specification of what the brain does? (MacKay, 1952, p. 86). We can, of course, specify all the things we can think of, which we have *observed* the brain to do; but by what algorithm are we going to make sure that we have left nothing out? Is not this in fact an ongoing process? Is it not likely to be as indefinitely ongoing as the process of exhausting the physical description of the universe, which the physicist is engaged on in other dimensions? We try to produce a fair specification of the things that *so far* we have noticed that the brain does. On the basis of it we make predictions; and inevitably — as in all other branches of science — we will find discrepancies. Eventually after a generation or two we wake up to the fact that, after all, there is another way of specifying what the brain does which we had not yet thought of. This has certainly been the story in physics — new ways of specifying 'what matter does' keep cropping up. So do not let us get the idea that we have brain imitation in our pocket just because, in principle, any specification we write can be programmed on a universal machine.

Secondly, although *given time* a suitably programmed universal machine can perform any specified task, this gives no guarantee that we could get any such machine, however large, to simulate all the multiple interactions in a brain *simultaneously*, and in *real time*, since the speed of electrical signals is finite. It may well be that only a special-purpose 'analogue' mechanism could meet all detailed needs with the required speed. It is for this reason, rather than from any mystical views of what happens when carbon and hydrogen get together, that I have speculated whether protoplasm might not turn out after all to offer the only adequate building material. More and more physiological evidence is accumulating that spatial relationships between neural components, and the properties of the intervening medium, can matter even more than the circuit wiring diagram. Without accepting all the stories about what happens to flatworms when you train them and then feed them on one another, there is enough evidence in this general area to suggest that we on the circuit side had better be very cautious before we insist that the kind of information processing that a brain does can be replicated in a realisable circuit. Some kind of 'wet' engineering may turn out to be inevitable.

If we grant for the sake of argument that some machine might be able to copy the brain, we have still to ask whether a *computer* does what brains do. When a digital computer solves a problem, is it doing what human brains do when they solve problems? I must confess that I doubt it. I think it would be fair — fair to the computer — to say that a computer does, and of course is designed to do, what people do with tokens and counters: not what their brains do, but what their *hands* do. This is what makes computers relevant to thinking at all.

Let me explain what I mean. Suppose we set up an abacus, a bead frame. These beads are bits of wood. What have they to do with thinking? Only that *we* set them up as tokens for the ideas of numbers. We push these bits of wood around as an aid to our thinking — manipulating tokens for ideas according to the rules of our calculation. If we now set up an electronic device to push pulses of electricity around instead of bits of wood, the principle is not affected. We can properly say that computers *manipulate tokens* for ideas in the way that people's hands do. But there is no need to press on behalf of the computer the claim that it does what our brains do. What we do with our hands as an aid in the process of our thinking may have no direct resemblance to the physiological information flow in our brains.

To see this point from another angle, consider the many everyday physical situations which simulate the elementary operations of a digital computer. When rain falls on a sloping windowpane, for example, it may easily happen that one (larger) drop falls off for every two incident raindrops. Such a situation could in principle be combined with others of the same sort to form a binary counter or indeed any 'logic-element' of a digital computer.

Are we then to say that this window is thinking? Is it doing arithmetic in the scale of two? If so, think of all the mountainsides in the world where rain is falling down rock faces so that, if not in the scale of two then in some other scale, arithmetic is also being done! All that distinguishes the operations in a computer from these is the fact that *for somebody* the computer's operations *betoken* ideas. Apart from this they are as devoid of mental significance as a shower of rain*.

What then of remembering? One need not lose much adrenalin over the metaphorical usage of the computer engineer who talks about a computer's 'memory'. He is poetically minded, but he knows the thing he is talking about, and it probably does no harm. If we are trying to think realistically about the relation between computer-talk and mind-talk, however, then to speak of a computer as 'remembering' is as much nonsense as to speak of brains remembering or computers thinking. We could as well say that when a stone rolls down a mountainside and lies where it falls, it 'remembers' where it has fallen: or that the earth, on which it has made a dent, 'remembers' the impact of the stone. Sheer animism! Remembering is something that *people* do. A change of the magnetic state of a core in the computer need no more be an instance of 'remembering' than a dent in the earth when a stone falls on it down a mountainside. Animistic superstition, I think, is a real trap here. If we want to be precise about what a computer's store does, we might liken it to a notebook and pencil. Notebooks do not remember; *we* remember. We may revive old memories by associating ideas

---

* Note that we are here discussing a computer as the tool of a man. The computing operations in a goal-seeking automaton are in a different category, since they may be said to betoken the ideas of the 'artificial agent' so embodied.

with the marks in our notebook but we don't (I suppose) attribute animistic thoughts or memories to it on that account.

Finally there is the question of personality. Do computers have personalities? If we pull a curtain round a computer and talk to it, its output can indeed resemble what comes out of a man with a certain personality. But if we want to argue that therefore the computer has a personality, we had better be careful. The programme of a general-purpose computer is strictly analogous to a book of rules. It would therefore be possible in principle to enjoy the same 'dialogue' (save for the curtain) by looking up the rule book oneself instead of employing a computer to do so. Where now is the 'personality'? Lurking in the rule-book?

It seems clear that in such talk there is a real danger of a new kind of superstition, which can do harm to the field of artificial intelligence if we do not eradicate it. The way to eradicate it, I suggest, is to keep our lines of thought straight by respecting the distinction between different levels of concepts, and not trying to claim for something at one level an attribute that makes sense only at the other. In short my plea is for more semantic hygiene, and in particular that we should recognize that mere imitation of external operations is not enough to justify the attribution of mentalistic properties. I have suggested elsewhere (MacKay 1962b, 1964) that before an artificial agent could meaningfully have personal qualities predicated of it, it must be so organized that it can act in our world and display goals which are potentially in *conflict* with ours. It is out of potential goal conflict, I think, that the discipline of language arises and the recognition of one another's personalities emerges. Even then, however, I would emphasize that this is only a necessary, and not by any means a sufficient condition for the validity of mind-talk in relation to the artificial situation.

In conclusion, may I say that what impresses me more and more is the element of irreducible mystery that attends our human condition — a mystery which the fullest of physiological understanding would not dispel. As we have seen, the necessity for 'mind-talk' cannot be removed by any appeal to 'brain-talk', since no adequate substitute for it exists in these terms. In the end, in line with ancient wisdom, we have to face an irreducible dualism in our own nature — not, of necessity, a dualism of 'stuffs', but a dualism of aspect which no mechanistic analysis can exhaust.

SUMMARY

The age-old problem of relating 'mind-talk' and 'brain-talk' has been given a new twist by the advent of computers for which mind-like powers are claimed. This paper examines the relation between brain processes, perception and action, and between each of these and the capabilities of artefacts.

The view of perception as the 'witnessing' of brain-processes is criticised on psychological as well as philosophical grounds. Similar objections are raised to the conception of the agent as 'controlling' brain processes. What is contended, however, is not that brain and mind are identical, but rather that the undeniable dualism of human nature is one of 'aspect' rather than of 'stuff'. Mental and physical categories are logically complementary, and careless mixing of them can lead to nonsense.

References p. 332

It is suggested that some claims made for computers are nonsensical in this respect. Neither brains nor computers (*qua* physical systems) think, feel, perceive, decide etc. These are the activities of people, not of brains. This does not mean that the artificial production of conscious beings is necessarily impossible, but only that it is not guaranteed merely by the imitation of conscious bodily behaviour; even our ability to specify the requisite behaviour remains to be shown.

REFERENCES

FECHNER, G. T., (1862); *Elemente der Psychophysik*. Leipzig. Breitkopf and Härtel. (pp. 584–560)

MACKAY, D. M., (1951); Mindlike behaviour in artefacts. *Brit. J. Phil. Sci.*, **2**, 105–121; **3**, 352–253.

MACKAY, D. M., (1952); Mentality in machines. (Third paper in symposium). *Proc. Aristotelian Soc.* Suppl., **26**, 61–86.

MACKAY, D. M., (1954); On comparing the brain with machines. *Advanc. Sci.*, **40**, 402–406; reprinted in *Amer. Scientist*, **42**, 261–268; and *Ann. Rept. Smithsonian Inst.*, 1954, 231–240.

MACKAY, D. M., (1956); Towards an information-flow model of human behaviour. *Brit. J. Psychol.*, **47**, 30–43.

MACKAY, D. M., (1957); Brain and Will. *The Listener*, May 9 & 16; reprinted in *Body and Mind*, G. N. A. Vesey, Editor. Allen and Unwin (pp. 392–402).

MACKAY, D. M., (1958); Complementarity II. *Proc. Aristotelian Soc.* Suppl. **32**, 105–122.

MACKAY, D. M., (1962a); *Theoretical Models of Space Perception. Aspects of the Theory of Artificial Intelligence*. C. A. Muses, Editor. New York. Plenum Press. (pp. 83–104).

MACKAY, D. M., (1962b); The use of behavioural language to refer to mechanical processes. *Brit. J. Phil. Sci.*, **13**, 89–103.

MACKAY, D. M., (1963a); Psychophysics of perceived intensity: A theoretical basis for Fechner's and Stevens' laws. *Science*, **139**, 1213–1216.

MACKAY, D. M., (1963b); Indeterminacy, uncertainty and information-content. *Nachr. techn. Z.*, **16**, 617–620.

MACKAY, D. M., (1964); Communication and meaning — a functional approach. *Cross-Cultural Understanding: Epistemology in Anthropology*. F. S. C. Northrop and H. Livingston, Editors. New York, Harper and Row. (pp. 162–179).

POPPER, K. R., (1950); Indeterminism in classical and quantum physics. *Brit. J. Phil. Sci.*, **1**, 117–133, 173–195.

ROSENBLUETH, A., WIENER, N., AND BIGELOW, J., (1943); Behaviour, Purpose and Teleology. *Philosophy of Science*, **10**, 19–24.

STEVENS, S. S., (1957); On the psychophysical law. *Psychol. Rev.*, **64**, 153–181.

STEVENS, S. S., (1961); Psychophysics of sensory function. *Sensory Communication*. W. A. Rosenblith, Editor. New York, M.I.T. and Wiley (pp. 806–813).

Mathematical Models for Verbal Learning

R. C. CALFEE, R. C. ATKINSON and T. SHELTON, JR.

Stanford University, Institute for Mathematical Studies in the Social Sciences,
Ventura Hall, Stanford, Calif. (U.S.A.)

The use of language is perhaps the most distinctive feature of human behavior. At an early age we learn the appropriate words for the objects and events which surround us, as well as how to communicate our needs and feelings to other people. As we grow older we develop associative relations of varying complexity among the words in our vocabulary, as for example in the use of grammatical rules to form sentences. To illustrate a simple type of verbal association, suppose someone asks you to respond with the first word that comes to mind when he says 'cat'; your response will probably be 'dog' or perhaps 'rat'. If he says 'black', undoubtedly you will say 'white'. The problem facing a french student, on the other hand, is to learn to respond to 'dog' with 'le chien' and to 'black' with 'noir'. The laboratory study of how such verbal associations are formed, in addition to having practical implications, has played an important role in testing theoretical ideas about the nature of the learning process. It is this last matter which will chiefly concern us in this paper, and we will concentrate our attention on a particular kind of verbal learning problem known as *paired-associate learning*.

In paired-associate learning, the subject learns to give the correct response as each stimulus from a list of stimulus items is presented. In the experiments considered in this paper, the subject is informed in advance of what responses he may use. He is then shown the stimuli one at a time in a random order, and is asked to guess which of the responses has been designated as the correct answer for that particular stimulus. After the response is made, the subject is told the correct answer and then the next stimulus is presented. After the entire list of stimulus items has been presented, the experimenter rearranges the items in a new random order and again presents the list to the subject. As each item is shown to him, the subject attempts to anticipate the correct response, following which he is informed of the right answer. Each run through the list constitutes a *trial*, and when the subject is told the correct answer, we will speak of this event as a *reinforcement*.

An example of one such paired-associate study is an experiment by Atkinson and Crothers (1964), in which the stimulus items were 18 Greek letters and the responses were three nonsense syllables, RIX, FUB, and GED. Each response was paired with six stimuli, so that the three responses were used equally often as the correct answer. Figure 1 presents the proportion of correct anticipations on each trial for this study.

References p. 348

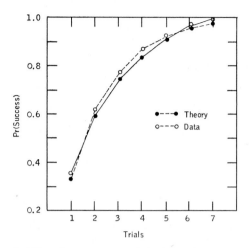

Fig. 1. The average probability of a success on trial *n* in Atkinson and Crothers' experiment.

On the first trial, the proportion of successes is very close to the value of 0.33 to be expected if the subject simply chose one of the responses at random as each stimulus was presented. The curve rises exponentially and gradually approaches an asymptotic value of 1, *i.e.*, eventually only correct anticipations occur.

One of the first theoretical attempts to account for data of this sort assumed that the effect of each reinforcement was to add an increment to the strength of the association between the stimulus and the correct response. Suppose that the probability of a correct anticipation on trial *n*, which will be denoted $\Pr(c_n)$, is taken as an estimate of the associative strength on trial *n*. The probability of an error on trial *n*, $\Pr(e_n)$, is an indication of how much remains to be learned. The basic assumption that is made in the 'incremental' theory is that the effect of the reinforcement on trial *n* is to increase the probability of a correct response by an amount which is a constant proportion θ of the amount remaining to be learned, *i.e.*,

$$\Pr(c_{n+1}) = \Pr(c_n) + \theta \Pr(e_n). \tag{1a}$$

Thus, every time a subject is told the correct answer to a stimulus item, there is an increase in the probability that the correct answer will be given when the item is presented again. Notice that this increase does not depend upon whether the correct or incorrect answer is given. Using the fact that $\Pr(e_{n+1}) = 1 - \Pr(c_{n+1})$, Eq. 1a may be rewritten as

$$\Pr(c_{n+1}) = (1 - \theta) \Pr(c_n) + \theta. \tag{1b}$$

In this form it is easy to see that the probability of a correct response on trial $n + 1$ is assumed to be a linear function of the probability on the preceding trial, and hence this model frequently is referred to as a *linear* model. The properties of this model have been extensively investigated (Bush and Mosteller, 1955; Estes and Suppes, 1959; Sternberg, 1963). In particular, it can be shown that $\Pr(c_n)$ may be written as a function of the parameter θ and g, (the guessing probability on trial 1 which will be the reciprocal of the number of responses); namely

$$\text{Pr}(c_n) = 1 - (1 - g)(1 - \theta)^{n-1}. \tag{2}$$

A derivation of Eq. 2 as the solution of the linear difference equation given in Eq. 1b may be found in any of the references above.

The theoretical curve in Fig. 1 was obtained from Eq. 2 with θ equal to 0.42, and it agrees very closely with the observed values. It is important ro realize that the learning process for each individual item in the list is represented by Eq. 2. That is, if the probability of a correct response for a given stimulus item could be measured by some hypothetical 'probability meter', the course of learning would resemble measurements from an analogue device such as a variable resistor operating in the following manner. On trial 1, the probability measurement would be equal to the guessing rate g, and on each succeeding trial the probability value would gradually move upward by some amount, as if the knob of the resistor were being turned in the same direction on each trial by an exponentially decreasing amount.

There have been objections to this type of representation of the learning process on several grounds. For example, some psychologists have argued that while very simple organisms might behave in this fashion, higher animals, especially when confronted with more complex problems, show learning of an *all-or-none* sort. It is not our intention to go into the history of the controversy concerning the relative merits of continuous and discontinuous characterizations of the learning process. (For some recent contributions to the issue see Bower, 1962; Estes, 1964; and Underwood and Keppel, 1962). Rather, we want to consider a model that assumes that learning is all-or-none, and then look at the kinds of differential predictions made by the two types of models.

Following the analogy between the linear model and a variable resistor, the all-or-none model may be represented by a two-position switch which operates in this manner: initially the switch is in the 'unlearned' position and responses are made at random from the available response set. After each reinforcement the switch is turned from the 'unlearned' to the 'learned' position with probability a, whereas with probability $1 - a$ the switch remains in the 'unlearned' position. Once the switch has been turned to the 'learned' position, it remains there, and the correct response is always given. More specifically, the model may be formulated as a two-state Markov process in which an item is assumed to be in the unlearned state U at the start of the experiment. When the subject is informed of the correct response to be associated with an item, then with probability a learning occurs, and there is a transition to the learned state L, whereas with probability $1 - a$, the item remains in state U. If an item is in state U, then the probability of a correct response is g, the guessing probability. Once an item is learned, however, then there will be no subsequent errors. These assumptions are incorporated in the matrix below, which specifies the transition probabilities between the two states U and L from trial n to trial $n + 1$, and the response vector which gives the probability of a correct response in each of the states:

$$
\begin{array}{cc}
 & \begin{array}{cc} L_{n+1} & U_{n+1} \end{array} \qquad \text{Pr(Success)} \\
\begin{array}{c} L_n \\ U_n \end{array} & \begin{bmatrix} 1 & 0 \\ a & 1-a \end{bmatrix} \qquad\quad \begin{bmatrix} 1 \\ g \end{bmatrix}
\end{array} \tag{5}
$$

For a detailed analysis of this model, see Bower (1961).

The probability of a correct response on trial n, $\mathrm{Pr}(c_n)$, for the all-or-none model is readily derived by considering the probability of an error on trial n. In order for an error to occur on trial n, (1) an item must remain in state U for $n-1$ trials, this with probability $(1-a)^{n-1}$, and (2) an incorrect guess must be made when this item is presented on trial n, this with probability $1-g$. Thus, $\mathrm{Pr}(e_n)$ is $(1-g)(1-a)^{n-1}$, and so

$$
\mathrm{Pr}(c_n) = 1 - \mathrm{Pr}(e_n) = 1 - (1-g)(1-a)^{n-1}. \tag{6}
$$

It is evident that when an identification is made between θ and a, the two models, though based on very different premises about the underlying learning process, predict the same mean learning curve.

As an example of a statistic that does differentiate the two models, consider, for a particular stimulus-response pair, the conditional probability of an error on trial $n+1$ given an error on trial n, *i.e.*, $\mathrm{Pr}(e_{n+1}|e_n)$. In the linear model the probability of an error on trial $n+1$ does not depend upon whether the preceding response was right or wrong, and so

$$
\mathrm{Pr}(e_{n+1}|e_n) = \mathrm{Pr}(e_{n+1}) = (1-g)(1-\theta)^n. \tag{7}
$$

Thus, for this model, the conditional probability of an error is an exponentially decreasing function of the trial number.

For the all-or-none models, however, the fact that an error occurs on trial n furnishes an important piece of information, *viz.*, the item must have been in the unlearned state at the beginning of trial n, since no errors can occur once the item becomes learned. In order for an error to occur on trial $n+1$, therefore (1) learning must *not* have occurred following the reinforcement on trial n, that with probability $1-a$, and (2) an incorrect response must be made on trial $n+1$, that with probability $1-g$; therefore

$$
\mathrm{Pr}(e_{n+1}|e_n) = (1-g)(1-a). \tag{8}
$$

Thus, the linear model predicts that $\mathrm{Pr}(e_{n+1}|e_n)$ will decrease exponentially over trials, whereas the all-or-none model predicts that this probability will remain constant over trials. In Fig. 2 the conditional probability from Atkinson and Crothers' experiment is presented, along with the predictions from the all-or-none and linear models based on the same parameter value used to fit the mean learning curve. Although the conditional probability does tend to decrease over trials, the data are more in agreement with the constancy prediction of the all-or-none model, than with the decrease predicted by the linear model. Nevertheless, the noticeable decline over trials in the data of Fig. 2 has been found to characterize many paired-associate studies, and when appropriate statistical tests are applied, this decline has proven to differ significantly from the constancy predicted by the all-or-none model. (For similar ex-

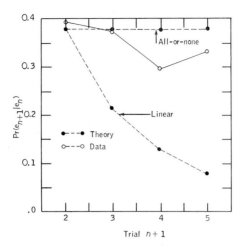

Fig. 2. Average probability of an error on trial $n + 1$, given an error on trial n for Atkinson and Crothers' experiment.

perimental results see Atkinson and Crothers, 1964; Estes, 1960; and Suppes and Ginsberg, 1963.)

Consequently, consideration has been given to ways in which the basic models described above may be modified so as to yield a more adequate account of paired-associate learning. We shall not attempt to deal with all the variations that have been proposed, but rather will restrict our attention to an extension of the all-or-none model suggested by Atkinson and Crothers (1964). As these authors point out, the inability of simpler models to account for all the details of the data indicates that one or more important psychological processes have been disregarded. For example, in paired-associate learning, it has been shown that considerable forgetting may result because the subject is trying to learn a number of stimulus-response pairs simultaneously (Melton, 1963; Murdock, 1961; Peterson and Peterson, 1959; Tulving, 1964). One way in which forgetting may affect the learning of paired-associates is suggested in the following analysis. Suppose we consider the course of learning for a single item i from a list. The item is presented to the subject, and following his response, he is told the correct answer. Now if item i is presented again immediately, it is very likely that the correct answer will be given. However, if other items from the list are interpolated between the two presentations of item i, the subject will be less likely to answer correctly on the second presentation of item i. The interpolated items are said to interfere with the retention of item i, or, more commonly, the subject forgets the association to item i. In general, as the number of interpolated items between the nth and $(n + 1)$st presentation of item i is increased, the amount of forgetting increases.

The two complementary processes — learning due to reinforcement, and forgetting due to interference — are both incorporated in the model that will be considered now. It will be assumed that each item in a list may be in one of three states: (1) state U is an unlearned state, in which the subject guesses at random from the set of response alternatives, (2) state S is a short-term memory state, and (3) state L is a long-term memory state. The subject will always give a correct response to an item in the short-term state, but it is possible for an item in state S to be forgotten, *i.e.*, to return to state U. Once an item moves to state L it is completely learned, in the sense that it will remain in state L and the correct response will always be given on subsequent presentations of the item.

The associative effect of a reinforcement is described by matrix **A** below:

$$
\begin{array}{c}
 \begin{array}{ccc} L & S & U \end{array} \\
\mathbf{A} = \begin{array}{c} L \\ S \\ U \end{array} \begin{bmatrix} 1 & 0 & 0 \\ a & 1\text{-}a & 0 \\ a & 1\text{-}a & 0 \end{bmatrix}
\end{array}
\tag{8}
$$

This matrix gives the probabilities of transitions between states for an item immediately after reinforcement. Thus, if an item is in the unlearned state, and the correct answer is told to the subject, then with probability a the item is learned (*i.e.*, it moves to state L), whereas with probability $1-a$ it moves to short-term memory. Thus, immediately following a reinforcement, an item will be either in long-term or short-term memory, and if the item is immediately presented again, the subject will give the correct response.

The effect of an interpolated unlearned stimulus-response pair on the learning state of a particular item is described by matrix **F**;

$$
\begin{array}{c}
 \begin{array}{ccc} L & S & U \end{array} \\
\mathbf{F} = \begin{array}{c} L \\ S \\ U \end{array} \begin{bmatrix} 1 & 0 & 0 \\ 0 & 1\text{-}f & f \\ 0 & 0 & 1 \end{bmatrix}.
\end{array}
\tag{9}
$$

If an item is in short-term memory and an unlearned stimulus-response pair is presented, then the interference produced by the unlearned pair results in forgetting of the item (*i.e.*, transition to state U) with probability f, whereas with probability $1-f$ the item remains in short-term memory. If an item is in long-term memory, the interference has no effect, and if an item is in the unlearned state then again the interference will have no effect.

The matrix describing the transitions between states from trial n to trial $n+1$ for a given item, which will be denoted $\mathbf{T}_n$, is found by taking the product of **A** and the Z_nth power of **F**, where Z_n is the number of unlearned pairs which intervene between the nth and $(n+1)$st presentations of the particular item. The association matrix **A** represents the reinforced presentation of the item, and the forgetting matrix **F** is applied Z_n times, once for each of the intervening unlearned pairs. Performing the matrix multiplication yields

$$\mathbf{T}_n = \begin{array}{c} \\ \mathbf{L}_n \\ \mathbf{S}_n \\ \mathbf{U}_n \end{array} \begin{array}{c} \mathbf{L}_{n+1} \quad \mathbf{S}_{n+1} \quad\quad \mathbf{U}_{n+1} \\ \left[\begin{array}{ccc} 1 & 0 & 0 \\ a(1{-}a) & (1{-}\mathbf{F}_n) & (1{-}a)\mathbf{F}_n \\ a(1{-}a) & (1{-}\mathbf{F}_n) & (1{-}a)\mathbf{F}_n \end{array} \right] \end{array} \tag{10}$$

where $\mathbf{F}_n = 1 - (1{-}f)^{\mathbf{Z}_n}$.

Unfortunately, there is no way of extracting from the data the exact value of $\mathbf{Z}_n$, the number of interpolated pairs which are not in state L. If an incorrect response is given to an intervening stimulus-response pair, then the pair must be in the unlearned state, but if a correct response occurs, then the pair may be in either long-term or short-term memory, or it may even be that the intervening pair is in the unlearned state and the correct response occurred by chance. Since the exact value of $\mathbf{Z}_n$ is indeterminate, as an *approximation* we will use the expected number of unlearned items intervening between the nth and $(n+1)$st presentation of an item. Suppose that there are $X + 1$ items in the list being learned. On the average, X items will be interpolated between any two consecutive presentations of a particular item. Since the items are arranged in random order, the average position of a particular item will be in the middle of a trial. Thus, for half the interpolated items, (those which follow item i on trial n), the probability of being either in state U or state S will be $(1{-}a)^{n-1}$. Similarly, for the other half of the interpolated items, (those which precede item i on trial $n + 1$), the probability that learning has not taken place is $(1{-}a)^n$. Combining these results, the expected number of unlearned items intervening between the nth and $(n+1)$st presentation of item i will be $X(1{-}a/2)(1{-}a)^{n-1}$, and it is this value which will be used as an approximation to $\mathbf{Z}_n$ in Eq. 10.

Next we turn to the derivation of several statistics of interest for this model. In these derivations, it should be kept in mind that $\mathbf{F}_n$ is a function of $\mathbf{Z}_n$, for which the approximation just discussed will be used. The mean learning curve may be obtained by noting that for an error to occur on trial $n + 1$ (1) an item must have failed to move to the long-term state on n preceding trials, which has probability $(1{-}a)^n$, (2) the item must change from state S to state U between the nth and $(n+1)$st presentations, which occurs with probability $\mathbf{F}_n$, and (3) while in state U an incorrect guess must be made with probability $1{-}g$; hence

$$\Pr(c_{n+1}) = 1 - (1{-}g)(1{-}a)^n \mathbf{F}_n \tag{12}$$

For fixed values of a and f, as the length of the list is increased (*i.e.*, as X becomes larger) $\mathbf{F}_n$ increases and therefore $\Pr(c_{n+1})$ will decrease. In other words, the model predicts that the longer lists will be more difficult to learn, which of course is in agreement with empirical findings.

The probability of an error conditional on an error, $\Pr(e_{n+1}|e_n)$, is also found by noting that if an error occurs on trial n, then the item must have been in the unlearned state. Thus the probability of an error on the next trial is

$$\Pr(e_{n+1}|e_n) = (1{-}g)(1{-}a)\mathbf{F}_n \tag{13}$$

since (1) learning must fail, with probability $1{-}a$, to result in transition to state L, (2) forgetting must occur with probability F_n, and (3) an incorrect guess must be made. Since F_n decreases over trials, $Pr(e_{n+1}|e_n)$ will also decrease over trials.

Because the amount of forgetting is a function of the trial number, this model will be referred to as the trial-dependent-forgetting (TDF) model. In the remainder of this paper we will present the results of a paired-associate study in which list length was varied, and each of the three models discussed here will be applied to the data in order to determine their relative merits.

The subjects for the experiment were three groups of 25 college students, each of whom learned a single paired-associate list. The stimulus member of each pair consisted of a two-digit number, and the response member was one of three nonsense syllables RIX, FUB or GED. A set of 21 stimulus items was chosen on the basis of low inter-item association value, and for Groups 9, 15 and 21, the experimental list consisted of a selection of 9, 15 or 21 items, respectively, from this set. For Group 21, the entire set of stimulus items was used, whereas for the other groups a different subset was randomly selected for each subject. Each of the three response alternatives was assigned as the correct response equally often for each subject. The list was learned to a criterion of two consecutive errorless trials or ten trials, whichever was shorter. The subject was first given instructions about the nature of the task and then ran through a practice list of four items to minimize warmup effects. The subject

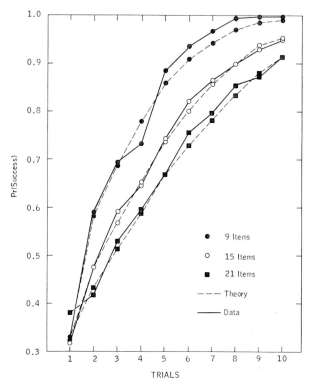

Fig. 3. Average probability of a success on trial n for three groups with different list lengths. See text for description of theoretical curves.

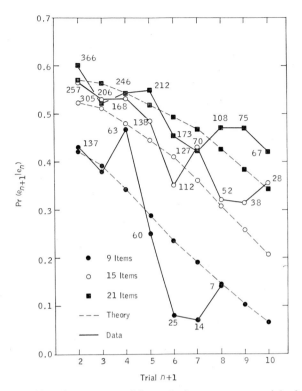

Fig. 4. Average probability of an error on trial $n + 1$, given an error on trial n for three groups with different list lengths.

was asked if he had any questions, and then the experimental run was begun. In order to reduce primacy effects (Peterson and Peterson, 1962), the first three stimulus items shown to the subject were two-digit numbers which were not in the set of 21 experimental items; these three items did not reoccur on later trials. Then, without interruption, the experimental list, arranged in a random order, was presented to the subject, and for each item, the subject was required to choose one of the three responses, following which he was informed of the correct answer. After the entire list had been presented in this fashion, the second trial then proceeded without interruption in the same manner with the items arranged in a new random order. Thus, the procedure involved the continuous presentations of items with no breaks between trials.

The mean learning curves for the three groups are presented in Fig. 3. As may be seen, the three curves are ordered according to list length, *i.e.*, as the number of items in the list is increased, there is a concomitant decrease in the mean proportion of successes on trial n. The curves for $Pr(e_{n+1}|e_n)$ are shown in Fig. 4. The three curves are again ordered by list length, and there is a decrease in the conditional probability over trials for each of three groups. (The numerals by each of the data points represent the number of observations on which the point is based.)

In order to determine the quantitative accuracy of the various models that have been presented, it is necessary to obtain parameter estimates. There are a number of alternative procedures for estimation; we will use the technique of chi-square minimization on specific response sequences suggested by Atkinson and Crothers (1964). This method yields parameter estimates having certain desirable properties and also provides a goodness-of-fit test. We begin by looking at the sequence of responses of a single subject for one stimulus item. This response is rewritten as a string of c's representing correct responses and e's representing errors. For example, the response sequence for a particular subject-item, beginning at trial 1 and ending at trial 10, might be written *eceececcec*. For parameter estimation, those portions of the sequence from trials 2 to 5 and from trials 6 to 9 will be used; in the example above, these subsequences are *ceec* and *eccc*, respectively. The 2^4 or 16 combinations of c's and e's possible in each four-trial block are listed in Table I. Also in Table I are the observed frequencies with which each combination occurred for the three experimental groups for trials 2 to 5; the data for trials 6 to 9 are in Table II. For example, the sequence *cccc*, no errors on trials 2 through 5, was observed in 83 out of a total of 225 subject-items in Group 9.

For notational purposes, let $O_{i,j,n}$ denote the ith sequence listed in the table for experimental group j, where the sequence starts at trial n, and let $N(O_{i,j,n})$ be the observed frequency of this sequence. The predicted relative frequency of each of the specific response sequences is derived for the models presented above. For the all-or-none model, for example, the probability of the sequence, no successes from trial 2 through trial 5, is found to be the probability that the item is not learned by trial 5, and that four incorrect guesses occur, which is $(1-g)^4 (1-a)^4$. The same sequence is predicted by the linear model to occur with probability $(1-g)^4 (1-\theta)^{10}$, since on each trial $Pr(e_n)$ is equal to $(1-g) (1-\theta)^{n-1}$ in the model. The derivation of the theoretical expressions for these sequences is very lengthy, and the interested reader is referred to the Atkinson and Crothers paper (1964) for further details.

Suppose that for an arbitrary model, $Pr(O_{i,j,n}; p)$ is the predicted probability of the ith sequence for group j starting at trial n and ending at trial $n+3$, where the prediction depends on a particular choice of the parameter(s), p, of the model. Further, let the total number of subject-item combinations in a given block of four trials for group j be denoted by T_j. Then we define the function

$$\chi^2_{i,j,n} = \frac{[T_j Pr(O_{i,j,n}; p) - N(O_{i,j,n})]^2}{T_j Pr(O_{i,j,n}; p)}. \tag{14a}$$

A measure of the discrepancy between a model and the data from group j is found by taking the sum of Eq. 14a over the sixteen sequences and two blocks of four trials; *i.e.*,

$$\chi^2_j = \sum_{i=1}^{16} \chi^2_{i,j,2} + \sum_{i=1}^{16} \chi_{i,j,6} \tag{14b}$$

In the case of the all-or-none and linear models, estimates of the parameters a and θ were found which minimized Eq. 14b for each group. This minimization is not readily performed by analytic means, and so a high-speed computer was programmed to find parameter estimates by a search procedure on the parameter space. If the set of subject-items is homogeneous and stochastically independent, then under the null

TABLE I

OBSERVED AND PREDICTED FREQUENCIES FOR SPECIFIC RESPONSE SEQUENCES FROM TRIALS 2 THROUGH 5

Trial				9 Items					15 Items					21 Items				
2	3	4	5	Observed	Linear	All-or-none	TDF	TDF-Revised	Observed	Linear	All-or-none	TDF	TDF-Revised	Observed	Linear	All-or-none	TDF	TDF-Revised
c	c	c	c	83	59.0	88.4	69.3	79.0	98	39.9	103.7	94.6	88.0	97	45.4	112.6	124.8	102.0
c	c	c	e	3	9.5	1.3	6.0	4.2	10	17.8	3.8	6.4	5.6	11	24.2	6.8	7.3	6.6
c	c	e	c	10	15.2	3.0	9.5	8.7	13	23.9	6.6	10.5	11.3	14	31.5	10.3	11.9	13.3
c	c	e	e	4	2.4	2.7	4.8	3.6	10	10.7	7.6	8.4	9.0	12	16.8	13.5	12.0	14.3
c	e	c	c	18	25.7	10.4	17.2	18.1	25	33.1	17.3	21.6	22.9	35	42.2	23.0	26.2	26.4
c	e	c	e	2	4.1	2.7	5.7	4.3	4	14.8	7.6	9.6	10.0	14	22.5	13.5	13.0	15.1
c	e	e	c	10	6.6	6.1	9.0	8.2	7	19.8	13.3	15.7	16.7	17	29.3	20.7	21.3	23.3
c	e	e	e	3	1.1	5.3	4.5	3.4	12	8.9	15.2	12.6	13.2	20	15.6	27.1	21.4	25.1
e	c	c	c	40	48.3	41.9	36.3	40.0	58	48.7	57.3	55.7	54.7	78	59.4	67.6	74.3	66.2
e	c	c	e	3	7.8	2.7	6.7	4.2	6	21.8	7.6	10.6	8.4	15	31.7	13.5	13.7	11.7
e	c	e	c	12	12.5	6.1	10.5	9.4	16	29.2	13.3	17.3	18.0	22	41.2	20.7	22.5	24.3
e	c	e	e	2	2.0	5.3	5.3	3.9	12	13.0	15.2	13.9	14.3	30	22.0	27.1	22.6	26.1
e	e	c	c	14	21.1	20.8	19.1	19.7	31	40.5	34.6	35.6	36.3	47	55.2	46.0	49.3	48.3
e	e	c	e	2	3.4	5.3	6.3	4.7	11	18.1	15.2	15.8	15.8	16	29.5	27.1	24.4	27.7
e	e	e	c	13	5.4	12.2	10.0	9.0	32	24.2	26.5	25.9	26.4	42	38.3	41.4	40.1	42.6
e	e	e	e	6	0.9	10.7	5.0	3.7	30	10.8	30.3	20.8	21.0	55	20.4	54.1	40.4	45.8
χ^2					73.5	42.5	17.5	10.9		173.2	30.3	21.7	23.2		180.5	21.8	23.6	19.8

References p. 348

TABLE II

OBSERVED AND PREDICTED FREQUENCIES FOR SPECIFIC RESPONSE SEQUENCES FROM TRIALS 6 THROUGH 9

Trial 6	7	8	9	9 Items Observed	Linear	All-or-none	TDF	TDF-Revised	15 Items Observed	Linear	All-or-none	TDF	TDF-Revised	21 Items Observed	Linear	All-or-none	TDF	TDF-Revised
c	c	c	c	205	177.7	192.2	164.1	192.1	271	156.3	263.9	251.6	259.3	319	178.1	309.7	339.5	310.4
c	c	c	e	0	5.3	0.3	4.2	1.2	6	26.1	1.6	5.5	3.5	8	39.5	3.5	5.9	4.9
c	c	e	c	0	7.9	0.7	6.3	2.8	8	32.8	2.7	8.6	7.3	13	48.4	5.4	9.4	9.9
c	c	e	e	0	0.2	0.6	1.6	0.3	2	5.5	3.1	3.7	2.5	4	10.7	7.1	5.7	6.2
c	e	c	c	12	5.0	2.5	10.2	6.4	13	41.6	7.1	15.0	15.4	27	59.8	12.0	17.8	20.2
c	e	c	e	0	0.4	0.6	1.9	0.5	1	6.9	3.1	4.5	3.1	6	13.3	7.1	6.7	7.1
c	e	e	c	1	0.5	1.5	2.9	1.0	2	8.7	5.4	7.0	6.1	11	16.3	10.8	10.7	12.5
c	e	e	e	0	0.0	1.3	0.7	0.1	5	1.5	6.2	3.1	2.1	10	3.6	14.1	6.5	7.8
e	c	c	c	13	18.3	10.1	17.6	14.4	24	53.5	23.5	30.2	34.7	55	74.8	35.3	40.5	47.4
e	c	c	e	0	0.5	0.6	2.3	0.6	2	8.9	3.1	5.3	3.3	10	16.6	7.1	7.7	6.5
e	c	e	c	0	0.8	1.5	3.5	1.4	11	11.2	5.4	8.3	7.3	5	20.3	10.8	12.4	14.0
e	c	e	e	0	0.0	1.3	0.9	0.2	1	1.9	6.2	3.6	2.5	3	4.5	14.1	7.5	8.7
e	e	c	c	1	1.2	5.0	5.6	3.1	15	14.2	14.2	14.6	15.5	17	25.1	24.0	23.4	28.5
e	e	c	e	0	0.0	1.3	1.1	0.2	5	2.4	6.2	4.3	3.1	7	5.6	14.1	8.8	10.0
e	e	e	c	0	0.1	2.9	1.6	0.5	5	3.0	10.9	6.8	6.2	11	6.8	21.6	14.1	17.6
e	e	e	e	0	0.0	2.6	0.4	0.1	4	0.5	12.4	3.0	2.1	19	1.5	28.3	8.5	11.0
χ^2					25.5	21.3	43.7	10.6		210.0	52.0	17.2	20.5		428.9	76.0	39.2	33.7

hypothesis, it can be shown that the χ^2 from Eq. 14b has the usual limiting distribution with 29 degrees of freedom for each group; one degree of freedom is subtracted from each of the two sets of sixteen frequencies because of the requirement that each set must sum to the total number of subject-item combinations, and another degree of freedom is subtracted for the parameter estimate. The total χ^2 value summed over the three experimental groups will have 87 degrees of freedom.

Since the TDF model is formulated in a fashion that takes list length into account, values of a and f were found for this model that jointly minimized the χ^2 function for all three groups. That is, we define the function

$$\chi^2 = \sum_{j=1}^{3} \chi_j^2 \tag{14c}$$

and find the values of a and f which minimize Eq. 14c. Since two parameters are estimated over the three groups, the χ^2 from Eq. 14c will have 88 degrees of freedom.

The response-sequence frequencies predicted by each of the models for trials 2 through 5 are listed in Table I, and in Table II we present the predictions for trials

TABLE III

PARAMETER ESTIMATES FOR VARIOUS MODELS AND TOTAL χ^2 VALUES OVER GROUPS

Model	Parameter	9 Item	15 Item	21 Item	χ^2 Value		
					Trials 2–5	Trials 6–9	Total
Linear	θ	0.32	0.17	0.15	427.2	664.4	1091.6
All-or-none	c	0.30	0.20	0.15	94.6	149.3	243.9
TDF	a	0.16	—	—	62.8	100.1	162.9
	f	0.22	—	—			
TDF Revised	a	0.37	—	—			
	b	0.11	—	—	53.9	64.8	118.7
	f	0.15	—	—			

6 through 9. In Table III the parameter estimates obtained by the minimization procedure are presented, as well as the minimum χ^2 values for each of the models over all groups. The linear model is definitely inferior to the all-or-none model, and the TDF model does a better job than either of the other two, although one less parameter has been estimated from the data for this model.

In spite of the fact that the TDF model provides a more adequate account of the data than the other models, there is some cause to be dissatisfied with this formulation. For one thing, the overall χ^2 value is about 163, which with 88 degrees of freedom far exceeds the 0.001 level of significance. More importantly, there is evidence that the association parameter, a, is not independent of list length. It will be recalled that in the analysis above, parameter estimation for the TDF model was carried out under the assumption that the parameters a and f are invariant over list lengths. The appropriateness of this assumption was evaluated by finding the best estimate of the two parameters separately for each experimental group; *i.e.*, estimates of a and f were obtained using Eq. 14b for each list length. Good agreement was found among the three estimates of the forgetting parameter f; the estimates were 0.25 ,0.25 and 0.21 for groups 9, 15 and 21, respectively. However, the separate estimates of the association parameter a were ordered according to the number of items in the list; for groups 9, 15 and 21, the estimates were 0.20, 0.17 and 0.14.

Consequently, consideration was given to modifications of the TDF model which would give a more adequate account of the data and also yield parameter values that would be relatively invariant over the list length variable. In the association phase of the model as originally formulated (Eq. 8), it was assumed that the probability of moving to long-term memory was the same whether an item was in the unlearned state or the short-term state; in both instances the transition probability was a. In the revised TDF model which will now be described, it will be assumed that the effect of a reinforced presentation of an item will depend on the state of the item at the time of reinforcement. If the item has been forgotten and is in state U, then there is a transition to long-term memory with probability b, whereas with probability $1—b$ the item goes to short-term memory. If an item is in state S (*i.e.*, it has not been learned, but neither has it been forgotten since the last reinforced presentation), then with probability a the item is learned and moves to long-term memory, whereas with probability $1—a$ it remains in state S. Thus matrix **A** (Eq. 8) is replaced by matrix **A'** below,

$$\mathbf{A'} = \begin{matrix} & \begin{matrix} L & S & U \end{matrix} \\ \begin{matrix} L \\ S \\ U \end{matrix} & \begin{bmatrix} 1 & 0 & 0 \\ a & 1—a & 0 \\ b & 1—b & 0 \end{bmatrix} \end{matrix}. \tag{15}$$

In all other respects the revised model is unchanged from the original formulation, and, in particular, the expected value of Z_n will be used as an approximation to Z_n in deriving statistics. That is, suppose that $\Pr(L_n)$ is the probability of being in long-term memory on trial n which, for the revised TDF model, is a function of a, b, f, and X. Then the expected number of unlearned stimulus-response pairs between the nth and $(n + 1)$st presentations of an item will be

$$X \{1 — \tfrac{1}{2} [\Pr(L_n) + \Pr(L_{n+1})]\}.$$

The minimum χ^2 estimation procedure was used to obtain estimates of a, b and f for the three experimental groups jointly, using Eq. 14c. The results are presented in Tables I, II and III as the revised TDF model. As may be seen, the introduction of the parameter b reduced the overall χ^2 value of the original TDF model by more than 25 per cent, from 163 to 119, which represents a considerable improvement. Moreover, when estimates of the parameters a, b and f were obtained separately for each of the experimental groups, it was found that the three estimates of f were quite consistent with one another, and that the variations in a and b were unrelated to list length.

It is of interest to note that the probability that an item is learned is more than three times larger if the item is in short-term memory than if it is in the unlearned state, *i.e.*, the estimate of the parameter a is 0.37, while b is 0.11. This relation between a and b suggests an explanation for the dependency between the association parameter in the original TDF model and the length of the paired-associate list. The effect of increasing list length in these models is to make it more likely that an item is in state U. In the original model, where a and b are assumed to be equal, the estimate of the associative effect of a reinforcement will be some weighted average of a and b, which we will call $\bar{a}$. In the case of a list with very few stimulus-response pairs, the probability that an item is in state S is larger than when there are many pairs, since as the number of pairs becomes larger, more forgetting will occur and hence an item is more likely to be in state U. Thus the relative contribution of the parameter a to the average $\bar{a}$ will decrease as list length increases, and as list length becomes very large, $\bar{a}$ will approach b. Since a is greater than b, the finding that $\bar{a}$ decreases with increasing list length in the original TDF model would be expected.

Fig. 3 presents the mean learning curves predicted by the revised model for each of the three list lengths. As may be seen, there is good agreement between the data and the theoretical curves. The model also was used to predict the curves for $Pr(e_{n+1}|e_n)$ which are shown in Fig. 4 along with the observed values. The data points are fairly variable, but overall the theoretical curves fit reasonably well. One way of directly testing the interference assumptions of the TDF model embodied in Eq. 9 would be to look at the probability of a correct response on trial $n+1$ as a function of the number of items interpolated between the nth and $(n+1)$st presentations of a particular stimulus-response pair. This probability should decrease exponentially according to the interference hypothesis of the TDF model. Unfortunately, when the experiment reported in this paper was conducted, no record was made of the specific presentation order within a trial, and so this direct test cannot be made. In an unreported study by Shelton, within-trial presentation order was recorded. Examination of these data clearly indicates that the probability of a success was a decreasing function of the number of interpolated items.

It has been our goal in presenting this analysis of paired-associate learning to illustrate the manner in which mathematical representations of psychological processes may be used to test specific hypotheses about the way in which these processes operate. While the revised TDF model is sufficiently complex to present serious difficulties in carrying out mathematical derivations, it is unlikely that the behavioral situation is as simple as the model indicates. Indeed, although the revised model is the most adequate formulation that has been presented, it is not satisfactory in a number of respects. For one thing, the χ^2 value of 119 with 87 degrees of freedom would lead to rejection of the null hypothesis at the 0.05 level of significance. This is not a serious fault *per se*, since we would certainly not discard the model until a more adequate representation of paired-associate learning could be suggested.

A more serious type of criticism involves the application of the model to data from other experiments to determine its generality. Revisions will certainly be necessary to account for some aspects of paired-associate learning that are not brought out by the experiment reported in this paper. For example, suppose that when a subject makes an incorrect response he is given a second guess at the right answer. According to the TDF model, the second guess should be chosen at random from the reduced set of response alternatives. In fact, the probability of a correct response on the second guess is found to be somewhat greater than this chance expectation (Binford and Gettys, 1964).

While it is always possible to modify any particular model to account for empirical findings, some other formulation might be preferred on the basis of simplicity and parsimony. Within the limits of the study reported in this paper, however, the TDF model is successful in providing a relatively good account of the data, both qualitatively and in quantitative detail. Moreover, it does so by incorporating both association and forgetting processes known to be important in paired-associate learning; further these processes are represented in such a fashion that changes in the data produced by variations in list length are accounted for by the representation of the learning process, rather than by changes in the parameter values.

ACKNOWLEDGEMENT

The preparation of this document was supported by the National Institute of Health (Grant USPHS-5 R01 HD 00918–03) and by the National Science Foundation (Grant 24264).

SUMMARY

A number of alternative models are proposed to account for the learning of simple verbal associations. In the linear model, which is considered first, it is assumed that learning of an association proceeds gradually in an incremental fashion. The all-or-none model presented next assumes that learning takes place on a single trial; prior to that trial, the subject responds at random. The third model presented (the TDF model) postulates all-or-none acquisition and interference-produced forgetting. The models are applied to an experiment in which subjects were required to learn lists of 9, 15, or 21 stimulus-response pairs. The effect of increasing the number of pairs is to increase the number of errors in a way which is well accounted for by the TDF model.

REFERENCES

ATKINSON, R. C., AND CROTHERS, E. J., (1964); A comparison of paired-associate learning models having different acquisition and retention axioms. *J. math. Psychol.*, **1**, 285–315.

BINFORD, J. R., AND GETTYS, C., (1965); Non-stationarity in paired-associate learning as indicated by a second-guess procedure. *J. Math. Psychol.*, **2**, 190–195.

BOWER, G. H., (1961); Application of a one-element model to paired-associate learning. *Psychometrika*, **26**, 255–280.

BOWER, G. H., (1962); A model for response and training variables in paired-associate learning. *Psychol. Rev.*, **69**, 34–53.

BUSH, R. R., AND MOSTELLER, F., (1955); *Stochastic Models for Learning*. New York. John Wiley and Sons.

ESTES, W. K., (1960); Learning theory and the new mental chemistry. *Psychol. Rev.*, **67**, 207–223.

ESTES, W. K., (1964); All-or-none processes in learning and retention. *Amer. Psychologist*, **19**, 16–25.

Estes, W. K. and Suppes, P., (1959); Foundations of linear models. *Studies in Mathematical Learning Theory*. R. R. Bush and W. K. Estes, Editors. Stanford, Calif., Stanford University Press (pp. 137–179).

Melton, A. W., (1963); Implications of short-term memory for a general theory of memory. *J. verb. Learn. verb. Behav.*, **2**, 1–21.

Murdock, Jr., B. B., (1961); The retention of individual items. *J. exp. Psychol.*, **62**, 618–625.

Peterson, L. R., and Peterson, M. J., (1959); Short-term retention of individual verbal items. *J. exp. Psychol.*, **58**, 193–198.

Peterson, L. R., and Peterson, M. J., (1962); Minimal paired-associate learning. *J. exp. Psychol.*, **63**, 521–527.

Sternberg, S., (1963); Stochastic learning theory. *Handbook of Mathematical Psychology*. R. D. Luce, R. R. Bush, and E. Galanter, Editors. Vol. 2. New York: John Wiley and Sons (pp.1–120).

Suppes, P., and Ginsberg, R., (1963); A fundamental property of all-or-none models, binomial distribution of responses prior to conditioning, with application to concept formation in children. *Psychol. Rev.*, **70**, 139–161.

Tulving, E., (1964); Intratrial and intertrial retention: notes towards a theory of free recall verbal learning. *Psychol. Rev.*, **71**, 219–237.

Underwood, B. J., and Keppel, G., (1962); One-trial learning. *J. verb. Learn. verb. Behav.*, **1**, 1–13.

Probability-Statistical Model of the Brain Organisation

A. B. KOGAN

The Rostov-Don State University, The Chair of Physiology of Man and Animals,
Rostov on Don (USSR)

All of us are at present witnesses of the great successes made by cybernetics — quite a new field of science, the appearance and rapid development of which is connected with the name of Norbert Wiener. It is he who stressed the 'principal Unity of a number of problems, in the centre of which there were the problems of connections control and statistical mechanics, and besides, both in the machine and in the living tissue' (1948). Such a principal unity allows to recreate in the models the main properties of the brain, both for the theoretical cognition of its work and for the practical use of this knowledge in technique. Besides, many difficulties arising on this way, may have the reason, that the similarity of the model and the original often push into the background the features of their difference.

Although the question about how far the analogy is going between the computer and the brain is subject to a heated discussion opened by Turing (1950), most of the statements lead us to the opinion expressed by George (1961) that the laws studied by cybernetics 'concern to an equal degree both the not living and the living systems'. However, if we single out the leading cybernetic law — the expedient self-regulation (not including into this concept 'expedience', anything more than adaptivity of behaviour) and raise the question 'whether it exists in living nature', it becomes clear that cybernetics deals with the category of phenomenon which appeared together with life. In the phenomenon that a man who falls, rises to his feet, and a stone which falls, remains lying on the ground, there is nothing vitalistic. In these phenomena we see the mechanism worked out by a thousand ages old evolution, the mechanism of self-regulation with a useful affect 'on oneself'. Such mechanisms do not appear in not living nature. Therefore, instead of the thesis about 'equal degree', it seems to us more right that cybernetics studies the specific vital phenomena and their reproduction in the machines created by man by his likeness.

However, the modern machines, reproducing the functions of the logical activity of the brain appear to be immeasurably less effective than their living prototypes.

Numerous examples show that the thing is not only in the quality of the technical materials or the insufficient application of the means already existing in the technique. For example, the calculation of the parameters of work of the system of the brain optic analyzer, carried out on the grounds of physiological experiments and morphological observations, showed that the wonderful stability with which its activity is been carried out, cannot be explained by means of doubling and reserving elements (Kogan, 1962). There is nothing vitalistic in this either. We can only mark the presence of certain pecularities in the organization of the nervous system. Recently these pecularities draw more and more attention of the investigators.

The accumulating physiological knowledge about the structural bases of the nervous activity and the behaviour of separate cells more clearly lays the stress on the fact that the primary theory of the nerve nets of formal neurons (McCulloch and Pitts, 1943) has a purely logical sense and does not describe the origanization of real neurons. In contrast to the required by formal logics one-way determinism of the path of the passing of the signal, the nerve connections, particularly when performing the highest brain functions, display extraordinary plasticity and nonspecifity. Yet Lashley (1929) showed that when removing different parts of the cortex, the conditioned reflexes very little depend on the topography of the removal.

In Fig. 1 we see the scheme of experiments carried out at our laboratory (Glumov, 1962). From these experiments we can see that temporal connections of the conditional reflex can be realized in different ways. Not a single one of these ways is absolutely necessary for their realization.

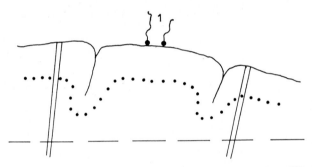

Fig. 1. The summary scheme of operations made on two cats who had conditioned food reflexes worked out on the direct irritation of a point of the cortex. The conditioned reflex was preserved for both cats, although the cut of the first cat (interrupted line) cleaved the paths along which there was carried out the conditioned excitation for the second cat after making her a cut (doubled line) and *vice versa*.

The development of investigations with applying technique of simultaneous micro-electrode recording of impulse activity of several neurons showed that the succession of the passage of rhythmical impulses through the neurons discovered by Verzeano and collaborators (1960) is rather an exception than a rule. The comparative physio-logical investigations carried out at our laboratory allow to mark some tendencies, that can be the indication of the peculiarities of the evolution of neuron organization (Fig. 2).

Thus, in a comparatively primitive ganglionic nervous system of molluscs there prevail right rhythms of impulses, often synchronous, or divisible ones for different neurons (Karpenko, 1963). The neurons of the middle and fore-brain of the frog to a certain extent lose the regularity and bonds of the rhythm (Chorayan, 1963). The

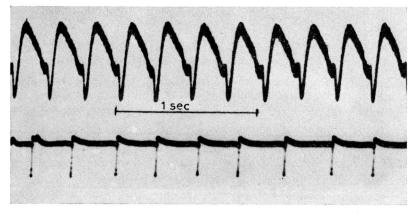

Fig. 2a

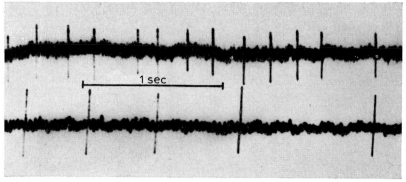

Fig. 2b

Fig. 2. The simultaneous recording of the spontaneous activity of two neurons having the distance about 200 μ between them. A — suboesophageous ganglion of the *Helix pomatia*. B — the lobi optici of a frog.

neurons of the cortex of rabbits and cats are still more unrhythmical and unsyn-chronous.

We think that these tendencies of arhythmiation and unsynchronization of the impulse activity of neurons should be put in connection with the evolutionary in-crease of the quantity of interneuron connections. The increase of possibilities of interaction leads to a more strongly pronounced variety of the plural interference of impulses.

If taken into consideration that according to the data of D. Sholl (1956), one neuron of the cortex can interact with 4000 other neurons, it becomes quite clear that the plurality of connections in the highest parts of the brain has reached such a degree at which it is impossible to say that one of them can determine the path of the signal.

All the given facts and considerations have led us to the conclusion that the specifity of the organization of the higher parts of the brain, providing their wonderful properties of high efficiency, flexibility and stability of functioning, is connected with the transition from the one-way determinism of the 'scheme of connections' to the probability determinism of random interaction of neurons. This view point was expressed in the hypothesis of probability–statistical principle of the organization of neuron elements in the functional systems of the brain (Kogan, 1962, 1964).

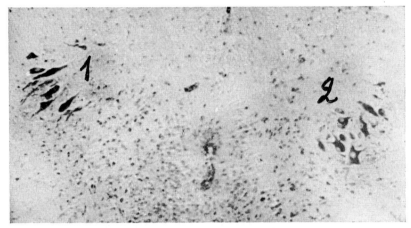

Fig.3 a

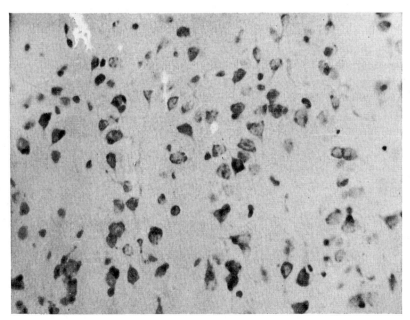

Fig. 3b

Fig. 3. The photo of the histochemical preparation. The Brachet's reaction on the ribonucleic acid. A — motoneurons of the nuclei of triceps femori of the frog one-sided reflectory excitation after 3 min (1). The other side-non exsided (2). B — The cells of the cortical part of the visual analyzer in the zone of the excitation caused by the flashes of the light.

According to this hypothesis the ensembles of neurons of the type described by Hebb (1949), form the mosaic of the probability distribution of activity in space and time. A great number of random interacting elements statistically determine the resulting total pattern of the regular reaction of the system. The nature of the high effectiveness of the higher nerve activity mechanisms becomes clearer. The probability character of the participation of separate neurons in the realization of the reflex conditions the wide interchangeability of the paths, and the statistical results allow to preserve it even when a part of the elements is excluded.

The difference between the organization of neurons of the lowest and highest levels of the nerve system can be clearly seen from the cytochemical indices of distribution of the excited and inhibited cells during the reflexes of the spinal cord centre and the analysatory cortex (Fig. 3). If in the first case all the motoneurons of the triceps showed after 15 sec of the reflex activity, similar accumulation of ribonucleic acid, reflecting their excited state, in the second case we can see that the neurons with increased and decreased content of ribonucleic acid, that is the excited and inhibited neurons are intermixed.

These data which are in agreement with the results of the study of the impulse activity relations allow to draw a conclusion that the transition from the 'schematic' organization of the neurons to the probability–statistical organization was carried out on the basis of the structural reorganization of the parallelly doubled homogeneous elements into a dynamic mosaic of elements of hetergeneous functional state.

SUMMARY

The analysis of the regulating processes in animate and inanimate nature shows that cybernetics studies laws which appeared with the beginning of life.

Still, the models of logical activity of the brain, based on the formal logic of the nervous nets don't reflect the main property of the living systems — their changeability and adaptability. It was supposed on the ground of morphological and physiogical facts that these properties are caused by the probability of distribution of activity in ensembles of neurons and by the statistical result of their interaction (Kogan, 1962, 1964).

Some facts are given about evolutionary increasing arhythmia and decreasing synchronization of the impulses as the result of the increase in number of interneuronic connections, and about cytochemical manifestations of two types of neuronic organization — homogeneous and mosaic.

REFERENCES

GLUMOV, G. M., (1962); Comparative roles of horizontal and vertical connections within cerebral hemispheres. *Fisiol. Zhurn. SSSR*, **48**, 1437–1443.

KARPENKO, L. M., (1963); Unit activity of the nervous cells of the Helix pomatia. *Electrophysiology of the Nervous System.* A. B. Kogan, Editor, Transactions of the IV Conference. Rostov-on-Don, University Press (p. 182).

KOGAN, A. B., (1962); Some principal peculiarities of the organisation of the brain information mechanisms. *Problems of neurocybernetics*. A. B. Kogan, Editor. Transactions of the I Conference. Rostov-on-Don. University Press (p. 16).

KOGAN, A. B., (1964); Probability-statistical principle of the brain functional systems organisation. *Dokl. Acad. Nauk SSSR*, **154**, 1231–1234.

TCHORAJAN, O. G., (1963); Contribution to functional neuronal architectonics. *Fiziol. Zhurn. SSSR*, **49**, 1026–1029.

GEORGE, F. H., (1961); *The brain as a computer*. Pergamon Press, Oxford, London, New York, Paris.

HEBB, D. O., (1949); *The Organization of Behaviour*. John Wiley. New York.

LASHLEY, K. S., (1929); *Brain Mechanisms and Intelligence*. University. Chicago Press.

McCULLOCH, W. S., AND PITTS, W., (1943); A logical calcula of the ideas immanent in nervous activity. *Bull. Mathemat. Biophys.*, **5**, 115–133.

SHOLL, D. A., (1956); *The organisation of the cerebral cortex*. John Wiley. New York.

TURING, A. M., (1950); *Mind*, **59**, 433–460.

WIENER, N., (1948); *Cybernetics*. The Technology Press of M.I.T. and John Wiley,

VERZEANO, M., AND NEGISHI, K., (1960); Neuronal activity in cortical and thalamic networks. *J. Gen. Physiol.*, **43**, 177–183.

An Outline of the Development of a Neuron Model

F. JENIK

T. H. Darmstadt, Institut für Allgemeine Nachrichtentechnik (West Germany)

CONTENTS

1. INTRODUCTORY REMARKS

In general, models are applied if the investigation of the original system is difficult, dangerous or very expensive. As the observation of pulse processing in the nervous system is rather difficult, the application of neuron models seems to be appropriate. The advantage of neuron models is, that most parameters can easily been altered, that undesired afferences may be excluded and that the input–output relationships are easily to observe.

In the first part of this paper the development of a neuron model will be outlined by means of block diagrams. Block diagrams are graphical representations of biological, physical or mathematical relationships. With neurons three parts may be distinguished that are important for pulse processing (Fig. 1): the synapses (S) the synapse-free membrane (M) of the soma and of the dendrites and the axon (A).

A presynaptic impulse, a presynaptic action potential u arriving at a synapse, in general activates this synapse and causes an alteration of the ionic conductances g of the subsynaptic membrane. The conductance change evokes ionic membrane currents and a postsynaptic response, indicated by the membrane voltage u_M. An

Fig. 1. Simple block diagram of a neuron. S: synapse; M: synapse-free membrane of the soma and of dendrites; A: axon; u: action potential in afferent and efferent fibres; g: the ionic conductance of the subsynaptic membrane of the soma influenced by u; u_M: displacement of membrane potential from resting value.

action potential is generated if the postsynaptic response is excitatory and supra-threshold. The action potential is propagated over the axon and appears as another input impulse u at the next neuron.

The present discussion will be limited to a particular neural element, to the giant synapse (distal synapse) in the squid stellate ganglion. This element is an axo-axonal synapse. Therefore the diagram of Fig. 1 may be replaced by the diagram of Fig. 2 representing the giant synapse (S) and the surrounding membrane of the giant axon

Fig. 2. Simple block diagram of the axo-axonal giant synapse in the stellate ganglion of the squid *Loligo*. In this case the nerve cell is far from the synapse and has negligible influence on pulse transmission. The presynaptic impulses are immediately transmitted to the postsynaptic axon. The same designations as in Fig. 1.

(A) at which both, the subthreshold postsynaptic responses and the action potential are evoked. This element has been chosen, because an excellent model of the giant axon has been worked out by Hodgkin and Huxley (1952). For the work leading finally to the development of the model, Hodgkin and Huxley have been awarded the Nobel Prize for medicine in 1963. Furthermore comprehensive experiments have been carried out by Bullock and Hagiwara (1957), Hagiwara and Tasaki (1958), and Takeuchi and Takeuchi (1962), revealing many of the properties of the giant synapse. Based on these findings a simple synapse model may be developed that can be combined with the axon model of Hodgkin and Huxley, thus providing a model of a neural element.

2. THE SYNAPSE MODEL

2.1 The synaptic terminal

The synapse consists of three parts (Fig. 3): the synaptic terminal or synaptic knob (SK), the synaptic cleft (SC) and the subsynaptic portion (SM) of the postsynaptic membrane. A presynaptic impulse u activates the synaptic knob and causes the

Fig. 3. Simple block diagram of the synapse. SK: synaptic terminal; SC: synaptic cleft; SM: subsynaptic area of the postsynaptic membrane. u: presynaptic action potential; s: amount of liberated transmitter substance; m: actual transmitter substance acting upon the subsynaptic membrane; g: ionic conductance of the subsynaptic membrane influenced by m.

liberation of an amount s of transmitter substance. The liberated transmitter substance diffuses through the synaptic cleft. A part m of s acts upon the subsynaptic membrane and causes an alteration of the ionic conductance g.

The task is now to find a simple model for this system that approximates the

experimental results as close as possible. Hagiwara and Tasaki (1958) have excited
the giant synapse by presynaptic spikes of various amplitudes $\hat{u}$ and have recorded
the amplitudes $\hat{u}_M$ of the excitatory postsynaptic potentials (EPSP's). The curve in
Fig. 4 gives the relationship between the amplitudes $\hat{u}_M$ of the EPSP's and the relative
amplitudes of the presynaptic spikes $\hat{u}_r$. This curve may be called input characteristic

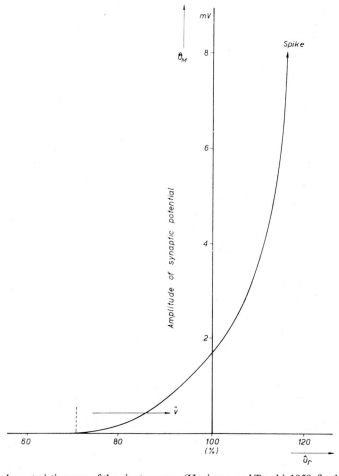

Fig. 4. Input characteristic curve of the giant synapse (Hagiwara and Tasaki, 1958, fig. 13). Horizontal
axis: amplitude of the presynaptic spike relative to a normal value. Vertical axis: amplitude of the
excitatory postsynaptic potentials (EPSP) observed at the giant synapse.

curve. It exhibits two important features: (1) There exists a presynaptic threshold at
approximately 70% of the normal spike amplitude. A postsynaptic response can be
observed only if the amplitude of the presynaptic spike exceeds the threshold. (2) The
relationship between the amplitude of the EPSP and the suprathreshold part v of the
presynaptic spike is strongly non-linear.

   According to present theory (Hagiwara and Tasaki, 1958; Takeuchi and Takeuchi,
1962; Eccles, 1964, p. 78, 82) the cause for both phenomena is thought to be in the

synaptic terminal. It is assumed that a remarkable release of transmitter substance takes place only if the amplitude of the presynaptic action potential exceeds a threshold and that the relationship between the suprathreshold part v of the presynaptic spike u and the released amount s of transmitter substance is non-linear.

If these assumptions hold the development of the synapse model should be started by introducing a threshold block (a, Fig. 5). Input of this block is the presynaptic

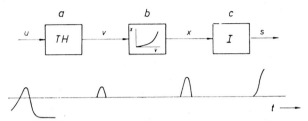

Fig. 5. Partial block diagram of the synaptic terminal of the giant synapse. Block a: threshold block, simulating presynaptic threshold; input: presynaptic action potential u; output: v, suprathreshold part of u. Block b: non-linearity simulating partially the non-linear input characteristic; input: v; output: an auxiliary variable x. Block c: integrator, simulating the release of transmitter substance s. The curves of u, v, x and s are sketched below the blocks.

action potential u, output is the suprathreshold part of u that has been designated v. By the next block (b) the non-linearity of the input characteristic may be simulated. Input variable of this block is the suprathreshold part v of the presynaptic spike, output is an auxiliary variable x. If v is an impulse, than x will be also an impulse (Fig. 5). Compared to v the amplitude of x will be distorted according to the non-linear transfer characteristic of block b. At present x can not be physically interpreted.

The next block simulates the release of transmitter substance s. From the occurrence of miniature endplate potentials (EPP) and of synaptic vesicles in the synaptic terminals it has been concluded that the transmitter substance is released in quanta (Eccles, 1961, p. 329, 338). Eccles applies this assumption to motoneurons and estimates that by one presynaptic spike, arriving at a synaptic knob, two or three quanta of transmitter substance might be liberated (1961, p. 339). In this case an extremely non-linear relationship of staircase form would hold between x and s. With the giant synapse Takeuchi and Takeuchi (1962, p. 1192) have estimated the quantum content of a synaptic potential to be 700. Because of this great number of quanta the staircase form of the release may be approximated by a smooth curve.

The exact relationship between the auxiliary variable x and the amount of released transmitter substance is not known. Therefore appropriate assumptions must be made. Following notions of Küpfmüller (1959, Küpfmüller and Jenik, 1961) it is assumed that the intensity of release is proportional to the instantaneous value of x (mathematically $ds/dt = k \cdot x$). This means that the total amount s of transmitter substance released by one impulse x, is proportional to the area of the impulse. The mathematical model for this relationship is the integration. Therefore block c in Fig. 5 represents an integrator.

Takeuchi and Takeuchi have excited the giant synapse by a train of action potentials

References p. 368

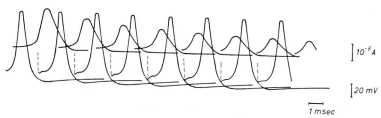

Fig. 6. Experimental data, published by Takeuchi and Takeuchi (1962, fig. 3). The giant synapse is excited by presynaptic action potentials (lower trace) arriving at a rate of 2 pps. The upper trace shows the corresponding synaptic currents evoked in the postsynaptic membrane which is voltage clamped. The great intervals of 500 ms between consecutive impulses have been omitted.

at a rate of 2/sec. They have recorded simultaneously the afferent impulses and the currents evoked in the postsynaptic membrane during voltage clamp (Fig. 6). These records exhibit three important features: (a) the amplitudes of the currents in the postsynaptic membrane decay over five to seven impulses and then attain a plateau that is maintained for a long time, (b) the currents show a steep rise and a fast decay, (c) there is a synaptic delay of approximately 1 msec between the onset of the presynaptic impulse and the onset of the postsynaptic current.

The cause for the decay of the amplitudes of the postsynaptic currents is again thought to be in the synaptic terminal. Eccles (1961, p. 338) points out: "Previous investigations on many different types of synapses have given rise to the suggestion that repetitive synaptic activation involves two opposing processes: depletion of the available transmitter and a mobilization of transmitter". If this holds for the giant synapse, too, then the decrease of the first current amplitudes in Fig. 6 may be explained by prevailing depletion. After five to seven impulses depletion and mobilization balance one another and a steady state is attained.

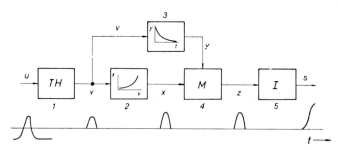

Fig. 7. Simple block diagram of the synaptic terminal of the giant synapse. Blocks 1, 2 and 5 correspond to blocks a, b, c of Fig. 5. Block 3 represents an ordinary differential equation providing a time dependent variable y that decreases if impulses u arrive. Block 4: Multiplier, performing multiplication of x and y. The output impulses z of block 4 agree with the input impulses x except for the amplitude. The amplitude of z decreases proportional to y. Attention: The insert of block 3 shows the time dependence of y, while the insert of block 2 shows the relationship between the amplitudes of x and v. The curves of u, v, x, z and s are sketched below the blocks.

In the model this process may be realized by introducing a multiplier between the nonlinear and the integrating block of Fig. 5 (see Fig. 7). Inputs of this block are the auxiliary variables x and y, output is the auxiliary variable z. There holds $z = x \cdot y$.

In the inactivated state let be $y = 1$. A first impulse x evoked under this condition will be transformed into an impulse z without any distortion. If more impulses arrive y must be controlled in such way that it shows the same decrease as the current amplitudes of Fig. 6. The variable z and the released transmitter substance s are proportional to y and show the same decrease. In the model it has been assumed that y is controlled by the impulses v. Block 3 transforms the impulses v into a decaying variable y as shown approximately by the inserted curve. In the simplest case block 3 represents a linear differential equation.

2.2 The synaptic cleft and the subsynaptic membrane

Two processes occur in the synaptic cleft: (a) The diffusion of the transmitter substance from the synaptic terminal to the subsynaptic membrane, (b) the abolition of the transmitter substance by enzymatic effects and by diffusion out of the synaptic cleft.

The diffusion of the transmitter substance across the synaptic cleft takes some time that accounts for most of the synaptic delay (Hagiwara and Tasaki, 1958). The rate of abolition, the rate of decay of the transmitter substance is important for pulse processing. If the decay is slow, the transmitter substance released by one impulse acts for a long time on the subsynaptic membrane and may evoke many action potentials, as can be observed with Renshaw cells and interneurons. With fast decay one input pulse can evoke only one output pulse. An exact mathematical description of diffusion and abolition requires the application of partial differential equations as shown by Eccles and Jaeger, 1958. For the present purpose only the time course of the transmitter substance at the subsynaptic membrane is of interest. It is assumed that the synaptic currents observed during voltage clamp of the postsynaptic membrane (Fig. 6) are proportional to the transmitter substance at the subsynaptic membrane thus providing data of the decay of the transmitter substance.

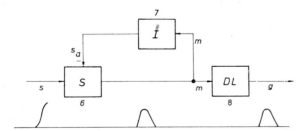

Fig. 8. Simple block diagram of the synaptic cleft (block 6 and 7) and of the subsynaptic area of the postsynaptic membrane (block 8). Block 6: Subtractor; s represents the released transmitter substance, s_a the abolished and m the actual transmitter acting upon the subsynaptic membrane. Block 7: integrator. Block 8 simulates the influence of the transmitter substance m on the ionic conductance g of the postsynaptic membrane; it performs some time delay (DL) but no pulse shaping. The shapes of the variables are shown below the block diagram.

In the model the abolition of the released transmitter substance can be simulated by subtraction (block 6 in Fig. 8). Inputs of the subtractor block 6 are the released transmitter substance a and the abolished transmitter substance s_a. The difference of

362 F. JENIK

these quantities is the actual transmitter substance *m*. An analysis of the decay of the membrane currents shows that the decay can be roughly approximated by an exponential curve. This permits to control s_a by *m*, if the relationship between these variables is realized by an integrator (block 7).

The transmitter substance *m* causes an alteration of the ionic conductance *g* of the subsynaptic membrane. According to the above assumptions the alteration of the membrane conductance is proportional to *m*, except for some time delay. Therefore block 8 simulating the relationship between *m* and *g* performs only some time delay but no pulse shaping. In neurons three factors contribute to the synaptic delay (Eccles, 1964, p. 82): (a) the liberation of transmitter substance, (b) the diffusion of the transmitter across the synaptic cleft, (c) the attachment of the transmitter to the receptor sites and the alteration of the ionic conductance of the subsynaptic membrane. In the present model the total synaptic delay has been simulated by block 8, because exact data of the particular contributions are not available. The block diagrams of Figs. 7 and 8 represent a simple model of the giant synapse. This model will be combined with the Hodgkin–Huxley model of the giant axon.

3. THE EXTENDED HODGKIN–HUXLEY MODEL

3.1 The Hodgkin–Huxley model

Hodgkin and Huxley (1952) have introduced the electrical circuit of Fig. 9 that simulates many processes occurring in the giant axon. The model consists of the membrane capacitance C_M, the membrane conductances for the sodium (g_{Na}), potassium (g_K) and the other (g_L) ions, and the equilibrium potentials for the sodium (Φ_{Na}), the potasium (Φ_K) and the other (Φ_L) ions. Fig. 9A shows the classical 'closed'

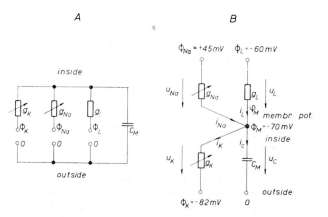

Fig. 9. Circuit diagram of the electrical model for the giant axon of the squid (Hodgkin and Huxley, 1952). *A*: closed form, *B*: open form. C_M: membrane capacitance; g_{Na}, g_K, g_L: ionic membrane conductances; Φ_{Na}, Φ_K, Φ_L: equilibrium potentials; i_{Na}, i_K, i_L, i_c: membrane currents; u_{Na}, u_K, u_L, u_c: driving voltages; φ_M: membrane potential ($\Phi_M = -70$ mV resting value of φ_M); u_M: membrane voltage ($u_M = \varphi_M - \Phi_M$).

configuration. The 'open' equivalent of Fig. 9B shows clearly that the model essentially is a voltage divider.

The membrane capacitance C_M, the conductance g_L and the equilibrium potentials Φ_{Na}, Φ_K, Φ_L are constant; the sodium conductance g_{Na} and the potassium conductance g_K are variable. In the resting state the membrane potential φ_M assumes a resting value of —70 mV that results from division of the equilibrium potentials by the conductances g_{Na}, g_K and g_L. An increase of the sodium conductance g_{Na} causes a positive displacement of the membrane potential, a depolarization, an increase of the potassium conductance g_K causes a negative displacement of φ_M, a hyperpolarization.

Hodgkin and Huxley have shown that the sodium and the potassium conductances are influenced by the membrane potential via feedback. The relationships are shown by a simplified block diagram in Fig. 10. There is a central block (*IF*) representing the

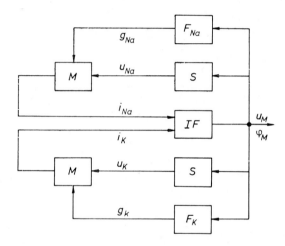

Fig. 10. Simple block diagram of the Hodgkin–Huxley model for the giant axon. *IF*: integrating pulse shaper, corresponding to C_M and g_L of Fig. 11; S = subtractor; M = multiplier; F_{Na} and F_K complex mathematical functions describing the relationships between the membrane potential (φ_M) and the membrane conductances for the sodium (g_{Na}) and potassium (g_K) ions.

membrane capacitance C_M and the leakage conductance g_L. Output of this block is the membrane potential φ_M or the membrane voltage u_M, inputs are the sodium (i_{Na}) and the potassium (i_K) currents. The membrane currents are generated according to Ohm's law by multiplication of the driving membrane voltages (u_{Na}, u_K) and the membrane conductances (g_{Na}, g_K). The ionic conductances and the driving voltages depend on the membrane potential φ_M, thus constituting feedback loops. There is a sodium feedback and a potassium feedback. Each feedback consists of a voltage path and a conductance path. The sodium conductance path (F_{Na}) exhibits positive feedback that causes the raise of the action potential. Both voltage paths and the potassium conductance path (F_K) provide negative feedback, that effects the decrease of the action potential.

3.2 The complete model

The conductances of the synapse-free membrane for the sodium, the potassium and
the other ions are in the model (Fig. 9A and B) realized by g_{Na}, g_K and g_L, respective-

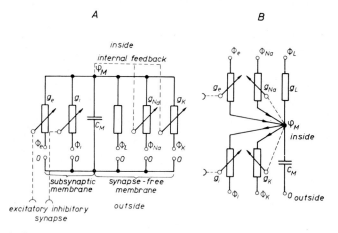

Fig. 11. Electrical circuit diagram of the axon model extended by the ionic conductances g_e, g_i of
the subsynaptic membrane of an excitatory and an inhibitory synapse. A closed version, B: open
version.

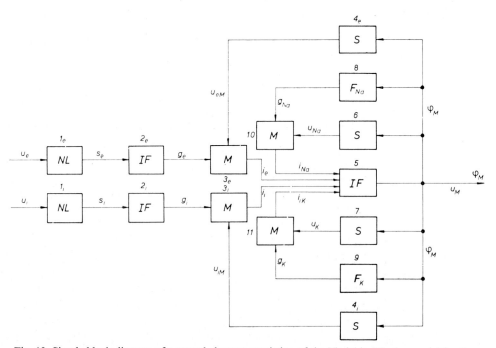

Fig. 12. Simple block diagram of a neural element consisting of the Hodgkin–Huxley model for the
giant axon (blocks 5–11) extended by an excitatory synapse (blocks 1e–4e) and an inhibitory synapse
(block 1i–4i).

ly. During the activity of the synapses the conductances of the subsynaptic areas are in parallel to the membrane conductances (Eccles, 1964 p. 49, 154). In Fig. 11 the conductances of an excitatory (g_e) and of an inhibitory (g_i) subsynaptic area have been introduced, g_i being merely hypothetical. The equilibrium potential Φ_e of the excitatory processes is close to zero (Hagiwara and Tasaki, 1958; Eccles, 1964, p. 50). An increase of g_e causes depolarization. On the other hand it is assumed that the equilibrium potential Φ_i for the inhibitory processes approaches the potassium potential Φ_K. An increase of g_i therefore causes hyperpolarization.

A simplified block diagram of the complete system is shown in Fig. 12. There is the feedback system of Fig. 10 consisting of blocks 5 to 11, simulating the activity of the synapse-free membrane. The excitatory synapse is simulated by blocks 1e to 4e, the inhibitory by blocks 1i to 4i. The block diagram is the graphical representation of a system of non-linear differential equations, describing the activity of synapses and of the synapse-free membrane concentrated at one point. It does not account for the spatial extension of the synapse and of the membrane. If the spatial extention should be accounted for, partial differential equations must be applied (Hodgkin and Huxley, 1952; Eccles and Jaeger, 1958). In terms of electrical circuits and of block diagrams spatial extension could be approximated by connecting several systems of Figs. 11 and 12 in parallel (Freygang, 1959; Rall, 1962). The advantage of mathematical models is that they give the relationships between many variables of a system in an exact and concise way. For practical purposes, however, the relationships between all variables are less interesting than the response of one variable, *e.g.* the membrane potential, to particular stimuli. Such responses can be calculated from

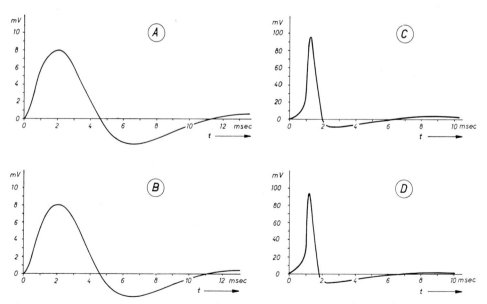

Fig. 13. Excitatory postsynaptic potentials (A, B) and action potentials (C, D) of giant synapse of *Loligo* (A: Takeuchi, Takeuchi, 1962; C: Hagiwara, Tasaki, 1958) and of extended Hodgkin–Huxley system (B, D: Hoehne, 1962); A: 10–15°C; B: 11°C; D = 18°C; C: Peak of spike restored. Vertical axis: displacement from resting potential. Horizontal axis: time.

the model by digital computers. A digital computer programmed with the extended Hodgkin–Huxley system represents an electronic model of the giant synapse.

Fig. 13 shows excitatory postsynaptic potentials and action potentials observed at the giant synapse and calculated by the extended Hodgkin–Huxley model. There is rather close agreement between the actual and the calculated responses.

4. THE ν-DIAGRAM

The principal purpose of neuron models is not the reproduction of single impulses but the investigation of pulse processing in cell networks. If the models shall be applied for this purpose there must be agreement between neuron and model not only for individual impulses but over the complete operation range. The operation range of a neuron can be defined by the set of all input situations and all output situations. The number of all input and output situations is very great. Therefore it is impractical to test a cell at all input and output situations and appropriate test functions must be chosen. In communication engineering similar problems occur: many various apparatus must be tested and compared with regard to pulse transmission and pulse processing. Here periodic wave forms turned out to be appropriate test functions. By means of the frequency response all apparatus can be compared.

This experience has been applied to neuron models. The models have been tested by application of an excitatory periodic pulse train of intensity e and of frequency f_e. The output rate r_a has been observed. The input variables have been varied between minimal and maximal values, that define the input operation range. The operation range of the input frequency extends between 0 and 1000 pps:

$$0 \leq f_e \leq 1000 \text{ pps.}$$

The input intensity indicates the amplitude of the presynaptic action potential and the number of synchronously activated synapses. Threshold intensity has been chosen as unity $e_{TH} = 1$. For subthreshold intensities there is $e < 1$, for suprathreshold intensities holds $e > 1$. The intensity range has been chosen as

$$0 \leq e \leq 5.$$

The results of a test may be plotted as characteristic curves (Harmon, 1961) or in the diagram of Fig. 14, that has been called ν-diagram (Küpfmüller and Jenik, 1961). According to suggestions of Küpfmüller the input frequencies have been plotted against the horizontal axis and the input intensities against the vertical. The area encompassed by the axes represents the input operation range under test conditions. Each point in this area represents the input situation of a particular test specified by particular values of e and f_e. At each point has been assigned the ratio ν of output rate r_a to input frequency f_e ($\nu = r_a : f_e$) that results from the corresponding input situation.

It turned out that there are distinctly bounded ν-areas, that are characteristic for a particular model. $\nu = 0$ indicates the subthreshold operation range, where no output pulses occur. In the area $\nu = 1$ each input pulse evokes one output pulse. Of particular

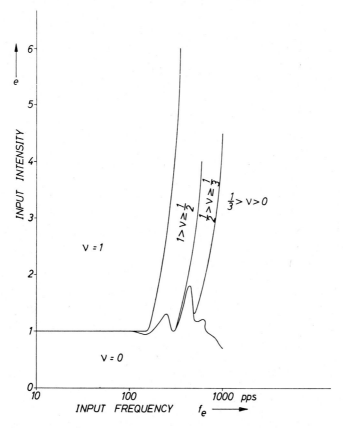

Fig. 14. v-diagram of a simplified version of the extended Hodgkin–Huxley model. In the model tested here the non linear blocks 1 and 2 have been replaced by linear ones, and blocks 3 and 4 providing adaptation have been omitted. The model is excited by one periodic pulse train of intensity e and frequency f_e. Each point in the area encompassed by the axes represents one input situation, defined by e and f_e. The ratio v of the resultant output rate r_a to the input frequency f_e has been assigned to each point. In the area $v = 0$ no output pulse and in $0 < v < 1$ frequency division occurs. (Jenik, 1964).

interest for pulse processing is the area where v-values between 0 and 1 can be obtained and where frequency division occurs. In the v-diagram of Fig. 14 frequency division occurs only above $f_e = 100$ pps. Average frequencies in this range may often occur if several afferent fibres are activated by various pulse trains.

A detailed analysis shows that the shapes of the v-areas are determined by the properties of cells that are important for pulse processing. By means of the v-diagrams models and neurons could be compared. The model is appropriate for the investigation of pulse processing only, if there is sufficient agreement between the shapes of the v-areas or between the boundary curves. Agreement between particular uncritical v-values $e.g.$ points A, B, C in Fig. 14 is not sufficient.

At present v-diagrams of neurons have not yet been worked out. The determination of v-diagrams of neurons would be very desirable.

ACKNOWLEDGEMENT

The author is grateful to Prof. Dr. Ing. e.h. K. Küpfmüller for advice and discussion, to Dipl. Ing. H. Hoehne for computer programming and calculations and to Deutsche Forschungsgemeinschaft for financial support. All calculations have been made at Deutsches Rechenzentrum, Darmstadt.

SUMMARY

The development of a neuron model is discussed by means of block diagrams. The systems consists of a model for the giant synapse of the squid and of the Hodgkin–Huxley membrane model. The synapse model is a non-linear system that simulates some adaptive properties. Calculated EPSP's and action potentials are shown and compared with actual ones. The model has been tested by periodic pulse trains. The results are plotted in a v-diagram.

REFERENCES

BULLOCK, TH. H., AND HAGIWARA, S., (1957); Intracellular recording from the giant synapse of the squid. *J. Gen. Physiol.*, **40**, 565–577.

ECCLES, J. C., (1961); The mechanism of synaptic transmission. *Ergebn. Physiol.*, **51**, 299–431.

ECCLES, J. C., (1964); *The Physiology of Synapses*. Springer, Berlin.

ECCLES, J. C., AND JAEGER, J. C., (1958); The relationship between the mode of operation and the dimensions of the junctional regions at synapses and motor end-organs. *Proc. Roy. Soc.*, **B 148**, 38–56.

FREYGANG, JR., W. H., (1959); Some functions of nerve cells in terms of an equivalent network. *Proc. Inst. Radio Eng.*, **47**, 1862–1869.

HAGIWARA, S., AND TASAKI, I., (1958); A study on the mechanism of impulse transmission across the giant synapse of the squid. *J. Physiol.*, **143**, 114–137.

HARMON, L. D., (1961); Studies with artificial neurons: I. Properties and functions of an artificial neuron. *Kybernetik*, **1**, 89–101.

HODGKIN, A. L., AND HUXLEY, A. F., (1952); A quantitative description of membrane current and its applications to conduction and excitation in nerve. *J. Physiol.*, **117**, 500–544.

JENIK, F., (1964); *Pulse processing of neuron models. Neural Theory and Modeling*. R. F. Reiss, Editor. Stanford Univ. Press.

KÜPFMÜLLER, K., (1959); Informationsverarbeitung durch den Menschen. *Nachrichtentechn. Z.*, **12**, 68–74.

KÜPFMÜLLER, K., AND JENIK, F., (1961); Über die Nachrichtenverarbeitung in der Nervenzelle. *Kybernetik*, **1**, 1–6.

RALL, W., (1962); Electrophysiology of a dendritic neuron model. *Biophys. J.*, **2**, (2) 145–167.

TAKEUCHI, A., AND TAKEUCHI, N., (1962); Electrical changes in pre- and postsynaptic axons of the giant synapse of Loligo. *J. Gen. Physiol.*, **45**, 1181–1193.

A Model of Learning Mechanisms in the Brain

W. K. TAYLOR

University College London, Department of Electrical Engineering, London (Great Britain)

INTRODUCTION

The numerous attempts that have been made to construct mathematical and electronic models of neural networks vary considerably in the degree of complexity of the individual neuron model employed and in the number of model neurons considered. At the level of complexity corresponding to the Hodgkin–Huxley axon membrane model investigators usually consider a single axon since the computations of interaction between several neurons in this detail would be impractical even on the largest digital or analogue computers. Any simplifications of the individual neuron model must produce some effect on the behaviour of an assembly and it is important to make simplifying assumptions that produce little distortion of the network properties from those obtained with the more exact neural models.

The most fundamental property of a neuron is its capacity for generating impulses at a frequency that is approximately proportional to the amount by which the resultant applied stimulus exceeds a threshold. This property is independent of the exact origin of the stimulus and any influence that tends to reduce the negative internal potential appears to be capable of firing a neuron. The firing rates of cortical neurons for example can be increased or decreased by feeding minute currents through the brain in the appropriate direction or by changing the composition of locally applied chemicals (Krnjević, 1963). Natural stimulation also modifies the firing rate (Lippold, 1963) and in this case the neurons are probably responding to the release of chemical transmitter substances at a proportion of the thousands of synaptic endings that cover the cell body and dendrites. McIntyre (1956) has demonstrated that temporal summation at some central synapses may last for 100 milliseconds or more so that spatial summation can occur when the afferent impulses are widely separated in time as well as in space. This picture is further complicated by the fact that a given size of stimulus may produce a greater increase in the firing rate of a given neuron at different times, depending on the intervening history of stimulation (Lippold, 1963). It seems improbable that this increase is due to a change in the size or frequency of the afferent axon action potential and an attractive hypothesis is that it is due to an increase in the amount of the transmitter substance released by each nerve impulse. Indirect support for this hypothesis also comes from electron micrographs of synapses in the brain which show considerable variability of the area of contact between axon and neuron membranes and also variation in the number of synaptic vesicles (Gray, 1959).

If the synaptic vesicles store the packets of transmitter substance that are released by the axon action potentials then one would expect changes in the firing rate produced by a standard stimulus to accompany any change in the number of synaptic vesicles.

In order to construct models of neural networks in which there is interaction between the neurons it is necessary to define the model of synaptic transmission. The model proposed by Taylor (1955) is reproduced in Fig. 1. Permanent learning is only

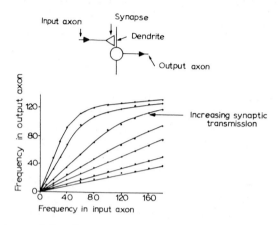

Fig. 1. Input–output characteristics of model neuron for different values of synaptic transmission.

possible in networks that contain synapses with this type of characteristic for which the synaptic transmission, defined as the change in output firing rate produced by unit change in input firing rate, is changed by activity. It has recently been shown (Taylor, 1964) that the magnitude of the change in transmission required for learning behaviour need only be a very small percentage of the initial or 'birth' value. A restriction of the magnitude of the synaptic transmission is obviously required if a neuron with thousands of synapses is not to be overdriven when a large percentage of excitatory synaptic endings are bombarded almost simultaneously at moderate impulse frequencies. Since an overdriven neuron ceases to produce impulses it represents a serious loss of information. If we accept that this is to be avoided so far as possible there must be restrictions on the maximum resultant stimulation that a neuron can receive. The word resultant is important here since stimulation can be excitatory or inhibitory, or positive and negative. Thus an excitatory stimulus many times the value required to drive a neuron at its maximum frequency could be almost exactly balanced by an inhibitory stimulus. The probability of this state existing by chance is extremely low, however, and its seems more feasible that it could only be maintained by negative feedback circuits. It is known that negative feedback plays an important role in the position control systems of the spinal cord (Taylor, 1957) and there is increasing evidence that the feedback principle is also employed throughout the brain. Analogue computers and control systems also make considerable use of the negative feedback principle and it is in these systems that the closest analogues of many neural circuits are to be found.

NEURONS AS CIRCUIT ELEMENTS

The various shapes of neuron found in the cerebral cortex have been classified by Sholl (1956). Examples of the two main types, pyramidals and stellates, are shown in Fig. 2, which suggests a possible way of representing them as circuit elements. Four synapses are shown in the pyramidal neuron, two excitatory and two inhibitory.

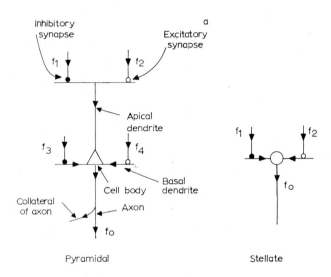

Fig. 2. Representation of pyramidal and stellate neurons as circuit elements.

When a nerve impulse arrives at an excitatory synapse it releases a transmitter substance that makes the membrane more permeable to sodium ions, thereby allowing a depolarizing inward current to flow. At the inhibitory synapse a different transmitter substance makes the membrane more permeable to potassium and possibly chloride ions, thereby allowing a polarizing current to flow until an equilibrium value of internal negative potential is reached. If steady inward and outward currents flow simultaneously and the cell is prevented from firing the internal potential will reach a resultant potential v_r that may be above or below the threshold potential v_t. If $v_r > v_t$ the cell fires at a rate proportional to $v_r - v_t$. Thus if v_t is —60 mV and v_r is —50 mV, the firing rate is proportional to $(-50) - (-60) = + 10$ mV. When $v_r < v_t$ the cell does not fire but a small increase in depolarization makes it fire if v_r is just below v_t. For strong inhibition v_r cannot go far below v_t since the limiting value of the potassium equilibrium potential is reached and the relationship between potential and current is highly non-linear. For this reason it is more convenient to deal with currents rather than potentials since if the potential in the synaptic region does not depart significantly from the resting potential the changes in current flow will be approximately proportional to the changes in membrane conductance. Also, if the latter changes are proportional to the concentration of transmitter substance which in turn is proportional to the rate at which transmitter is released by afferent impulses, there should be an overall steady state relationship of the following form for the pyramidal neuron in Fig. 2

$$f_0 = (t_1 f_1 + t_2 f_2 + t_3 f_3 + t_4 f_4) \tag{1}$$

where the t's are the transmissions of the synapses and are given in general by

$$t_r = \left(\frac{\mathrm{d}f_0}{\mathrm{d}f_r} \right) \ (\mathrm{d}f_n = 0, \ n \neq r) \tag{2}$$

i.e. t_r is the change in f_0 produced by a unit change in f_r when all other inputs are held constant and the neuron is firing at a rate f_0 before the change to $f_0 + \mathrm{d}f_0$ occurs. Thus to find t_2, f_2 is increased to $f_2 + \mathrm{d}f_2$ and f_0 increases to $f_0 + \mathrm{d}f_0$ if t_2 is an excitatory synapse or f_0 decreases to $f_0 - \mathrm{d}f_0$ if t_2 is an inhibitory synapse. In the first case

$$f_0 + \mathrm{d}f_0 = t_1 f_1 + t_2(f_2 + \mathrm{d}f_2) + t_3 f_3 + t_4 f_4$$

and subtracting equation (1) from this expression yields

$$\mathrm{d}f_0 = t_2 \mathrm{d}f_2 \ \text{ or } \ t_2 = \frac{\mathrm{d}f_0}{\mathrm{d}f_2}$$

For the inhibitory synapse with transmission t_3

$$f_0 - \mathrm{d}f_0 = t_1 f_1 + t_2 f_2 + t_3(f_3 + \mathrm{d}f_3) + t_4 f_4$$

and subtraction gives

$$- \mathrm{d}f_0 = t_3 \mathrm{d}f_3 \ \text{ or } \ t_3 = - \frac{\mathrm{d}f_0}{\mathrm{d}f_3}$$

Inhibitory synapses may thus be considered to have negative transmission.

The general expression for the steady state firing rate of a neuron with n synapses becomes

$$f_0 = \sum_{r=1}^{n} t_r f_r \tag{3}$$

It is possible that groups of synapses originate from the same afferent axon and in this case there is only one value of f_r for the group. For these cases the t_r can be interpreted as the equivalent resultant transmission of the group.

A representation of the cause-effect sequence from an afferent axon to the firing rate of the post-synaptic neuron is shown in Fig. 3.

This simple picture only represents the steady state equation (3) and the dynamic response must also be considered. It seems quite possible that there are several different transmitter substances and that each has a characteristic time course of action.

Microelectrode recordings obtained by McIntyre (1956) and Krnjević (1963) reproduced in Fig. 4 illustrate this point. Quite apart from the magnitudes of the effect which can be represented by the transmission t_r there is a wide range of possible time courses for the rise and decay of excitation and inhibition following the arrival of an afferent impulse at a synapse.

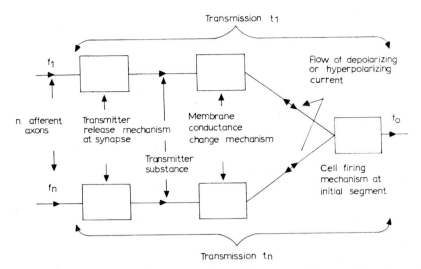

Fig. 3. Representation of cause—effect sequence from afferent axon firing rates $f_1 \ldots f_n$ to rate of post-synaptic neuron; f_0.

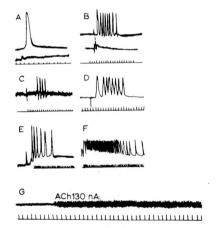

Fig. 4. Microelectrode recordings showing prolonged discharge following release of slowly decaying transmitter.

Strictly speaking the word frequency has no meaning except in the steady state where $f_r = \dfrac{1}{T_r}$ and T_r is the time interval between impulses. It is useful, however, to introduce the concept of instantaneous frequency at time t and to define it as the reciprocal of the time interval between the last impulse and the present impulse at time t. This instantaneous frequency $f_r(t)$ is illustrated in Fig. 5. Thus $f_r(t)$ can be interpreted as the reciprocal of the 'local' time interval between impulses at time t and there is little loss of useful information if $f_r(t)$ is regarded as a continuous curve through the points. If, for example, $f_r(t)$ is as shown in Fig. 5 it is possible to reconstruct the corresponding nerve impulse pattern by using the function $f(t_0) = \dfrac{1}{t_0}$

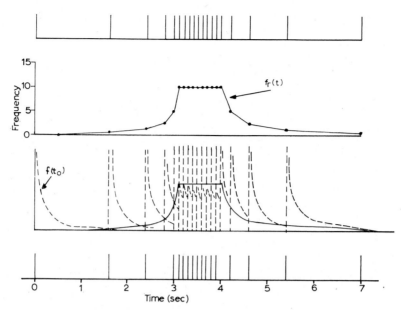

Fig. 5. Instantaneous frequency representation of nerve impulse patterns.

as a template with the origin ($t_0 = 0$) situated initially where $f_r(t)$ becomes non-zero, *i.e.* at the first impulse position. The second impulse is then situated at the point where the curve $\dfrac{1}{t_0}$ crosses $f_r(t)$. Similarly the third impulse is found by placing the template origin at the second impulse and so on. If $f_r(t)$ represents the resultant flow of current into the neuron then the pattern of nerve impulses generated can be expected to resemble the pattern derived by the above procedure, except at very low frequencies. If, however, the impulse pattern represents the input to a synapse r having $t_r = 1$, then f_0 cannot in general be expected to be a reproduction of the impulse pattern except perhaps in the steady state and even then there may be a grouping of impulses so that only the average of f_0 is equal to f_r. This distortion of the impulse pattern as it passes through a synapse and neuron can be expected whenever the synapse has a memory effect of any duration from a few milliseconds upwards. Synaptic transmitter memory effects that decay with time constants of approximately 50 msec and 60 sec are illustrated in Fig. 4 at F and G respectively. The first shows the response of a neuron that continues to fire long after the occurrence of a short volley of synaptic bombardment. The second memory effect is produced by releasing a small amount of acetylcholine near a cortical neuron. In both cases the firing continues after the initial stimulus is removed and it is probably due to the slow decay of the transmitter and ACh. concentrations respectively. In the case of cholinergic neurons the transmitter itself may well be ACh, which appears from the results of Krnjević to have much longer rise and decay times than laevo-glutanate and γ-aminobutyric acid (GABA) which produce excitation and inhibition respectively. The depolarizing and hyperpolarizing currents that might be expected to flow if small quantities of these substances are released by a nerve impulse arriving at a synapse containing one of them is illustrated in Fig. 6. It is assumed that each impulse produces the same peak value of current.

MAGNITUDE OF SYNAPTIC TRANSMISSION

The average steady state magnitude of the synaptic current presumably depends on the following factors:

(a) The quantity of transmitter released by an action potential in the presynaptic axon. Other things being constant, this quantity will be assumed to be proportional to the magnitude of the action potential.

(b) The strength or concentration of the transmitter.

(c) The rate of decay of the transmitter.

A function that gives a good approximation to the rise and fall of the synaptic current following an impulse is ate^{-bt} where the value of a represents the combined effect of (a) and (b) above and $\frac{1}{b}$ is the decay time constant.

For a constant presynaptic axon frequency f_i the depolarizing (or hyperpolarizing) current will rise to a mean value with a superimposed fluctuation, as shown in Fig. 6.

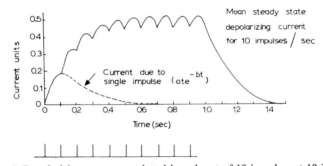

Fig. 6. Depolarizing current produced by a burst of 10 impulses at 10 i/sec.

SYNAPSES WITH PERMANENT MEMORY

The slow decay of transmitter at some synaptic endings can be regarded as a short term memory but this effect cannot form a satisfactory basis for permanent memory even if the transmitter decay time constant $\frac{1}{b}$ is infinite since this would result in increasingly high rates of spontaneous firing in the absence of stimulation and there is no evidence for this. The advantage of a short term transmitter substance memory is that it can be used over and over again to store different information for short periods since the memory is automatically erased as the transmitter decays to zero. The nature of permanent memory appears to be fundamentally different in that it is still present in the absence of transmitter substance and when the neurons are not firing. The most reasonable hypothesis is that permanent memory resides in changes of synaptic transmission and only becomes apparent when the synapse is 'interrogated' by nerve impulses. This synaptic transmission hypothesis of permanent memory in its simplest form assumes that the transmission of a specialized 'memory synapse' commences at some initial value t_0 and increases by a very small amount Δt_0 each time an impulse arrives at the synapse.

The interpretation of the experiment performed by Lippold *et al.* (1962) on the above hypothesis is that the current fed into the cortex increases the synaptic transmission at certain neurons which thenceforward fire at a higher rate when the same natural stimulus is repeated.

NEURAL CIRCUITS WITHOUT SIGNIFICANT MEMORY

(a) Collateral feedback

Feedback from a neuron to itself via a recurrent collateral may be positive or negative as illustrated in Fig. 7. The relationship between input and output changes in firing rate are

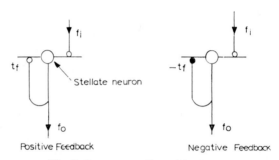

Fig. 7. Recurrant collateral feedback.

$$f_0 = f_i t_i + f_0 t_f \qquad \text{for positive feedback}$$

$$f_0 = f_i t_i - f_0 t_f \qquad \text{for negative feedback}$$

Hence

$$f_0 = \frac{f_i t_i}{1 - t_f} \qquad \text{(positive feedback)}$$

$$f_0 = \frac{f_i t_i}{1 + t_f} \qquad \text{(negative feedback)}$$

It follows that positive feedback can cause a neural circuit to be unstable if t_f, or more generally the resultant transmission round a positive feedback path, is equal to or greater than unity. If $t_f \geqslant 1$ a single afferent impulse causes f_0 to suddenly jump from zero to a maximum possible firing rate at which the impulses become so small that t_f is effectively reduced to unity by non-linearity. Negative feedback, however, cannot cause instability, and if t_f becomes $\gg 1$ f_0 is given by $f_0 = \frac{t_i}{t_f} f_i$ and if in particular both t_i and t_f are much greater than unity and $t_i = k_i t_f$ then $f_0 = k_i f_i$

with a high degree of stability that is largely independent of electronical conduction from neighbouring neurons. This is illustrated in Fig. 8.

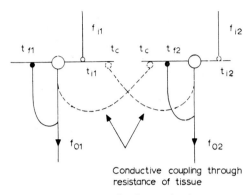

Conductive coupling through resistance of tissue

Fig. 8. Interaction by conduction.

Let the coupling due to the spread of current produce an effective transmission t_c of unity so that

$$f_{02} = f_{i2}t_{i2} + f_{01}t_c - f_{02}|t_{f2}|$$

from which

$$f_{02} = \frac{f_{i2}t_{i2} + f_{01}t_c}{1 + |t_{f2}|}$$

Thus if the transmitter has a powerful action that is 100 times greater than the spread of current so that

$$t_{i2} = 100\ t_c$$

$$|t_{f2}| = 100\ t_c$$

then

$$f_{02} \approx f_{i2} + f_{01}/100$$

But if $t_{i2} = t_c = 1$ and $t_{f2} = 0$ then $f_{02} = f_{i2} + f_c$

In other words, the firing of neuron (2) is largely controlled by its synaptic input frequency if this is of the same order as f_{01} and is very insensitive to the firing of neighbouring neurons that are not in synaptic contact with it. A special case of interest arises, however, when f_{i2} is zero or much smaller than f_{01}. It is then possible for the interaction effect to become dominant so that groups of neighbouring neurons become synchronized at a low frequency. It is suggested that this may be one reason why α rhythm tends to occur when the inputs f_i are small and why it disappears when they are large and the firing rates become independent and unsynchronized.

(b) Reciprocal feedback

The broken lines in Fig. 8 indicate interaction due to the spread of current but there is considerable evidence for axonic connections of this type at which t_c is produced by chemical transmission and may be of the same order of magnitude as t_i. If t_f is absent the circuit lateral inhibition becomes as shown in Fig. 9 and

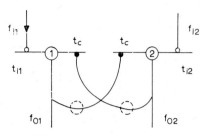

Fig. 9. Reciprocal feedback.

$$f_{01} = t_{i1}f_{i1} - |t_c|f_{02}$$

$$f_{02} = t_{i2}f_{i2} - |t_c|f_{01}$$

These are now simultaneous equations and solution gives

$$f_{01} = \frac{t_{i1}f_{i1} - |t_c|f_{i2}}{1 - t_c^2}$$

$$f_{02} = \frac{t_{i2}f_{i2} - |t_c|f_{i1}}{1 - t_c^2}$$

Thus if $|t_c| = \frac{1}{2}$ and $t_{i1} = t_{i2} = 1$

$$f_{01} = \frac{f_{i1} - \frac{1}{2}f_{i2}}{\frac{3}{4}}$$

$$f_{02} = \frac{f_{i2} - \frac{1}{2}f_{i1}}{\frac{3}{4}}$$

or

$$f_{01} = 4/3\,f_{i1} - 2/3\,f_{i2}$$

$$f_{02} = 4/3\,f_{i2} - 2/3\,f_{i1}$$

If these functions are plotted as they stand as a function of f_{i2} when $f_{i1} = 10$ the broken lines shown in Fig. 10 are obtained.

The solutions that predict negative values of frequency are impossible, however, and must be modified. The true solution is obtained by first replacing all negative frequencies by zero and then going back to the original equations. Thus from $0 \leqslant f_{i2} \leqslant 5$, f_{02} must be zero and we have

$$f_{01} = f_{i1} = 10$$

Also from $20 \leqslant f_{i2}$, $f_{01} = 0$ and

$$f_{02} = f_{i2}$$

In the spinal cord this type of circuit produces reciprocal innervation of flexor and

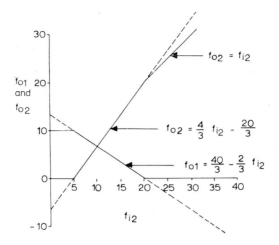

Fig. 10. Response of reciprocal feedback network.

extensor muscles. The neurons (1) and (2) are motoneurons and the inhibitory connexions are made through Renshaw cells, shown by broken circles in Fig. 9 (Taylor, 1957). It is sometimes useful to simplify neuronal circuits by omitting any neurons that are not firing. For the above example the equivalent circuits are as shown in Fig. 11 for the specified ranges of f_{i2}.

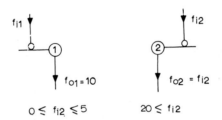

Fig. 11. Equivalent circuits.

It will be noted from the general expression

$$f_{01} = \frac{t_{i1}f_{i1} - |t_c|f_{i2}}{1 - t_c^2}$$

that t_c cannot be as large as unity since this makes the effective transmission infinite, *i.e.* the network becomes unstable. This is because there is positive feedback from each neuron to itself if the other neuron is firing. A small increase in f_{01} reduces f_{02} and this in turn removes some inhibition from neuron 1 and causes its frequency to increase still further until neuron 2 is cut off. Thus if f_{i1} and $f_{i2} = 10$ $t_c = t_{i1} = 1$, then it is possible to have $f_{01} = 10$ and $f_{02} = 0$ or $f_{01} = 0$ and $f_{02} = 10$. A momentary inhibition of the active neuron will cause the state to change over so that under these conditions the circuit can be said to remember which neuron was inhibited last.

(c) Combined positive and negative feedback. The amplitude sensitive trigger circuit

If a neuron has both excitatory and inhibitory self feedback as shown in Fig. 12 then the resultant output when the neuron is firing in a stable state is given by the solution of

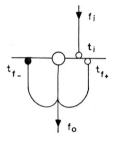

Fig. 12. Combined excitatory and inhibitory self feedback.

$$f_0 = f_i t_i + f_0 t_{f+} - f_0 |t_{f-}|$$

$$i.e. \; f_0 = \frac{f_i t_i}{1 + (|t_{f-}| - t_{f+})}$$

Thus if $|t_{f-}| = t_{f+}$ the net effect of the feedback is zero. If $|t_{f-}| > t_{f+}$ the circuit is stable and has a reduced overall gain and if $|t_{f-}| < t_{f+}$ but $(1 + |t_{f-}|) > t_{f+}$ the circuit is stable and the overall gain is increased. The gain becomes infinite when $(1 + |t_{f-}|) = t_{f+}$ *e.g.* when $|t_{f-}| = 1$ and $t_{f+} = 2$. A case of special interest arises when $(1 + |t_{f-}|) > t_{f+}$, and both feedback paths are inhibited, the inhibition of the negative feedback path exceeding the inhibition of the positive feedback path as shown in Fig. 13.

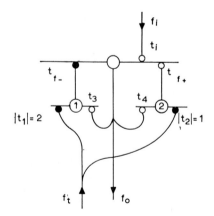

Fig. 13. An amplitude sensitive trigger circuit.

To take a specific example of this case let us assume the following values of transmission:

$$t_i = 1 \qquad\qquad |t_1| = 2$$

$$t_{f+} = 1 \qquad\qquad |t_2| = 1$$

$$|t_{f-}| = 1 \qquad\qquad t_3 = 1$$

$$t_4 = 1$$

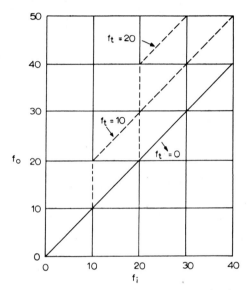

Fig. 14. Characteristics of trigger circuit.

As f_i increases from zero for various fixed values of f_t the values of f_0 shown in Fig. 14 are obtained. Thus when $f_t = 0$, f_0 is simply given by

$$f_0 = \frac{f_i}{1 + 1 - 1} = f_i$$

The outputs of neurons 1 and 2 are given by

$$f_{01} = f_0 - 2f_t$$

$$f_{02} = f_0 - f_t$$

so that for $f_t = 10$ neuron 2 is inhibited until $f_0 = 10$ but neuron 1 is inhibited until $f_0 = 20$. Thus as soon as $f_0 = f_t = 10$ the equation for f_0 changes from $f_0 = f_i$ to $f_0 = f_i + t_{f+} (f_0 - f_t)$ or

$$f_0 = \frac{f_i - f_t t_{f+}}{1 - t_{f+}} = \frac{f_i - f_t}{0}$$

i.e. the gain becomes infinite and f_0 increases rapidly. In practice f_0 can only increase at a finite rate determined by the membrane time constant and rate of increase of excitatory transmitter at synapse t_{f+}. The increase continues until $f_0 = t_1 f_t = 20$ and at this point the equation changes to

$$f_0 = f_i + t_{f+}(f_0 - f_i) - |t_{f-}|(f_0 - 2f_t)$$

$$f_0 = \frac{f_i + f_t(2t_{f-} - t_{f+})}{1 + |t_{f-}| - t_{f+}} = f_i + 10$$

The net result is that the output f_0 is equal to the input f_i until it reaches a threshold point f_t. At this point the output suddenly increases by an amount f_t and the circuit can be said to trigger. The input frequency f_t controls the threshold or trigger level and the size of the jump is proportional to this threshold.

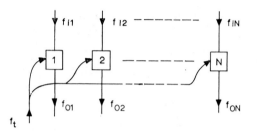

Fig. 15. Assembly of trigger circuits.

An assembly of trigger circuits as shown in Fig. 15 will indicate which of the increasing inputs is the first to reach the common trigger level, as determined by f_t, *i.e.* the maximum firing rate in a set of axons. Alternatively the trigger level may be reduced until the first circuit to trigger indicates the maximum, irrespective of its absolute magnitude.

(d) Maximum amplitude filter (MAF)

This circuit can be regarded as an extension of reciprocal feedback to more than two neurons and is shown in Fig. 16. The inputs are $f_{i1} \ldots f_{iN}$ and all but one of the outputs $f_{01} \ldots f_{0N}$ are required to be zero, the non-zero output being equal to the

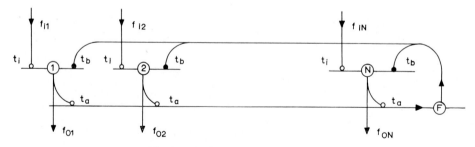

Fig. 16. Maximum of amplitude filter.

maximum input frequency. If N is the number of neurons in the filter then the feedback neuron F has N independent inputs from $f_{01} \ldots f_{0N}$ through the N synapses with transmission t_a giving

$$f_f = f_{01}t_a + f_{02}t_a \ldots \ldots f_{0N}t_a$$

$$f_f = t_a \left(f_{01} + \ldots \ldots f_{0N} \right)$$

When the filter is operating as required only one output f_{0m} is non-zero and $f_{0r} = f_{ir}$. For this active neuron

$$f_{0m} = \left(f_{im}t_i - f_f |t_b| \right)$$

$$\therefore f_{0m} = f_{ir}t_i - |t_b|t_a \left(f_{0r} \right)$$

$$\therefore f_{0m} = \frac{f_{im}t_i}{1 + |t_b|t_a} = f_{im} \quad \text{if} \quad \frac{t_i}{1 + |t_b|t_a} = 1$$

If for example $t_a = 1$ then $t_i = 1 + t_b$ and this is approximately satisfied if $t_i = |t_b| \gg 1$. To take a specific example let $t_a = 1$, $|t_b| = 19$, $t_i = 20$, $N = 20$. The filter will operate correctly providing the largest input exceeds the second largest input by an amount d_f which can be determined by substituting $f_{im} = f_i + d_f$ and

$$f_{ir} \leqslant f_i \qquad (r \neq m)$$

$$f_{0m} = (f_i + d_f) \frac{t_i}{1 + |t_b|t_a}$$

$$\therefore f_f = t_a f_{0r}$$

$$f_{0r} = f_{ir}t_i - f_f |t_b|$$

$$r \neq r_m$$

$$f_{0r} \leqslant f_i t_i - \frac{|t_b|t_a t_i}{1 + |t_b|t_a} \cdot (f_i + d_f)$$

for f_{0r} to be just zero

$$1 - \frac{|t_b|t_a}{1 + |t_b|t_a} = d_f \frac{t_b t_a}{1 + |t_b|t_a}$$

or

$$d_f = \frac{f_i}{|t_b|t_a}$$

Thus for $d_f = 1$ and a maximum input $f_{im} = 20$, all other inputs may have any value up to 19 and the corresponding outputs will be zero as required.

The possible range of transmission values in this circuit may be estimated from the basic assumption that each neuron has a maximum synaptic capacity related to the total surface area of its dendrites and a maximum firing rate of 1000 impulses/sec. If each neuron is to be potentially capable of firing up to the maximum rate when the filter is operating correctly then $f_f = 1000$ when $f_{0m} = 1000$, which means that t_a must be unity. There are N effective transmissions t_a and if these cover the surface area of neuron F the total transmission for the whole neuron is $Nt_a = N$ since $t_a = 1$. Neurons $1 \ldots \ldots N$ only have two sets of synaptic inputs and if each set covers half of the neuron surface the total transmission per set will again be N if each set occupies the same area as neuron F, i.e. if neurons $1 - N$ have twice the surface area of F. The values of transmission t_b and t_i that satisfy these simple physiological and geometrical restrictions are thus of the same order as N, the values required for correct operation of the MAF.

The case of exactly equal inputs is of interest since the d_f requirement is then not satisfied. By symmetry the outputs will all be f_0 if the inputs are all f_i. If we assume that neuron F is not overdriven then

$$f_f = N f_0 \, (t_a = 1)$$

also

$$f_0 = t_i f_i - |t_b| N f_0$$

and

$$f_0 = \frac{t_i f_i}{1 + N|t_b|}$$

and since

$$t_i \approx |t_b|, \quad N|t_b| \gg 1 \quad f_0 \approx \frac{f_i}{N} \text{ and } f_f \approx f_i$$

The outputs are all very small and F is not overdriven under these conditions.

SHORT TERM AND LONG TERM MEMORY

The sensitivity of the MAF to very small values of $d_f \to 0$ can be increased by substituting the trigger circuits for neurons $1 - N$. The first circuit to trigger then generates a significantly larger frequency than all the other circuits and the MAF operates reliably even if the original d_f is practically zero and down to the neuron noise level or spontaneous fluctuation. Under these conditions the active output is selected at random by the inherent noise and becomes quite unpredictable. This effect may well be mechanism for generating trial behaviour when the weight of evidence in favour of all alternatives becomes equal. As d_f increases with the success

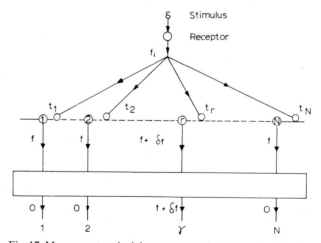

Fig. 17. Memory network giving output at r in response to stimulus s.

of certain trials the probability of these trials increases. This is illustrated in Fig. 17 which shows how a particular stimulus S can elicit different responses depending on which axon carries the frequency $f + d_f$. If all the t's are equal and all the neurons $1 - N$ are identical then d_f will be zero and responses will be selected at random. There are two ways in which d_f can become non-zero. The first possibility is that one of the neurons is firing at a rate d_f above all the rest before S is applied, as shown in Fig. 18 so that when S is applied the rth input is the first to cross the trigger level (broken lines in Fig. 18). It seems probable that this could be the basis of short term memory, d_f being due to the slow decay of transmitter released by activity that precedes S by up to several minutes.

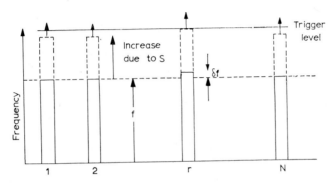

Fig. 18. Short term memory based on distribution of initial firing rates before stimulus is applied.

The second possibility is that one transmission is slightly larger than the rest by d_t so that the outputs of the N neurons driven by S become $f = f_i t$ except for the one with increased transmission which becomes $f + d_f = f_i (t + d_t)$ with $d_f = f_i d_t$. This is considered to be the basis of permanent memory, d_t being due to the fact that this synapse has received more nerve impulses than the remainder over its lifetime, irrespective of how long ago the impulses were present. As the circuit is drawn there is no way in which the imbalance required for either short term or permanent memory can be brought about and it is clear that this requires additional signals to control the flow of impulses from S to the neurons $1 - N$. Before considering this problem in more detail it will be useful to look at the properties of basic neural circuits incorporating the short term or '*transmitter*' memory and the permanent or '*transmission memory*'.

BASIC NEURAL CIRCUITS WITH TRANSMITTER MEMORY

1. Temporal pattern recognition

The short term transmitter memory requires a transmitter substance like acetylcholine that can have a decay time constant measured in terms of seconds and possibly minutes. Cholinoceptive neurons are particularly numerous in the primary visual area where they may serve to store visual information for short periods and one would expect to find them in other sensory areas.

Temporal patterns such as a gestures of the hand or spoken words can only be recognized with certainty by the brain when the pattern is completed and the earlier parts of the pattern are stored, so that recognition can be based on the complete temporal pattern. The transmitter memory network shown in Fig. 19 satisfies this

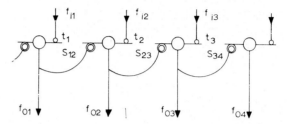

Fig. 19. Temporal pattern recognition network with transmitter memory.

condition and has the effect of converting temporal patterns to spatial patterns, providing the temporal pattern is completed before the transmitter memory of the initial portions decays to zero.

Synapses with an excitatory transmitter memory like s_{12} and s_{23} are denoted by two concentric open circles. The particular network shown is one of the possible permutations and is most sensitive to the temporal pattern in which activity progresses

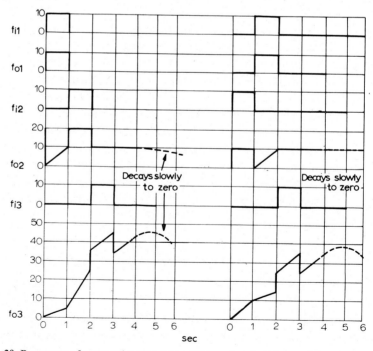

Fig. 20. Responses of temporal pattern recognition network with transmitter memory.

sequentially from input 1 to input 3. If the sequence is changed in any way the maximum output attained is less than when the sequence is 1, 2, 3 and the neurons 'tuned' to the new sequence will give the largest output.

Let us assume that each impulse releases a small amount of depolarizing transmitter d that does not decay appreciably during the temporal pattern. This is approximately true for example for a temporal pattern lasting three seconds when the transmitter decay time constant is one minute. The transmitter released at synapse S_{12} due to a constant input $f_{01} = t_1 f_{i1}$ is given by $f_{01} d.t$, i.e. a linear increase so that f_{02} increases linearly if $f_{i2} = 0$. The network thus behaves like a chain of integrators in cascade and the response to two temporal patterns is as shown in Fig. 20 if d = 1 and all inputs are 10 impulses /sec. If connections are made at random in large numbers then networks sensitive to all possible temporal patterns will be formed in approximately equal numbers. When the sequence f_{i1}, f_{i2}, f_{i3} occurs the largest output after the pattern is completed in f_{03} and other sequences such as f_{i2}, f_{i1}, f_{i3} produce a smaller output at f_{03} but a large output at a neuron with appropriate connections. A maximum amplitude filter supplied by the above networks will thus indicate the temporal pattern that has occurred. The longest temporal pattern that can be recognized unambiguously by this type of network depends on the length of the longest unbroken chain of connections.

Patterns of longer duration may also be recognized by several layers of the network, each layer having longer synaptic decay time constants than the one above. Thus relatively short sound patterns such as words could be recognized by the first layers and longer patterns such as sentences by following layers.

2. A temporary learning mechanism employing transmitter memory

A typical learning situation is one in which an animal confronted with a new stimulus S_k selects a motor response R_l at random initially. If this response leads to a reward, such as food F, the memory is changed so that the probability of the animal choosing the same response in the future, when confronted with the same stimulus, is increased. If a transmitter memory is involved the memory gradually decays to zero so that without reinforcement the animal eventually makes other exploratory responses. A learning mechanism of this type is shown in Fig. 21.

In general there will be K stimulus patterns $S_1 \ldots S_k \ldots S_K$ and L response patterns $R_1 \ldots R_l \ldots R_L$. Only one stimulus pattern is shown in Fig. 21 and the whole network is repeated K times so that each stimulus is potentially capable of eliciting any response. The maximum amplitude filter and trigger circuit ensures that only one response is selected at any particular instant of time. The functioning of the network is illustrated by the waveforms shown in Fig. 22 which indicate how the food input F inhibits all responses except the one that was made before the food was obtained.

It is assumed for simplicity that there is no transmitter memory at the L afferent synapses $a1 \ldots al \ldots aL$ and that the response R_l is initially selected at random at time T_1 by the stimulus S_k. The burst of impulses representing R_L is fed back to

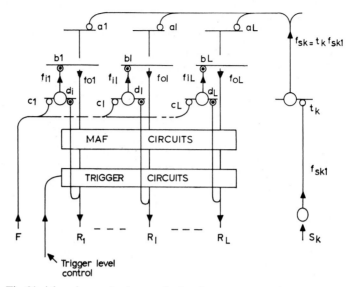

Fig. 21. A learning mechanism employing short term transmitter memory.

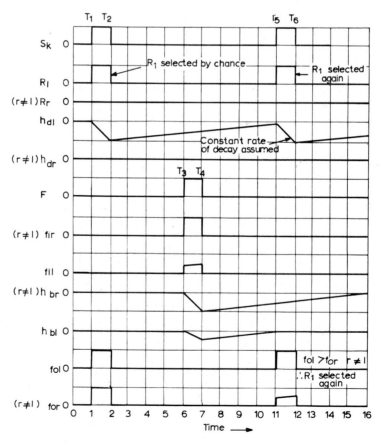

Fig. 22. Typical wavevorms for network shown in Fig. 21.

the transmitter memory synapse dl where it produces a hyperpolarization current h_{dl}. If food F is obtained before this hyperpolarization decays to zero, which may be several minutes, the frequency of firing f_{il} is less than the frequencies $f_{i1} \ldots f_{iL}$ and in consequence there is less hyperpolarization at synapse bl than at any other synapse $b1 \ldots bL$. Thus if the same stimulus S_K is repeated before the latter hyperpolarizations have decayed to zero the firing rate f_{ol} will be the maximum of the set $f_{o1} \ldots f_{oL}$ and the same response R_l will be selected. The memory gradually fades as the transmitter concentrations decay to zero. It will be observed that the transmitter memory only involves summation of slowly decaying hyperpolarizing and depolarizing currents whereas the permanent transmission memory described in the next section involves multiplication by a permanently changed transmission.

NEURAL CIRCUITS WITH TRANSMISSION MEMORY

The experimental results obtained by Lippold (1962) seem to indicate an approximately linear rate of transmission increase of the form $t_{io} + k_i \int_o^t f_i \, dt$ where t_{io} is the initial transmission at time $t = 0$, *i.e.* before the synapse is used, and k_i is a constant that determines the rate of increase in transmission when the synapse receives impulses at a rate f_i. This is illustrated in Fig. 23a which shows an excitatory synapse with transmission memory as an open triangle.

If f_i becomes non-zero and constant at $t = 0$, as shown in Fig. 23b, f_o commences at $t_{io}f_i$ and gradually increases. There must clearly be some limit t_{max} to the increases in transmission and the time taken to reach the limit may be several years if f_i is present continuously or much longer if f_i is only non-zero for short periods, as, for example, is the output of a rapidly adapting receptor or neuron.

The nervous system contains a certain amount of noise that has the effect of super-

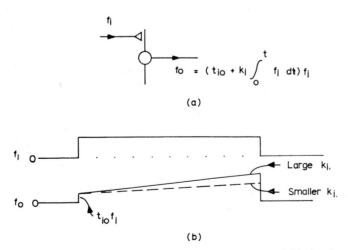

$$f_o = (t_{io} + k_i \int_o^t f_i \, dt) f_i$$

(a)

(b)

Fig. 23. (a) Representation of a synapse with transmission memory and (b) the characteristics of the synapse.

imposing firing rates of a few impulses/sec on the firing rates due to transmitter action. Reliable operation therefore requires a value of f_i of say 10 i/sec at least, which in turn implies that the change in transmission produced by 10 i/sec acting for a few seconds must be very small if the memory is not to be saturated after many years. Consequently the constant k_i must be very small. An estimate can be made by assuming that a typical axon supplying a transmission memory synapse is only active on the average for 100 sec per day at 10 i/sec. If t_{io} is 0.1 and $t_m = 1$ then k_i 10 $\times$ 100 $D = 0.9$ where D is the number of days to reach the maximum transmission. Thus if $D = 1000$ days the change of transmission produced by one impulse is required to be $k_i = 0.9 \times 10^{-6}$.

The neural circuit for combined positive and negative feedback (Fig. 12) gave an output

$$f_0 = \frac{f_i t_i}{1 + (|t_{f-}| - t_{f+})}$$

If the feedback synapses have transmission memory as shown in Fig. 24 for a pyramidal neuron then the values of the feedback transmissions become $t_{f+} = t_o + dt_+$ and $|t_{f-}| = t_o + dt$ which give

$$f_0 = \frac{f_i t_i}{1 + (dt_- - dt_+)} \approx f_i t_i (1 + dt_+ - dt_-) \quad \text{(for small changes)}$$

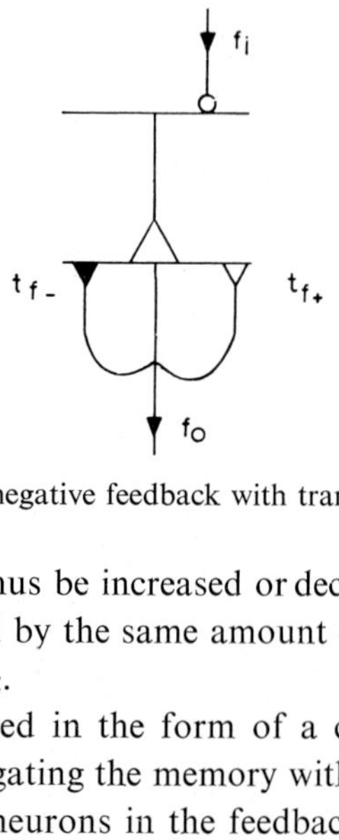

Fig. 24. Positive and negative feedback with transmission memory.

The effective transmission can thus be increased or decreased by increasing t_{f+} or $|t_{f-}|$ respectively. If both are changed by the same amount ($dt_+ = dt_-$) the overall transmission remains unchanged at t_i.

Information can only be stored in the form of a change in the effective transmission and retrieved by interrogating the memory with f_i. The effective transmission can be controlled through interneurons in the feedback loops as shown in Fig. 25. There are three control inputs f_+, f_- and f_l. The latter is produced by the response or its after discharge due to transmission memory. A response that follows the stimulus S_k and meets with success, i.e. is followed by a 'good' input stimulus G, leads to an increase in f_+ and a decrease in f_- so that f_l is allowed to increase t_{f+} more than t_{f-} with a resultant increase in the effective transmission. The reverse is true if the response is followed by an unfavourable or 'bad' stimulus B, so that f_- exceeds f_+. In general f_k can have any value between 0 and 1000 i/sec, and it seems probable that only firing

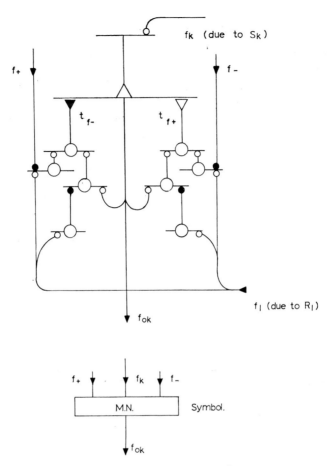

Fig. 25. Transmission memory network.

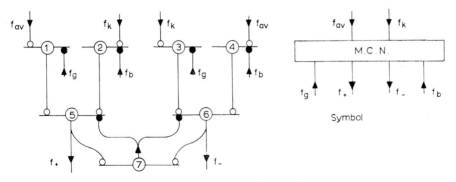

Fig. 26. Memory control network.

rates above a threshold are significant. On the other hand it is difficult to imagine a fixed threshold that would make the best use of high signal/noise ratios and a threshold proportional to the average firing rate of $f_1 \ldots f_K$ would appear to be a simple alternative. The impulses f_+ would then only be present when f_k is greater than $f_{av} = \frac{1}{K}(f_1 + f_2 \ldots + f_K)$ and a reward is obtained. A network that generates f_+ and f_- is shown in Fig. 26. This will be called a Memory Control Network (MCN).

There are two ways in which each output f_+ and f_- can be non-zero and these are summarized as follows:

$$f_+ = f_k \text{ if } f_k > f_{av} \text{ and } f_g \text{ inhibits neurons 1 and 3}$$
$$f_+ = f_{av} \text{ if } f_k < f_{av} \text{ and } f_b \text{ inhibits neurons 2 and 4}$$
$$f_- = f_k \text{ if } f_k > f_{av} \text{ and } f_b \text{ inhibits neurons 2 and 4}$$
$$f_- = f_{av} \text{ if } f_k < f_{av} \text{ and } f_g \text{ inhibits neurons 1 and 3}$$

It is assumed for simplicity that either f_g or f_b is zero (*i.e.* they are outputs of a MAF), and that the synapses have appropriate transmissions. Possible sources of the 'good' and 'bad' inputs f_g and f_b are receptors sensitive to edible and poisonous substances respectively. These specific connections could have evolved by natural selection to become what might be regarded as a third type of memory, the structural memory, that lacks the flexibility of the transmitter or transmission memories but serves to control their formation.

MODELS OF CORTICAL LEARNING MECHANISMS

It has been suggested on anatomical and physiological grounds (Taylor, 1964) that several kinds of specific neural circuit exist at various depths in the cerebral cortex and that correct functioning of cortical learning mechanisms depends more on intact

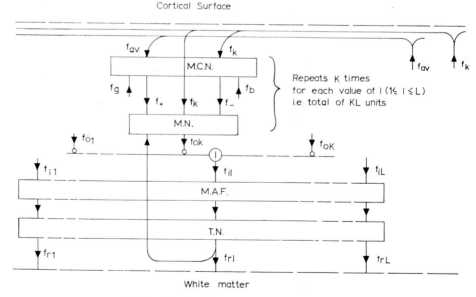

Fig. 27. Model of cortical learning mechanism.

vertical units rather than on lateral spread. The composition of a typical vertical unit is shown in Fig. 27.

The unit repeats KL times, where K is the number of independent input fibres and L is the number of independent output fibre groups. The actual number of fibres may be considerably larger than the number of independent groups if many fibres carry the same message. The input fibres having impulse rates denoted by $f_1 \ldots f_k \ldots f_K$ originate in sensory areas or in other memory areas. The output fibres having impulse rates $f_{r1} \ldots f_{rl} \ldots f_{rL}$ supply pre-motor areas or the inputs to other memory areas so that associations between different sensory modalities may be formed in 'mixed' areas.

ELECTRICAL SIMULATION OF THE MODEL

A specially constructed analogue computer containing 4000 motor driven potentiometers simulating transmission memory has been used to simulate the model of cortical learning mechanisms shown in Fig. 27. The input frequencies $f_1 \ldots f_k \ldots f_K$

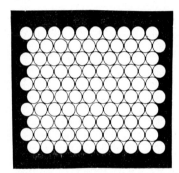

Fig. 28. Photomultiplier sensory field.

Fig. 29a. Stimulus patterns.

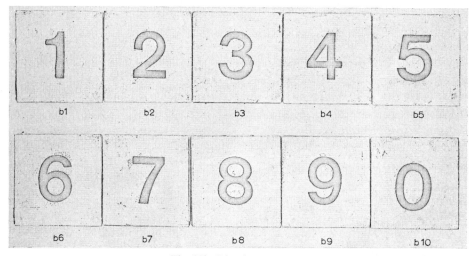

Fig. 29b. Stimulus patterns.

are represented in analogue form by the output voltages of one hundred photo-multipliers ($K = 100$) arranged to simulate a small 10×10 cone area of fovea as shown in Fig. 28. A lens is placed before the photomultipliers so that the image of any object presented at a suitable distance is focussed on them. The connections between the photomultipliers and the outputs or responses are so general, *i.e.*, each photomultiplier to each response via a memory network, that the mechanism should be initially capable of learning the best response to any visual stimulus pattern that can be resolved by the memory. As the number of stimulus patterns increases, how-ever, there is the possibility of confusion due to overloading the memory.

Many different forms of stimulus pattern have been used but the extremes are well

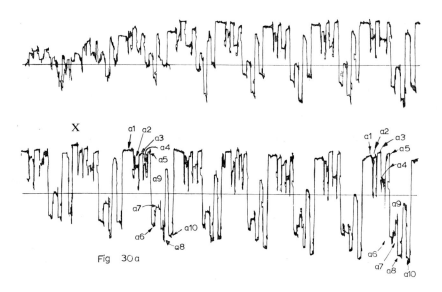

Fig 30a

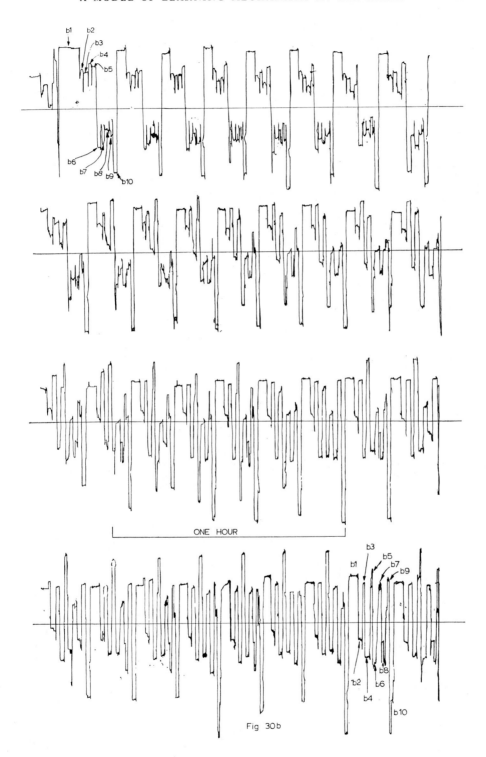

ONE HOUR

Fig 30b

illustrated by the faces and numerals shown in Fig. 29. For simplicity of describing the output only two responses will be considered since these may be represented by positive and negative deflections of a pen recorder connected between response 1 and response 2. It is, however, more instructive to record the inputs to the MAF since these are analogue signals that indicate the 'level of confidence' with which each decision to select response 1 or 2 is made. Thus if f_{01} is much greater than f_{02} the pen gives a large $+ve$ deflection indicating a strong preference for response 1. If, however, $f_{01} \approx f_{02}$ there is no deflection of the pen and the response is selected at random.

The results of a typical teaching experiment in which the model was trained to give positive responses to the women's faces and negative responses to the men's faces are shown in Fig. 30a. The faces are presented sequentially in the order shown together with signals indicating the 'good' response. The latter signals are omitted when the mechanism gives the correct response and they may thus be considered to be error correcting inputs. The results show that the responses are initially weak and that they become stronger as the training proceeds. After 16 presentations of each face the responses are all correct and the time taken to reach this stage was approximately three hours. It will be noted that nine out of the ten faces produce the correct responses after only $1\frac{3}{4}$ h (X) and that the remainder of the time is consumed in training that face a9 is that of a man since there is a strong tendency for it to be treated as a woman's face.

The results of an experiment using numbers as the stimulus patterns are shown in Fig. 30b. The initial $4\frac{1}{2}$ h of this experiment are omitted and the records commence at a point where the model has been trained to give positive responses to patterns b1, b2, b3, b4 and b5 and negative responses to patterns b6, b7, b8, b9 and b10. The object of the experiment that follows is to retrain the model so that odd number patterns give positive responses and even number patterns give negative responses. This result is just achieved in $4\frac{1}{2}$ h, but a further $1\frac{3}{4}$ h are required to produce a level of confidence or output signal strength comparable with the level at the beginning of the experiment.

These experiments for $K = 100$ and $L = 2$ only make use of 200 memory networks or 400 potentiometers simulating synapses with transmission memory. The capabilities of the model will obviously increase when the larger memory is employed and the next stage of the research will be devoted to the problem of estimating the size of memory required for specific learning tasks.

REFERENCES

BINDMAN, L. J., LIPPOLD, O. C. J., AND REDFEARN, J. W. T., (1962); Long-lasting changes in the level of the electrical activity of the cerebral cortex produced by polarizing currents. *Nature (London)*, **196**, No. 4854, 584–585.

GRAY, E. G., (1959); Axosomatic and axodendritic synapses of the cerebral cortex: an electron microscope study. *J. Anat. (London)*, **93**, 420–433.

KRNJEVIČ, K., AND PHILLIS, J. W., (1963); Pharmacology of cholinoceptive cells. *J. Physiol.*, **166**, 328–350.

MCINTYRE, A. K., (1956); Multiple firing at central synapses. *Nature (London)*, **178**, 302–304.

SHOLL, D. A., (1956); *The organization of the cerebral cortex*. London, Methuen, 1956.

TAYLOR, W. K., (1955); *Electrical simulation of some nervous system functional activities. Information theory.* Edited by Colin Cherry. London, Butterworths, pp. 314–328.

TAYLOR, W. K., (1957); Measurement and control in the human operator. *Trans. Soc. Instr. Technol.,* **9**, No. 3.

TAYLOR, W. K., (1964); Cortico-thalamic organization and memory. *Proc. Roy. Soc. B,* **159**, 466–478

Norbert Wiener (1894–1964)

Perspectives in Cybernetics

by

the late NORBERT WIENER

Massachusetts Institute of Technology, Cambridge, Mass. (U.S.A.)

I propose to devote this inaugural lecture to a discussion of the role of randomness in organization and in particular in the organization of the nervous system, both structurally and functionally. By now we are quite familiar with mechanical devices imitating the action of living organisms. We have computing machines to do our arithmetic for us, automatic devices to turn on the current in our toaster, and a myriad of other devices. Most of these devices represent 'inventions', that is concatenations of mechanical and electrical operations which have been put together by human ingenuity and which could scarcely be thought of as occurring by an accident of nature. Nevertheless living organisms did originate at some time or other, and we generally conceive of them as having originated by an accident of nature. The question that arises is: is the difference between living organisms and the artificially constructed mechanical surrogates one of principle, or can we find any intermediate systems binding together the two sides of the gap?

Under these conditions it is not unnatural that we have turned to the study of chance and randomness to supply in living organisms that external design which seems to be missing in their origin. In this way we are only going again over the path trod by Darwin in his theory of natural selection.

In the 18th century the general view concerning the multiplicity of animals and plants was that the species went back to the original creation by the deity. Long after, doubts began to be expressed about this by eccentrics as Lamarcq and Erasmus and Darwin. People began to search for some mechanisms, other than creation, which could account for the origin of species. Here Darwin's suggestion of natural selection won the day. This was that species of animals or plants which were originally close enough to one another to interbreed freely, became more and more differentiated in the course of time until this possibility of free interbreeding became lost, thus breaking up the breeding continuity into several separate breeding communities. Some of these had a good balance with their environment, including as a

---

* During his stay at the Central Institute for Brain Research, Amsterdam, as visiting professor in cybernetics, Norbert Wiener prepared an inaugural lecture to be delivered in April 1964. Before his trip to Stockholm he dictated a first draft to one of our secretaries. In concert with Mrs. Margaret Wiener I prepared the final draft of this lecture.

J. P. SCHADÉ

part of it their own nature. These flourished and multiplied, giving rise in turn to new species. The others which were not as well adjusted to their environment sooner or later dwindled and became extinct. Thus the pattern of species, according to Darwin, is a fragmentation pattern due to the development of gaps in what was originally — at least as a possibility — a more or less random distribution, and the formation of these gaps was itself a random phenomenon. This gives a hint of how random developments may lead us to an apparently well defined pattern.

When Darwin developed his theory of natural selection we knew far less about the mechanisms available for this than we have found out since. The fundamental machinery of heredity consists of genes and their combinations and recombinations. This was not known to Darwin although the basic experimental work was already being done in Brünn by the Abbot Mendel. Even in Mendel's work these bearers of unitary characteristics, known as genes, were only discovered by physiological influences and Mendel knew nothing or next to nothing about the nuclear elements, the chromosomes which carry these genes, and the arrangements of genes or the chromosomes themselves. It is because of this later work that we have been able to supplement Darwin's conjectures by a very fair study of the dynamics of the multiplication of species and races, and by the statistical study of the frequencies of the various dynamic combinations.

We are now at the stage in which the dynamics of the physiology of the individual is going through a period of investigation which parallels that carried out earlier by Darwin, Mendel and their followers into the dynamics of the genetics of the race. The queen of all the physiological sciences is the physiology of the nervous system. It is thus not at all remarkable that the picture which is now being formed of nervous activity has a very considerable resemblance to the picture of natural selection.

We are living in an age in which automata have become part of our daily life. Most of these automata have very little resemblance in their operation to the living organisms which perform similar functions. To think of the structure of this unnatural thing multiplying itself and producing other systems with the same property, is repugnant to our way of thinking. I will not say it is impossible, for I have myself developed an account of how one operative mechanism may at the same time act as a template for the design and production of other mechanisms with the same function. Nevertheless for such a method to have any naturalness it must have probability and we must consider the prospect of the development and multiplication of such a system from this statistical point of view.

The need for this statistical element in the study of live processes in general, and processes of the nervous system in particular, has been felt by many physiologists and has been emphasized explicitly by Dr. W. Ross Ashby. However, the notion of the statistical description of a dynamical system, and for that matter the notion of a dynamical system itself, is neither trivial nor easy and requires a considerable sophistication in mathematics and mathematical systems. It is my intention in this talk to stress some of the points which must be considered in a sophisticated approach to such matters.

Most of our present approaches to the nervous system are centered around the nerve fiber, which is the prime conductive mechanism of this system. We know that along the length of the nerve fiber a message is carried by a spike-like wave of electrical activity which travels along the fiber at a fairly definite velocity and then leaves a temporary inactive period behind it before it can be stimulated again. We have a fairly good physical-chemical-electrical account for how such an impulse travels along a fiber. As this is one of the few phenomena in the nervous system which can be studied in relative isolation there has been a great tendency to build up operational models of the nervous system out of elements which are essentially those of nerve fibers.

Now the nerve fibers of which the white matter in the nervous system consists and the elements of which the gray matter consists, although the gray matter is itself largely fibers, have one great difference: the fibers of the white matter are much longer than the fibers of the gray matter. Very likely the fundamental molecular process of conduction is the same in both, although it is carried on without essential change for a much longer time in the white fibers. I remember that when I was a child I read a popular article for children about the nervous system which compared the firing of a nerve to the falling down in succession of a sequence of domino's stood on end where each one upsets the next one. This is a good analogue if we do not go into it too much in detail, and it indicates that the process of propagation of the nerve message represents a repeated iteration of the action which is transformed anew each time. The result is that after a long sequence of such repetitions the pattern of the action has been remade very many times and can be expected to have assumed an asymptomatic form in which no trace of the form of the original activity will survive. An impulse goes along a nerve either to disappear in the course of time and space, or to assume a standardized form. This is manifestly the origin of the remarkable all-or-none phenomenon observed in nervous conduction.

It is now clear that this all-or-none character is the result of the long duration in time and the long continuence in space of nervous conduction under essentially constant conditions. It is not to be expected then in a short fiber in which the remaking of the initial impulse has not had headway enough to assume its final shape or in which there are non-homogeneities such as incoming or outcoming branches as in the teledendron or the dendrites. Therefore the pattern of all-or-none activity, where highly suitable for the conduction of nervous activity in the white matter, is by no means so suitable for the study of the same sort of activity in the gray matter. As a matter of fact I believe there is positive evidence that the all-or-none hypothesis applied to the gray matter leads to false conclusions.

This is an elementary example of the caution with which we must take the account of the mechanism of action of the nervous system. The simple pattern of activity along the nerve is not sufficiently elaborate to cover the whole subject. Moreover it is difficult to supplement this information by other equally valid information concerning the gray matter.

The gray matter is a forest where we can literally not see the forest for the trees nor the trees for the forest. We have many techniques of studying its histology and several for studying its physiology. Each of these techniques gives us information about some phases of the nervous system at the cost of suppressing the other phases, and it is most difficult to get these different elements of information onto the same screen. If we wish to know the ramifications of the individual fiber in the nervous system to the highest possible degree of accuracy, we use a staining method like that of Golgi, which seems to dye fortuitously one fiber out of many with a metalic deposit. The knowledge that we receive concerning the individual fiber is precise in the extreme. But the knowledge as to its real orientation to other fibers is scanty and misleading. On the other hand we can use a colored stain which will bring out a large part of the fibers at the cost of representing them as an inextricable tangle. To interpret the information obtained by these two methods, so as to understand the relevance of the one picture to the other, we must use mixed methods of staining in which we get as much information concerning the trees or the forest as we do by the pure methods, but in which we get much more information, partial though it be, concerning the relation between the trees and the forest.

Thus we may say that our actual knowledge of the functional organization of the nervous system, and of its permanence in time, is minimal. Obviously there is enough permanence that certain processes which retain past impressions may be attributed to the reverberations of very large and permanent circuits of information in the nervous system. This is one sort of memory, but it is almost certainly not the only sort. It is highly improbable that this is the sort of memory upon which are impressed the rather specific and long-lasting impressions to which we refer in psycho-analysis.

The psycho-analysist is familiar with impressions received in early childhood and which, though they appeared to be utterly lost, can be brought back in a very explicit and detailed way into consciousness by appropriate psycho-analytic procedures. The fondling of a child by its mother, shocking experiences of the family life, and the relations between the parents can all be brought back to full and detailed consciousness by processes which have a certain formal likeness to the processes by which an apparently lost photographic image can be developed and fixed. The use of certain drugs or techniques of hypnosis show us that the stored repertory of the nervous system is enormously greater than that which we should imagine without these radical techniques of investigation. These hidden memories, in addition to their multiplicity and detail, are not easily accessible to the person who carries them. They need to be brought out by elaborate techniques which are themselves time consuming. They seem to be not like reverberations of circuits which are there more or less all the time, and which we should expect to find fugitive and easily erased by even a temporary interruption, but rather like engrams burnt into the very intimate structure of mental and nervous organization. This is not to say that these deep memories do not have physiological carriers. Short of the dogmatic and sterile vitalism, we must suppose that they have identifiable physico-chemical correlates. It does mean, however, that these correlates must be sought at a level much finer than that of the fiber structure of the nervous system and must go back to a structure of a finer texture than that which we observe with the ordinary microscope. Perhaps the electron-microscope is the appropriate tool for investigating them, or even analytical tools going further still into the molecular structure.

What type of structure do other parallel physiological processes suggest as the carrier of these long-term memories? Here we are not on solid ground, but we have ample basis for speculation. In addition to the memories carried by the nervous system of the individual there are certain rational memories which last not only for the life time of a single plant or animal, but for ages of geological history. These memories are the genetic memories and are carried, at least in large measure, by the genes in the chromosomes.

There are types of animal or plant which have remained without radical change for millions of years. Of course we are not in a position to make a direct experiment of how the living beings of early times carried their hereditary qualities, but it is highly reasonable to suppose that these beings, very similar to those existing nowadays, carried their natural memories in the same way as those of the present. Here we know that the chief bearer of hereditary properties is the nucleus of the germ cell and that within this nucleus the hereditary properies are carried in minute organs, known as the chromosomes. Even within the chromosome we have a chain of still more minute carriers of heredity which are known as genes and whose arrangement we are able to infer to a great degree. The last decade has greatly increased our knowledge of the physical chemistry of these genes themselves and has given clear indication of the very specific and rather complicated intercalation of nucleic acids and amino acids in the form of the double spiral. This spiral seems under certain conditions to split into its two components, single spirals, and each of them seems to pick from the nutritive medium in which they are immersed the necessary complementary parts, to reconstitute again a double spiral of the same sort as the original one.

It is this which is the fundamental phenomenon of genetics rather than the phenomena of sex. In order for the fusion of elements from the two parents to constitute the primordium of the new individual the genes themselves must produce more similar molecules.

This process may seem to be explained by the double spiral hypothesis, but this is incomplete in some parts. Not only must the double spiral split, but the dynamics of its splitting and of its taking on new elements from the nutritive medium needs to be explained. This dynamics is a much more complicated matter than the more switching circuitry of the nervous network. This dynamics of nucleic acids is not confined to the genes. There is a good deal of evidence nowadays that viruses are closely related to genes. They are nucleic acid complexes which multiply as do the genes at the expense of constitutive materials, to be found in the host animal or plant. In this sense they are parasites, although to sue the word "parasite" with a strict meaning the viruses should be "alive". However, the question of whether a virus is alive or not is highly academic, for the word "life" does not come to us with a pre-defined meaning.

Thus the multiplicity of viruses is the same sort of phenomenon as the elementary multiplication of genes. There may be nucleic acid complexes other than genes or viruses which have a familiar mechanism of multiplication. Such substances are beautifully adapted to carry memories, not only in the race but in the individual. It is an observation which has been made within the last few years, that nucleic acid complexes are to be found in the nervous system more readily than in other tissues. Not only are they to be found in the nervous system but they seem to be largely located in the neighbourhood of the synapses, in other words, in the places where the nerve fibers communicate with one another and where we should naturally suppose that some of the most critical nervous activity takes place.

Thus it is quite reasonable to suppose that the stable memory which is not so instantaneously available, is carried not by reverberating circuits in the nervous system but by nucleic acid complexes. Our pattern is not a switching pattern but a pattern of some molecular activity, let us say of molecular vibrations. This is the sort of dynamics which we study in solid state physics. And if we wish to tie up nervous activity with statistical mechanics this may well be the phenomenon which we should investigate.

In order to see what sort of activity may be involved in nucleic acid memory, let us take the much simpler solid state phenomenon, that of crystal habit. We are all of us familiar with the regularity of snowflakes, which are crystals of water. We do not need at present to account for the six-fold symmetry of snowflakes as such because it corresponds to the hexagonal lattice of hydrogen and oxygen in the crystals. However, the symmetry of the snowflake is more than the symmetry of the lattice. Not all snowflakes have a gross hexagonal symmetry, but many of them do. In this there is the remarkable correspondence between the different limbs of the crystal. We do not in general find crystals where one limb is taken from one snowflake, another limb from another, and so on. The resemblance between the different limbs is great and very possibly too great to be accounted for by the similar states of deposit through which all six limbs have gone. There seems to be some active force adapting the limbs to one another and this force is probably connected with the vibrations of the snowflake, magnetic or electrical, or both. Thus the organization of the snowflake may be sought in the dynamics of its oscillations. This dynamics is not merely linear and the whole general problem of crystal habit cannot be separated from the active nonlinear dynamics of crystals.

Now if we go back to nucleic acid complexes it is an ascertained fact that some of them are crystals. Tobacco mosaic virus has been crystallized for a matter of decades and recently some of the cancer viruses in man have been crystallized. Thus it is quite conceivable that in the dynamics of the formation of these crystals vibration phenomena play a role just as they do in the formation of snowflakes. At least a part of these vibration phenomena may be electro-magnetic vibrations. In this case the double spiral statics of the formation of genes and viruses, as well as of the carriers of long-term memory, would be the electromagnetic molecular vibrations of the spirals, which are by their very nature incipient crystals. Here we must realize that the possibility that these vibrations are the heart of the phenomenon does not mean that these vibrations have enough power to act at a distance. Nevertheless it may be possible to produce such vibrations at really high levels of energy. The recent work being done with lasers indicates that crystals can be made to vibrate with power according to highly specific models. Perhaps it may be possible to take some of the virus- or gene-crystals, and make them vibrate in a similar specific manner. If this were the case it is quite conceivable that this sort of light or radiation energy may itself have an aspect of the multiplicity of the nucleic acid complexes. If it is in fact a substance of the nucleic acid complex type which has effected a nervous memory specific radiation may well be important in the dynamics of this memory.

One matter which has made me suspect that the vibrations of the molecules in nucleic acid complexes may be responsible for their behaviour as organized systems is that in dynamical systems of a much coarser texture the vibration properties play a large part in their organization. This is true both with biological and with engineering systems. In the ordinary system of electric alternators which constitutes the source of power for our electric lights, the various generators are pulled together in their frequency or speed of rotation by their interaction which tends to slow down the rotation of those generators which are going fast and to speed up the rotation of those which are going slow and thus to produce a system with stability of frequency greater than that which would be obtained by the regulatory mechanisms of each generator independently. This pulling together of frequencies is an example of what we call 'a nonlinear phenomenon' or, in other words, one in which adding of inputs does not add outputs. It is only in systems of this sort that different frequencies of oscillation can interact.

This is a prototype for the phenomenon of organization which takes place very frequently in biology. It takes place e.g. in the frequencies of oscillation of the brain and seems to produce the remarkbable dominance of frequencies of about 10 oscillations per second which is known as the α-rhythm. It is also probably responsible for the flashing in unison of fireflies on a tree in a tropical forest.

This phenomenon of behaviour in unison which is observed with fireflies can be duplicated with many other communities of animals as e.g. that of baby chicks, with which we are experimenting now here in Amsterdam. These chicks have a peculiar cry of terror which under certain circumstances tends to be given more or less at the same frequency and the same phase by all the members of the community. In explaining the production of this cry we must remember that the chicks can both make a sound and hear it. If this cry is recorded by the magnetic tape at its usual frequency and time, and is played back to the chicks then the chicks may take up the cry and echo it with a remarkable consistency of period. This periodic cry may continue for several cycles after the tape has been turned off. This suggests that under appropriate circumstances it may continue indefinitely, with the cry of the other chicks acting as the tape has acted. Thus we have a self organizing process in which the necessary nonlinear interaction of the chicks produces a process with a recognizable structure.

These phenomena of entrainment and of mutual entrainment seem to have a very wide range in life processes. The suggestion which I have made concerning the self-organization of nucleic acid complexes is that the molecular vibration is subject to similar entrainment.

While entrainment, as we have seen, is not necessarily a random process, the sort of self-entrainment that we find in the community is generally a random process. It is a random process rather closely related to that by which the molecular vibrations of the particles of air combine to produce organized sound waves. Here I must go into the history of random motion.

In the middle of the last century Clark Maxwell developed the statistical theory of gases. The pressure-volume-temperature relations of gas are derived from the random collisions of particles not unlike miniature billiard balls. The theory was first developed in the case of particularly elastic collisions between balls of negligeable size and it led to the theory of the perfect gas, in which the product of pressure and specific volume is proportional to the temperature. Later on it was found that this theory was not adequate to cover the experimental observations and it was modified by Van der Waals into a theory taking into account the specific volume of the particles and the fact that their interaction was distributed over a certain range of distances. Nowadays in the theory of plasmas we are forced to consider sound in media in which the range of interaction between two particles is infinite, and it has not been too easy to accommodate Van der Waals' theory to this case.

However, the basis for a wider statistical theory suitable to plasma theory and also to the far more complicated dynamics of biological interactions was being developed at the same time by Hamilton in Ireland and was later carried further by Willard Gibbs in the United States. In this the basis for the statistical theory lay not in the multiplicity of the molecular particles but in what is known as 'phase space'. Phase space has dimensions of position and momentum, and has as a fundamental invariant an energy which is the sum of potential and kinetic energy. This energy quantum is known as the Hamiltonian theorem and the whole dynamics of the system may be expressed in terms of it. This is the classical basis of Hamiltonian statistical dynamics although certain refinements of it, such as those involving the theory of relativity, may concern themselves with more complicated structures of space and time.

Statistical dynamics consider the development of a dynamical system in time, but not of a *single* system. It deals rather with the distribution of systems spread according to a certain basis of probability. To give an account of this distribution one must be able to average over distributions in phase space. This is a field of work to which I have devoted myself for years, and we can use a very rigorous mathematical theory as our basis for statistical mechanics. It can be referred back to a one-dimensional theory in which we have a quantity distribution over a line in such a way that the amount over a given interval is independently distributed, compared with the amount of a nonoverlapping interval at where the distribution depends only on the length of the interval. With this distribution as a basis it is possible to build a very elaborate theory of many other distributions dependent upon it and to apply this to statistical mechanics.

Here let me remark improvidently that the statistical mechanics of the present day has been radically modified by the introduction of ideas from quantum theory. By this, probability has been submitted to new postulates. In the earliest days of quantum theory these postulates seemed to be somewhat arbitrary and it was not easy to understand why they should be applicable to probabilities which would associated with the frequencies of the various natural phenomena. It has been possible, however, to carry back this newer statistical mechanics of quantum theory to a statistical mechanics associated with a theory much more of a classical type. This work has engaged my attention for some years and I have carried it out with the collaboration of two colleagues, Armand Siegel of Boston University and Giacomo della Ricca of the Institute for Theoretical Physics at Naples. This work is far from complete but it gives us a good expectation of a statistical mechanics which will be universal and cover quantum phenomena as well as classical phenomena.

Once one is in possession of the statistical mechanics of the Hamiltonian-Gibbsian basis, one finds that it is after all not so different from the statistical mechanics of Maxwell's basis to which one has been accustomed for years. After all, if we deal with the molecules of the gas, their positions are expressed in the position coordinates of phase space and their momentary coordinates. Thus Maxwellian statistical mechanics can automatically be expressed as a particular case of a Gibbsian one, where we ignore those properties which are unchanged by the interchange of molecules. This is a direction of work in which much remains to be done and in which it is natural to develop *e.g.* a theory of sound with long range forces such as occur in plasmas. It is this Gibbsian frame which seems to me most suitable for the statistical mechanics which we need in the study of nucleic acid complexes and other biological phenomena and particularly in the study of life and nervous phenomena.

I repeat: since this statistical mechanics is largely the work of the future (although we have a solid mathematical basis upon which to develop it), unlike the statistical mechanics of nerve nets it does not involve a permanent structure of connections which is subject to later modifications. In the theory of this latter type it would be easier to deal with memory structures which can be transferred from one place in the anatomical system to another. In other words it is quite possible that the suspicions which people like Ashby have, that the basis of nervous organization is statistical, need not to be attributed to the existence of a certain permanent network of anatomical connections carrying an independent statistical ensemble of messages. A statistical neurology is just as compatible with what I have called the *wet* neurophysiology as with the *dry* neurophysiology.

I have not been able to bring this résumé of these ideas to a final state in which all that the future investigator will have to do is to fill in details in pattern which has already been rendered explicit and closed. However, I think that I have helped to suggest the liberty to think of neurological and other physiological problems on a statistical basis without tying them down to an anatomical rigid notion of the nervous system. In dealing with an organization of such almost inconceivable complexity it would be fatal to limit one's possibilities of thought too narrowly at the beginning. The remaking of neurophysiology on a mechanistic basis is only half of the problem, which is faced by the physiologists of the future. I am convinced that when the balance of the intellectual developments of the future is cast we shall find that it is not only the physiologists who have taken over the ideas of the physicists, but the physicists as well who will have taken over many of the ideas of the physiologists.

We are in physics in a stage in which we no longer possess a single authoritative physical system like that of Newton. The fundamental particles of modern physics are of the greatest possible importance but they are not fundamental in the sense of being ultimate. Relativity and quantum theory both represent valid moments in the development of physics but the difficulties of Einstein and Bohr remain, and the unified field theory on which Einstein counted is still a pious hope. We are all expecting a new synthesis of ideas, which will certainly not be final but will give us a new plateau on which physics can operate for decades, if not for centuries. However, when we attain to this among the phenomena whose study has contributed to this new unified physics of the future biological phenomena will be an essential part of the conceptual basis which has led to the new synthesis, and I think it is safe to predict that the physical part of our unified science will show much modification by the inclusion of phenomena which we now consider to belong explicitly to the world of life.

Bibliography

(1913–1964)

of

the late NORBERT WIENER

BIOGRAPHY

Nov. 26, 1894	Born in Columbia, Missouri
	Parents: Leo Wiener, Bertha Kahn Wiener
1906	Graduated from Ayer, Massachusetts, High School
1909	A.B., Tufts College
1909	
1909–1910	
1910–1911	Cornell University
1911–1913	Harvard, M.A., 1912; Ph.D., 1913
1913–1914	John Thornton Kirkland Fellow of Harvard (travel), Study with Bertrand Russell at Cambridge, England, and with Hilbert in Goettingen, Germany
1914–1915	Frederick Sheldon Fellow of Harvard (travel), Study with Russell and Hardy at Cambridge, England, and at Columbia University
1915–1916	Harvard, Docent Lecturer in Department of Philosophy
1916–1917	University of Maine, Instructor in Mathematics
1917–1918	General Electric Corporation, Lynn, Mass.
1918	Staff Writer for Encyclopedia Americana, Albany, N.Y.
1918–1919	U.S. Army, Aberdeen Proving Ground, Maryland
1919	The Boston Herald
1919–1924	MIT, Instructor of Mathematics
1924–1929	MIT, Assistant Professor of Mathematics
1929–1932	MIT, Associate Professor of Mathematics
1932–1959	MIT, Professor of Mathematics
1926–1927	Guggenheim Fellowship, Study at Goettingen and Copenhagen
1929–1930	Exchange Professor of Mathematics at Brown University
1931–1932	Lecturer at Cambridge University, England
1935–1936	Visiting Professor at Tsing Hua University, Peiping, China
Fall 1947, '49, '51	Collaborator with Dr. Arthuro Rosenblueth at the Instituto Nacional de Cardiologia, Mexico, on a Rockefeller Foundation grant
1951	Fulbright Teaching Fellowship, University of Paris, College de France
1955–1956	Visiting Professor at the Indian Statistical Institute, Calcutta, India
1956, '59, '61, '63	Summer Course, UCLA, Los Angeles, Calif.
1960	Fall Semester, University of Naples, Italy
1962	University of Naples, Italy
1964	Visiting Professor in Cybernetics at the Netherlands Central Institute for Brain Research, Amsterdam
1964, March 18	Died at Stockholm, Sweden
1959–1960	MIT, Institute Professor
1960–1964	MIT, Institute Professor, Emeritus

PRIZES: Bowdoin Prize, Harvard, 1914
            Boucher Prize, American Mathematical Society, 1933
            Lord and Taylor American Design Award, 1949
            ASTME Research Medal, 1960
            The National Medal of Science, 1963

MEMBER: American Mathematical Society (Vice President, 1935–1937)
            London Mathematical Society
            Appalachian Mountain Club
            Royal Society of Arts
            International Brain Research Organization (Honorary member)

HONORARY DEGREES: Sc.D. (Hon.), Tufts, 1946
            Sc.D. (Hon.), University of Mexico, 1951
            Sc.D. (Hon.), Grinnell College, 1957

PUBLICATIONS: 207 papers in mathematical and scientific journals (see bibliography)
Books: The Fourier Integral and Certain of its Applications, Cambridge University
            Press, 1933
            Cybernetics. The Technology Press of MIT and John Wiley & Sons, Hermann
            et Cie, Paris, 1948
            Extrapolation, Interpolation and Smoothing of Stationary Time Series, with
            Engineering Applications. The Technology Press and John Wiley & Sons, 1949
            The Human Use of Human Beings. Houghton Mifflin Co., 1950
            Ex-Prodigy. Simon & Schuster, 1953
            I Am a Mathematician. Doubleday & Co., Inc., 1956
            Nonlinear Problems in Random Theory. The Technology Press of MIT and
            John Wiley & Sons, Chapman and Hall, London, 1958
            The Tempter. Random House, Inc., 1959
            Cybernetics. The Technology Press and John Wiley & Sons, 2nd edition (two
            new chapters) 1961
            God and Golem, Inc. The MIT Press, 1964
Editorships: Nerve, Brain and Memory Models. Progress in Brain Research, Vol. 2. (with
            J. P. Schadé) Amsterdam-New York, Elsevier, 1963
            Cybernetics of the Nervous System. Progress in Brain Research, Vol. 17.
            (with J. P. Schadé). Amsterdam-New York, Elsevier, 1964
            Progress in Biocybernetics, Vols. 1–3. (with J. P. Schadé). Amsterdam-New
            York, Elsevier. 1964–1965

1913 On the rearrangement of the positive integers in a series of ordinal numbers greater than that
      of any given fundamental sequence of omegas. *Mess. Math.*, **3**.
1914 The highest good. *J. Phil. Psych. Sci. Method*, **9**, 512–520.
1914 Relativism. *J. Phil. Psych. Sci. Method*, **9, 21**, 561–577.
1914 A simplification of the logic relations. *Proc. Camb. Phil. Soc.*, **27**, 387–390.
1914 A contribution to the theory ot relative position. *Ibid.*, 441–449.
1915 Studies in synthetic logic. *Proc. Camb. Phil. Soc.*, **18**, 24–28.
1915 The shortest line dividing an area in a given ratio. *J. Phil. Psych. Sci. Method*, **V**, 568–574.
1917 Certain formal invariance in boolean algebras. *Trans. Am. Math. Soc.*, **18**, 65–72.
1920 Bilinear operations generating all operations rational in a domain. *Ann. Math.*, **21**, 157–165.
1920 A set of postulates for fields. *Trans. Am. Math. Soc.*, **21**, 237–246.
1920 Certain iterative characteristics of bilinear operations. *Bull. Am. Math. Soc.*, **27**, 6–10.
1920 The mean of a functional of arbitrary elements. *Ann. Math.*, **22**, 66–72.
1920 On the theory of sets of points in terms of continuous transformations. *G. R. Strasbourg
      Math. Congr., 1920.*
1920 Certain iterative properties of bilinear operations. *G. R. Strasbourg Math. Congr., 1920.*
1921 A new theory of measurement: A study in the logic of mathematics. *Proc. Lond. Math. Soc.*,
      181–205.
1921 A new vector in integral equations (with F. L. Hitchcock). *J. Math. Phys.*, **I**.
1921 The average of an analytical functional. *Proc. Nat. Acad. Sci.*, **7**, 253–260.

1921   The average of an analytical functional and the Brownian movement. *Ibid.*, **10**, 294–298.

1921   The isomorphisms of complex algebra. *Bull. Am. Math. Soc.*, **27**, 443–445.

1922   The relation of space and geometry to experience. *Monist.*, **32**, 12–60, 200–247, 364–394.

1922   The group of the linear continuum. *Proc. Lond. Math. Soc.*, **2 (20)**, 329–346.

1922   A new type of integral expansion. *J. Math. Phys.*, **I**, 167–176.

1922   Limit in terms of continuous transformation. *Bull. Soc. Math. France*, 119–134.

1922   Certain notions in potential theory. *J. Math. Phys.*, **3**, 24–51.

1922   The equivalence of expansions in terms of orthogonal functions (with J. L. Walsh). *Ibid.*, **1**, 103–122.

1923   On the nature of mathematical thinking. *Austr. J. Psych. Phil.*, **1**, 268–272.

1923   Note on a paper of M. Bauaeh. *Fund. Math.*, **4**, 136–143.

1923   Nets and the dirichlet problem (with H. B. Phillips). *J. Math. Phys.*, **2**, 105–214.

1923   Differential space. *Ibid.*, **2**, 131–174.

1923   Note on a new type of summability. *Amer. J. Math.*, **45**, 83–86.

1923   Discontinuous boundary conditions and the dirichlet problem. *Trans. Am. Math. Soc.*, **25**, 307–314.

1923   Note on the series $\Sigma\,(+\,1/n)$. *Bull. Acad. Polon.*, A, 87–90.

1924   In memory of Joseph Lipka. *J. Math. Phys.*, **3**, 63–65.

1924   The quadratic variation of a function and its fourier coefficients. *Ibid.*, **3**, 72–94.

1924   The dirichlet problem. *J. Math. Phys.*, **3**, 127–147.

1924   Une condition nécessaire et suffisante de possibilité pour le problème de dirichlet. *C.R.*, **178**, 1050–1053.

1924   The average value of a functional. *Proc. Lond. Math. Soc. (2)*, **22**, 454–467.

1924   Un problème de probabilités dénombrables. *Bull. Soc. Math. France*, **11**, 3–4.

1925   Note on a paper of O. Perron. *J. Math. Phys.*, **4**, 21–32.

1925   The solution of a difference equation by trigonometrical integrals. *Ibid.*, **4**, 153–163.

1925   A contribution to the memory of interpolation. *An. Math. (2)*, **26**, 212–216.

1925   Note on quasi-analytic functions. *J. Math. Phys.*, **4**, 193–199.

1925   On the representation of functions by trigonometrical integrals. *Math. Ztschr.*, **24**, 576–616.

1925   Verallgemeinerte trigonometrische Entwicklungen. *Gött. Nachr.*, 151–158.

1926   A new formulation of the laws of quantization for periodic and aperiodic phenomena (with M. Born). *J. Math. Phys.*, **5**, 84–98.

1926   Eine neue Formulierung der Quantengesetze für periodische und nicht periodische Borganze. *Z. Phys.*, **36**, 174–187.

1926   The harmonic analysis of irregular motion. *J. Math. Phys.*, **5**, 99–121.

1926   The harmonic analysis of irregular motion (second paper). *J. Math. Phys.*, **5**, 158–189.

1926   The operational calculus. *Math. Ann.*, **95**, 557–584.

1926   Analytical approximation to topological transformations (with P. Franklin). *Trans. Am. Math. Soc.*, **28**, 762–785.

1927   On the closure of certain assemblates of trigonometrical functions. *Proc. Natl. Acad. Sci.*, **13**, 27–29.

1927   Laplacians and continuous linear functionals. *Szedged Acta*, **3**, 7–16.

1927   The spectrum of an array and its application to the study of the translation properties of a simple class of arithmetical functions. *J. Math. Phys.*, **6**, 145–157.

1927   Quantum theory and gravitational relativity (with D. J. Struik). *Nature*, **119**, 853–854.

1927   A relativistic theory of quanta (with D. J. Struik). *J. Math. Phys.*, **7**, 1–23.

1927   Sur la théorie rélativiste des quanta (with D. J. Struik). *C. R.*, **185**, 42–44.

1927   On a new definition of almost periodic functions. *Ann. Math.*, **28**, 365–367.

1927   On a theorem of Bochner and Hardy. *J. Lond. Math. Soc.*, **2**, 118–123.

1927   Sur la théorie rélativiste des quanta. *C.R.*, **18**, 184–185.

1927   Une généralization des fonctionelles à variation bornée. *C.R.*, **18**, 65–67.

1927   Une méthode nouvelle pour la démonstration des théorèmes de Tauber. *C.R.*, **184**, 793–795.

1928   The fifth dimension in relativistic quantum theory (with D. J. Struik). *Proc. Natl. Acad. Sci.*, **14**, 262–268.

1928   The spectrum of an arbitrary function. *Proc. Lond. Math. Soc. (2)*, **27**, 287–496.

1928   Coherency matrices and quantum theory. *J. Math. Phys.*, **1**, 109–125.

1928   A new method in Tauberian theorems. *J. Math. Phys.*, **7**, 161–184.

1929   Harmonic analysis and the quantum theory. *J. Franklin Inst.*, **207**, 525–534.

1929   Hermitian polynomials and Fourier analysis. *J. Math. Phys.*, **8**, 70–73.

1929 Harmonic analysis and group theory. *J. Math. Phys.*, **8**, 148–154.

1929 On the spherically symmetrical statistical field in Einstein's unified theory of electricity and gravitation. *Proc. Natl. Acad. Sci.*, **15**, 353–356.

1929 On the spherically symmetrical statistical field in Einstein's unified theory: a correction. (with M. S. Vallarta). *Proc. Natl. Acad. Sci.*, **15**, 802–804.

1929 A type of Tauberian theorem applying to Fourier series. *Proc. Lond. Math. Soc. (2)*, **30**, 1-8.

1929 Fourier analysis and asymptotic series. Appendix to V. Bush, *"Operational Circuit Analysis"*. Wiley, New York, 366–379.

1930 Generalized harmonic analysis. *Acta Math.*, **55**, 117–258.

1932 Tauberian theorems. *Ann. Math.*, **33**, 1–100.

1932 A note on Tauberian theorems. *Ann. Math.*, **33**, 787.

1932 A new deduction of the Gaussion distribution. *J. Math. Phys.*, **10**, 284–288.

1932 Characters of infinite Abelian groups (with R.E.A.C. Paley). *Intern. Math. Congr., Zürich, 1932*.

1932 Über eine Klasse singulärer Integralgleichungen (with E. Hopf). *Sitzungsber. Preuss. Akad. Wiss.*, 696.

1933 Review: Harald Bohr. Fastperiodische Funktionen. *Math. Gaz.*, **17**.

1932 Review: Besicovitch, A. S. Almost periodic functions. *Math. Gaz.*, **16**.

1933 *The Fourier integral and certain of its applications.* Cambr. Univ. Press.

1933 Notes on the theory and application of Fourier transforms. I, II. *Trans. Amer. Math. Soc.*, **35**, 348–355.

III, IV, V, VI, VII. *Trans. Am. Math. Soc.*, **34**, 761–791.

1933 A one-sided Tauberian theorem. *Math. Zeitschr.*, **36**, 787–789.

1933 R.E.A.C. Paley, In memoriam. *Bull. Amer. Math. Soc.*, **39**, 476.

1933 Characters of Abelian groups (with R. E. A. C. Paley). *Proc. Natl. Acad. Sci.*, **19**, 253–257.

1933 Review of Titchmarsch, E.C. The Fourier integral and certain of its applications. *Math. Gaz.*, **17**, 129; *Science*, **132**, 731.

1933 Notes on random functions (with R. E. A. C. Paley and A. Z. Zygmund). *Math. Zeitschr.*, **37**, 647–668.

1933 The total variation of *g (x h) — f (x)* (with R. C. Young). *Trans. Amer. Math. Soc.*, **35**, 327–340.

1934 Leibnitz and Haldane. *Phil. Sci.*, **1**.

1934 Notes on the Kron theory of tensors in electrical machinery, abstract. *J. Electr. Eng. China*, **7**, 3–4.

1934 A class of gap theorems. *Ann. Scuola Normale Sup. Pisa*, **E**, 1–6.

1934 Fourier transforms in the complex domain (with R. E. A. C. Paley). *Amer. Math. Soc. Colloq. Publ.*, **19**.

1934 Random functions. *J. Math. Phys.*, **14**.

1935 The closure of bessel functions (abstract). *Amer. Math. Soc. Bull.*, **41**.

1935 Fabry's gap theorem. *Sci. Repts. Natl. Tsing Hua Univ., Ser. A*, **3**, 239–245.

1935 A theorem of Carleman. *Sci. Repts. Natl. Tsing Hua Univ., Ser. A*, **3**, 291–298.

1935 Math. in American Secondary Schools. *J. Math. Assoc. Japan Sec. Educ.*

1936 The role of the observer. *Phil. Science*, **3**, 307–319.

1936 Sur les séries de Fourier lacunaires. Theorème direct (with S. Mandelbrojt). *C. R.*, **203**, 34–36.

1936 Séries de Fourier lacunaires. Theorème inverse. *C.R.*, **203**, 233–234.

1936 Gap theorems. *C.R. Congr. Intern. Math.*

1937 Taylor's series of entire functions of smooth growth (with W. T. Martin). *Duke Math. J.*, **3**, 213–223.

1937 Random waring's theorems, abstract (with N. Levison). *Science*, **85**, 439.

1938 On absolutely convergent Fourier Stieltjes transforms (with H. R. Pitt). *Duke Math. J.*, **4**.

1938 Fourier-Stieltjes transforms and singular infinite convolutions (with A. Wintner). *Amer. J. Math.*, **LX**.

1938 Remarks on the classical inversion formula for the LaPlace integral (with D. V. Widder). *Bull. Amer. Math. Soc.*

1938 The homogeneous chaos. *Am. J. Math.*, **LX**.

1938 The decline of cookbook engineering. *Tech. Rev.*, **41**, 23.

1938 Review: Hogben, L. science for the citizen. *Tech. Rev.*, **41**, 66–67.

1938 The historical background of harmonic analyiss. *Amer. Math. Soc. Semicent. Publ.*, **II**.

1939 Review: Burlingame, Roger, March of the iron men. *Tech. Rev.*, **41**, 115.

1939 Convergence properties of analytic functions of Fourier-Stieltjes transforms (with Cameron). *Trans. Amer. Math. Soc.*, **46.**

1939 Generalization of Ikehara's theorem (with H. R. Pitt). *J. Math. Phys.*, **XVII.**

1939 On singular distribution (with A. Wintner). *J. Math. Phys.*, **XVII.**

1939 A new method in statistical mechanics, abstract (with B. McMillan). *Amer. Math. Soc. Bull.*, **45**, 234. *Science*, **90.**

1939 The ergodic theorem. *Duke Math. J.*

1939 The use of statistical theory in the study of turbulence. *Nature*, **144**, 728.

1940 A canonical series for symmetric functions in statistical mechanics, abstract. *Amer. Math. Soc. Bull.*, **46.**

1940 Fukamiya, M. On dominated ergodic theorems in Lp $(p \geqq L)$, 1939. *Math. Rev.*, **1**, 148.

1940 Review: Fukamiya, M. The Lipschitz condition of random functions, 1939. *Math. Rev.*, **1**, 149.

1940 Review: De Donder, T. L'Energétique déduit de la mécanique statistique générale. 1939. *Math. Rev.*, **1**, 192.

1941 Harmonic analysis and ergodic theory (with A. Wintner). *Amer. J. Math.*, **LXIII.**

1941 On the ergodic dynamics of almost periodic systems. *Amer. J. Math.*, **63.**

1942 On the oscillation of the derivatives of a periodic function (with G. Polya). *Trans. Amer. Math. Soc.*, **52**, 249–256.

1943 Ergodic dynamics of almost periodic systems (with A. Wintner). *Math. Rev.*, **4**, 15; *Amer. J. Math*, **63**, 794–824.

1943 Behavior, purpose and teleology (with A. Rosenblueth and J. Bigelow). *Phil. Sci.*, **10.**

1943 The discrete chaos (with A. Wintner). *Math. Rev.*, **4**, 220; *Amer. J. Math.*, **65**, 279–298.

1945 The role of models in science (with A. Rosenblueth). *Phil. Sci.*, **12**, 316–322.

1945 La teoria de la extrapolacion estadistica. *Soc. Math. Mex. Bul.*, **2**, 37–45.

1946 Conduction of impulses in cardiac muscles (with A. Rosenblueth) *Sobri. de Arch. Inst. Cardiol. Mex.*. **16**, 205–265; *Bull. Soc. Math. Mex.*, **2**, 37–42.

1946 Theory of statistical extrapolation. *Math. Rev.*, **7**, 461.

1946 Generalizations of the Wiener-Hopf integral equation (with A. E. Hei). *Proc. Natl. Acad. Sci.*, **32**, 98–101; *Math. Rev.*, **8**, 29 (1947).

1948 Wiener, N, and Mandelbrojt. *Math. Rev.*, **9**, 230.

1947 A scientist rebels. *Atl. Monthly*, **179**, 46.

1948 Teleological mechanisms (with L. K. Frank, G. E. Hutchinson, W. K. Livingston and W. S. McCulloch). *Ann. N.Y. Acad. Sci.*, **50**, 187–278.

1948 Review: Infeld, L. Whom the Gods love: The story of Evariste Galois (New York, 1948). *Scripta Math.*, **14**, 273–274.

1948 *Cybernetics*. The Technology Press and John Wiley and Sons, Hermann et Cie. Paris.

1948 A rebellious scientist after two years. *Bull. Atom. Scient.*, **4**, 338.

1948 Time, communication and the nervous system. *Ann. N.Y. Acad. Sci.*, **50**, 197–219.

1948 Cybernetics. *Scientific American*, **179**, 14–18.

1948 An account of the spike potential of axons (with A. Rosenblueth, W. Pitts and J. Garcia Ramos). *J. Comp. Physiol.*

1949 Sur la théorie de la prévision statistique et du filtrage des ondes. *An. Harmonique, Colloques Internationaux du CNRS*, **15**, 67–74. Centre National de la Recherche Scientifique, Paris.

1949 *Extrapolation and interpolation and smoothing of stationary time series with engineering applications.* The Technology Press and John Wiley and Sons.

1949 New concept of communication engineering. *Electronics*, **22**, 74–77.

1949 Godfrey Harold Hardy, 1877–1947. *Bull. Amer. Math. Soc.*, **55**, 72–77.

1949 Sound communication with the deaf. *Phil. Science*, **16.**

1949 Some problems in sensory prosthesis (with L. Levine). *Science*, **110.**

1950 The thinking machine. *Time*, **55.**

1950 Some prime-number consequences of the Ikohara theorem (with L. Geller). *Acta Scientiarum Mathematicarum, Adiuvanta Academia Scientiarum Hungarica, Szeged.*

1950 *The human use of human beings.* The Houghton Mifflin, Boston.

1950 Cybernetics. *Bull. Amer. Acad. Arts Sci.*, **III.**

1950 Some maxims for biologists and psychologists. *Dialectica*, **4.**

1950 Purposeful and non-purposeful behavior (with A. Rosenblueth). *Phil. Science.*

1950 Speech, language and learning. *J. Acoust. Soc. Amer.* **22**, 690–697.

1950 Comprehensive view of prediction theory. *Proc. Intern. Congr. Math.*, Cambridge, 1950: *Amer. Math. Soc.*, **II.**

1950 Entropy and information. *Proc. Symp. Appl. Math.*, **2**.

1951 Problems of sensory prosthesis. *Amer. Math. Soc. Bull.*, **57**.

1951 Homeostasis in the individual and society. *J. Franklin Inst.*, **251**.

1952 *The brain (ss)*. The Tech. Eng. News, 1952 (reprinted in paperback anthology, Crossroads in Time, Ed. Groff Conklin, publ. by Doubleday, Garden City, New York, 1953).

1953 *Les machines à calculer et la pensée humaine*. Coll. Int. Centre Nat. Rech. Sci., Paris, 8–13, 1951 (1953).

1953 A new form for the statistical postulate of quantum mechanics (with A. Siegel). *Phys. Rev.*, **91**.

1953 Mécanique quantique — Distributions quantiques dans l'espace différentiel pour les fonctions d'ondes dépendant du spin. *C.R.*

1952 Miracle of the broom closet (ss). *Tech. Eng. News*, **33**. (repr. in Mag. Fantasy Sci. Fiction, 1954, by Anthony Boucher).

1953 *Ex-prodigy*. Simon and Schuster.

1953 The concept of homeostasis in medicine. *Trans. Stud. Coll. Physic. Phil.*, **20**.

1953 The differential space theory of quantum mechanics (with A. Siegel). *Phys. Rev.*, **91**, 1551.

1953 Optics and the theory of stochastic processes. *J. Optical Soc. Amer.*, **43**, 225–228.

1953 The future of automatic machinery. *Mech. Eng.*, 130–132.

1954 *Nonlinear prediction and dynamics*. Proc. Third Berkeley Symp. Math. Stat. Probl., Univ. Calif. Press.

1955 The differential space theory of quantum systems (with A. Siegel). *No. 4 del Supplemento al 2, Ser. X del Nuovo Cimento*, 982–1003.

1955 On the factorization of matrices. *Comm. Math. Helv.*, **29**.

1955 Thermodynamics of the message. *Neurochem.*

1955 *Time and organization*. Sec. Fawley Found. Lecture, Univ. Southampton.

1956 The "theory of measurement" in differential quantum theory (with A. Siegel). *Phys. Rev.*, **101**, 429–432.

1956 *The theory of prediction*. Modern Math. for the Engineer.

1956 *I am a mathematician*. Doubleday, New York.

1956 Brain waves and the interferometer. *J. Physiol. Soc. Jap.*, **18**.

1956 Moral reflections of a mathematician. *Bull. Atom. Scient.*, **XII**, 53–57. Reprinted from "*I am a Mathematician*".

1957 Rhythms in physiology with particular reference to encephalography. *Proc. Rudolf Virchow Med. Soc. City New York*, **16**, 109–124.

1957 The definition and ergodic properties of the stochastic adjoint of a unitary transformation (with E. J. Akutowicz). *Rend. Circolo Matem. Palermo*, **II**, 1–13.

1957 Notes on Polya's and Turan's hypotheses concerning Liouville's factor. *Rend. Circolo Matem. Palermo*, **II**, 1–9.

1957 The role of the mathematician in a materialistic culture. (A scientists's dilemma in a materialistic world). *Columbia Eng. Quart. Proc. Sec. Combined Plan Conference*, 6–9 Oct.

1957 On the non-vanishing of Euler products (with A. Wintner). *Amer. J. Math.*, **LXXIX**, 801–808.

1957 The prediction theory of multivariate stochastic processes, Part I (with P. Masani). *Acta Math.*, **98**, 111–150.

1958 The prediction theory of multivariate stochastic processes, Part II (with P. Masani). *Acta Math.*, **99**, 93–137.

1958 *Logique, probabilité et méthode des sciences physiques*. La méthode dans les sciences modernes, éditions science et industrie, Francois le Lionnais (Ed.), Paris, 111–112.

1958 My connection with cybernetics. Its origin and its future. *Cybernetica*, Namur, Belgium, 1–14.

1958 Random time. *Nature*, **181**, 561–562.

1958 Time and the science of organization. *Scientia*.

1958 *Nonlinear problems in random theory*. Techn. Press MIT and John Wiley and Sons, New York.

1959 A factorization of positive hermitian matrices (with E. J. Akutowicz). *J. Math. Mech.*, **8**, 111–120.

1959 *The temper*. Random House.

1960 *Preface to "Cybernetics of natural systems"* by D. Stanley-Jones.

1960 "*The grand privilege*", Saturday Rev.

1960 Some moral and technical consequences of automation. *Science*, **131**.

1960 *Kybernetik*. Contribution to "*Das soziologische Wörterbuch*".

1961 Ueber Informationstheorie. *Die Naturwissenschaften*, **7**, 174–176.

1961 Science and society. *Voprosy Filos.*, **7**.

1961   *Cybernetics*. 2nd. ed., MIT Press and John Wiley and Sons, New York.

1962   L'homme et la machine. *Proc. Colloques Philosophiques Internationaux de Royaumont*.

1962   Contribution to *Proc. Int. Symp. Applic. Autom. Control Prosthetics Design*.

1962   *The mathematics of self-organizing systems*. Recent developments in information and decision processes. MacMillan, New York.

1963   *Introduction to neurocybernetics and epilogue* (with J. P. Schadé). Progr. Brain Res., **2**, 264–268.

1963   Random theory in classical phase space and quantum mechanics (with Giacomo della Riccia). *Proc. Int. Conf. Functional Analysis*, *MIT*, Cambridge.

1963   On the oscillations of nonlinear systems. *Proc. Symp. Stochastic Models Med. Biol., Math. Res Center, US Army*.

1964   *God and Golem*. MIT Press.

1964   Dynamical systems in physics and biology. Contribution to Series "*Fundamental Science in 1984*", *New Scient*.

Author Index*

---

* Italics indicate the pages on which the author's contribution appears in this volume.

Subject Index